FHG

The original and u

Pets Welcome 2004

with

including

Holidays with Horses **and** ***Narrow Boat holidays***

Pet's Products Section

Guide to Pet Friendly Pubs

For Contents see page 3

For Index of towns/counties see back of book

Part of IPC Country and Leisure Media

CONTENTS

Pets Welcome 2004 First Edition

ENGLAND

SCOTLAND

WALES

IRELAND

Ratings You Can Trust

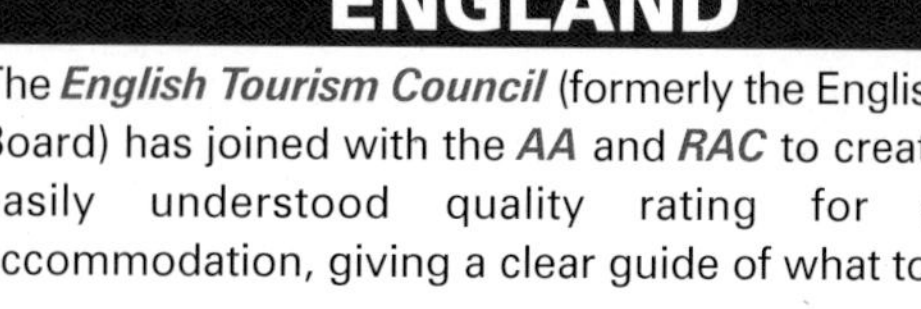

ENGLAND

The ***English Tourism Council*** (formerly the English Tourist Board) has joined with the ***AA*** and ***RAC*** to create a new, easily understood quality rating for serviced accommodation, giving a clear guide of what to expect.

HOTELS are given a rating from One to Five ***Stars*** – the more Stars, the higher the quality and the greater the range of facilities and level of services provided.

GUEST ACCOMMODATION, which includes guest houses, bed and breakfasts, inns and farmhouses, is rated from One to Five ***Diamonds***. Progressively higher levels of quality and customer care must be provided for each one of the One to Five Diamond ratings.

HOLIDAY PARKS, TOURING PARKS and CAMPING PARKS are now also assessed using ***Stars***. Standards of quality range from a One Star (acceptable) to a Five Star (exceptional) park.

Look out also for the new *SELF-CATERING* Star ratings. The more ***Stars*** (from One to Five) awarded to an establishment, the higher the levels of quality you can expect. Establishments at higher rating levels also have to meet some additional requirements for facilities.

SCOTLAND

Star Quality Grades will reflect the most important aspects of a visit, such as the warmth of welcome, efficiency and friendliness of service, the quality of the food and the cleanliness and condition of the furnishings, fittings and decor.

THE MORE STARS,

THE HIGHER THE STANDARDS.

The description, such as Hotel, Guest House, Bed and Breakfast, Lodge, Holiday Park, Self-catering etc tells you the type of property and style of operation.

WALES

Places which score highly will have an especially welcoming atmosphere and pleasing ambience, high levels of comfort and guest care, and attractive surroundings enhanced by thoughtful design and attention to detail

STAR QUALITY GUIDE FOR

HOTELS, GUEST HOUSES AND FARMHOUSES

SELF-CATERING ACCOMMODATION
(Cottages, Apartments, Houses)

CARAVAN HOLIDAY HOME PARKS
(Holiday Parks, Touring Parks, Camping Parks)

★★★★★	*Exceptional quality*
★★★★	*Excellent quality*
★★★	*Very good quality*
★★	*Good quality*
★	*Fair to good quality*

In England, Scotland and Wales, all graded properties are inspected annually by Tourist Authority trained Assessors.

YORKSHIRE DALES to
SCOTTISH HIGHLANDS
Over 600 superb, personally inspected, self catering holiday properties in beautiful rural and coastal locations. From Yorkshire's Dales and Moors, the Lakes and Cumbria, through Northumbria and the Borders to Scotland's Highlands and Islands. Cosy cottages to country houses, many welcome pets and most are open all year.
2004 Dales Quality Approved Holiday Cottages
Yorkshire
Cumbria
The Lake District
Northumbria
The Borders
Scotland
Dales Holiday Cottages
01756 799821 & 790919
Skipton, North Yorkshire, BD23 2AA.
www.dalesholcot.com
English Tourism Council
Committed to ETC Quality Assurance

Country Holidays
BRITAIN'S FAVOURITE COTTAGE HOLIDAYS
With over 3,000 quality graded cottages throughout the UK, catering from two to twenty-two, you're sure to find the right property for you. Many of our properties also accept pets so none of your family need miss out.
Every kind of property for every kind of holiday
Look & Book at: www.country-holidays.co.uk or call 0870 442 5240 for your 2004 brochure.

Cornwall & Dorset
Three award winning family holiday parks in stunning locations. All are close to safe sandy beaches and fantastic visitor attractions. We have designated dog walking areas at all of our Parks.
0870 444 0080
Quote WP
Weststar
HOLIDAY PARKS
book online: www.weststarholidays.co.uk/pw
Kynance Cove
near Mullion
Mullion near Helston, Cornwall ☆ Looe Bay near Looe, Cornwall ☆ Sandford near Poole, Dorset

PENMORVAH MANOR HOTEL

Falmouth, Cornwall TR11 5ED

- 3 Star Country House Hotel and Self Catering Courtyard Cottages
- Situated in 6 acres of mature gardens and woodland
- Ideal for visiting Cornwall's superb gardens
- Close to Falmouth and Coastal paths • Well-behaved dogs welcome
- Ground floor bedrooms for easy pet access • Ample car parking

Tel: 01326 250277 • Fax: 01326 250509
e-mail: reception@penmorvah.co.uk
website: www.penmorvah.co.uk

Paul & Barbie Higgins
Trewith, Duloe, near Liskeard
Cornwall PL14 4PR

TREWITH HOLIDAY COTTAGES

Self Catering Accommodation Open All Year

Tel: 01503 262184
mobile: 07968 262184

Situated in a superb elevated position of outstanding natural beauty. Just 1 1/2 miles from Looe. Choice of 4 refurbished cottages with 1-3 bedrooms. Fully-equipped and tastefully furnished with full central heating. Use of laundry room. Peaceful location with delightful walks. Many beaches, coves, fishing, shopping close by in Looe. Because of ponds young children need supervision. Well-behaved dogs welcome.

E-mail: holiday-cottages@trewith.freeserve.co.uk
www.trewith.freeserve.co.uk

TREMAINE GREEN

for MEMORABLE HOLIDAYS

"A beautiful private hamlet" of 11 award-winning traditional cosy **Cornish** craftsmen's cottages between **Looe** and **Polperro.** Clean, comfortable and well equipped, with a warm friendly atmosphere, for pets with 2 to 8 people. Set in lovely grounds, only 12 miles from the **Eden Project** with country and coastal walks nearby. Pets £16 pw; owners from only **£112:**

- Towels, Linen, Electricity & Central Heating included • Dishwashers in larger cottages • Power shower Baths • Launderette
- Games Room • Tennis Court • TV/Videos • Cots & Highchairs available • Pubs & Restaurants in easy walking distance

Mr & Mrs J Spreckley, Tremaine Green Country Cottages, Pelynt, Near Looe, Cornwall PL13 2LT
Tel: 01503 220333 • e-mail: stay@tremainegreen.co.uk • web: www.tremainegreen.co.uk

Near Perranporth

Greenmeadow Cottages

Highly praised luxury cottages. Sleep 6. Superbly clean, comfortable and spacious. Open all year. Short Breaks out of season. Pets welcome in two of the cottages. Non-smoking available. Ample off-road parking.

For brochure and bookings

Tel: 01872 540483

Step onto The Coastal Path...

Escape the pressures of life. Relax! explore the Cornish Coast from Green Door Cottages in Port Gaverne.

8 comfortable, restored 18th Century cottages set around a sheltered courtyard, plus 2 prestigious apartments with panoramic sea views beside a picturesque cove, directly on the Coastal path, less than half a mile from Port Isaac.

An ideal location for your holiday and short breaks. Well behaved dogs are very welcome.

Call now for a brochure on:
01208 880293

PORT GAVERNE
email: enquiries@greendoorcottages.co.uk
web: www.greendoorcottages.co.uk

- Caravan Holiday Homes
- Touring & Camping
- North coast 3 miles, Truro 5
- Families & couples
- Pets welcome
- Peace and quiet
- No club or bar
- Shop/Off-licence
- Laundry room • Games room
- Children's play area
- Electric hook-ups
- Satellite TV in all units

Chiverton Park

Set in the heart of glorious Cornish countryside, yet only a short distance from the A30, this spacious, well-run park offers peace and relaxation in a delightful 4-acre rural setting. Holiday homes are fully equipped (except linen, which may be hired)

Chiverton Park, Blackwater, Truro TR4 8HS • 01872 560667
info@chivertonpark.co.uk • www.chivertonpark.co.uk

Dalswinton
HOUSE

A Victorian stone built Cornish house of character in a glorious rural setting. Standing in 10 acres of formal gardens and meadowland, the house overlooks the Vale of Lanherne and the village of St Mawgan with views to the sea at the dog friendly beach of Mawgan Porth. Our Hotel offers a comfortable, friendly atmosphere and great food prepared with fresh local produce. Regret no children under 16.

- Dogs free of charge and allowed everywhere (except the dining room)
- 8 Acres of private meadowland for dog exercise
- Bed & Breakfast from £32.00 per person per night
- Short Break and weekly rates available
- Car parking and heated outdoor pool
- All rooms en suite
- Tea/coffee & colour TV in all rooms
- Licensed bar and a restaurant serving 3 course dinner
- Garden chalet for self catering or inclusive terms
- Easy access to Newquay airport and The Eden Project

Proprietors: Stuart and Sal Hope

Dalswinton House, St Mawgan-in-Pydar, Cornwall TR8 4EZ

Tel/Fax: 01637 860385

Visit us at www.dalswinton.com e-mail: dalswinton@bigwig.net

Within the sound of the sea at Trevaunance Cove…

Delightful old inn with enormous beams

• Log fires
• Real Ale
• Malt Whisky
• Upstairs Eating Areas

The Driftwood Spars Hotel

Walkies Country

All bedrooms have excellent facilities, some with wonderful views

OPEN ALL YEAR • AMPLE PARKING

Now Brewing Own Beer

The Driftwood Spars Hotel, Trevaunance Cove, St Agnes, Cornwall TR5 0RT

Tel: 01872 552428 • www.driftwoodspars.com

BOSINVER HOLIDAY COTTAGES

Nestling in a hidden valley near the sea, the Eden Project and Lost Gardens of Heligan, our small farm has friendly animals and ponies. Choose from our 16th Century thatched farmhouse or cottages privately set in their own gardens surrounded by wildflower meadows. Wander down to the fishing lake or village pub, swim in the pool, play tennis, or relax and listen to the birdsong. No pets during Summer school holidays please.

Brochure from: Mrs Pat Smith, Bosinver Farm,
Trelowth, St Austell, Cornwall PL26 7DT. • Tel: 01726 72128
E-mail: reception@bosinver.co.uk • Website: www.bosinver.co.uk

The Rosevine Hotel

Porthcurnick Beach, Portscatho, St Mawes, Cornwall TR2 5EW

Tel: 01872 580206 • Fax: 01872 580230

e-mail: info@rosevine.co.uk • website: www.rosevine.co.uk

• Cornwall's "AA TOP 200" luxury hotel • De luxe bedrooms and suites • Award-winning cuisine • • Beautiful sub-tropical gardens facing directly over the safe, sandy beach fronting the National Trust coastline • • Warm heated indoor pool • • Children and pets most welcome •

CORNWALL'S ONLY RAC THREE DINING AWARDS AND BLUE RIBBON HOTEL RAC ★★★ AA ★★★ 82%

White Lodge Hotel

Mawgan Porth Bay, Near Newquay, Cornwall TR8 4BN
Tel: 01637 860512

e-mail: adogfriendly@aol.com • website: www.dogfriendlyhotel.co.uk

GIVE YOURSELVES & YOUR DOGS A BREAK

at our family-run White Lodge Hotel overlooking beautiful Mawgan Porth Bay, near Newquay, Cornwall

- ★ Dogs most welcome- FREE OF CHARGE
- ★ Your dogs sleep with you in your bedroom.
- ★ Direct access to sandy beach and coastal path.
- ★ Dog loving proprietors with 20 years' experience in catering for dog owners on holiday with their dogs.
- ★ ALL bedrooms with colour TV, tea/coffee makers, alarm clocks, radios, heaters etc.
- ★ Fantastic sea views from most rooms.
- ★ Well-stocked residents' lounge bar, dining room & sun patio with outstanding sea views across the bay.
- ★ Large free car park within hotel grounds.

SPECIAL 6 DAYS (5 NIGHTS) CHRISTMAS BREAK **ONLY £305** *Half Board*

SPECIAL 6 DAYS (5 NIGHTS) NEW YEAR BREAK **ONLY £260** *Half Board*

SPECIAL 6 DAYS (5 NIGHTS) BREAKS **ONLY £200-£212.50** *BB & Evening Meal*

WEEKLY TERMS **FROM £280-£297.50** FOR 5-COURSE EVENING DINNER, BED AND 4-COURSE BREAKFAST WITH CHOICE OF MENU

This Hotel is now open all year – Winter Break packages available

Phone Patsy Powell
for free colour brochure

ALL PRICES INCLUDE VAT AT 17½%

WILLAPARK MANOR HOTEL

Bossiney, Tintagel, Cornwall PL34 0BA

Tel: (01840) 770782

One of the most beautifully situated hotels in England

set in 14 acres of landscaped gardens and secluded woodland with spectacular views of Bossiney Bay and the rugged unspoilt coastline towards Boscastle. The lawns in front of this character country house sweep down to meet the cliffs where a hidden gate leads to the coast path and beach. This unique situation, well appointed en suite rooms, exceptional cuisine and friendly atmosphere, combined with the professionalism gained by years of experience make people return every year. A warm welcome and memorable holiday assured for you and your dog.

English Tourism Council ★★ HOTEL

Tariff: En suite room, breakfast and 4 course dinner from £275.00 weekly or £46.00 daily inc. VAT.

www.willapark.co.uk

- Character 40 Bedroom Hotel • Set in an area of outstanding natural beauty
- Adjacent to its own 18 hole golf course • Magnificent panoramic sea views
- Good food, wines & service • Health & Fitness facilities • Indoor heated pool

Tel: 01503 230276 Fax: 01503 230329

www.whitsandbayhotel.co.uk Email: info@whitsandbayhotel.co.uk

Greenhowe Caravan Park

Great Langdale, English Lakeland.

VERY GOOD

Greenhowe is a permanent Caravan Park with Self Contained Holiday Accommodation. Subject to availability Holiday Homes may be rented for short or long periods from 1st March until mid-November. The Park is situated in the heart of the Lake District some half a mile from Dungeon Ghyll at the foot of the Langdale Pikes. It is an ideal centre for Climbing, Fell Walking, Riding, Swimming, Water Skiing or just a lazy holiday.

Please ask about Short Breaks.

Greenhowe Caravan Park
Great Langdale, Ambleside
Cumbria LA22 9JU

For free colour brochure

Telephone: (015394) 37231
Fax: (015394) 37464
Freephone: 0800 0717231

Rose Cottage

Lorton Road, Cockermouth CA13 9DX

Family-run guest house on the outskirts of Cockermouth. Warm, friendly atmosphere. Ample off-road parking. All rooms en suite with colour TV, tea/coffee, central heating and most have double glazing.

Pets most welcome in the house (excluding dining room), and there are short walks nearby. Ideal base for visiting both Lakes and coast.

Tel & Fax: 01900 822189 **website: www.rosecottageguest.co.uk**

The Coppermines & Coniston Lakes Cottages

ETC ★★ to ★★★★★

50 unique Lakeland cottages for 2-30 of quality and character in stunning mountain scenery. Log fires, exposed beams. Weekends and Short Breaks.

Book online: www.coppermines.co.uk

01539441765 **Pets very welcome!**

"Your own country house in the Lakes"

Two luxury holiday houses available to rent in the Lake District.

Routen House

Routen House is a beautiful old farmhouse set in 4 acres in an outstanding position with fabulous views over Ennerdale Lake. Fully modernised while retaining the character of the old farmhouse, it has been furnished to a very high standard. Sleeps 12 plus cot.

Little Parrock is an elegant Victorian Lakeland stone house with large rooms and a wealth of period features. Lovely private garden. Fully modernised to a very high standard; real log fires. Sleeps 10 plus cot.

Little Parrock

Both houses are non-smoking but pets are very welcome. Please contact:

Mrs J. Green • Tel & Fax: 01604 626383 • e-mail: joanne@routenhouse.co.uk

www.routenhouse.co.uk

Thwaite Howe Hotel

Situated in its own grounds, with magnificent mountain views to Skiddaw, our hotel has a very peaceful location, yet is within easy reach of all the Lake District's attractions and also the Cumbrian coast. We are a small, friendly country house hotel specialising in delicious home cooking, complemented by an excellent selection of fine wines. All eight bedrooms have en suite bathrooms, colour televisions, radio, tea and coffee making facilities, direct dial telephones, hair dryers and thermostatically controlled radiators. We have a residents' lounge and a well stocked bar. Unfortunately the hotel is unsuitable to accommodate children under 12 years of age. Well behaved dogs are welcome (subject to conditions available from the hotel). Non-smoking rooms. Call for brochure.

ETC ★★

Thornthwaite, Near Keswick CA12 5SA

Tel: 017687 78281 • Fax: 017687 78529

An unrivalled location in the heart of The Lake District

Derwentwater Hotel

Portinscale, KESWICK,
Cumbria, CA12 5RE, England
www.derwentwater-hotel.com

An award-winning hotel set on the shores of Derwentwater - QUEEN OF THE ENGLISH LAKES

The epitome of a late Victorian Country House Hotel, **The Derwentwater** stands on the shore of Derwentwater itself, in the small village of Portinscale 1 mile West of Keswick.

Owned and managed by the same owners for 18 years, **The Derwentwater** has been completely refurbished and modernised under their careful and discerning eye. With 48 rooms all en-suite and unrivalled views from the conservatory, across the head of the lake to the fells and mountains beyond.

The Hotel is an ideal base for touring the area. You can drive through the glories of the Borrowdale valley at the head of Derwentwater, with its charming fell farms, and its rugged mountain backdrop, or explore the nearby market towns and villages with their wealth of interesting galleries, antique salerooms, cafes and country pubs.

Derwent Manor

Portinscale, KESWICK
Cumbria, CA12 5RE, England
www.derwent-manor.com

Individually designed Luxury Apartments PLUS . . . All the services of a three star hotel

Enjoy the freedom and space of a carefree seasonal break, staying in the superbly appointed and beautifully situated, luxury apartments at **Derwent Manor.** This, the former majestic residence of an eminent Manchester Alderman, has been tastefully converted into stylish, fully equipped apartments, designed to give comfort and privacy in the tranquil setting of Portinscale, near Keswick, Cumbria.

Derwent Manor stands in its own landscaped garden grounds adjacent to the **Derwentwater Hotel** AND . . . residents of the **Manor** have full use of the **Derwentwater Hotel** facilities including bar, restaurant, games room, lounges, and garden, as well as access to the lakeside walks across the 16 acres of 'Wetlands' conservation grounds, with free lake and river fishing, 9 hole putting green and ample free parking in our extensive grounds.

WE WELCOME WELL-MANNERED PETS

MANOR LOUNGE

NEARBY 'OXLEY'S' LEISURE CLUB

MANOR APARTMENT

Call us now for our full colour brochure on 017687 72538

Midtown Cottages, High Lorton

These two cottages have both been awarded four stars and are electrically centrally heated for all year round use. Built around a courtyard area, they are 'upside down' – the bedrooms (one double, one twin) being downstairs with the lounge, dining area and small but well equipped kitchen with dishwasher and freezer upstairs to make the most of the views over the fells. Whilst the two cottages are not absolutely identical, they are both furnished to the same high standard. They are both non-smoking, but pets are very welcome. Cot & high chair available if required. Lorton lies at the northern end of Lorton Vale, a beautiful valley which runs from Cockermouth in the west to Buttermere in the east. The river Cocker runs the full length of the valley, and at the end of the 18th century its fast flowing streams that flow down from the fells, through the village were used as the motive power for flour and linen mills. Some of these mill buildings survive today, having later been used by the Jennings family as their brewery. The 'Yew Tree Hall', now the village hall, was once the brewery malt house. Jennings ales are still brewed in nearby Cockermouth.

Complete weeks £420(High Season), £360 (Mid Season), £240 (Low Season). Short breaks from £160

Please contact: Mr & Mrs M. Burrell • Tel: +44(0) 1264 710165
e-mail: info@midtown-cottages.com • website: www.midtown-cottages.com

Holbeck Ghyll Lodge

Tel: 01484 684605 ***ETC***
Fax: 01484 689051 **★★★★**

Extremely comfortable traditional Lakeland stone lodge with enclosed garden at rear. Two twin bedded bedrooms. Dining/living room with open fire and sofa bed. Fully equipped oak fitted kitchen. Bathroom with bath and shower. Antique pine furniture throughout. One double bedroom with en suite shower and toilet. Ample parking. House situated for local walks, lake and pubs. Secure covered way for bikes. Available Easter to end of October. Saturday change over.

Mrs Kaye, Holmdene,
Stoney Bank Road, Holmfirth HD9 7SL
e-mail: maggiekaye@hotmail.com

Your Stepping Stone to the Cumbrian Lake District

Carrock Cottages are three recently renovated stone built cottages set on the fringe of the Lakeland Fells. A quiet rural location near the lovely villages of Hesket Newmarket with its award winning brewery, Caldbeck and Greystoke.
Explore the beauty of the Lake District National Park or head North to historic Carlisle and on to Hadrians Wall.
Fell walking & other activities close to hand as well as excellent restaurants.
A warm welcome guaranteed.
Accommodation for 1 to 12 people.

Carrock House, Hutton Roof, Penrith, Cumbria CA11 0XY
Tel: Malcolm or Gillian on 01768 484 111 or Fax: 017684 888 50

WWW.CARROCKCOTTAGES.CO.UK

Tanglewood Caravan Park

CAUSEWAY HEAD, SILLOTH-ON-SOLWAY, CUMBRIA CA7 4PE

Tanglewood is a family-run park on the fringes of the Lake District National Park. It is tree-sheltered and situated one mile inland from the small port of Silloth on the Solway Firth, with a beautiful view of the Galloway Hills. Large modern holiday homes are available from March to October, with car parking beside each home. Fully equipped except for bed linen, with end bedroom, central heating in bedrooms, electric lighting, hot and cold water, toilet, shower, gas fire, fridge and colour TV, all of which are included in the tariff. Touring pitches also available with electric hook-ups and water/drainage facilities, etc. Play area. Licensed lounge with adjoining children's play room. Pets welcome free but must be kept under control at all times. Full colour brochure available.

TEL: 016973 31253

e-mail: tanglewoodcaravanpark@hotmail.com
website: www.tanglewoodcaravanpark.co.uk

LONSDALE HOUSE HOTEL

11 Daltongate, Ulverston, Cumbria LA12 7BD

LONSDALE HOUSE HOTEL – situated right in the heart of Ulverston (South Lakes festival town). Offering friendly service, great food and comfortable accommodation. Dogs are most welcome, provided they are accompanied by well-behaved owners, and can stay in the rooms. A short walk from the hotel, on the edge of the National Park overlooking Ulverston, is Sir John Barrow's Monument on Hoad Hill. A popular place for walking with superb views of the Lake District peaks and panoramic view of Morecambe Bay. There are also some good walks along the bay coast a short drive from the hotel. Lonsdale House Hotel is an excellent base to explore the Lake District because we are only 15 minutes from Lake Windermere and about 30 minutes from Windermere Village, Coniston and Cartmel.

Phone **01229 582598**
for a brochure and find out about our Special Breaks.
www.lonsdalehousehotel.co.uk

Smallwood House Hotel

Ambleside, Central Lake District LA22 9DJ • 015394 32330

En suite rooms • Large Breakfast selection • Car park
Secure cycle storage • Local leisure club membership

New – luxury one-bedroom self-catering flat

"Where Quality & the Customer Come First"

www.smallwoodhotel.co.uk • enq@smallwoodhotel.co.uk

DENE CREST
Guest House

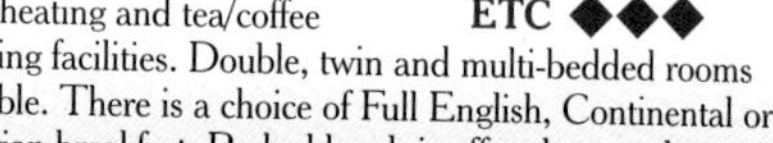

ETC ◆◆◆

Guests are welcomed to a comfortable, tastefully decorated Guesthouse. All rooms are fully en suite and have colour TV, shaver points, central heating and tea/coffee making facilities. Double, twin and multi-bedded rooms available. There is a choice of Full English, Continental or Vegetarian breakfast. Packed lunch is offered as an alternative or can be purchased for a small fee. Only two minutes away from Bus and Rail Station, very close to town centre and amenities, yet surprisingly quiet. Discounts on long stays. Pets Welcome. Terms from £18pp per night, depending on month. Open all year. Short Break terms available. Proprietors: Anne & Peter Watson.

DENE CREST GUEST HOUSE • Woodland Road, Windermere LA23 2AE
Tel: 015394 44979 • e-mail: denecrest@btinternet.com • www.denecrest.com

Kirkwood

Guest House, Prince's Road, Windermere LA23 2DD

KIRKWOOD occupies a quiet spot between Windermere and Bowness, offering guests a warm and friendly atmosphere with an individual personal service. Rooms are large and all en suite with TV and tea/coffee making facilities; some have four-poster beds. Your hosts will be pleased to help plan tours or walks with maps provided.

Three-night Special Breaks available. B&B £25 – £30.

Tel & Fax: 015394 43907
e-mail: info@kirkwood51.co.uk
website: www.kirkwood51.freeserve.co.uk

Hargate Hall, Wormhill, Near Buxton
Derbyshire SK17 8TA
Tel/Fax: 01298 872591 • www.hargate-hall.co.uk

Twelve Luxury Apartments

In a fine country house set in over 5 acres of parkland within the Peak District National Park. Sleep 2-9. All equipped to the highest standard, with satellite TV, hi-fi and video. Open all year.

Facilities include:

- mountain bikes
- full-size snooker table
- games room
- adventure playground

Well-behaved pets permitted

Toad Hall Cottages

Pets very welcome with well behaved humans!

200 outstanding and unusual quality cottages throughout Devon, Cornwall & Exmoor. Situated in fabulous walking countryside, with magical scenery, dog friendly beaches and pubs so your humans will enjoy their holiday too!

08700 777345

www.toadhallcottages.com

or email: thc@toadhallcottages.com

Blagdon Manor Hotel & Restaurant

Ashwater, North Devon EX21 5DF
Tel: 01409 211224
Fax: 01409 211634
stay@blagdon.com
www.blagdon.com

AA ★★ 84%

Liz and Steve along with our 2 Chocolate Labradors, Nutmeg and Cassia, look forward to welcoming you to Blagdon Manor

Restaurant: Enjoy excellent cuisine using locally sourced produce. Dinner available every night for residents. **Accommodation:** 7 en suite bedrooms *Panoramic views of the Devon countryside and Dartmoor. Beautifully restored Grade II Listed building. Enjoy a peaceful location halfway between Dartmoor and Exmoor and only 20 minutes from the North Cornish coast at Bude.*

3 acres of gardens and 17 acres of fields • Dogs welcome.
Children over the age of 12.
Double/twin rooms £90.00 per night, based on two sharing.
Single occupancy £72.00. Dogs £5.00 per night.

'Easily the best choice of cottages in Devon...'

...and comfortably the best value

Contact us now for a free colour guide and unbiased recommendation service to the 400 best value cottages around Exmoor and Devon's unspoilt National Trust Coast.

Bargain breaks from only £35 per person to luxury manor house for 16 from only £995 per week.

North Devon Holiday Homes

Barnstaple, Devon EX31 1BD

Tel: 01271 376322 ❖ Fax 01271 346544

e mail: info@northdevonholidays.co.uk www.northdevonholidays.co.uk

The Church House Inn, Holne

Tucked away in the beautiful, quiet countryside of South Dartmoor, a warm welcome awaits you at this 14th century inn, renowned for its high quality food.

- Bar menus feature local produce.
- Imaginative à la carte menu.
- Award-winning chefs.
- Fine wines and real ales.
- Six comfortable rooms.
- Families and dogs welcome.
- Dogs free of charge.
- Open all year.

Tel. 01364 631208 • Fax: 01364 631525
www.churchhouse-holne.co.uk

Jan & Tony Skerritt, Paul & Jane Silk

LILAC COTTAGE

Smallridge, Axminster

Lilac Cottage is a very pretty rose and vine covered detached cottage in the middle of charming Smallridge. It has been carefully renovated, retaining the inglenook fireplace, oak beams, floors and doors. Oil-fired central heating, colour TV, fully-equipped all-electric kitchen. Furnished to a high standard, sleeps six plus cot. Tenants return year after year. Children and pets are welcome. Walled garden and garage. West Country Tourist Board Registered. The villages and surrounding countryside are beautiful on the borders of Devon, Dorset, and Somerset. Many seaside towns within a seven to ten mile radius, e.g. Lyme Regis, Charmouth and Seaton. Telephone or SAE to:

Mrs J.M. Stuart, Manor Farm House, Deane, Basingstoke, Hants RG25 3AS
Tel & Fax: 01256 782961 or Mrs Young: 01386 840341
E-mail: joanna.sb@free.fr

View from balcony of beach and sea

Instow Beach Haven Cottage

Seafront cottage overlooking the sandy beach. Instow is a quiet yachting village with soft yellow sands and a pretty promenade of shops, old houses, pubs and cafés serving drinks and meals. Beach Haven has extensive beach and sea views from the house and garden, sleeps 5, own parking, gas fired central heating, colour TV, washing machine. Lawned garden overlooking sea with terrace and garden furniture. Coastal walks and cycle trails, boat to Lundy Island. Dog welcome.Other sea front cottages available.

Ring 01237 473801 for prices and vacancies only or send SAE for brochure to Mrs P.I. BARNES, 140 Bay View Road, Northam, Bideford, Devon EX39 1BJ

Northcott Barton Farm Cottage

Beautifully equipped, spotlessly clean three bedroom cottage with large enclosed garden. A walker's and country lover's ideal: for a couple seeking peace and quiet or a family holiday. Very special rates for low season holidays, couples and short breaks. Near golf, riding, Tarka trail and R.H.S. Rosemoor. Character, comfort, beams, log fire, *"Perfick"*. Pets Welcome, no charge.

For availability please contact Sandra Gay,
Northcott Barton, Ashreigney, Chulmleigh, Devon EX18 7PR
Tel/Fax: 01769 520259
e-mail: sandra@northcottbarton.co.uk
web: www.northcottbarton.co.uk

Give yourselves and your dogs the break you deserve at

Woodlands Guest House

Parkham Road, Brixham, South Devon TQ5 9BU

Overlooking the beautiful Brixham Harbour and Torbay – The English Riviera

- Dogs most welcome – free of charge
- Your dogs sleep with you in your bedroom
- Near dog friendly parks and beaches
- Most bedrooms en suite
- Dog loving proprietors with 19 years experience in catering for dog owners on holiday with their dogs
- All bedrooms with colour TV, tea/coffee making facilities, mini fridges etc.
- Fantastic panoramic views over Brixham, Harbour, Marina, the Sea and Torbay
- Only just a short walk away from the busy Shopping Centre with its many quality English, Continental and fish Restaurants, Pubs, Clubs, Shops and Banks
- Ideal holiday base from which to explore Glorious South Devon
- Car Park within grounds and unrestricted on-road parking outside

BED & 4-COURSE BREAKFAST WITH CHOICE OF MENU – **EN SUITE ROOMS – ONE NIGHT FROM ONLY £24.00 TO £26.00 PER PERSON INCLUSIVE – REDUCTIONS FOR LONGER STAYS.**

PHONE 01803 852040 JOHN OR DIANE PARRY FOR FREE COLOUR BROCHURE.

E-mail:Dogfriendly2@aol.com

Website:www.dogfriendlyguesthouse.co.uk

YOUR PET STAYS FREE

ETC ★★★

Sandy Cove Hotel stands in 20 acres of cliff, coast and garden. The Hotel Restaurant overlooks the sea and cliffs with spectacular views of the bay. You will probably wonder how we can do it for the price when we offer a FIVE-COURSE MEAL including seafood platters with lobster, smoked salmon and steak. Every Saturday a Swedish Smorgasbord and Carvery carved by the Chef, and followed by dancing till late. Live entertainment weekly from Whitsun until September. All bedrooms have colour TV, telephone, teamaking and are en suite. The cocktail bar overlooks the bay and you have the use of the hotel's 80° heated indoor pool and recreation centre with sauna, sunbed, gym equipment and whirlpool, ALL FREE OF CHARGE.

Please return this advertisement to qualify for "Pets Stay Free" offer. Bargain Breaks and weekly rates available all year. Includes 5-course Evening Meal and coffee. Children – free accommodation. Please send for free brochure pack. Children under 5 years completely free, including meals.

Sandy Cove Hotel

Combe Martin Bay,
Devon EX34 9SR
Tel: (01271) 882243 & 882888
E-mail: rg14003483@aol.com

Indoor pool heated to 80°F with roll-back sides to enjoy the sun

Where else would you rather walk your dog?

PRINCE HALL *Hotel*

Two Bridges
Dartmoor
Devon PL20 6SA

Recommended in 2004 by
AA, Best Loved Hotels,
Good Hotel Guide, ETC,
Which? Hotel Guide

Tel: 01822 890 403
Fax: 01822 890 676
e-mail: info@princehall.co.uk
website: www.princehall.co.uk

"Supreme Accolade 2004" Voted one of the AA top 200 hotels in Britain and Ireland

WINNERS OF "BEST HOTEL RESTAURANT" WEST COUNTRY FOOD AWARDS 2000

International Caravan & Camping Park

A small country estate surrounded by forest in which deer roam. Situated in an area of outstanding natural beauty.

Large, flat, sheltered camping/touring pitches Modern facilities building, luxury 2/6 berth full service holiday homes, also self contained flat for 2 persons.

CULLOMPTON
DEVON
EX15 2DT

COLOUR BROCHURE ON REQUEST
Tel: (01404) 841381 (Evgs to 8pm)

Fax: (01404) 841593 • www.forest-glade.co.uk • email: enquiries@forest-glade.co.uk

THE LORD HALDON COUNTRY HOUSE HOTEL

The Lord Haldon Country House Hotel is the perfect venue for a quiet get-away break with your beloved pet. Acres of private grounds, mile of driveway for exercise and animals are welcome in guests' bedrooms by arrangement.The hotel stands in its own grounds, four miles south west of Exeter, set 400 feet above sea level above the Haldon Hills. It is family Hotel run by the Preece family, owners for over 21 years. The hotel is AA* recognised with two Red Rosettes for its restaurant, which is open seven days a week, lunch times and evenings. There is also an intimate Lounge Bar which serves bar food. The Lord Haldon is the only hotel in Devon that is a member of Relais du Silence, an independent hotel consortium dedicated to fine food, service, peace and quiet. For further information about how you can enjoy the finest part of Devon, please telephone for a free hotel brochure, or visit our website: www.lordhaldonhotel.co.uk**

THE LORD HALDON
Privately Owned Country Hotel

Dunchideock, Near Exeter
Devon EX6 7YF
Tel: 01392 832483
Fax: 01392 833765
e-mail: enquiries@lordhaldonhotel.co.uk

BADGER'S HOLT • Dartmoor National Park

Luxury self catering holiday accommodation nestling by the River Dart at the foot of Yar Tor adjacent to the famous Badger's Holt tea rooms – a traditional Devonshire cream tea not to be missed! Two purpose-built apartments, fully equipped and maintained to the highest standard.

"Bench Tor" • 2 bedroom sleeps 4
"Yar Tor" • 3 bedroom, 2 bathrooms sleeps 6-8

Accommodation available all year • Pets welcome
Tea rooms open March to October

Enquiries to Badger's Holt, Dartmeet, Dartmoor PL20 6SG • Tel: 01364 631213 • Fax: 01364 631475

Watermill Cottages

Down a narrow lane lies a secret valley just over a mile inland from Slapton sands. There you will find the six delightful **Watermill Cottages** on the banks of a small river by an old mill house. A peaceful haven with wonderful walks and freedom for children to explore. Home cooking available. Winter breaks from **£95**.

Hansel, Dartmouth, South Devon TQ6 0LN
website: www.watermillcottages.co.uk

For our colour brochure call 01803 770 219 or e-mail: graham@hanselpg.freeserve.co.uk

Flear Farm Cottages

nestle in a softly curving valley close to the village of East Allington, amidst their own 75 acres of fields and woods. Steeped in history, these substantial Devon stone barns have been generously converted with care and imagination into ten cottages.

All the cottages are light and fresh, and decorated in an elegantly simple style with warm pine, whitewashed walls and exposed beams.

With beaches close by, this exceptional setting, together with the luxurious standard of the cottages and facilities, makes Flear Farm the perfect place to stay.

Children can explore Flear and Oxen Wood, and have hours of fun in the large indoor pool and well-equipped play area. Parents can relax in the sauna, take a dip in the pool, play a set or two of tennis before a leisurely lunch.

Flear has plenty to offer all year round. The cottages are warm and cosy with central heating and woodburning stoves. Walks in and around Flear are a pleasure at any time of the year and the stunning South Devon coastline, with an unbelievable number of coves and beaches, is within an eight mile radius.

Flear Farm Cottages

in the heart of the Devon countryside

Flear Farm Cottages, East Allington, Totnes, Devon TQ9 7RF

Tel: 01548 521227 • Fax: 01548 521600

www.flearfarm.co.uk • e-mail: flearfarm@btinternet.com

★★★★ - ★★★★★ ETC

BLACKWELL PARK, LODDISWELL, KINGSBRIDGE

Bed, Breakfast and Evening Meal is offered in Blackwell Park, a 17th century farmhouse situated 5 miles from Kingsbridge. Seven bedrooms, some en suite, and all with washbasins and tea-making facilities. Games room; large garden, also adjoining 54 acres of woodland/Nature Reserve. Ample food with a choice of menu.

CHILDREN AND PETS ESPECIALLY WELCOME; babysitting, DOGSITTING. Pets welcome FREE of charge. Dartmoor, Plymouth, Torbay, Dartmouth and many beaches lie within easy reach.

Bed and Breakfast. Evening Meal optional.
Proprietress: Mrs B. Kelly Tel: 01548 821230
Blackwell Park, Loddiswell TQ7 4EA

Brendon House

A charming 18th century licensed Country House, nestling in the delightful wooded Lyn Valley on Exmoor. Brendon House offers fully equipped en suite bedrooms, a comfortable residents' lounge, dining room and spacious gardens bordering onto the Lyn salmon and trout river, all this against a backdrop of stunning Exmoor scenery.

For dinner you can choose from our menu of delicious Devon country fare, our Exmoor Game Selection and local seafood dishes. Vegetarian dishes are also available.

B&B from £24 • Four-course dinner £16 • Pets stay FREE

For reservations or a colour brochure: Ian & Sandra Rigby, Brendon House Hotel, Brendon, Lynton EX35 6PS
website: www.brendonvalley.co.uk/Brendon_House.htm
e-mail: brendonhouse4u@aol.com • Tel: 01598 741206

Moorlands

Where countryside and comfort combine

Woody Bay, Devon EX31 4RA
www.moorlandshotel.co.uk
Tel: 01598 763224

Two self-contained apartments within a family-run guesthouse sleeping two or three persons. Our ground floor apartment is one bedroom, lounge, kitchen and bathroom and has its own entrance and private patio area.

The second apartment is on the first floor, comprising two bedrooms, lounge with screened kitchen and shower room. The house is set in six acres of garden surrounded by Exmoor countryside.

Guests are welcome to use all the hotel amenities, including the bar, dining room and outdoor swimming pool.

Telephone for brochure. Dogs welcome with well-behaved owners.

DOGS WELCOME FREE

Quality en suite accommodation in small, friendly hotel magnificently situated on cliff-side above secluded cove with spectacular sea views. Superb food, well-stocked licensed bar lounge. TV and tea-making facilities in all rooms. ***Please write or telephone for full details.***

AA ★★

Lundy House Hotel

Mortehoe, North Devon EX34 7DZ • Tel: 01271 870372

E-mail: info@lundyhousehotel.co.uk • Website: www.lundyhousehotel.co.uk

Situated in the pretty village of Mortehoe The Smugglers offers luxury accommodation from twin rooms to family suites. Treat yourselves and your pets to beautiful coastal walks and golden beaches, before you sample our delicious home-cooked meals, real ales and warm, year-round hospitality.

The Smugglers

North Morte Road, Mortehoe, N. Devon EX34 7DR

Tel/Fax: 01271 870891

Holiday Homes & Cottages S.W.

www.swcottages.co.uk

Large selection of cottages in Devon & Cornwall. Pets welcomed. ETC rated. Coastal and Rural locations.

Tel: 01803 663650

Fax: 01803 664037

AMBER HOUSE HOTEL

6 Roundham Road, Paignton, Devon TQ4 6EZ Tel: 01803 558372

* Family-run licensed Hotel. * Colour TVs and tea/coffee making facilities in all rooms. * En-suite facilities and ground floor rooms. * Restricted smoking. * Good food, highly recommended. * Large car park. * Spacious suntrap garden and patio. * Park and beach 5 minutes' walk. * We pride ourselves on our high standards.* A warm welcome assured to pets and their families. * B&B from £18 per night. * PETS FREE.

Val & James Banks.

Write or telephone now for further details

Give your pets a holiday at

Churchwood Valley

Seven times David Bellamy Gold Award Winner

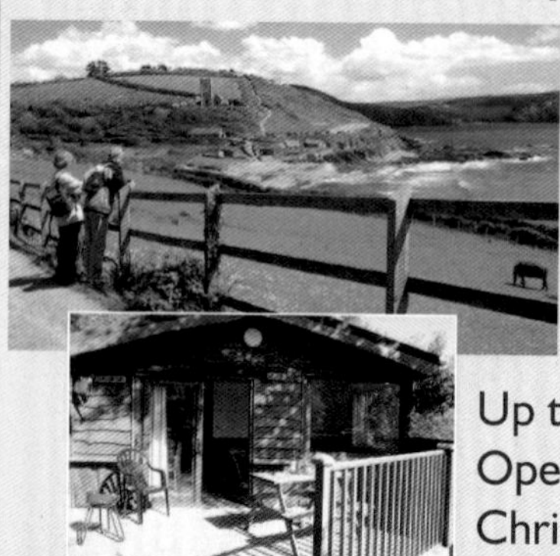

Relax in one of our comfortable log cabins, set in a peaceful wooded valley near the beach.
Enjoy wonderful walks in woods and along the coast. Abundance of birds and wildlife.
Up to two pets per cabin.
Open April to January including special Christmas and New Year Breaks.

Wembury Bay, South Devon

e-mail: Churchwoodvalley@btinternet.com

Tel: 01752 862382

❖ Bolberry Farm Cottages ❖

Bolberry, Near Salcombe, Devon TQ7 3DY

Luxury two and three bedroom barn conversion cottages
• Private gardens • Shared orchard • Views across valley • Gas, coal, open fires
• Parking • Finished to a very high standard • Linen and towels included
• Central heating • Close to coastal path and pet friendly beaches
• No charge for pets • Dog wash • Short Breaks out of season • Special couples rate
• Discount on meals taken at our Hotel nearby – Port Light Hotel
Credit/Debit cards accepted

Tel: 01548 561384 • e-mail: info@portlight-salcombe.co.uk
www.bolberryfarmcottages.co.uk • Hazel & Sean Hassall

❖ The Pet Holiday Specialist ❖

Hope Cove

Blue Bay
Apartments

Hope Cove, Near Salcombe

- *Four sunny apartments ~ Sleep 2-6 people*
- *Beach and Cliff Walks 300 yards*
- *Lovely Sea and Country Views*
- *Children and Pets Very Welcome*

Tel: 01548 511400
website: www.blue-bay-apartments.co.uk

SAND PEBBLES HOTEL & RESTAURANT

Hope Cove, near Salcombe. Friendly family-run Hotel 300 yards from delightful sandy beaches and coastal walks. Refurbished 2003. Relaxing restaurant renowned for excellent food and service. Come and stay with us and...

"Let Us Spoil You"

Telephone: 01548 561673
website: www.sandpebbleshotel.co.uk

SEE OUR ENTRY UNDER DEVON – SALCOMBE

• HOUSEBOAT HOLIDAYS •

SALCOMBE BOAT & MARINE Co. Ltd
Strand Court, Whitestrand, Salcombe, Devon TQ8 8ET

RELAX ON SALCOMBE'S BEAUTIFUL TRANQUIL ESTUARY
Well equipped Houseboats for self-catering
Motor boat & rowing dinghy included
CHILDREN AND PETS VERY WELCOME
For our Brochure please telephone: 01548 843730

Seamark

Six 2/3 bedroom Cottages set in two acres of gardens. Indoor swimming pool. Sauna. Games room. Beach. Golf and Windsurfing close by.

www.seamarkdevon.co.uk
Thurlestone Sands, Near Salcombe, Devon TQ7 3JY • Tel/Fax: 01548 561300

MILKBERE COTTAGE HOLIDAYS ◆ 3 FORE STREET ◆ SEATON ◆ DEVON EX12 2LE
Tel: (01297) 22925 – COLOUR BROCHURE
e-mail: info@milkberehols.com ◆ website: http//www.milkberehols.com

17th Century Farmhouse with seven individual cottages, lovingly converted from period farm buildings, each with its own enclosed, delightful garden.

Cradled in 45 acres of peaceful valley amid glorious Devon countryside. Abundant wildlife. Art Studio facilities in restored historical Victorian building with stunning views. All weather tennis court, trout pond. Idyllic walks in Area of Outstanding Natural Beauty, two miles from beach and World Heritage Coastline.

14th Century Inn and amenities within walking distance. Open all year. ETC ★★★★

SIDMOUTH'S MULTI AWARD WINNING TOURING & HOLIDAY HOME PARK
Weston - Sidmouth - Devon - EX10 0PH
Telephone: Park/Reservations 01297 680387 • Fax: 01297 680541
e-mail: oakdown@btinternet.com
www.bestcaravanpark.co.uk

Welcome to Oakdown "Caravan Holiday Park of the Year" in the Excellence in England Awards 2003 – Sidmouth's multi award winning park. Set within the East Devon World Heritage Coast, Oakdown is level, sheltered and landscaped into groves to give privacy. Our luxurious amenities include aids for the disabled. Enjoy our Field Trail to the famous Donkey Sanctuary.

Free colour brochure with pleasure.

FHG

Publisher's Note

While every effort is made to ensure accuracy, we regret that FHG Publications cannot accept responsibility for errors, omissions or misrepresentations in our entries or any consequences thereof. Prices in particular should be checked because we go to press early. We will follow up complaints but cannot act as arbiters or agents for either party.

Torcross Apartments

Situated directly on the beach in the unspoilt countryside of the South Hams between the blue waters of Start Bay and the Slapton Ley Nature Reserve. Seven miles to Dartmouth. Winter breaks. Central heating. Ground floor apartments and lift to all floors. In-house bar and restaurant; take-away food service. Lovely walks on coastal path.

Brochure with pleasure or visit our **website** on **www.torcross.com**

Torcross, South Devon TQ7 2TQ Tel: 01548 580206 • Fax: 01548 580996

e-mail: enquiries@torcross.net

The best of both worlds!...

★ *Indoor and Outdoor Swimming Pools* ★ *Spa Pool*
★ *Licensed Restaurant* ★ *Gym*
★ *Beauty Salon* ★ *Sauna*
★ *Launderette* ★ *Solarium*
★ *Indoor Recreation Room*

We've joined together the friendly service and facilities of the 2 star Red House Hotel for those wanting a traditional hotel atmosphere, with the privacy and freedom of Maxton Lodge's 24 self-contained holiday apartments. Two styles of accommodation sharing the same conveniently located grounds and superb range of facilities, so whether you're a working conference delegate or a fun loving family you'll find a style to suit you.

AA ★★

Red House Hotel, Rousdown Road, Chelston, Torquay TQ2 6PB
Tel: (01803) 607811
Fax: (01803) 605357
E-mail: Stay@redhouse-hotel.co.uk
Web: www.redhouse-hotel.co.uk

Sunnymeade Country Hotel

West Down,
Near Woolacombe,
North Devon EX34 8NT

Small, friendly, comfortable country hotel with our own large enclosed garden set in beautiful countryside.

- *A few minutes away from Ilfracombe, Exmoor and Woolacombe's Blue Flag Beach, (where dogs are allowed).*
- *Award-winning home cooked traditional English food, using fresh local produce.*
- *Special diets can be accommodated* • *Vegetarian choice always available*
- *Licensed Bar* • *Deaf accessible* • *10 en suite rooms, 4 on the ground floor.*
- *Open all year including Christmas.*
- *Pets Welcome – dogs are free*
- *Lots of lovely walks accessible right from the door.*

Telephone: 01271 863668 • Fax: 01271 866061

website: www.sunnymeade.co.uk

THE KNOLL HOUSE

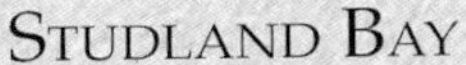

ESTABLISHED 1931

A peaceful and relaxing holiday for all ages.
An independent country-house hotel, in an unrivalled position above three miles of golden beach. Dogs are especially welcome and may sleep in your room. Special diets arranged. Our 100 acre grounds offer nice walks; squirrels and rabbits!

~

Good food and a sensible wine list.
Tennis courts; nine acre golf course and outdoor heated pool.
Health spa with Jacuzzi, Sauna, Turkish room, plunge pool and gym.
Many ground-floor and single rooms for older guests.

~

Family suites, of connecting rooms with bathroom, separate young children's dining room.
Playrooms and fabulous SAFE adventure playground.

~

Daily full board terms: £97-£130. Children less, according to age.

~

Open Easter - end October

For Colour Brochure
TEL 01929 · 450450 FAX 01929 · 450423
Email: enquiries@knollhouse.co.uk
Website: www.knollhouse.co.uk

Country Inn set in the heart of lovely Piddle Valley. Within easy reach of all Dorset's attractions. All rooms en suite with colour TV, tea and coffee, telephone; swimming pool (May-September). Riverside garden, restaurant where Half Board guests choose from à la carte menu at no extra cost.

Telephone: 01300 348358; Fax: 01300 348153

e-mail: thepoachersinn@piddletrenthide.fsbusiness.co.uk website: www.thepoachersinn.co.uk

Bed and Breakfast
£30 per person per night.
Dinner, Bed and Breakfast
£45 per person per night.
10% discount for seven nights.
Low Season Breaks
two nights Dinner, Bed and Breakfast
£90 per person.
Third night Dinner, Bed and Breakfast – FREE. (OCT-APR)
(excluding Bank Holiday weekends)

Send for brochure

ETC/AA

◆◆◆◆

Little Hewish Barn

A 150 year old brick and flint barn, converted to provide comfortable accommodation of a very high standard, including oil-fired central heating. There are two double bedrooms (one converts to twin), both with en suite bath/shower facilities. Spacious open-plan living/dining area features a wood-burning stove, fully-equipped kitchen, dishwasher, washer/dryer, TV/video, stereo etc. Children and well-behaved pets are very welcome. Fully-enclosed patio garden and ample on-site parking. Prices are all inclusive – no hidden extras. 'Per person per night' pricing outside of peak periods.

Little Hewish Barn, Milton Abbas, Blandford Forum, Dorset DT11 0DP
Tel: 01258 881235 • Fax: 01258 881393 • E-mail: terry@littlehewish.co.uk

Langtry Manor

Somewhere Special... for Someone Special

Built by Edward VII as a Lovenest for Lillie Langtry. A rare gem of a hotel where the building, food, service and history blend to form something quite exceptional. Four posters, Jacuzzi's, complimentary leisure club and award-winning restaurant. Midweek and weekend breaks. As featured on BBC Holiday Show. Pets welcome by arrangement.

Derby Road, East Cliff, Bournemouth BH1 3QB
Tel: (01202) 553887 www.langtrymanor.com

Cromwell House Hotel

Lulworth Cove, Dorset

Catriona and Alistair Miller welcome guests to their comfortable family-run hotel, set in secluded gardens with spectacular sea views. Situated 200 yards from Lulworth Cove, with direct access to the Dorset Coastal Footpath. A heated swimming pool is available for guests' use from May to October. Accommodation is in 17 en suite bedrooms, with TV, direct-dial telephone, and tea/coffee making facilities; most have spectacular sea views. Restaurant, bar wine list. Two nights dinner, bed and breakfast (fully en suite) from £90. Off peak mid week breaks available. Open all year except Christmas.

Cromwell House Hotel, Lulworth Cove, Dorset BH20 5RJ
Tel: 01929 400253/400332 • Fax: 01929 400566

ETC/AA/RAC ★★

- Gothic National Trust Hotel
- Set in 20 acres overlooking Studland Bay
- Superb food & rooms • Sea views & 4 posters • Log fires
- Tennis, golf, horse-riding • 2 minute walk to beach

The Manor House Hotel,
Studland Bay, Near Swanage, Dorset BH19 3AU
Tel/Fax: 01929 450288
www.themanorhousehotel.com

Eype's Mouth Country Hotel

Situated in a secret spot, down a leafy lane, just a five minute walk from the sea. All 18 rooms en suite, with colour TV, tea and coffee making facilities and trouser press. Two of the rooms having four-poster beds. Restaurant with views over Lyme Bay. Smugglers Bar serving bar snacks lunchtimes and evenings with patio overlooking the sea. Enjoy the spectacular walks or just take in some of the many places of interest in the area. Don't just drive through Dorset, come and stay a while and experience the peace and tranquillity that still exists in this beautiful part of Dorset. Heidi our Dalmatian looks forward to meeting you and your Fido. Three day breaks available.

Eype's Mouth Country Hotel, Eype, Bridport DT6 6AL
Tel: 01308 423300 • Fax: 01308 420033
e-mail: eypehotel@aol.com • website: www.eypehotel.co.uk

Gorselands Caravan Park

"Peaceful and Pretty"

ROSE AWARD CARAVAN HOLIDAY PARK

*** Fully Serviced caravans**
*** Shop**
*** Launderette**

*** Self contained flats**
*** Village Pub 100 yards**
*** Beach car park 3 mins by car**

Attractive secluded park set in coastal valley overlooking Chesil Beach, part of Dorset's World Heritage Jurassic Coastline. Tourist Board graded. Glorious sea views. Country and seaside walks. An ideal base for discovering Dorset's charming villages and Heritage coastline. The beach is a mile either by car or through the meadows, and the fishing is excellent. Pets are most welcome.

Colour brochure: Dept. PW
Gorselands Caravan Park
West Bexington-on-Sea, Dorset DT2 9DJ
Tel: 01308 897232 • Fax: 01308 897239

Low Lands Farm

Low Lands, Cockfield, Bishop Auckland, Co. Durham DL13 5AW
Tel 01388 718251 • Mobile: 07745 067754
e-mail: info@farmholidaysuk.com • website: www.farmholidaysuk.com

farm STAY UK

Two award-winning, beautifully renovated self-catering cottages on a working family farm. If you want peace and quiet in an area full of beautiful unspoilt countryside packed with things to see and do, then come and stay with us. Each cottage sleeps up to four people, plus cot. Beams, log fires, gas BBQ, own gardens and parking. Close to Durham City, the Lake District and Hadrian's Wall. Pets and children most welcome; childminding and equipment available. Terms from £150 to £295, inclusive of linen, towels, electricity and heating.

Please contact Alison or Keith Tallentire for a brochure.

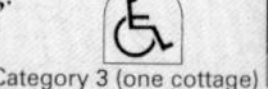
Category 3 (one cottage)

Egon Ronay Recommended
All pets welcome
Plenty of space to exercise pets.

20 Ensuite Rooms Inc. 5 luxury suites

* * * * *

Renowned Carvery and A la carte restaurant

* * * * *

Conservatory with Games * Licensed Bar
Mini breaks available all year

Jersey Farm is family run by the original owners still with the farm animals in the fields. We guaranteea relaxing time in this peaceful and scenic part of England

Jersey Farm Hotel, Darlington Road, Barnard Castle, Co Durham DL12 8TA
Tel: 01833 638223 Fax: 01833 631988 Web: www.jerseyfarm.co.uk

A historic country hotel whose heritage dates from the 13th Century, situated in the heart of the Forest of Dean, close to the Wye Valley. The hotel retains many of its original features, including beams, timber panelling and oak spiral staircases. 22 en suite bedrooms are located throughout the hotel grounds, including Four-Poster rooms and a Cottage Suite. All bedrooms are en suite and have colour TV, direct dial telephones and tea and coffee making facilities. Our Red Rosette candlelit restaurant is renowned for its quality cuisine and friendliness of service. Tudor Farmhouse is the ideal retreat to relax and unwind.

GWESTY ★★★ HOTEL

AA ★★ 74%

Tudor Farmhouse Hotel & Restaurant

Clearwell, Near Coleford, Gloucestershire GL16 8JS
Freephone: 0800 7835935 • Fax: 01594 837093
e-mail: info@tudorfarmhousehotel.co.uk • website: www.tudorfarmhousehotel.co.uk

Attention All Dog Lovers!

Romantic 18th Century Coach House in the heart of the beautiful Cotswold Hills. Sleeps four adults and two children. Beams, woodburners, outdoor heated swimming pool and bubbling hot tub. Hillside garden and twenty acres of woodlands. Free private kennel facilities (optional). Breaks £115 - £550

Also available Pear Tree Cottage close to 600 acres of National Trust common. Sleeps four + one child. Luxurious outdoor jacuzzi. £120 - £300. Colour brochure from Ros Smith.

The Old Coach House

Edgecombe House, Toadsmoor Road, Brimscombe, Stroud GL5 2UE • Tel: 01453 883147

Dear Rover,

Well, we've just got back from our holidays – absolute bliss and what a lovely place the Downfield is – we got a really warm welcome from the owners. Great walks in the Cotswolds, comfy rooms, a bar, delicious food and the Joneses I brought with me were really pleased as well. I made lots of new friends – there were even some cats to chase! Why don't you come with me next year and bring your owners with you – Just call Nigel or Maura on the dog and bone on

Lots of licks, Toby

ETC/AA/RAC ◆◆◆

The Downfield Hotel

134 Cainscross Rd, Stroud, Gloucestershire GL5 4HN
01453 764496
e-mail: info@downfieldhotel.co.uk
www.downfieldhotel.co.uk

Relaxation, comfort and tranquillity

The Woodlands Lodge Hotel

Bartley Road, Woodlands, New Forest, Hampshire SO40 7GN
Reservations: (023) 80 292257 • Fax: (023) 80 293090
e-mail: reception@woodlands-lodge.co.uk www.woodlands-lodge.co.uk

The Woodlands Lodge Hotel is a luxuriously restored Georgian Country House, set within the beautiful New Forest, yet only 15 minutes from Southampton. Our attractive gardens have direct access to the forest and are ideal for romantic walks. Golf, fishing and horse riding are available nearby and the hotel is perfectly situated for touring the area. Come and unwind from the stress of everyday life and enjoy pure luxury without ostentation.

AA ★★★

All bedrooms enjoy full en suite facilities of whirlpool bath and separate shower and have king sized beds and a full range of amenities. The quality four-course menu is changed seasonally to make use of local produce and is complemented by an interesting wine list. The service is friendly, efficient and informal.

Woodlands Lodge – where a warm welcome awaits you.

The Crown Hotel, New Forest

Tired of the same old walks? Enjoy forest, heath and the beach whilst staying at The Crown Hotel. 38 en suite rooms, all individual and recently refurbished.

Our Chef of thirty years, Stephen Greenhalgh, delights us with his imaginative menus using local produce wherever possible, either in the informal bar or the Restaurant overlooking our water-featured garden.

Dogs are welcome to bring their well-behaved owners!

High Street, Lyndhurst, Hampshire SO43 7NF • Tel: 023 8028 2922 • Fax: 023 8028 2751

E-mail: reception@crownhotel-lyndhurst.co.uk • Web: www.crownhotel-lyndhurst.activehotels.com

AA ★★

Ye Hostelrie Hotel

English Tourism Council ★★ HOTEL

GOODRICH, ROSS ON WYE,
HEREFORDSHIRE HR9 6HX

Tel: 01600 890241 • Fax: 01600 890838
e-mail: info@ye-hostelrie.co.uk
website: www.ye-hostelrie.co.uk

Enjoy comfort and good food at this fully centrally heated 17th Century Inn. Situated near to Goodrich Castle in a beautiful part of the Wye Valley, it affords easy access to the Forest of Dean, rural Herefordshire and Wales; although in a quiet village it is only a mile from the A40. Dine in the elegant surroundings of the restaurant, or the cosy atmosphere of the bar choosing from our extensive menu of home made dishes. A choice of real ales and fine wines, Morning Coffee and Afternoon Cream Tea is also available.

Prices: Bed and Breakfast in a double, twin bedded room or family room with en suite facilities, colour television, courtesy tray, clock radio, from: Double £50, Single £32.50; a cot can be provided.

• Pets are welcome in the bedrooms and garden. •

the Inn on the Wye
Quality Food with Excellent Service!
A beautifully restored 18th Century coaching inn with views of Goodrich Castle on the banks of the River Wye. All bedrooms en-suite with colour TV, telephone, & usual facilities. Ala carte & bar snack menus offering home cooked food.
Peaceful country walks - ideal base for touring.
Families welcome. Children's play area and gardens.
Open all day, seven days a week. Large car park.
Pets welcome by arrangement.
Kerne Bridge, Goodrich,
Nr Ross-on-Wye, HR9 5QS
Tel: 01600 890872 Fax: 01600 890594
E-mail: theinnonthewye@kernebridge.freeserve.co.uk
www. theinnonthewye.co.uk
RAC

"A Peaceful Retreat in the tranquil walking/biking countryside of West Wight"

The Country Garden Hotel

Church Hill, Totland Bay, Isle of Wight PO39 0ET

A five minute stroll to the Solent, surrounded by lovely walks and hikes, and a short drive to the bustling sailing port of Yarmouth, this personable intimate hotel offers the best of all worlds. Ashley Courtenay sums it up: "a really superb hotel set in beautiful gardens - relish the superb cuisine" in one of the Isle's finest restaurants overlooking the gardens. **Garden & sea-view rooms available**, all en suite with TV, fridge, duvets and down pillows, bathrobes, phone, central heating, hairdryer, tea/coffee. ***ASHLEY COURTENAY RECOMMENDED***

ANY DAY TO ANY DAY, B&B, HALF BOARD

Adults Only • Doubles • Twins • Singles • Suite • Ground floor rooms

FERRY INCLUSIVE RATES OCTOBER THRU APRIL

B&B from £41pp/day ; DB&B from £55pp/day, £365pp/week

For brochure, tariff, sample menu and testimonials from recent guests:

Phone/Fax: 01983 754521
e-mail: countrygardeniow@aol.com
website: www.thecountrygardenhotel.co.uk

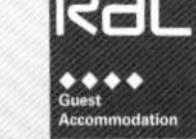

SENTRY MEAD HOTEL

Sentry Mead is a tranquil Country House set in its own spacious gardens where well-behaved dogs are welcome throughout the hotel (except in the dining room) and to sleep in guests' bedrooms; our own Labrador and Retriever always make our canine visitors feel at home as soon as they arrive. Personal care and attention to detail make this a very special 3 star hotel for both pets and people for either a short break or a longer stay.

Mike & Julie Hodgson

Sentry Mead Hotel, Madeira Road, Totland Bay
Isle of Wight PO39 0BJ
Tel/Fax: 01983 753212

e-mail: pets@sentry-mead.co.uk • website: www.sentry-mead.co.uk

"....a jewel in the crown of the West Wight"

Garden of England

Cottages in Kent & Sussex

Tel: 01732 369168
Fax: 01732 358817
The Mews Office
189A High Street
Tonbridge
Kent TN9 1BX

holidays@gardenofenglandcottages.co.uk
www.gardenofenglandcottages.co.uk

Accommodation for all seasons

Big paws and little paws are welcome in many of our holiday homes, plus **pets go free** with every well-behaved owner

All properties ETC quality assessed

Short Breaks available all season from £60. 1st pet £5, 2nd pet free

SUPERB VALUE FOR 2004 SEASON

Carefree HOLIDAYS

A warm welcome for you and your pets. Inexpensive, 'live-as-you-please' self-catering holidays in beautiful Norfolk. Chalets, Bungalows, and Cottages near Great Yarmouth & Norfolk Broads.

Booking Hotline
Tel: 01493 732176
All calls personally answered

Colour Brochure : Carefree Holidays, Chapel Briers, Yarmouth Road, Hemsby, Norfolk NR29 4NJ.
Find us on the internet: www.carefree-holidays.co.uk

Set in the UK's most beautiful village of Burnham Market, this stylish, fabulous hotel provides a friendly atmosphere with attentive service. This privately owned inn offers individually designed bedrooms with a high degree of comfort, air-conditioned dining rooms in which modern British brasserie-style food is served, a traditional bar with log fire, which attracts many of the locals and is the sort of place where nice dogs like to meet, a sunny patio and garden in which to relax with dogs, and a conservatory which is tastefully furnished.

Owner Paul Whittome with Augustus and Sweep, affectionately known as "the boys"

Amazing value midweek Dinner, Bed and Breakfast Breaks.

Johansens "Inn of the Year"
Egon Ronay "Inn of the Year"
Good Hotel Guide Cesar Awards "Inn of the Year"
Norfolk Dining Pub of the Year
Voted by The Times as their 2nd Favourite Hotel in England
Catey Award Winner
AA 2 Rosette Restaurant

Beach and Woodland Walks 1 Mile Away.

The Hoste Arms Hotel, The Green, Burnham Market, Norfolk PE31 8HD
Tel: 01328 738777 • Fax: 01328 730103
E-mail: reception@hostearms.co.uk • Web: www.hostearms.co.uk

Pet welcome free of charge

Comfortable, well-equipped chalets situated on beautiful, landscaped, quiet site. Ideally placed for walks to adjacent woods, cliffs and sandy beaches. 10 minutes' walk to town. Golf course and local shops nearby. Plenty of local places of interest to visit. One twin, one double room, bathroom, colour TV, microwave, well-equipped kitchenette. Children welcome.

Short Breaks in Spring/Autumn 2 nights or more from £70
Spring/Autumn £120-£185 per week
June-September £195-£265 per week

DETAILS FROM: MRS I. SCOLTOCK, SHANGRI-LA, LITTLE CAMBRIDGE, DUTON HILL, DUNMOW, ESSEX CM6 3QU • TEL: 01371 870482

Kings Chalet Park
Cromer, Norfolk

Sleep 2-4
Open March to October

4B&B STRENNETH

Country Bed and Breakfast

Airfield Road, Fersfield, Diss, Norfolk IP22 2BP

STRENNETH is a well-established, family-run business, situated in unspoiled countryside just a short drive from Bressingham Gardens and the picturesque market town of Diss. Offering first-class accommodation, the original 17th Century building has been carefully renovated to a high standard with a wealth of exposed oak beams and a newer single storey courtyard wing. There is ample off-road parking and plenty of nice walks nearby. All seven bedrooms, including a Four-Poster and an Executive, are tastefully arranged with period furniture and distinctive beds. Each having remote-control colour television, hospitality trays, central heating and full en suite facilities. The establishment is smoke-free. Dinners are served by arrangement. There is an extensive breakfast menu using local produce. Ideal touring base. Pets most welcome at no extra charge. Outside kennels with runs if required. Bed and Breakfast from £25.00.

Telephone: 01379 688182 • Fax: 01379 688260
E-mail: pdavey@strenneth.co.uk • Website: www.strenneth.co.uk

Experience the great joy of Norfolk...

We offer your pets 8 acres of lawns, paddock and woodland as a play area with Norfolk's vast beaches within a few minutes drive. We offer the rest of the family a choice of 14 superbly equipped cottages, leisure centre with heated indoor pool, sauna, solarium and games room. Animal farm, children's play area, enchanted wood, grass tennis court and croquet lawn.

Idyllic Cottages @ Vere Lodge

Vere Lodge, South Raynham, Fakenham, Norfolk NR21 7HE
Tel: 01328 838261 (24 hour answering service)
Fax: 01328 838300 E-mail: major@verelodge.co.uk

www.idylliccottages.co.uk
for those who demand the very best

The Lifeboat Inn

16th Century Smugglers' Ale House

Ship Lane,Thornham,
Norfolk PE36 6LT
Tel: 01485 512236 • Fax: 01485 512323
E-mail: reception@lifeboatinn.co.uk

THE LIFEBOAT INN has been a welcome sight for the weary traveller for centuries – roaring open fires on a frosty night, real ales and a hearty meal awaiting. The Summer brings its own charm – a cool beer, gazing over open meadows to the harbour, and rolling white horses gently breaking upon Thornham's sandy beach.

Dogs are welcome in all our bars and we provide the sort of breakfast that will enable you to keep up with your four-legged friend on the way to the beach!

Guests arriving at reception are greeted by our grand old fireplace in the lounge – ideal for toasting your feet after a day walking the coastal path – if you can coax your sleeping dog out of prime position!

The restaurant (AA rosette) opens every evening offering a varied selection of dishes to suit all tastes. Our extensive bar snack menu is also available if guests wish their pets to join them in the bar.

Bird watchers, walkers and nature lovers are spoilt for choice. A walk from our front door will take you to Thornham beach in no time at all and onto the Holme Nature Reserve. The Titchwell Marsh Nature Reserve is 2 miles away and Snettisham, Blakeney, Holkham and Cley Nature Reserves are all within short driving distance.

There are numerous and varied walks along miles of open beaches, across sweeping sand dunes, through pine woods or along chalk and sandstone cliff tops. It is truly a walker's paradise - especially if you're a dog.

We hope you will come and visit us. For our brochure and tariff which includes details of breaks please ring 01485 512236 or visit our website www.lifeboatinn.co.uk

Other FHG Holiday Guides

100's of places to stay!

SELF-CATERING HOLIDAYS in Britain

One of the best and perhaps the widest selection of self-catering accommodation, covering the whole of the UK. Established 30 years, and with over 1,000 entries it is firmly established as the market-leader for self-catering holiday choices throughout Britain.

From modern apartment complexes to hidden forest cabins, there is a holiday to suit every need. There is also a large selection of caravan holidays. The guide has proved popular with families and couples who enjoy the freedom of a direct-booked self catering holiday.

CARAVAN & CAMPING HOLIDAYS

This handy sized guide is one of our most popular titles and has been a best-seller for over 20 years. This guide covers every type of caravan and camping facility with user-friendly symbols to show grading of standards and facilities. As a longtime best-seller our Guide to Caravan & Camping Holidays continues to offer advertisers low cost year-long exposure to the largest single category of holiday-maker throughout the UK.

BRITAIN'S BEST HOLIDAYS

An extremely popular and inexpensive quick reference guide for all kinds of holiday opportunities throughout Britain. The extensive range of holidays is split into four main categories – Board (hotels, guest houses, farms, bed & breakfast, etc); Self-Catering (houses, cottages, flats, chalets); Caravans (solus sites, parks and camping sites); Activity holidays (camping, golfing, sporting holidays) This guide is very user-friendly with self-explanatory symbols to show services and amenities. It is most popular amongst families and those looking for the easiest route to making a direct booking.

FHG

Guides available from most bookshops and larger newsagents

FHG Publications Ltd. Abbey Mill Business Centre, Seedhill, Paisley PA1 1TJ

Prices: Caravan & Camping and Britains Best Holidays only £4.99

Self Catering Holidays only £6.99

NOTE

All the information in this guide is given in good faith in the belief that it is correct. However, the publishers cannot guarantee the facts given in these pages, neither are they responsible for changes in ownership or facilities that may take place after the date of going to press.

Readers should always satisfy themselves that the facilities they require are available and that the terms, if quoted, still apply.

PETS WELCOME FREE

IN THE BEAUTIFUL EXMOOR NATIONAL PARK

The DUNKERY BEACON HOTEL

WOOTTON COURTENAY
WEST SOMERSET TA24 8RH
www.dunkerybeaconhotel.co.uk

Country house hotel in fabulous unrivalled setting.

The superb views can be absorbed at leisure from the terrace or lawns and gardens.

• Fully en suite rooms • Colour TV • Coffee and tea making facilities
• Hairdryers • Car park • Lots of lovely "walkies" • No single supplement
Complimentary tray of tea and biscuits on arrival

No restriction on dog access, apart from the main dining room (usual exceptions)

Special Breaks Spring/Summer/Autumn

For full information and brochure write or telephone Kenneth or Daphne Midwood

TELEPHONE 01643 841241 • E-mail: Dunkery.Beacon@virgin.net

YOU WILL BE WARMLY WELCOMED ON ARRIVAL,
BUT IT IS QUITE POSSIBLE THAT YOUR PET WILL GET EVEN MORE FUSS

Meet our two Old English sheepdogs Poppy and Sweet Pea

"I knew we were in the right place when the afternoon tea came with dog biscuits!

Ralegh's Cross Inn

Brendon Hill, Exmoor, Somerset TA23 0LN

Situated high in the beautiful Brendon Hills, Exmoor National Park, the warmest of welcomes awaits everyone who steps over the threshold of this 16th century coaching inn. Only 14 miles from Taunton and the M5, but a million miles from the stresses of modern life! All rooms are en suite with hospitality tray, colour TV and direct dial telephone.

As well as our daily specials board, we also boast an extensive menu of freshly prepared starters, home-cooked main courses and a tempting range of home made desserts. We are very famous locally for our tasty farmer's carvery.

As well as being a walker's, rider's and fisherman's paradise, there are many places of interest for the tourist too. We offer a range of seasonal leisure breaks; telephone for a brochure, or view our comprehensive website.

Tel: 01984 640343
Fax: 01984 641111
enquiry@raleghscross.co.uk
www.raleghscross.co.uk

Edgcott House

Exford
Somerset
TA247QG
Tel/Fax: 01643 831 495

Marc Watts may have relocated from Cornwall's Trevaunance, but his blend of warm and mildly eccentric hospitality is unchanging.

Edgcott House is a 17th Century country house, in the village of Exford right in the heart of the magnificent Exmoor National Park.

Edgcott House is a country house of great charm and character set amidst mature, secluded gardens in beautiful lush countryside. Experience the sound of birdsong & bubbling brook, the comfort of open log fires, newly refurbished bedrooms - all with ensuite, and delicious full Exmoor breakfast.

Exmoor •• The Pack Horse

Allerford, Near Porlock, Somerset TA24 8HW
Tel/Fax: 01643 862475
www.thepackhorse.net • e-mail: holidays@thepackhorse.net

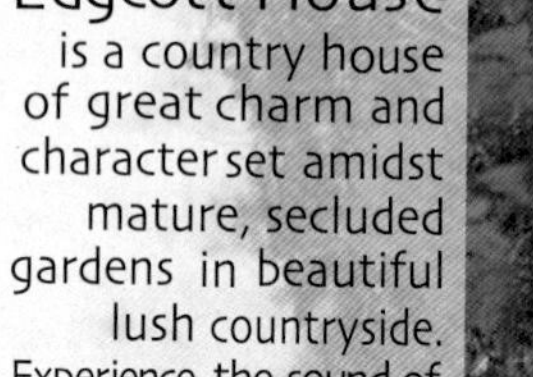

Our self-catering apartments and cottage are situated in this unique location within a picturesque National Trust village which has local amenities. The Pack Horse sits alongside the shallow River Aller, overlooking the famous bridge. Enjoy immediate access from our doorstep to the beautiful surrounding countryside, pretty villages, spectacular coast, and Exmoor.

Terms from £220 to £450 per week

OPEN ALL YEAR • PRIVATE PARKING • SHORT BREAKS

Very warm welcome assured

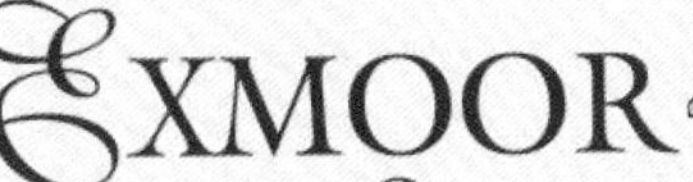

... for all Seasons

The Exmoor White Horse Inn

Exford, Exmoor National Park, Somerset, TA24 7PY

Tel: (01643) 831229

Your dream of an Olde Worlde 16th Century Inn, with log fires, standing on the green by the side of a trickling stream of one of Exmoor's most beautiful villages comes true before your eyes. Horses all around, the blacksmith busy over the road and rolling moor waiting for you at the edge of the village.

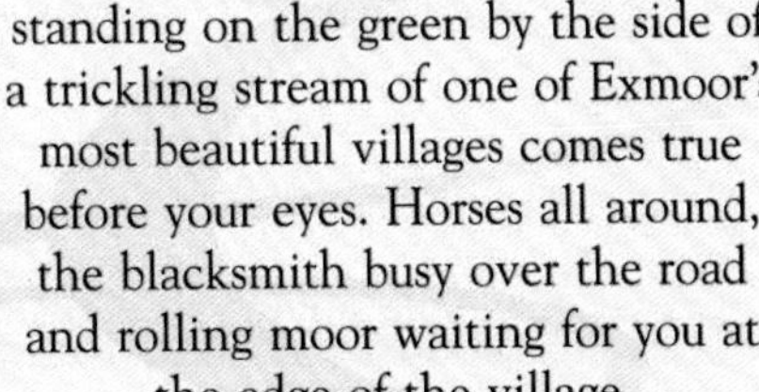

26 sumptious ensuite rooms with colour TV, tea and coffee making facilities and direct dial telephones, which invite you to kick off your shoes and relax. Enjoy a 5 course candlelit dinner prepared with fresh local produce including smoked Salmon, Lobster, Venison and Game specialities, and mouth-watering sweets from our traditional pudding board.

There are days and days of exploring to do on Exmoor or along its spectacular coast - ride or walk over the moor 'on safari' in search of wild red deer. Riding, fly fishing tuition, shooting (Clays), walking (8 circular walks from Inn) can be arranged. Enjoy full use of our leisure facilities at our sister hotel.

www.exmoor-hospitality-inns.co.uk

The Castle Hotel

Porlock, Somerset TA24 8PY

Tel & Fax: 01643 862504

E-mail: castlehotel@btconnect.com

The Castle Hotel is a small, fully licensed family-run hotel in the centre of the lovely Exmoor village of Porlock. It is an ideal holiday location for those who wish to enjoy the grandeur of Exmoor on foot or by car. The beautiful villages of Selworthy and Dunster with its castle are only a short distance away. There are 13 en suite bedrooms, all fully heated, with colour TV and tea/coffee making facilities.The Castle Hotel has a well-stocked bar with Real Ale. Draught Guinness and Cider. A full range of Bar Meals is available at lunchtimes and evenings or dine in our Restaurant. Children and pets are most welcome. Dog walking field. Darts, pool and skittles.

✤ ✤ ***Special Breaks available*** ✤ ***Extremely low rates*** ✤✤

PASSION
ANDREWS ON THE WEIR
Restaurant with Rooms

PERFECT

Overlooking Porlock Weir, where Exmoor meets the sea, is a restaurant with rooms where every meal is an experience; where each room is individual; and where pets are just as welcome as their owners. Discover the perfect break on Exmoor at Andrews.

Porlock Weir, Porlock, Somerset TA24 8PB
Tel: 01643 863300 Fax: 01643 863311
www.andrewsontheweir.co.uk

Knights Holiday Homes

at Kessingland on the Suffolk Heritage Coast

THE BEST OF BRITISH SELF-CATERING HOLIDAYS

at the 'Seaview' and 'Alandale' Holiday Parks on the peaceful Suffolk Coast

CHILDREN AND PETS WELCOME
OPEN ALL YEAR

'Kessingland: Most easterly village in the United Kingdom. First to greet the sun. Once known as the richest village in England because of its prolific fishing. Now known for its peaceful, pleasant surroundings, its beautiful spacious beach and its Suffolk countryside, where you can relax in peace and watch the boats sail by on the North Sea's Herring Pond.'

Seaview Bungalows
These bungalows are situated on a quiet, attractive estate set in nine acres of lawns overlooking the sea. There is a made-up roadway round the estate and parking near your door. Your bungalow has three bedrooms, bathroom and toilet, kitchen and lounge with a sun door opening onto the lawns. A walkway leads immediately from the estate to the promenade and the beach.
SHOPS ARE APPROXIMATELY 450 YARDS AND BUS STOP 300 YARDS.

THE BUNGALOWS
- 1-6 persons
- Colour Television
- Bed linen supplied • Fully equipped kitchens
- Full size cookers and refrigerators
- Microwaves, video recorders
- Cots and Highchairs are available
- Electrically heated - no meters • Parking

THE VILLAGE
- Clean Beach Award
- Mother Hubbard's Cupboard – Kessingland Art Centre and Gift Shop
- Suffolk Wildlife Park
- Shops • Pubs
- Restaurants • Cafes • Bus Service

BROCHURE ◆ CALENDAR ◆ OFFER LETTER ◆ BOOKING FORM from

 **Knights Holiday Homes, 198 Church Road, Kessingland, Suffolk NR33 7SF Freephone 0800 269067** VISA

NOTE

All the information in this guide is given in good faith in the belief that it is correct. However, the publishers cannot guarantee the facts given in these pages, neither are they responsible for changes in ownership or facilities that may take place after the date of going to press.

Readers should always satisfy themselves that the facilities they require are available and that the terms, if quoted, still apply.

LITTLE HEMINGFOLD HOTEL

★ **Relax** and enjoy the friendly and tranquil atmosphere of our part 17th century and early Victorian farmhouse.

★ **Meander** through our 40 acres of farm and woodland with endless walks in the adjoining countryside.

★ **Treat** your pets to one of our courtyard garden rooms, all en suite and some with log-burning stoves.

★ **Fish**, row and swim in our two-acre trout lake or take up a challenge on our grass tennis court.

Discounts for children 7-14 years old. and FREE accommodation for pets. Weekly Dinner, Bed and Breakfast from £64 per person per night. Two day breaks from £64 per person per night.

Please ring or write to Paul and Alison Slater

LITTLE HEMINGFOLD HOTEL, TELHAM, BATTLE, EAST SUSSEX TN33 0TT

Tel: 01424 774338 • Fax: 01424 775351

E-mail: littlehemingfoldhotel@tiscali.co.uk • Website: www.littlehemmingfoldhotel.co.uk

ETC ◆◆◆ **'Special Places to Stay'** **RAC**

JEAKE'S HOUSE

Mermaid Street, Rye, East Sussex TN31 7ET
Telephone: 01797 222828 Fax: 01797 222623

E-mail: jeakeshouse@btinternet.com • Website: www.jeakeshouse.com

Dating from 1689, this beautiful Listed Building stands in one of England's most famous streets. Oak-beamed and panelled bedrooms overlook the marsh to the sea. Brass, mahogany or four-poster beds with linen sheets and lace; honeymoon suite; TV, radio, telephone. Book-lined bar. Residential licence. Traditional and vegetarian breakfast served. £37.00–£58.00pp. Private car park. Visa and Mastercard accepted.

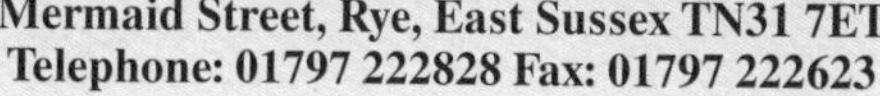

AA ◆◆◆◆◆ PREMIER SELECTED   RAC ◆◆◆◆◆ Sparkling Diamond & Warm Welcome Award   Good Hotel Guide César Award

Fairhaven Holiday Cottages

Fairhaven offers a wide selection of holiday homes for 2 - 12 people as well as comprehensive local knowledge and a friendly service. We specialise in Kent and Sussex with a few properties in Wiltshire and in Wales. Our directors personally visit all of our properties to ensure quality and up-to-date information. Pets are welcome in many properties and short breaks are available out of season.

For full details of all our properties visit our website

www fairhaven-holidays.co.uk

Alternatively request a colour brochure by telephone, fax or e-mail
Tel: 08452 304334 • Fax: 01634 570157 • e-mail: enquiries@fairhaven-holidays.co.uk

Little Oaks Farley Way, Fairlight East Sussex

Luxury bungalow on one level set in quiet coastal village with clifftop parklands, close to ancient towns of Rye, Battle and Hastings. Furnished to a very high standard, the spacious accommodation comprises double bedroom with en suite shower and sauna, twin bedroom, lounge with TV, dining room, fully equipped kitchen/diner, bathroom, conservatory and balcony overlooking beautiful secluded garden and garage. No smoking in bungalow. Pets welcome. Rates on application, which include central heating, electricity, bed linen and towels.

Contact: Ray and Janet Adams, Fairlight Cottage, Warren Road, Fairlight, East Sussex TN35 4AG • Tel/Fax: 01424 812545

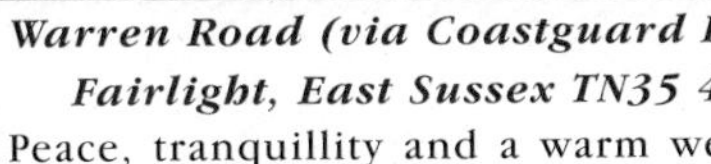

FAIRLIGHT COTTAGE

Warren Road (via Coastguard Lane), Fairlight, East Sussex TN35 4AG

Peace, tranquillity and a warm welcome await you at our comfortable country house, adjoining 650 acres of country park in an area of outstanding natural beauty – a paradise for dogs and owners. Panoramic sea views from large balcony. Centrally heated en suite bedrooms with beverage trays and colour TV. Comfortable guest lounge. Delicious breakfasts. No smoking. Ample parking. Pets stay with owners (free of charge).

B&B from £27.50 pppn. • Single supplement
Janet & Ray Adams • 01424 812545

ETC/AA ◆◆◆◆

ST ANDREWS LODGE

Chichester Road, Selsey, West Sussex PO20 0LX
Tel: 01243 606899 • Fax: 01243 607826
e-mail: info@standrewslodge.co.uk
web: www.standrewslodge.co.uk

Welcoming, family-run hotel with a reputation for an excellent hearty breakfast. Situated on the Manhood peninsula just south of Chichester, close to unspoilt beaches and countryside. Ten bedrooms, all en suite, with direct-dial telephones, TV, fridge and tea-making facilities; some on ground floor. Spacious lounges with log fire; friendly bar for residents only. Wheelchair accessible room. Large secure car park. Dogs welcome in rooms overlooking large garden. Apply for brochure, prices and details of special winter offers October to February.

Two Self-Catering Holiday Cottages • West Sussex • Steyning, Near Worthing

Five Star rating by an independent holiday cottage agency

PEPPERSCOMBE FARM, NEWHAM LANE, STEYNING, WEST SUSSEX BN44 3LR • Tel: 01903 813868
e-mail: johncamilleri@btopenworld.com

Each cottage is designed to sleep 2 adults only.

LOCATION is peaceful and quiet, nestling in a combe beneath the South Downs Way, just a few minutes from the old historic market town of Steyning. We offer a direct link to the Downs and the foot and bridle path network, and are close to many places of interest. Previously a dairy farm, part of which is now converted to spacious, comfortable cottages with oak beams, and, for winter lets, have a very efficient underfloor heating system, making them both a warm and cosy place to stay.

Prices from £350 varying to £475 for 7 nights. Pets are welcome at £15 each per week.
Please phone for further information and details.

DORMY HOUSE

Willersey Hill, Broadway, Worcestershire WR12 7LF
Telephone: Broadway (01386) 852711 Telefax: (01386) 858636
e-mail: reservations@dormyhouse.co.uk
website: www.dormyhouse.co.uk

The 17th century Dormy House Hotel is set high in the rolling Cotswold countryside between the picturesque villages of Broadway and Chipping Campden, with Stratford-upon-Avon only a short drive away. Adjacent to Broadway Golf Course, it is a really lovely place in which to relax with your dog(s) and enjoy a one night stay, or classic Dormy Break for two or more nights. Telephone for brochure or booking, or visit our website.

Experience the unique atmosphere and traditional hospitality at...

Simonstone Hall, Hawes, North Yorkshire DL8 3LY

Set in magnificent countryside near the market town of Hawes, Simonstone Hall is a beautifully restored country house hotel with spectacular views over the dale and surrounding fell.
• Outstanding Bar Meals and Sunday Lunches served in the Game Tavern. • Our Restaurant provides an elegant setting for our wide selection of fine foods and wines.
• An excellent base for walking and exploring the Dales.
• Pets welcome in most rooms • Kennels provided if required.
A relaxed, friendly establishment with open fires, four-poster beds and experienced staff to look after all your needs.

Telephone: 01969 667255 • Fax: 01969 667741
E-mail: information@simonstonehall.demon.co.uk
Website: www.simonstonehall.co.uk AA ★★

LUXURY COTTAGES AND TIMBER LODGES IN BEAUTIFUL SURROUNDINGS

FOLLIFOOT,
HARROGATE HG3 1JH

TEL: 01423 870439
FAX: 01423 870859

e-mail:holiday-park@ruddingpark.com
www.ruddingpark.com

- **Deer House family pub**
- **Children's adventure playground**
- **Pets welcome**
- **Heated outdoor swimming pool and paddling pool**
- **Games room**
- **18 hole pay & play golf course plus floodlit driving range**

RELAX IN THE HEART OF YORKSHIRE

Panoramic views, waterfalls, wild birds and tranquillity

Stone farmhouse with panoramic views, high in the Yorkshire Dales National Park (Herriot family's house in 'All Creatures Great and Small' on TV). Three bedrooms (sleeps 6-8), sitting and dining rooms with wood-burning stoves, kitchen, bathroom, WC. House has electric storage heating, cooker, microwave, fridge, washing machine, colour TV, telephone. Garden, large barn, stables. Access from lane, private parking, no through traffic. Excellent walking from front door, near Wensleydale, Pets welcome. Self-catering from £400 per week.

Westclose House (Allaker),
West Scrafton, Coverdale, Leyburn, North Yorks DL8 4RM
For bookings telephone 020 8567 4862
e-mail: ac@adriancave.com • www.adriancave.com/yorks

Holidays for Discriminating Dogs

Yorkshire Dales

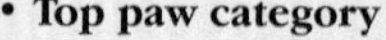
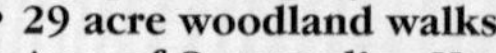
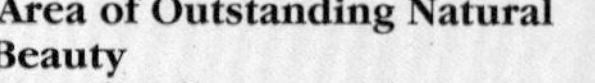
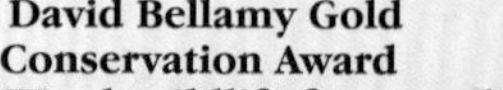

- Sniffing trails
- Top paw category
- 29 acre woodland walks
- Area of Outstanding Natural Beauty
- David Bellamy Gold Conservation Award
- Watch wildlife from quality accommodation
- Central: Harrogate, York, Skipton, Herriot/Bronte Country

See advert in Harrogate Section

Hill House Farm Cottages

Julie & Jim Griffith
Hill House Farm
Little Langton, Northallerton DL7 0PZ
Tel: 01609 770643 Fax: 01609 760438
e-mail: info@Hillhousefarmcottages.com

These former farm buildings sleeping 2/6 have been converted into 4 well-equipped cottages, retaining original beams. Cosily heated for year-round appeal. Peaceful setting with magnificent views. Centrally located between Dales and Moors with York, Whitby and Scarborough all within easy driving distance. Pets welcome. Exercise Field. Weekly rates from £150 incl. all linen, towels, heating and electricity. Short Breaks available.

• Pub food 1 mile • Golf 2 miles • Shops 3 miles

For a free colour brochure please call 01609 770643

"the best of Yorkshire – coast, city and countryside..."

Deceptively spacious luxury cottage in conservation village, on delightful cul-de-sac with thatched roof cottages and charming ivy-clad pub. Ideal Whitby, Scarborough and York.

The cottage sleeps 2-8 + cot in 4 bedrooms. Mediterranean style, south-facing patio area with gas barbecue for lazy summer evenings. Off-street parking. Pets and children very welcome. Non-smoking. Open all year. Other properties available – all ETC 4 Star.

Coronation Farm Cottage

Tel: 01653 698251 • Fax: 01653 691962

e-mail: enquiries@coronationfarmcottage.co.uk • web: www.coronationfarmcottage.co.uk

Tel: 01484 851413 Fax: 01484 851843

DURKER ROODS HOTEL

WEST YORKSHIRE'S WARMEST WELCOME

Extensively refurbished, Durker Roods, a former Victorian gentleman's residence, has an excellent reputation for the warmth of its welcome.

Located close to major road networks, it is an ideal base from which to explore 'Last of the Summer Wine' country, and the foothills of the Peak District National Park. Golf Breaks available; many leisure facilities close by.

All 30 bedrooms offer en suite facilities, TV and hospitality trays; some ground floor rooms are suitable for disabled visitors. The elegant restaurant features British and Mediterranean-style dishes using fresh seasonal produce, and the newly refurbished bar has a warm, relaxing atmosphere.

Durker Roods Hotel, Bishopsway, Meltham, Huddersfield HD9 4JA

e-mail: spencer@durkerroodshotel.co.uk • www.durkerroodshotel.co.uk

The Estate lies along the beautiful Deveron River and our traditional stone cottages nestle in individual seclusion. Visitors can explore one of the ancient baronies of Scotland. The sea is only nine miles away, and the market town of Turriff only two miles, with its golf course, swimming pool, etc. Places of interest including the Cairngorms, Aviemore, picturesque fishing villages and castles, all within easy reach on uncrowded roads. See our Highland cattle. 6 miles of own walks.

Terms: from £159 weekly. Special Winter lets. 10 cottages sleeping 6-9. Children and reasonable dogs welcome. STB Inspected.

For a brochure contact: ***Mrs P. Bates, Holiday Cottages, Forglen Estate, Turriff, Aberdeenshire AB53 4JP***
Tel: 01888 562918/562518 • Fax: 01888 562252
website: www.forglen.co.uk

A LUXURY DOG'S LIFE AT MELFORT PIER & HARBOUR

Private beach, Hill walking, Underfloor heating, dog sitter.
Luxury Lochside Houses with Sauna, Spa bath, Sat.TV, Tel, e-mail.
Right on the shores of Loch Melfort. Close-by Restaurants/Bars.
Excellent base for touring Argyll and the surrounding islands.
From £85 – £220 per house per night. Open all year.
Sleep 2-6 persons. Min. stay 2 nights, start any day of the week.
2 Pets welcome. 1 pet stays free when you mention Pets Welcome!

Tel: 01852 200 333 • Fax: 01852 200 329

e-mail: melharbour@aol.com • website: www.scotland2000.com/melfort

Lagnakeil HIGHLAND LODGES

STB ★★★★ Self-Catering

Our timber lodges and three houses are set in a tranquil, scenic wooded glen overlooking Loch Feochan, only 3½ miles from Oban, 'Gateway to the Isles'. Lodges are fully equipped to a high standard, including linen. Country pub only a short walk up the Glen. OAP discount. Free loch fishing. Special breaks from £39 per lodge per night, weekly from £195. Lodges/houses sleep 2-10 comfortably in 1-4 bedrooms.
Our colour brochure will tell lots more. Please phone or write to:

Colin & Jo Mossman, Lagnakeil Highland Lodges, Lerags, Oban PA34 4SE • 01631 562746 • Fax: 01631 570225 • e-mail: lagnakeil@aol.com • website: www.lagnakeil.co.uk •

Seil Island, by Oban, Argyll P34 4TJ
Telephone: 01852 300276
Web page: WWW.willowburn.co.uk
Personally run and managed by Jan Wolfe and Chris Wolfe.

Willowburn Hotel and Restaurant

The Willowburn Hotel garden reaches down to the peaceful waters of Clachan Sound. Inside, the lounge, dining room and most of our comfortable en suite bedrooms enjoy this wonderful view – we see otters, seals, deer and a huge variety of birds.
We are informal and relaxed and take pride in what we offer – in particular our food, which is imaginative and varied, as is our wine list. There's some wonderful walking in the area, wildlife, wild flowers, gardens, boat trips, and places and opportunities just to sit and ponder.
We are non-smoking, pet-friendly and we just want you to relax and enjoy yourselves.

Good Food Guide 2003 • Which! Hotel Guide 2003 • Scottish Small Hotel ★★★★ • The Taste of Scotland • AA ★★ Hotel 76% • AA Rosette 2001

Cairndow, Argyll.
At The Head Of Loch Fyne

Two comfortable holiday cottages at the head of the longest sea loch in Scotland. **INVERFYNE** (pictured left), a very spacious cottage with 4 twin bedded rooms, overlooks the estuary. There is a piano in the 32 foot living room and a large utility/drying room. **BRIDGE COTTAGE** (pictured right), is a traditional stone cottage and sleeps four, overlooks the bottom pool of the river Fyne. Linen and electricity are included. Achadunan Estate is set amidst lovely walking country. The bird life is fascinating and the deer graze the river banks and the hills behind the cottages. Brochures available from:

Mrs Delap, Achadunan, Cairndow, Argyll PA26 8BJ
Tel & Fax: +44 (0) 1499 600 238
Web: www.argyllholidaycottages.com

Tralee Bay Holiday Park achieved the Gold David Bellamy award 99, 00, 01 and 02 for the wild life and conservation. Located on the beautiful West Coast of Scotland near Oban, overlooking Ardmucknish Bay. The wooded surroundings and sandy beach make Tralee the ideal destination for a self-catering lodge or caravan holiday at any time of the year. The park offers something for everyone with play area, mini golf, fly fishing, diving, nature walks and boat slipway. Set in breathtaking Highland countryside, the gateway to the Isles. The choice of self catering accommodation ranges from 2003 model 2/6 berth caravans to brand new lavishly furnished lodges. Pets welcome in specific units.

TRALEE BAY HOLIDAYS

Tel: 01631 720255/217

Tralee Bay Holidays, Benderloch, by Oban, Argyll PA37 1QR
E-mail: tralee@easynet.co.uk Web: www.tralee.com

COLOGIN COUNTRY CHALETS
Oban

All Scottish Glens have their secrets: let us share ours with you – and your pets !

- Tranquil country glen, just 3 miles from Oban
- Free fishing and dinghy use on our hill loch.
- Excellent walks for you and your dogs.
- Home-cooked food and licensed bar in our converted farm-yard byre.
- A safe haven for pets and children.
- A friendly, family-run complex with a good range of facilities.

PETS WELCOME

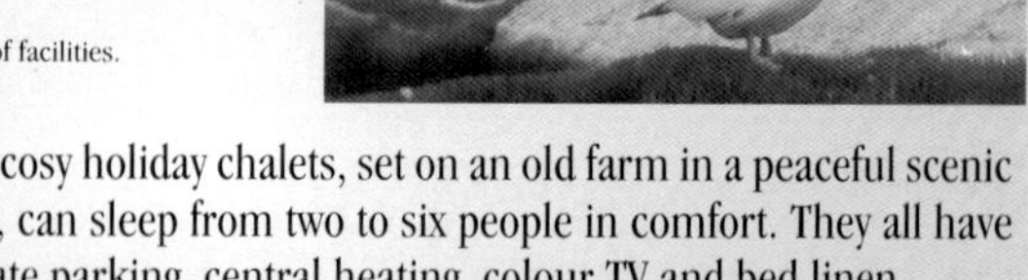

Our cosy holiday chalets, set on an old farm in a peaceful scenic glen, can sleep from two to six people in comfort. They all have private parking, central heating, colour TV and bed linen.

Call now for our colour brochure and find out more:

MRS LINDA BATTISON, COLOGIN FARMHOUSE, LERAGS GLEN, BY OBAN, ARGYLL PA34 4SE

Tel: Oban (01631) 564501 Fax: (01631) 566925

E-mail: cologin@west-highland-holidays.co.uk

www.west-highland-holidays.co.uk

STB ★★★ to ★★★★ Self Catering

Open all year round.
Rates from £180 to £510 per week.
Autumn Gold breaks and mid-week deals also available.

ABBOT'S BRAE HOTEL

West Bay, Dunoon, Argyll PA23 7QJ

Tel: 01369 705021 • Fax: 01369 701191

e-mail: info@abbotsbrae.co.uk • website: www.abbotsbrae.co.uk

Award-winning, small Country House Hotel set in its own secluded woodland garden with breathtaking views of the sea and hills. Very spacious en suite bedrooms including four-poster, king-size and twin rooms. The welcoming, homely atmosphere, peaceful surroundings and appetising menus will ensure a memorable stay. Special offers in spring and autumn. Pets stay free. Ideal base to explore the Western Highlands, situated at the Gateway to Scotland's first National Park.

For further details contact either Helen or Gavin.

Westwood House – Kelso

Overlooking Scotland's famous River Tweed

TOTAL "OFF LEAD" FREEDOM FOR DOGS IN ENCLOSED AND SECLUDED GROUNDS

Renovated riverside cottage with 12 acres of paths, through walled gardens and on own private island. 4 bedrooms sleeping 2 - 8 (+ child), 2 bathrooms, period features, cosy log fire and centrally heated.

• ½ mile Kelso town • one hour Edinburgh/Newcastle • ½ hour Berwick (station) and Northumberland coast

DOGS WELCOME FREE

For Brochure and tariff, from £325 per week fully inclusive of all linen and towels, electricity and heating. 2-person discounts available. Trout fishing also included.

Debbie Crawford, Tel: 07788 134 832

Pippin Heath Farm, Holt, Norfolk NR25 6SS

e-mail: westwood.house@btinternet.com

ACHIEVING GOLD IN GREEN TOURISM AND 'HIGHLY COMMENDED' IN SCOTTISH THISTLE AWARDS

Slipperfield House

West Linton EH46 7AA

Scottish Tourist Board ★★★★ Self Catering — **America Cottage**

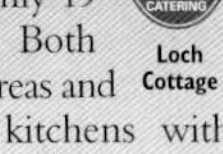

Loch Cottage

Two well-equipped cottages a mile from West Linton at the foot of the Pentland Hills, set in 100 acres of lochs and woodlands. Only 19 miles from Edinburgh City Centre. Both Cottages have sitting rooms with dining areas and digital colour TV; modern bathrooms and kitchens with washing and drying machines, microwave oven and telephone.

Details from Mrs C.M. Kilpatrick

• Dogs welcome • Ample parking

• Car essential • Central Edinburgh 19 miles

• Golf and private fishing • Available all year.

This is an ideal dog-friendly location for a family holiday near Edinburgh.

Tel and Fax: 01968 660401 e-mail: cottages@slipperfield.com website: www.slipperfield.com

For free colour brochure write to:

The Barniken House Hotel, Duns, Berwickshire, S.E. Scotland TD11 3DE

Tel: 01361 882466

Give yourself and your dogs a quality holiday break in beautiful Duns, Berwickshire, South East Scotland

The Barniken House Hotel

• Dogs most welcome • Your dogs sleep with you in your bedroom

• Satellite TV, tea/coffee making in all bedrooms • Central heating • Sun lounge

• Luxurious Lounge Bar (with 100 Malt Whiskies) and Dining Room, both furnished to a very high standard • Large garden with 9-hole putting green and patio

• Large car park • 18 hole course • Near spectacular scenery and ideal walks for dogs

• Within easy reach of sandy beaches

Bed, Breakfast and Evening Dinner from ONLY £175 per week.

Special 6-day Spring & Autumn Breaks: ONLY £30 per day Dinner, Bed and Breakfast.

Special 6-day Christmas Break: ONLY £195 Dinner, Bed and Breakfast.

Special 6-day New Year Hogmanay Break: ONLY £300 Dinner, Bed and Breakfast.

All prices include VAT.

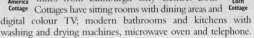

Cumbria ~ Scottish Borders

• Superb character cottages set in historic landscape on conservation farm with panoramic views • High quality furnishings • Wood-burning stoves • Stabling facilities - bring your own horse • Great walking, cycling, riding, forest tracks, bridleways, rivers and wooded valleys • Explore the Lake District, Hadrian's Wall, Solway Coast, historic Carlisle and return to a barbecue on your own patio, or relax by the fire. • Sleep up to 7 + cot • Open all year • £250-£450 per week.

Jane Gray, Saughs Farm & Cottages, Bailey, Newcastleton TD9 0TT (016977 48346/48000; Fax: 016977 48180)

e-mail: skylark@onholiday.co.uk
website: www.skylarkcottages.co.uk

Lockerbie Manor

COUNTRY HOTEL

The 1814 former home of the Marquis of Queensberry is a tranquil haven ideal for pets and owners. Set in 78 acres of wooded parkland only half-a-mile off the M74, the hotel is ideally situated to use as a touring base, for an activity break or just to relax, unwind and enjoy the countryside. You and your pets will feel most welcome with our "home away from home" comforts and hospitality. **Pets Welcome at no charge**

BORELAND RD, LOCKERBIE DG11 2RG • Tel: 01576 202610/203939 • Fax: 01576 203046
e-mail: info@lockerbiemanorhotel.co.uk • website: www.lockerbiemanorhotel.co.uk

A privately owned hotel set in 14 acres of mature woodland and gardens within walking distance of Castle Douglas. Galloway is one of the most beautiful and diverse areas of countryside in Britain - offering everything from golden sandy beaches to grouse moors, and picturesque harbour villages to forest walks. Panelled walls, log fires and a cosy Sportsman's Bar with over 50 whiskies to offer. 17 en suite rooms, with colour TV, tea & coffee making facilities, hairdryer, trouser press and direct dial telephone.

The Urr Valley Hotel is delighted to welcome dogs and the intimate atmosphere of the building is increased by the presence of two 'in house' golden retrievers and one basset hound. We allow dogs into all areas except those where food is served and we have excellent outdoor watering facilities. The grounds are perfect for exercising pets and their owners, and we look forward to welcoming you in the near future. AA ★★

The Urr Valley Hotel,
Ernespie Road, Castle Douglas,
Dumfries & Galloway, Scotland DG7 3JG
Tel: 01556 502188 Fax: 01556 504055

e-mail:info@urrvalleyhotel.co.uk website: www.urrvalleyhotel.co.uk

AVIEMORE
PINE BANK CHALETS

Enjoy the stunning beauty of the Highlands and the Cairngorm Mountains from our choice of superbly appointed log cabins and chalets. Great location – close to Spey River. Peaceful and relaxing setting. Friendly service staff, selected Sky TV, video, barbecue, mountain bikes. Many activities available. Leisure pool and restaurants nearby. Large choice of style and price.

5 log cabins, 4 chalets, 2 Flats, sleeping up to 6
Open all year £255-£695 per week• Pets Welcome

Dalfaber Road, Aviemore, Inverness-shire PH22 1PX
Tel: 01479 810000 • Fax: 01479 811469
e-mail: pinebankchallets@btopenworld.com
website: www.pinebankchalets.co.uk

Speyside Cottages, Nethy Bridge, Scottish Highlands

SSC
Member of Association of Scotland's Self-Caterers

Choice of very comfortable modern cottages or converted smithy of unique character on river bank, set individually in this quiet Highland village. Fenced gardens. Sleep 2-9. Linen, towels, visitors' laundry, Sept. to May heating included. Good walking and touring centre. Close to RSPB reserve with river and forest walks at your doorstep.

Mr & Mrs J.B. Patrick,
1 Chapelton Place, Forres, Moray IV36 2NL
Tel/Fax: 01309 672505
E-mail: brian@speysidecottages.co.uk
Website: www.speysidecottages.co.uk

UP TO

Cairngorm Highland Bungalows

Glen Einich, 29 Grampian View,
Aviemore, Inverness-shire PH22 1TF
Tel: 01479 810653 • Fax: 01479 810262
e-mail: linda.murray@virgin.net
website: www.cairngorm-bungalows.co.uk

Beautifully furnished and well-equipped bungalows ranging from one to four bedrooms. All have colour TV, video, microwave, cooker, washer-dryer, fridge and patio furniture. Some have log fires. Leisure facilities nearby include golf, fishing on the River Spey, swimming, sauna, jacuzzi, tennis, skating and skiing. Within walking distance of Aviemore. Ideal touring base. Children and pets welcome. Phone for colour brochure. Open all year.

SOUTH LOCH NESS

Wildside Highland Lodges

Set on the banks of a rocky river deep in the countryside, amidst spectacular scenery, with a choice of accommodation.

• Cosy studio units built for two. • Well appointed stone and cedar lodges, some with wood fires, for up to 6. • Spacious grounds and private lawns. • Large picture windows to enjoy the scenery. • Country pub nearby and a choice of places to eat out. • Open all year round, with free central heating. • Mini breaks available and pets welcome.

• See our colour brochure before you choose your special holiday or visit our web site.

SSC

Wildside, Whitebridge, Inverness IV2 6UN Tel: 01456 486 373
Fax: 01456 486 371 e-mail: info@wildsidelodges.com
website: www.wildsidelodges.com

THISTLE COTTAGE

Torlundy, Fort William, Inverness-shire

In a rural area, 3½ miles north of Fort William in a beautiful quiet valley below Aonach Mor Ski Centre. Central for touring the Highlands. Warm and friendly welcome. Double and family rooms with TV and tea/coffee making facilities. En suite available. Ample parking. Pets welcome in bedroom. Open all year. Bed and Breakfast from £17 per person per night.

Contact Mrs M. Matheson on
01397 702428 for details
E-mail: moragmatheson@btopenworld.com
www.thistlescotland.co.uk

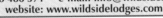

See advertisement under Perth & Kinross

Exceptional walking and wildlife area – deer, red squirrels and a great variety of birds. Twelve acres of formal and informal gardens and grounds. Walk straight from the door through woodlands onto the hillsides or around the loch.

The two log cabins and cottage are well furnished, equipped and heated. Cleaned and beds freshly made for your arrival. All linen, towels and electricity included.

Ardoch Lodge

Yvonne & John Howes, Ardoch Lodge, Strathyre, Perthshire FK18 8NF
Tel/Fax: 01877 384666 • E-mail: ardoch@btinternet.com

In the lodge all our bedrooms, which have outstanding views of the mountains, are spacious and have either en suite or private bathrooms. Deliciously imaginative food using local produce plus a high level of service and comfort provides an excellent base from which to tour this beautiful part of Scotland. Truly a place to unwind. Perfect for pets. ***Dogs most welcome, free of charge***

Visit our web site at www.ardochlodge.co.uk

Situated in the heart of the Ceiriog Valley, one of the most picturesque in North Wales.

This 18th century hotel offers peace and tranquillity. All rooms en suite, some with whirlpool baths and four-poster beds.

Excellent restaurant, old world charm bar with open fire, comfortable lounges, garden, patios and large car park.

Pets welcome in all rooms except restaurants and lounge.

Pets from £5 per night.

2 nights Dinner, Bed & Breakfast from £110pp.

Bed & Breakfast from £85, two sharing

★★★

GWESTY ★★★ HOTEL

Llwynmawr, Glyn Ceiriog, Near Llangollen LL20 7BB

Tel: 01691 718281 • Fax: 01691 718479

e-mail: goldenpheasant@micro-plus-web.net • website: www.goldenpheasanthotel.co.uk

SIR JOHN'S HILL FARM HOLIDAY COTTAGES

Laugharne, Carmarthenshire SA33 4TD

Tel: 01994 427667

In one of the finest locations in West Wales with spectacular views of coast and countryside, the three very comfortable cottages are the perfect place for a relaxing break.

If you really want to treat your dogs to a great holiday, bring them to Sir Johns Hill Farm. They will have a great time playing around the Farm which is well away from main roads, and there are lots of great country walks and long sandy beaches nearby too.

e-mail: liz.handford@sirjohnshillfarm.co.uk www.sirjohnshillfarm.co.uk

Furzewood, Granary & Stables Cottage, Amroth

In a spectacular setting of nine acres overlooking the bay with views to Caldey Island and the Gower, all our cottages offer 5 star comfort all year round. Just minutes from the safe sandy beach, Amroth village and the Pembrokeshire Coast Path and adjacent to Colby Estate, with its lovely sheltered wooded walks, we welcome children, pets and their owners! We have a large safe garden play area and fields to walk the dogs. Short Breaks available out of season. *For brochure contact:*

Mrs Green, Furzewood Farm, Amroth, Pembrokeshire SA67 8NQ

Tel: 01834 814674 • e-mail: info@amrothcottages.co.uk • www.amrothcottages.co.uk

★★★★★

Tel: 01348 837724
Fax: 01348 837622
E-mail: stay@lochmeyler.co.uk
Web: www.lochmeyler.co.uk

Mrs Morfydd Jones
Llandeloy,
Pen-y-Cwm,
Near Solva,
St. Davids, Pembrokeshire
SA62 6LL

A warm welcome awaits you at Lochmeyler, a 220 acre dairy farm in the centre of the St David's Peninsula.
It is an ideal location for exploring the beauty of the coast and countryside.
There are 15 bedrooms, eight of them in the adjacent cottage suites. All are en-suite, non-smoking, luxury rooms with colour TV, video and refreshment facilities. Rooms serviced daily. Children are welcome and there is a children's play area. Dogs free. Kennel facilities are free for owners wishing to leave their dogs during the day. Well behaved dogs can sleep in bedrooms providing they have their own bedding on the floor.

Closed Christmas & New Year
Credit cards accepted.
Colour brochure on request.

DAILY RATES

Bed & Breakfast per person per night min £20 – max £27.50

Children half price sharing family room

Dinner available Sat/Mon/Wed nights £15 per person. Children half price.

St Bride's Bay
COTTAGES

Cosy cottages and farmhouses near superb beaches and coastal path, around beautiful St.Brides Bay in Pembrokeshire. WTB graded. Sleeps 2-11. Pet welcome.

www.stbridesbaycottages.com

Tel: 0870 7572270

Croft Farm & Celtic Cottages
• Pembrokeshire •

Croft makes the ideal place for a main holiday or short break. Delightful barn conversions provide superbly comfortable accommodation. Enjoy the luxury indoor heated pool, sauna, spa pool and gym facilities. Close to sandy beaches, bays and coastal National Park. Good walking country. Indoor and outdoor play areas. Colourful gardens. Friendly farm animals. Pets welcome.

For a brochure please contact Andrew and Sylvie Gow,
Croft Farm & Celtic Cottages, Croft, Near Cardigan, Pembrokeshire SA43 3NT
Tel/Fax: 01239 615179 • www.croft-holiday-cottages.co.uk
• e-mail: croftfarm@compuserve.com

OAK WOOD LODGES
Llwynbaedd, Rhayader, Powys LD6 5NT

SELF CATERING LOG CABINS

Luxurious Norwegian log cabins situated at approximately 1000ft above sea level with spectacular views of the Elan Valley and Cambrian Mountains. Enjoy pursuits such as walking, pony trekking, mountain biking, fishing, and bird watching in the most idyllic of surroundings. Excellent touring centre. Dogs welcome. Short breaks as well as full weeks. Open all year round.

For more information and brochure call
01597 811422

Pet and Petcare Products and Services

QUALITY DOG COATS

Smart, light and custom designed for *every* size and breed of dog. Flectalon Thermal, Vent X Breathable Waterproof, Waterproof or Night Time Safety. Choice of Colours. Optional Extras: Tummy Protectors, Rear leg straps.

01271 376115 for a brochure
or www.gillrugs.com for the 'on-line' shop

Retired trailhound LASSIE thoroughly enjoyed her first holiday on canals.
sent by Tim Owen, Grange-over-Sands, Cumbria

NARROWBOAT HOLIDAYS FOR YOU AND YOUR PETS

A narrowboat holiday offers the best of both worlds – a chance to explore the countryside, visiting new places every day, and yet having the security of fixed accommodation with no worries about booking into a B&B for the night, and no packing and unpacking at each new destination.

Boats are well equipped and comfortable, a floating 'home from home', and ideal for all the family. Children especially love to be 'part of the crew' and are happy to follow the safety rules. Dogs also love the water and will quickly settle down on board, especially if you bring their own pet blanket or bed. Most boat owners are willing to allow pets but numbers may be limited and there may be restrictions on certain breeds. You should check on this when booking.

A little common sense and some consideration for others will ensure that everyone enjoys their holiday. However, the following points are important:

• You should keep your dog under control at all times for his own safety, and if he is likely to jump into the water it may be best to keep him on a lead. You might also consider obtaining a lifejacket for him if he is not a good swimmer.

• Make sure that your pet does not damage the furniture and fittings and discourage him from lying on beds or seating.

• NEVER leave your pet unattended on board, or elsewhere.

Finally, why not check out a nice pub on your trip?. There are many dog-friendly inns and pubs along Britain's waterways, some offering special facilities for dogs. See our Pet Friendly Pubs supplement at the back of the book for more details.

BOARDING YOUR PET by Kenn Oultram

THE remarkable growth of travel and tourism has provided satellite industries like **Animal Boarding Establishments (ABE)** with year-round financial benefits, though ABE owners will reveal they were never entirely dependent on the holiday-maker. For this is very much a service industry in its own right; greatly appreciated by, for example, pet owners who may be moving house...entering hospital...taking a work assignment abroad...having the builders in...throwing a fireworks party...coping with a bitch in season or, perhaps, a cat recuperating from surgery. As looking after pets is an awesome responsibility and a job for the professional, is it reasonable to expect a neighbour or pet-sitter to take this on?

Staff at an ABE must be alert for blood, constipation, diarrhoea, lethargy, coughing, fleas, incontinence, sneezing, worms and vomit! It is taken for granted that an ABE will accept the allergic, the arthritic, the diabetic, the epileptic, the hyper-active and the neurotic...and administer pills, drops and injections. Most of all they will be expected to guarantee the safe-keeping of your pet during your absence. Postmen may claim they face the risk of dog bites, but try opening the kennel door of an outsize hound with a 30 inch neck and two cute rows of flashing stained teeth.

Early advance booking at an ABE for your pet's boarding card is now essential as the equation of 5,000 kennels/catteries to cope with a potential 11 million UK dogs and cats simply doesn't balance and, at peak times, you'll discover there's no room at the inn.

All ABEs are inspected annually by an officer from the Environmental Health Department of the Local Authority which issues a licence to operate. It is illegal to run an ABE without a licence and this must be displayed for all to see (usually in the reception area).

Some general guidelines:

- A brochure indicates a professional approach. Ring round requesting these.
- Do NOT book if the ABE will not permit you to inspect the facilities. On arrival ask to see the exercise area for dogs (leaving dogs to their own devices all day in outside runs is NOT exercise). In catteries check that sneeze barriers are installed.
- If vaccinations are not necessary do NOT book; especially if dogs are not required to be vaccinated against kennel cough.
- Ask if the ABE's insurance covers your pet's stay; otherwise a nasty vet's bill could be awaiting your return.
- Many pet owners have more than one dog or cat. Look for family-sized units and check heating facilities (after all, our winters are twice the duration of our summers...and the ABE staff need to be kept warm too!)

- Check that your pet will not come into contact with another client's pet.
- On arrival – your ears, eyes and nose will tell all! You are looking for cleanliness, contented boarders and an experienced, caring staff. If apprehensive ask if you may send someone to visit your pet during its stay. You could also try your pet for a day (or a night) prior to the planned lengthy stay.
- If your pet is taken ill, ensure that the ABE is advised whether to call its own veterinarian or your own. Leave a contact number.
- If the ABE does not stock your pet's favourite food, offer to supply this, though there may not be any discount off your bill by doing so.
- Ask if a grooming service is offered. Some ABEs do. Others provide a collection and delivery service.

Finally, the time has surely come for an exhaustive, independent survey of British kennels and catteries with a one-to-four star ratings assessment. Perhaps one of the major motoring organisations should attempt this.... after all, 99% of ABE clients arrive on four wheels.

For free advice and addresses call the Animal Boarding Advisory Bureau on 01606 891303 or the Feline Advisory Bureau on 01747 871872 during office hours. For the boarding of house rabbits write to The British House Rabbit Association, Box 346, Newcastle-upon-Tyne NE99 1FA. You may even wish to recommend your own Animal Boarding Establishment.

Professional Boarding for Dogs and Cats since 1957
Animal Boarding Advisory Bureau at same address.

Clatterwick Lane
Little Leigh
Northwich
Cheshire
CW8 4RJ
Telephone: 01606 891 303
★ ★ ★ ★ ★

THE OTFORD BOARDING KENNELS
PILGRIMS WAY WEST,
OTFORD, SEVENOAKS, KENT TN14 5JN
Tel: 01959 525880
e-mail: hmosaic@aol.com

57 double licensed kennels. Open all year. 24 hour vet cover. Luxury heated individual kennels with attached covered runs. Free individual exercise in three grassed paddocks. Individual diets. Vaccination certificates must be produced. Pampered, people-loving pets only!

THE LINKS BOARDING KENNELS,
PEMBREY,
CARMARTHENSHIRE SA16 0HT
Tel: 01554 832409

Dogs and cats.
Individual heated kennels with large runs; two enclosed grass runs for dogs to run free; heated cattery with covered run. All animals must be inoculated. Other small domestic animals catered for.

Preparing your Dogs and Cats for travel abroad

How can my pet travel? Because of stringent requirements, dogs and cats travelling under the so-called pet passport scheme cannot make last minute reservations; in general, six-month advance planning is required. Veterinarians must implant a microchip in the animal, inoculate it against rabies, have a laboratory recognized by the Department for Environment, Food and Rural Affairs (DEFRA) confirm by blood sample that the vaccine is active, and issue a PETS certificate. Certificates are valid from six months after obtaining the blood sample results until the date of the animal's next rabies booster shot. (Dogs and cats resident in Britain whose blood sample was drawn before Feb 29, 2000 are exempt from this six month rule). Dogs and cats must also be treated against ticks and tapeworms no less than 24 nor more than 48 hours before check-in (when the animal enters carrier's custody). Animals travelling by air are placed in containers bearing an official seal (the number of which is also inscribed on the PETS certificate) to ensure animals are not exposed to disease en route. Sealing requirements do not apply to Cyprus or Malta. Owners must also sign a certificate attesting that the animal has not been outside participating territories in the last six months. Travellers are cautioned that Britain will enforce its rules rigorously.

Your pet must be injected with a harmless identification ISO (International Standards Organisation) approved microchip. This chip will be read by a handheld scanning device.

From and back to the UK.

Ask your vet to implant an ISO (International Standards Organisation) approved microchip - then to vaccinate against rabies recording the batch number of the vaccine on a veterinary certificate together with the microchip number.

Approximately 30 days later your vet should take a blood sample and send it to one of the DEFRA approved laboratories to check that the vaccine has provided the correct level of protection.

Your vet will then issue you with a certificate confirming all the above – in the UK this is called The Pet Travel Scheme Re-Entry Certificate. It is valid for the life of the rabies vaccine, so keep your rabies vaccine up to date and a new certificate will be issued without the need for further blood tests.

Six months from the taking of a successful blood test you will be able to enter or re-enter the UK from Western Europe and 28 other countries including Australia, Japan and Singapore.

Pets must be treated for ticks and for the echinococcus parasite by a qualified vet who will record this on an official UK certificate not less than 24 hours and not more than 48 hours before entry into the UK. We are trying to secure changes in this very awkward timetable, which is being rigidly enforced.

On entering the UK you must therefore have two official certificates; one for the microchip, rabies vaccine and blood test; the second for treatment against ticks and parasites. You will also have to sign a residence declaration form - provided by the travel operator who is carrying out the checking. It simply confirms that the pet has not been outside the approved countries in the previous six months.

From Europe to the UK

As above, you must microchip your pet, vaccinate against rabies and approximately 30 days later your vet will take a blood test sending it to one of the laboratories from the list of those approved by MAFF. SIX MONTHS after a successful blood test your pet will be allowed to travel to the UK providing it has been treated against ticks and worms.

Costs:

- Microchip: Should be in the region of £25.00
- Vaccine: Varies according to vet but again approximately £30.00
- Blood test: We know that the blood testing laboratory at Weybridge (VLA) charge £49.50 per test.

Therefore anything in addition is that levied by the vet. Providing the rabies vaccination is kept up to date the blood test will not have to be repeated. Should there be a break between rabies vaccines a further blood test would have to be taken and then a period of 6 months allowed before re-entry to the UK would be permitted.

Therefore: Microchip and blood-test are one-off costs but the rabies vaccination is a yearly or 2 yearly cost depending on the vaccine used.

DEFRA Help line Telephone Number is: 0870 241 17110

Current ports of entry are Dover (from Calais by ferry), Portsmouth (from Caen, Cherbourg, Le Havre or St Malo by ferry) and Folkestone (from Calais or Cheriton by Eurotunnel). London Heathrow is the authorised port-of-entry for : British Midland Airlines from Amsterdam-Schiphol, Brussels, Madrid, Palma Majorca, and Paris (Paris for guide dogs only); Finnair from Helsinki; and Lufthansa from Frankfurt.

The laboratories approved by MAFF for blood testing:

Veterinary Laboratory Agency New Haw, Addlestone Surrey KT15 3NB UNITED KINGDOM	Tel: (+44) 01932 357 345 Fax:(+44) 01 932 357 856 Costs: £49.50
BioBest Bush Loan - Paul Burns, Vet Penicuick Midlothian EH26 0PZ SCOTLAND	Tel: (+44) 0131 445 6101 Fax: (+44) 0131 445 6102 Costs: £32.50
Agence Francaise De Securite Sanitaire des Aliments Nancy Domaine de Pixerecourt B.P. 9F-54220 Maizeville, FRANCE	Tel: (+33) 3 83 298950 Fax:(+33) 3 83 298959 Costs: 425ff = approx £42
National Veterinary Institute Commission of Diagnosites Section of Diagnostic Department of Virology P.O. Box 585, BMCS-751 23 Uppsala SWEDEN	Tel: (+46) 1867 4000 Fax:(+46) 1847 14517 Costs: 500K=approx £40
Danish Veterinary Institute for Virus Research Lindholm DK-4771 Kalvehave DENMARK	Tel: (+45) 55 8602 00 Fax:(+45) 55 8603 00 Costs: 252K=approx £25
National Veterinary and Food Research Institute PL 368 (Heimmeentie 57) 00231 Helsinki FINLAND	Tel: (+35) 89393 1901 Fax:(+35) 89393 1811 Costs: 396.50 Fmark = approx £26.00
Institut fur Virologie Frankfurter Strasse 107 D35392 Giessen GERMANY	Tel: (+49) 641 99 38350 Fax: (+49) 641 99 38359 Costs: 72.60DM= approx £25
Dept. for Equine, Pets and Vaccine Control Virology Unit Federal Institute for the Control of Viral Infection in Animals Robert Kochgasse 17 2340 Modling AUSTRIA	Tel: (+43) 2236 46 640 902 or 906 Fax:(+43) 2236 46 640 941 Costs: 600 schillings= approx £30

Instituto Zooprotilattico Sperimentale delle Venezie Via Romea 14/A 1-35020 Legonaro (PD) ITALY	Tel: (+39) 04980 70 306 Fax:(+39) 04988 30 Costs: Price Unknown
Direccion General de Sanidad de la Produccion Agaria, Laboratono de Sanidad y Produccion Animal del Estado, Camino del Jau, S/N E-18320 Santa Fe (Granada) SPAIN	Tel: (+34) 958 44 03 75 Fax:(+34) 958 44 12 00 Costs: FREE
Institute Pasteur of Brussels Rue Engeland 642 B-i 180 Brussels BELGIUM	Tel: (+32) 2 373 31 58 Fax:(+32) 2 373 31 74 Costs: 1,500BF- approx £25
Institute of Veterinary Virology Schweizerische Tollwutzentrale Langgass-Strasse 122 CH-3012 Bern SWITZERLAND	Tel: (+41) 31 631 2378 Fax:(+41) 31 631 2534 Costs: 96.75 SF= approx £40
You can e-mail us at or write to our London address:	passports.forpets@virgin.net PASSPORTS FOR PETS

What we musn't forget?

Medicine, if needed

Toys

Health certificates

Food and drink dishes

The dog's basket or blanket – it is extremely important that your dog has something to make him feel at home

A thermometer

A bell to hang around the dog's collar.

A can opener if you have canned food

A deodorant for the hotel room

Paper towels

Brushes to brush your dog

A towel to dry the dog in case of rain or when you get back to the hotel room

Send us your favourite Pet Photo!

On the following pages are a selection of Pets photos sent in by readers of **Pets Welcome!**

If you would like to have a photo of your pet included in the Spring edition (published April 2004), send it along with a brief note of the pet's name and any interesting anecdotes about them. Please remember to include your own name and address and let us know if you would like the pictures returned.

Everyone sending a photo can select a **FREE** copy of any of FHG's year 2004 guides from the list shown at the back of this book. If your picture is featured in the next issue we will also pay £10.

We will be happy to receive prints, transparencies or pictures on disk or by e-mail to **fhg@ipcmedia.com** All pictures should be forwarded by the end of January 2004.

Thanks to everyone who sent in pictures of their pets and regret that we were unable to include all of them. ***See page 82 for this year's selection***

Send your Pet photo to: FHG Publications,
Abbey Mill Business Centre,
Seedhill, Paisley PA1 1TJ.

Have your pet's photo featured in Pets Welcome! and receive a FREE Live-a-Lot Pack

As the sponsor of **Pets Welcome! 2004** **Winalot** is offering readers the chance to win a **Live-a-Lot Pack** for every picture featured.
The special packs include a rucksack, fold away bowl, water bottle, frisbee and dog towel – an essential kit for everyday doggie outings.

Readers' Pets Pictures

We would like to thank readers for their response to our request for pictures in this issue, and are pleased to present the following selection.

Don't forget my toothbrush, says CHARLIE
sent by Mrs Armitage of Pontypool

Halt! Who goes there? says Blue Persian BASIL
sent by Nicola Howson

Having a "ball" at the beach
sent by Mr & Mrs Leeke of Wootton Bassett, Wiltshire

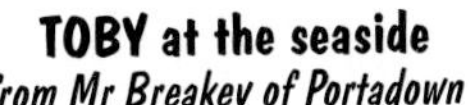

TOBY at the seaside
from Mr Breakey of Portadown

Maybe I'll grow into it
sent by Mrs PJ. Lewis of Kettering, Northamptonshire

SALLY loves the great outdoors
sent by Miss Matanie of Goffs Oak, Hertfordshire

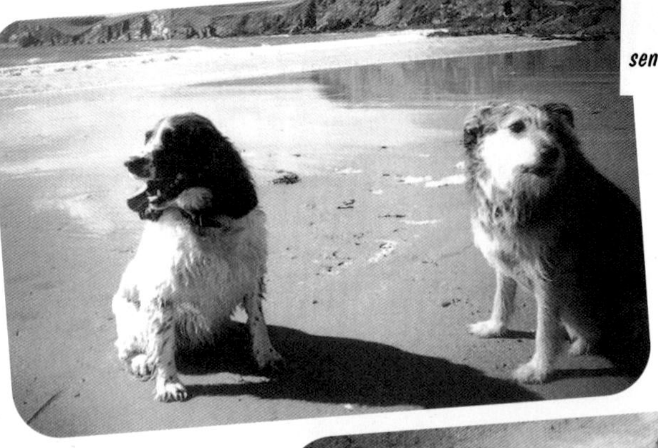

BONNIE & MICKEY
wait for their owners to catch up
sent by Mrs Langton of Bigbury-on-Sea, Devon

SOPHIE finds a shady spot
from Mr Cookson of Warrington.

It's nice to share
sent by Mrs St. Maur-Sheil
from Whitney, Oxfordshire

I'm ready, what's keeping you?
says LOU LOU
from Miss Barnes
of Oakham, Rutland

Where did all this white stuff come from? asks KASHKA
sent by Yvonne Baker of Wolverhampton

Snoozy TOBY
sent by Mr & Mrs Hall of Sheffield

OLIVER models the latest head-gear
sent by Helen Morgan of Sheffield

A welcome rest for HOLLY
sent by Natasha Herman from Hendon

BERTIE minds the baby minder
from Mrs Sanderson of Retford, Nottinghamshire

BEAU & BRANDY relax outdoors
sent by Mrs Milsom of Brantham, Suffolk

Come on in, the water's fine, says **KANE**
sent by Mrs Dewolfreys of Newquay, Cornwall

Who's missing a sock, says **KATIE**
from Mrs Peacock of Felixstowe, Suffolk

YASSKO
Searching
for buried treasure
from Mrs Halling of Bedford

CONNIE & BESS observing the marine life
sent by Josephine Gee of Dorchester, Dorset

FRED's the outdoor type
sent by Yvonne Baker of Wolverhampton

Last one in's a cissie
sent by Alison Ward and Dawn Myers of Portsmouth, Hampshire.

DOG FRIDAY
sent by Susan Wyatt of Lutterworth, Leicestershire

A gardener's work is never done, says SOPHIE
from Miss Thomson of Enfield, Middlesex

JASPER – totally laid back
sent by Mr Babb, Northop, Clwyd

JOCK, GEMMA-KELLY, JACK, OBAN & TOMMY
relaxing in the sun
sent by Elizabeth Walker of Leeds

Do you think it bites, asks CALLY
sent by Miss Kelson of Newport, South Wales

... and enjoying a nap

from Moira Bryan of Paisley

WHISKY exploring the garden...

Make sure you get my best side, says OLIVER
sent by Lisa de Angelis of Chesterfield

There's nothing like a nice rest after a bit of gardening
sent by Sandie Stimson of Peterborough, Cambridgeshire

If this is a desert, where's the camels, asks PENNY
sent by Mrs Manns, Welwyn Garden City, Hertfordshire

Now, where did I leave my owner, says BILLY
sent by Mrs Thomson of Louth, Lincolnshire

Do these shades suit me? asks MILLIE
from Peter & Cheryl Risely of Falmouth, Cornwall

BESSIE cools off in Coniston Water
from Mr & Mrs Gibbons of High Peak, Derbyshire

Let's get aboard, says PADDY
sent by Sharon Symons of Cornwall

BILLY & CHARLIE, the inseparable friends
sent by Dominique Wheelhouse

Opposites attract, CHARLIE & JENNY
sent by Janet Curtis of Axminster, Devon

DOLLY's jolly holiday
sent by Tracey Rees-Cooke

DogsTrust: A Dog is For Life

Are you thinking of going on holiday in the UK with your dog?

If so, the Dogs Trust has a free factsheet which will be of particular interest.

"Safe travel and happy holidays with your hound in the UK"

For this and any other of our free Dogs Trust factsheets please contact us at:

Dogs Trust,
17 Wakley St. London EC1V 7RQ.
Tel: 020 7837 0006
Website: www.dogstrust.org.uk
or e-mail us, info@dogstrust.org.uk

Last year Dogs Trust cared for over 11,500 stray and abandoned dogs at our network of 15 Rehoming Centres.
So if you are looking for a companion for your dog or you have a friend who might like a dog, just contact your nearest Dogs Trust Rehoming Centre.

We care for around 1,600 dogs on any given day, so we are sure we will be able to find your perfect partner. The Dogs Trust never destroys a healthy dog.
For details of our Sponsor-a-Dog scheme please call 020 7837 0006 or visit www.sponsoradog.org.uk

Dogs Trust Rehoming Centres

ENGLAND

Dogs Trust Canterbury
01227 792 505

Dogs Trust Darlington
01325 333 114

Dogs Trust Evesham
01386 830 613

Dogs Trust Ilfracombe
01271 812 709

Dogs Trust Kenilworth
01926 484 398

Dogs Trust Leeds
01132 613 194

Dogs Trust Merseyside
0151 480 0660

Dogs Trust Newbury
01488 658 391

Dogs Trust Roden
01952 770 225

Dogs Trust Salisbury
01980 629 634

Dogs Trust Shoreham
01273 452 576

Dogs Trust Snetterton
01953 498 377

WALES

Dogs Trust Bridgend
01656 725 219

SCOTLAND

Dogs Trust West Calder
01506 873 459

NORTHERN IRELAND

Dogs Trust Ballymena
028 2565 2977

Registered Charity No. 227523

YOUR DOG MAGAZINE

Your Dog is Britain's best-selling dog magazine, a monthly read that's packed with tips and advice on how to get the best out of life with your pet.

Every issue contains in-depth features on your dog's health, behaviour and training, and looks at issues such as how to pick the perfect puppy for your lifestyle.

Your Dog Essentials
Stress-free solutions, top tips and invaluable ideas on how to make life with a pet fun!

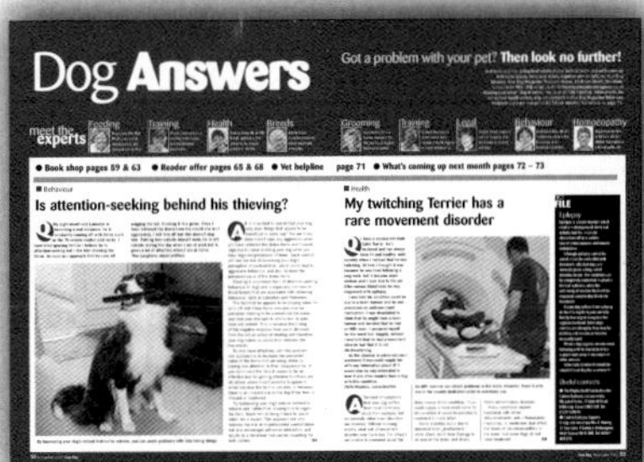

Dog Answers
Twenty pages of your problems solved by our panel of experts – everything from training, health, behaviour, feeding, breeds, grooming, legal and homoeopathy.

Breeds
Every month the spotlight falls on a different breed.

And lot, lots more...

Your Dog Magazine is available from your newsagent on the 7th of every month; price £2.95. Alternatively, why not take out a subscription? To find out more, contact the subscriptions hotline on tel. 01858 438854 and quote reference PW01.

The original and unique

FHG

Pets Welcome 2004

with

including

Holidays with Horses* and *Narrow Boat holidays
PETS' PRODUCTS Section
Guide to Pet Friendly Pubs

For Contents see page 3
For Index of towns/counties see back of book

Part of IPC Country and Leisure Media

43rd Edition © IPC Media Ltd 2003
ISBN 1 85055 349 1

Cover design: Focus Network
Cover Pictures: Kris Coppieters/Alamy

Cartography by GEO Projects, Reading

Maps are based on Ordnance Survey Maps with the permission
of the Controller of Her Majesty's Stationery Office,
Crown Copyright reserved.

Typeset by FHG Publications Ltd, Paisley.
Printed and bound in Great Britain by William Clowes, Beccles, Suffolk.

Distribution. Book Trade: Plymbridge House, Estover Road,
Plymouth PL6 7PY
(Tel: 01752 202300; Fax: 01752 202333).
News Trade: Market Force (UK) Ltd, 5th Floor Low Rise, Kings Reach Tower
Stamford Street, London SE1 9LS
(Tel: 0207 633 3450; Fax: 0207 633 3572).

Published by FHG Publications Ltd., Abbey Mill Business Centre,
Seedhill, Paisley PA1 ITJ (Tel: 0141-887 0428 Fax: 0141-889 7204).
e-mail: fhg@ipcmedia.com

Pets Welcome! is an FHG publication, published by
IPC Country & Leisure Media Ltd, part of IPC Media Group of Companies.

All the advertisers in PETS WELCOME! have an entry in the appropriate classified section and each classified entry may carry one or more of the following symbols:

- 🐕 This symbol indicates that pets are welcome free of charge.
- **£** The £ indicates that a charge is made for pets. We quote the amount where possible, either per night or per week.
- **pw!** This symbol shows that the establishment has some special provision for pets; perhaps an exercise facility or some special feeding or accommodation arrangements.
- ☖ Indicates separate pets' accommodation.

PLEASE NOTE that all the advertisers in PETS WELCOME! extend a welcome to pets and their owners but they may attach conditions. The interests of other guests have to be considered and it is usually assumed that pets will be well trained, obedient and under the control of their owner.

The original and unique Pets Welcome 2004

Foreword

The 43rd edition of Pets Welcome! is packed full of pet-friendly accommodation, so taking your dog on holiday has never been easier. Choices include hotels, B&Bs, self-catering properties, caravans amd Narrowboat Holidays.

All of our proprietors are happy to welcome pets, in fact many of them have pets of their own, but they do expect owners to be responsible. Pets should therefore be kept under control at all times and discouraged from jumping on beds and seating. They should never be left unattended, especially in a strange bedroom - a lonely or unhappy pet is very likely to get into mischief. Please remember that a little consideration and common sense now will ensure that you and your pets are welcome to return another time.

Most of our entries are of long standing and are tried and tested favourites with animal lovers. However as publishers we do not inspect the accommodation advertised in Pets Welcome! and an entry does not imply our recommendation. Some proprietors offer fuller facilities for pets than others, and in the classified entry which we give each advertiser we try to indicate by symbols whether or not there are any special facilities and if additional charges are involved. However, we suggest that you raise any queries or particular requirements when you make enquiries and bookings.

If you have any problems or complaints, please raise them on the spot with the owner or his representative in the first place. We will follow up complaints if necessary, but we regret that we cannot act as intermediaries nor can we accept responsibility for details of accommodation and/or services described here. Happily, serious complaints are few. Finally, if you have to cancel or postpone a holiday booking, please give as much notice as possible. This courtesy will be appreciated and it could save later difficulties.

Boarding your Pet (Page 74), Preparing your Dogs and Cats for Travel Abroad (Page 76), Holidays with Horses (Page 411), and The Guide to Pet Friendly Pubs (Page 415) are now regular features, and on page 100 you will find some useful information on keeping your pet happy in warm weather. Our latest selection of Pets Pictures appears on page 82.

We would be happy to receive readers' suggestions on any other useful features. Please also let us know if you have had any unusual or humorous experiences with your pet on holiday. This always makes interesting reading! And we hope that you will mention ***Pets Welcome!*** when you make your holiday inquiries or bookings.

Anne Cuthbertson, Editor

For many of us enjoying a country holiday also means taking our dogs on scenic walks, or for a journey in the car - often in warm weather, and at these times they may need a little extra care and attention. The following tips could make your pet's life on hot days considerably more comfortable:

WATER!

A normal 20kg dog will drink about one and a half pints of water a day. In the heat this can increase by 200 to 300%. Water should always be available. Make sure you take plenty for your pet, as well for yourself when out walking and in the car. Stabilising non-spill water bowls are great for travel, while handy inflatable bowls are ideal for stowing in your knapsack. You can even buy water bottles that your dog can carry.

SHADE

Encourage your dog to favour shady, cool spots when you stop for a rest - rather than sunbathe with the rest of the family!

CAR

NEVER leave your dog in the car unattended. Placing a dog in the back of any car even with an open rear window is undesirable and may be fatal. Remember - even a car parked in shade in the morning when it's cool could reach over 100 degrees very quickly as the sun moves. Heat stroke can occur within minutes.

EXERCISE

Plan your walk so you avoid strenuous exercise during the hottest part of the day. Some dogs like to paddle or swim - if there is no water around and your dog seems uncomfortably hot, seek a shady spot and provide water.

HEALTH

A dog's heat loss system is dependent on overall health. If your dog is fit, supple and active then walking will be a pleasurable experience, however, if there is any indication of heart or respiratory problems arising, controlled exercise in the cool is recommended. Veterinary advice should be sought if problems persist during heat stressful times.

HEAT STROKE

This is an emergency and potentially life threatening situation. If in doubt take the following action, then seek advice. A chilled dog is better than an overheated one.

- Cease any form of exercise.
- Move the dog into a cool place.
- Sponge the dog with cold water - all over, avoiding water round the mouth or nose.
- Do not offer food or fluids until evident recovery.
- Seek veterinary advice if in doubt.

THE FHG DIPLOMA

HELP IMPROVE BRITISH TOURIST STANDARDS

You are choosing holiday accommodation from our very popular FHG Publications.
Whether it be a hotel, guest house, farmhouse or self-catering accommodation, we think you will find it hospitable, comfortable and clean, and your host and hostess friendly and helpful.

Why not write and tell us about it?

As a recognition of the generally well-run and excellent holiday accommodation reviewed in our publications, we at FHG Publications Ltd. present a diploma to proprietors who receive the highest recommendation from their guests who are also readers of our Guides. If you care to write to us praising the holiday you have booked through FHG Publications Ltd. – whether this be board, self-catering accommodation, a sporting or a caravan holiday, what you say will be evaluated and the proprietors who reach our final list will be contacted.

The winning proprietor will receive an attractive framed diploma to display on his premises as recognition of a high standard of comfort, amenity and hospitality. FHG Publications Ltd. offer this diploma as a contribution towards the improvement of standards in tourist accommodation in Britain. Help your excellent host or hostess to win it!

FHG DIPLOMA

We nominate

Because

Name ....

Address...

....

Telephone No...

If you are planning a family day out and don't want to leave your pet behind, then check out the attractions listed below which allow pets (in most cases they must be kept on leads).

Bucks Goat Centre, Layby Farm, Stoke Mandeville, Aylesbury, Buckinghamshire HP22 5XJ
Tel: 01296 612983
e-mail: bucksgoat@ccn.go-free.co.uk
website: www.bucksgoatcentre.co.uk
The most comprehensive collection of goat breeds in Britain; other animals, shops and cafe.
Dogs must be kept on leads.

Buckinghamshire Railway Centre, Quainton Road Station, Quainton, Aylesbury, Buckinghamshire HP22 4BY
Tel: 01296 655720
website: www.bucksrailcentre.org.uk
A working steam railway centre. Steam train rides, minature railway rides, large collection of historic, preserved steam locomotives, carriages and wagons.

Launceston Steam Railway, St Thomas Hill, Launceston, Cornwall PL15 8DA
Tel: 01566 775665
Victorian locomotives haul from Launceston (buffet, museum, workshops, souvenirs, books) to Newmills (picnic, play area, riverside walk).
Dogs on lead at all times. They are charged 50p but get a ticket!

The China Clay Museum, Wheal Martyn, St Austell, Cornwall PL26 8XG
Tel: 01726 850362
e-mail: info@wheal-martyn.com
website: www.wheal-martyn.com
Industrial museum of the china clay industry. Historic trail with working water wheels; nature trail.
Dogs on leads welcome.

Peak Cavern, Castleton, Hope Valley, Derbyshire S33 8WS
Tel: 01433 620285
e-mail: info@peakcavern.co.uk
website: www.devilsarse.com
Guided tours of this vast limestone cave, whose entrance is so large it once contained a village and rope works.
Dogs must be kept on lead in the cave.

The Milky Way Adventure Park, Downland Farm, Clovelly, Bideford, Devon EX39 5RY
Tel: 01237 431255
e-mail: info@themilkyway.co.uk
website: www.themilkyway.co.uk
The largest all-weather facilities in North Devon including the Time Warp, a huge indoor play area, archery, birds of prey and other live shows.
Dogs must be kept on leads and not taken to live shows.

Beamish, The North of England Open Air Museum, Beamish, Durham DH9 0RG
Tel: 0191 370 4000
e-mail: museum@beamish.org.uk
website: www.beamish.org.uk
An open-air museum illustrating life in the 1800s and 1900s, set in 200 acres of beautiful countryside.
Dogs (except Guide Dogs) not allowed in refreshment areas or period buildings but are very welcome elsewhere at Beamish. Must be kept on a lead at all times.

Hever Castle and Gardens, Edenbridge, Kent TN8 7NG
Tel: 01732 865224
e-mail: mail@hevercastle.co.uk
website: www.hevercastle.co.uk
Thirteenth century castle, childhood home of Anne Boleyn set in award-winning gardens with Italian, Rose and Tudor gardens, topiary, lake, yew and water maze. Two licensed self-service restaurants. Gift, book and garden shops.
Dogs must be kept on lead at all times.

Forde Abbey Gardens, Chard, Somerset TA20 4LU
Tel: 01460 221290
e-mail: forde.abbey@virgin.net
website: www.fordeabbey.co.uk
30 acres of one of the top ten gardens in England surround the 12th century former abbey.
Dogs on short leads please.

Bowhill House and Country Park, Bowhill, Selkirk, Scottish Borders TD7 5ET
Tel: 01750 22204
e-mail: bht@buccleuch.com
Home of the Duke & Duchess of Buccleuch, with outstanding collections of art, silverware and porcelain.
Dogs must be kept on lead and stick to main tracks.

Bo'ness & Kinneil Railway, The Station, Bo'ness, West Lothian EH51 9AQ
Tel: 01506 822298
website: www.srps.org.uk
A living museum of steam and diesel locomotives, carriages and historic buildings.
Pets welcome on lead (not restaurant or museum).

FHG READERS' OFFER 2004

Leighton Buzzard Railway

Page's Park Station, Billington Road,
Leighton Buzzard, Bedfordshire LU7 4TN
Tel: 01525 373888
e-mail: info@buzzrail.co.uk • website: www.buzzrail.co.uk

One free adult/child with full-fare adult ticket

valid from 16/3/04 – 29/10/04

NOT TO BE USED IN CONJUNCTION WITH ANY OTHER OFFER

FHG READERS' OFFER 2004

Buckinghamshire Railway Centre

Quainton Road Station, Quainton, Aylesbury HP22 4BY
Tel & Fax: 01296 655720
e-mail: bucksrailcentre@btopenworld.com
website: www.bucksrailcentre.org.uk

One child FREE with each full paying adult

not valid for for special events

NOT TO BE USED IN CONJUNCTION WITH ANY OTHER OFFER

FHG READERS' OFFER 2004

Cars of the Stars Motor Museum

Standish Street, Keswick, Cumbria CA12 5HH
Tel: 017687 73757
e-mail: cotsmm@aol.com • website: www.carsofthestars.com

One child free with two paying adults

Valid 2004

NOT TO BE USED IN CONJUNCTION WITH ANY OTHER OFFER

FHG READERS' OFFER 2004

Windermere Steamboats & Museum

Rayrigg Road, Windermere, Cumbria LA23 1BN
Tel: 015394 45565 • e-mail:steamboat@ecosse.net
website: www.steamboat.co.uk

Two for the price of one (adults) OR 25% off family ticket

valid March to October 2004

NOT TO BE USED IN CONJUNCTION WITH ANY OTHER OFFER

FHG READERS' OFFER 2004

Blue-John Cavern

Castleton, Hope Valley, Derbyshire S33 8WP
Tel: 01433 620642 • e-mail: lesley@bluejohn.gemsoft.co.uk
website: www.bluejohn-cavern.co.uk

One child free with every paying adult

Valid until end 2004

NOT TO BE USED IN CONJUNCTION WITH ANY OTHER OFFER

A 65-minute journey into the lost world of the English narrow gauge light railway. Features historic steam locomotives from many countries.

PETS MUST BE KEPT UNDER CONTROL AND NOT ALLOWED ON TRACKS

Open: Sundays and Bank Holiday weekends 16 March to 29 October. Additional days in summer.

Directions: On A4146 towards Hemel Hempstead, close to roundabout junction with A505.

FHG PUBLICATIONS, ABBEY MILL BUSINESS CENTRE, PAISLEY PA1 1TJ

A working steam railway centre. Steam train rides, miniature railway rides, large collection of historic preserved steam locomotives, carriages and wagons.

Open: Sundays and Bank Holidays April to October, plus Wednesdays in June, July and August 10.30am to 5.30pm.

Directions: off A41 Aylesbury to Bicester Road, 6 miles north west of Aylesbury.

FHG PUBLICATIONS, ABBEY MILL BUSINESS CENTRE, PAISLEY PA1 1TJ

A collection of cars from film and TV, including Chitty Chitty Bang Bang, James Bond's Aston Martin, Del Boy's van, Fab1 and many more.

PETS MUST BE KEPT ON LEAD

Open: Daily 10am-5pm. Closed February half term. Weekends only in December.

Directions: In centre of Keswick close to car park.

FHG PUBLICATIONS, ABBEY MILL BUSINESS CENTRE, PAISLEY PA1 1TJ

World's finest steamboat collection and premier all-weather attraction. Swallows and Amazons exhibition, model boat pond, tea shop, souvenir shop. Free guided tours. Model boat exhibition.

Open: 10am to 5pm 3rd weekend in March to last weekend October.

Directions: on A592 half-a-mile north of Bowness-on-Windermere.

FHG PUBLICATIONS, ABBEY MILL BUSINESS CENTRE, PAISLEY PA1 1TJ

Large range of natural water-worn caverns featuring mining equipment, stalactites and stalagmites, and fine deposits of Blue-John stone, Britain's rarest semi-precious stone.

DOGS MUST BE KEPT ON LEAD

Open: 9.30am to 5.30pm.

Directions: Situated 2 miles west of Castleton; follow brown tourist signs.

FHG PUBLICATIONS, ABBEY MILL BUSINESS CENTRE, PAISLEY PA1 1TJ

FHG READERS' OFFER 2004

Crich Tramway Village

Crich, Matlock, Derbyshire DE4 5DP

Tel: 0870 7587267 • Fax: 01773 852326

e-mail: info@tramway.co.uk • website: www.tramway.co.uk

One child FREE with every full paying adult

valid during 2004

NOT TO BE USED IN CONJUNCTION WITH ANY OTHER OFFER

FHG READERS' OFFER 2004

Treak Cliff Cavern

HOME OF BLUE JOHN STONE

Castleton, Hope Valley, Derbyshire S33 8WP

Tel: 01433 620571

e-mail: treakcliff@bluejohnstone.com • website: www.bluejohnstone.com

10% discount (not valid on Special Events days)

valid during 2004

NOT TO BE USED IN CONJUNCTION WITH ANY OTHER OFFER

FHG READERS' OFFER 2004

The Big Sheep

Bideford, Devon EX39 5AP

Tel: 01237 472366

Admit one child FREE with each paying adult

valid during 2004

NOT TO BE USED IN CONJUNCTION WITH ANY OTHER OFFER

FHG READERS' OFFER 2004

The Gnome Reserve & Wild Flower Garden

West Putford, Near Bradworthy, Devon EX22 7XE

Tel: 01409 241435 • e-mail: info@gnomereserve.co.uk

website: www.gnomereserve.co.uk

One FREE child with full paying adult

Valid during 2004

NOT TO BE USED IN CONJUNCTION WITH ANY OTHER OFFER

FHG READERS' OFFER 2004

Killhope Lead Mining Museum

Cowshill, Upper Weardale, Co. Durham DL13 1AR

Tel: 01388 537505

e-mail: killhope@durham.gov.uk • website: www.durham.gov.uk/killhope

One child FREE with full-paying adult (not valid for Park Level Mine)

valid April to October 2004

NOT TO BE USED IN CONJUNCTION WITH ANY OTHER OFFER

A superb family day out in the atmosphere of a bygone era. Explore the recreated period street and fascinating exhibitions. Unlimited tram rides are free with entry. Play areas, shops, tea rooms, pub, restaurant and lots more.

Open: daily April to October 10 am to 5.30pm, weekends in winter.

Directions: Eight miles from M1 Junction 28, follow brown and white signs for "Tramway Museum".

FHG PUBLICATIONS, ABBEY MILL BUSINESS CENTRE, PAISLEY PA1 1TJ

An underground wonderland of stalactites, stalagmites, rocks, minerals and fossils. Home of the unique Blue John stone – see the largest single piece ever found. Suitable for all ages.

Open: Opens 10am. Enquire for last tour of day and closed days.

Directions: Half-a-mile west of Castleton on A6187 (old A625)

FHG PUBLICATIONS, ABBEY MILL BUSINESS CENTRE, PAISLEY PA1 1TJ

"England for Excellence" award-winning rural attraction combining traditional rural crafts with hilarious novelties such as sheep racing and duck trialling, Indoor adventure zone for adults and children.

Open: daily, 10am to 6pm April - Oct Phone for Winter opening times and details.

Directions: on A39 North Devon link road, two miles west of Bideford Bridge.

FHG PUBLICATIONS, ABBEY MILL BUSINESS CENTRE, PAISLEY PA1 1TJ

Visit 1000+ gnomes and pixies in two acre beech wood. Gnome hats are loaned free of charge - so the gnomes think you are one of them - don't forget your camera! Also 2-acre wild flower garden with 250 labelled species.

Open: Daily 10am to 6pm 21st March to 31st October.

Directions: Between Bideford and Bude; follow brown tourist signs from A39/A388/A386.

FHG PUBLICATIONS, ABBEY MILL BUSINESS CENTRE, PAISLEY PA1 1TJ

Britain's best preserved lead mining site – and a great day out for all the family, with lots to see and do. Underground Experience – Park Level Mine now open.

Open: April 1st to September 30th 10.30am to 5pm daily. Weekends and half term in October

Directions: Alongside A689, midway between Stanhope and Alston in the heart of the North Pennines.

FHG PUBLICATIONS, ABBEY MILL BUSINESS CENTRE, PAISLEY PA1 1TJ

FHG READERS' OFFER 2004

Barleylands Farm

Barleylands Road, Billericay, Essex CM11 2UD

Tel: 01268 290229 • e-mail: info@barleylands.co.uk
website: www.barleylands.co.uk

FREE adult ticket when accompanied by one child

Valid 1st March to 31st October. Not special event days

NOT TO BE USED IN CONJUNCTION WITH ANY OTHER OFFER

FHG READERS' OFFER 2004

NATIONAL WATERWAYS MUSEUM

Llanthony Warehouse, Gloucester Docks, Gloucester GL1 2EH

Tel: 01452 318200 • website: www.nwm.org.uk
e-mail: bookingsnwm@thewaterwaystrust.org

20% off museum admission (excludes combination tickets)

valid during 2004

NOT TO BE USED IN CONJUNCTION WITH ANY OTHER OFFER

FHG READERS' OFFER 2004

Cider Museum & King Offa Distillery

21 Ryelands Street, Hereford HR4 0LW

Tel: 01432 354207 • Fax: 01432 371641

e-mail: info@cidermuseum.co.uk • website: www.cidermuseum.co.uk

50p reduction on entry fee

valid during 2004

NOT TO BE USED IN CONJUNCTION WITH ANY OTHER OFFER

FHG READERS' OFFER 2004

Museum of Kent Life

Lock Lane, Sandling, Maidstone ME14 3AU

Tel: 01622 763936 • Fax: 01622 662024

e-mail: enquiries@museum-kentlife.co.uk • website: www.museum-kentlife.co.uk

Two tickets for the price of one (cheapest ticket FREE)

valid from March to November 2004

NOT TO BE USED IN CONJUNCTION WITH ANY OTHER OFFER

FHG READERS' OFFER 2004

Docker Park Farm

Arkholme, Carnforth, Lancashire LA6 1AR

Tel & Fax: 015242 21331

e-mail: info@dockerparkfarm.co.uk • website: www.dockerparkfarm.co.uk

One FREE child per one paying adult (one voucher per child)

valid from January to December 2004

NOT TO BE USED IN CONJUNCTION WITH ANY OTHER OFFER

Craft Village with animals, museum, blacksmith, glassblowing, miniature railway (Sundays and August), craft shops, tea room and licensed restaurant.

DOGS MUST BE KEPT ON LEAD

Open: Craft Village open all year. The Farm open 1st March to 31st October.

Directions: M25, A127 towards Southend. Take A176 junction off A127, 3rd exit Wash Road, 2nd left Barleylands Road.

FHG PUBLICATIONS, ABBEY MILL BUSINESS CENTRE, PAISLEY PA1 1TJ

On three floors of a Listed Victorian warehouse telling 200 years of inland waterway history.• Historic boats • Boat trips available (Easter to October) • Painted boat gallery • Blacksmith • Archive film • Hands-on displays "A great day out"

Open: every day 10am to 5pm (excluding Christmas Day).

Directions: Junction 11A or 12 off M5 – follow brown signs for Historic Docks. Railway and bus station - 15 minute walk. Free coach parking.

FHG PUBLICATIONS, ABBEY MILL BUSINESS CENTRE, PAISLEY PA1 1TJ

Discover the fascinating history of cider making. There is a programme of temporary exhibitions and events plus free samples of Hereford cider brandy.

Open: April to Oct
10am to 5.30pm (daily)
Nov to Dec 11am to 3pm (daily)
Jan to Mar 11am to 3pm (Tues to Sun)

Directions: situated west of Hereford off the A438 Hereford to Brecon road.

FHG PUBLICATIONS, ABBEY MILL BUSINESS CENTRE, PAISLEY PA1 1TJ

Kent's award-winning open air museum is home to a collection of historic buildings which house interactive exhibitions on life over the last 150 years.

Open: Seven days a week from March to November. 10am to 5.30pm.

Directions: Junction 6 off M20, follow signs to Aylesford.

FHG PUBLICATIONS, ABBEY MILL BUSINESS CENTRE, PAISLEY PA1 1TJ

We are a working farm, with lots of animals to see and touch. Enjoy a walk round the Nature Trail or refreshments in the tearoom. Lots of activities during school holidays.

Open: Summer: daily
10.30am to 5pm
Winter: weekends only
10.30am to 4pm.

Directions: Junction 35 off M6, take B6254 towards Kirkby Lonsdale, then follow the brown signs.

FHG PUBLICATIONS, ABBEY MILL BUSINESS CENTRE, PAISLEY PA1 1TJ

FHG READERS' OFFER 2004

Southport Zoo and Conservation Trust

Princes Park, Southport, Merseyside PR8 1RX

Tel: 01704 548894 • Tel & Fax: 01704 538102

e-mail: info@southportzoo.com • website: www.southportzoo.com

FREE Zoo Pack per family

valid during 2004 except Bank Holidays

NOT TO BE USED IN CONJUNCTION WITH ANY OTHER OFFER

FHG READERS' OFFER 2004

Newark Air Museum

The Airfield, Winthorpe, Newark, Nottinghamshire NG24 2NY

Tel: 01636 707170

e-mail: newarkair@lineone.net • website: www.newarkairmuseum.co.uk

Party rate discount for every voucher (50p per person off normal admission).

Valid during 2004

NOT TO BE USED IN CONJUNCTION WITH ANY OTHER OFFER

FHG READERS' OFFER 2004

Cogges Manor Farm Museum

Church Lane, Witney, Oxfordshire OX28 3LA

Tel: 01993 772602 • website: www.cogges.org

Two for the price of one

Valid April to end of November 2004

NOT TO BE USED IN CONJUNCTION WITH ANY OTHER OFFER

FHG READERS' OFFER 2004

Avon Valley Railway

Bitton Station, Bath Road, Bitton, Bristol, BS30 6HD

Tel: 0117 932 5538

e-mail: enquiries@avonvalleyrailway.co.uk • website: www.avonvalleyrailway.co.uk

One FREE child ticket with every fare-paying adult
(Not valid for "Day out with Thomas Events")

valid from May to October2004

NOT TO BE USED IN CONJUNCTION WITH ANY OTHER OFFER

FHG READERS' OFFER 2004

Easton Farm Park

Easton, Near Wickham Market, Ipswich, Suffolk IP13 0EQ

Tel: 01728 746475 • e-mail: easton@eastonfarmpark.co.uk
website: www.eastonfarmpark.co.uk

£1 per person off for up to 4 full paying admissions

Valid until end 2004

NOT TO BE USED IN CONJUNCTION WITH ANY OTHER OFFER

Lions, snow leopards, chimpanzees, otters, reptiles, aquarium and lots more, set amidst landscaped gardens. Gift shop, cafe and picnic areas.

Open: all year round from 10am

Directions: on the coast 16 miles north of Liverpool; follow the brown and white tourist signs

FHG PUBLICATIONS, ABBEY MILL BUSINESS CENTRE, PAISLEY PA1 1TJ

A collection of 65 aircraft and cockpit sections from across the history of aviation. Extensive aero engine and artefact displays.

Open: Daily from 10am (closed Christmas period).

Directions: Follow brown and white signs from A1, A46, A17 and A1133.

FHG PUBLICATIONS, ABBEY MILL BUSINESS CENTRE, PAISLEY PA1 1TJ

Historic manor house and farm with traditional animals. Work in the Victorian kitchen every afternoon.

Open: April to 2nd December: Tuesday to Friday 10.30am to 5.30pm. Saturday and Sunday 12-5.30pm.

Directions: Just off A40 Oxford to Cheltenham road at Witney.

FHG PUBLICATIONS, ABBEY MILL BUSINESS CENTRE, PAISLEY PA1 1TJ

The Avon Valley Railway offers a whole new experience for some, and a nostalgic memory for others. Steam trains operate every Sunday Easter to October, plus Bank Holidays and Christmas.

PETS MUST BE KEPT ON LEADS AND OFF TRAIN SEATS

Open: Steam trains operate every Sunday Easter to October plus Bank Holidays and Christmas

Directions: On the A431 midway between Bristol and Bath at Bitton

FHG PUBLICATIONS, ABBEY MILL BUSINESS CENTRE, PAISLEY PA1 1TJ

Lots of baby animals. FREE pony rides, face painting, green trail, 'pat-a-pet', indoor children's soft play area; gift shop, tearoom, pets' paddocks

DOGS MUST BE KEPT ON LEADS

Open: March to October 10.30am to 6pm

Directions: Follow brown tourist signs off A12 and other roads

FHG PUBLICATIONS, ABBEY MILL BUSINESS CENTRE, PAISLEY PA1 1TJ

FHG READERS' OFFER 2004

Buckley's Yesterday's World

High Street, Battle, East Sussex TN33 0AQ

Tel: 01424 775378 e-mail: info@yesterdaysworld.co.uk
website: www.yesterdaysworld.co.uk

50p off each admission

Valid until end 2004

NOT TO BE USED IN CONJUNCTION WITH ANY OTHER OFFER

FHG READERS' OFFER 2004

Wilderness Wood

Hadlow Down, Near Uckfield, East Sussex TN22 4HJ

Tel: 01825 830509 • Fax: 01825 830977

e-mail: enquiries@wildernesswood.co.uk • website: www.wildernesswood.co.uk

TWO for the price of ONE

valid during 2004

NOT TO BE USED IN CONJUNCTION WITH ANY OTHER OFFER

FHG READERS' OFFER 2004

Stratford Butterfly Farm

Swans Nest Lane, Stratford-upon-Avon, Warwickshire CV37 7LS

Tel: 01789 299288 • e-mail: sales@butterflyfarm.co.uk
website: www.butterflyfarm.co.uk

One child free with each paying adult

Valid during 2004

NOT TO BE USED IN CONJUNCTION WITH ANY OTHER OFFER

FHG READERS' OFFER 2004

Cholderton Rare Breeds Farm Park

Amesbury Road, Cholderton, Wiltshire SP4 0EW

Tel: 01980 629438

e-mail: sales@rabbitworld.co.uk • website: www.choldertonfarm.co.uk

One person FREE with two paying adults
(not valid on Public Holidays or weekends during July and August)

valid June to November 3rd 2004

NOT TO BE USED IN CONJUNCTION WITH ANY OTHER OFFER

FHG READERS' OFFER 2004

Embsay & Bolton Abbey Steam Railway

Bolton Abbey Station, Skipton, N. Yorkshire BD23 6AF

Tel: 01756 710614 website: www.embsayboltonabbeyrailway.org.uk

One adult travels FREE when accompanied by a full fare paying adult

valid during 2004, does not include Special Event Days

NOT TO BE USED IN CONJUNCTION WITH ANY OTHER OFFER

The past is brought to life at the top attraction in the South East 2002 (England for Excellence Awards). Step back in time and wonder through over 30 shop and room settings.

PETS NOT ALLOWED IN CHILDREN'S PLAY AREA

Open: 9.30am to 6pm (last admission 4.45pm, one hour earlier in winter).

Directions: Just off A21 in Battle High Street opposite the Abbey.

FHG PUBLICATIONS, ABBEY MILL BUSINESS CENTRE, PAISLEY PA1 1TJ

Wilderness Wood is a unique family-run working woodland in the Sussex High Weald. Explore trails and footpaths, enjoy local cakes and ices, try the adventure playground. Many special events and activities. Parties catered for.

Open: daily 10am to 5.30pm or dusk if earlier.

Directions: On the south side of the A272 in the village of Hadlow Down. Signposted with a brown tourist sign.

FHG PUBLICATIONS, ABBEY MILL BUSINESS CENTRE, PAISLEY PA1 1TJ

Wander through a lush landscape of exotic foliage where a myriad of multi-coloured butterflies sip nectar from tropical blossoms. Stroll past bubbling streams and splashing waterfalls; view insects and spiders all safely behind glass.

Open: 10am to 6pm summer, 10am to dusk winter.

FHG PUBLICATIONS, ABBEY MILL BUSINESS CENTRE, PAISLEY PA1 1TJ

Lovely rural farm with 50 breeds of rabbit, and several breeds of poultry, pig, sheep, goat, horses and ponies. Iron Age Roundhouse.
Cafe, craft shop, events throughout holidays, famous pig races, nature trail, indoor and outdoor play.

Open: 10.30am to 6pm in season, weekends 10am to 4pm in winter.

Directions: Near Stonehenge, just off the A303 at the intersection with A338 Salisbury/Swindon Road.

FHG PUBLICATIONS, ABBEY MILL BUSINESS CENTRE, PAISLEY PA1 1TJ

Steam trains operate over a 4½ mile line from Bolton Abbey Station to Embsay Station. Many family events including Thomas the Tank Engine take place during major Bank Holidays.

Open: steam trains run every Sunday throughout the year and up to 7 days a week in summer.
10.30am to 4.30pm

Directions: Embsay Station signposted from the A59 Skipton by-pass; Bolton Abbey Station signposted from the A59 at Bolton Abbey.

FHG PUBLICATIONS, ABBEY MILL BUSINESS CENTRE, PAISLEY PA1 1TJ

FHG READERS' OFFER 2004

Museum of Rail Travel

Ingrow Railway Centre, Near Keighley, West Yorkshire BD22 8NJ

Tel: 01535 680425 • e-mail: admin@vintagecarriagestrust.org
website: www.vintagecarriagestrust.org

"ONE for ONE" free admission

Valid during 2004 except during special events (ring to check)

NOT TO BE USED IN CONJUNCTION WITH ANY OTHER OFFER

FHG READERS' OFFER 2004

Thackray Museum

Beckett Street, Leeds LS9 7LN

Tel: 0113 244 4343 • Fax: 0113 247 0219

e-mail: info@thackraymuseum.org • website: www.thackraymuseum.org

TWO for ONE on the purchase of a full adult ticket

valid until July 2004 excluding Bank Holidays

NOT TO BE USED IN CONJUNCTION WITH ANY OTHER OFFER

FHG READERS' OFFER 2004

Dunaskin Heritage Centre

Waterside, Patna, Ayrshire KA6 7JF

Tel: 01292 531144

e-mail: dunaskin@btconnect.com • website: www.dunaskin.org.uk

TWO for the price of ONE

valid from 1st May to 31st October 2004

NOT TO BE USED IN CONJUNCTION WITH ANY OTHER OFFER

FHG READERS' OFFER 2004

Kelburn Castle & Country Centre

Fairlie, Near Largs, Ayrshire KA29 0BE

Tel: 01475 568685 • e-mail: info@kelburncountrycentre.com
website: www.kelburncountrycentre.com

One child FREE for each full paying adult

Valid until October 2004

NOT TO BE USED IN CONJUNCTION WITH ANY OTHER OFFER

FHG READERS' OFFER 2004

Scottish Maritime Museum

Harbourside, Irvine KA12 8QE

Tel: 01294 278283 • e-mail: smm@tildesley.fsbusiness.co.uk
website: www.scottishmaritimemuseum.org • Fax: 01294 313211

TWO for the price of ONE

Valid from January to December 2004

NOT TO BE USED IN CONJUNCTION WITH ANY OTHER OFFER

A fascinating display of railway carriages and a wide range of railway items telling the story of rail travel over the years.

ALL PETS MUST BE KEPT ON LEADS

Open: Daily 11am to 4.30pm

Directions: Approximately one mile from Keighley on A629 Halifax road. Follow brown tourist signs

FHG PUBLICATIONS, ABBEY MILL BUSINESS CENTRE, PAISLEY PA1 1TJ

A fantastic day out for all at the lively and interactive, award-winning Thackray Museum. Experience life as it was in the Victorian slums, discover how medicine has changed our lives and the incredible lotions and potions once offered as cures. Try an empathy belly and explore the interactive bodyworks gallery.

Open: daily 10am till 5pm, closed 24th - 26th and 31st December and 1st January.

Directions: from M621 follow signs for York (A64) then follow brown tourist signs. From the north, take A58 towards city and then follow brown tourist signs.

FHG PUBLICATIONS, ABBEY MILL BUSINESS CENTRE, PAISLEY PA1 1TJ

Set in the rolling hills of Ayrshire, Europe's best preserved ironworks. Guided tours, audio-visuals, walks with electronic wands. Restaurant/coffee shop.

Open: April to October daily 10am to 5pm.

Directions: A713 Ayr to Castle Douglas road, 12 miles from Ayr, 3 miles from Dalmellington.

FHG PUBLICATIONS, ABBEY MILL BUSINESS CENTRE, PAISLEY PA1 1TJ

The historic home of the Earls of Glasgow. Waterfalls, gardens, famous Glen, unusual trees. Riding school, stockade, play areas, exhibitions, shop, cafe and The Secret Forest.

PETS MUST BE KEPT ON LEAD

Open: daily 10am to 6pm Easter to October.

Directions: On A78 between Largs and Fairlie, 45 mins drive from Glasgow.

FHG PUBLICATIONS, ABBEY MILL BUSINESS CENTRE, PAISLEY PA1 1TJ

Scotland's seafaring heritage is among the world's richest and you can relive the heyday of Scottish shipping at the Maritime Museum.

Open: all year except Christmas and New Year Holidays. 10am - 5pm

Directions: Situated on Irvine harbourside and only a 10 minute walk from Irvine train station.

FHG PUBLICATIONS, ABBEY MILL BUSINESS CENTRE, PAISLEY PA1 1TJ

FHG
READERS' OFFER 2004

Almond Valley Heritage Centre

Millfield, Livingston, West Lothian EH54 7AR

Tel: 01506 414957

e-mail: info@almondvalley.co.uk • website: www.almondvalley.co.uk

Free child with adult paying full admission

Valid during 2004

NOT TO BE USED IN CONJUNCTION WITH ANY OTHER OFFER

FHG
READERS' OFFER 2004

MYRETON MOTOR MUSEUM

Aberlady, East Lothian EH32 0PZ

Tel: 01875 870288

One child FREE with each paying adult

valid during 2004

NOT TO BE USED IN CONJUNCTION WITH ANY OTHER OFFER

FHG
READERS' OFFER 2004

Highland and Rare Breeds Farm

Elphin, Near Ullapool, Sutherland IV27 4HH

Tel: 01854 666204

One FREE adult or child with adult paying full entrance price

valid May to September 2004

NOT TO BE USED IN CONJUNCTION WITH ANY OTHER OFFER

FHG
READERS' OFFER 2004

Landmark Forest Theme Park

Carrbridge, Inverness-shire PH23 3AJ

Tel: 01479 841613 • Freephone 0800 731 3446

e-mail: landmarkcentre@btconnect.com • website: www.landmark-centre.co.uk

10% DISCOUNT for pet owners. Free admission for pets!
Maximum of four persons per voucher

Valid during 2004

NOT TO BE USED IN CONJUNCTION WITH ANY OTHER OFFER

FHG
READERS' OFFER 2004

New Lanark World Heritage Site

New Lanark Mills, New Lanark. Lanarkshire ML11 9DB

Tel: 01555 661345• Fax: 01555 665738

e-mail: visit@newlanark.org • website: www.newlanark.org

One FREE child with every full price adult

valid until 31st October 2004

NOT TO BE USED IN CONJUNCTION WITH ANY OTHER OFFER

An innovative museum exploring the history and environment of West Lothian on a 20-acre site packed full of things to see and do, indoors and out.

Open: Daily (except Christmas and New Year) 10am to 5pm.

Directions: 15 miles from Edinburgh, follow "Heritage Centre" signs from A899.

FHG PUBLICATIONS, ABBEY MILL BUSINESS CENTRE, PAISLEY PA1 1TJ

On show is a large collection, from 1899, of cars, bicycles, motor cycles and commercials. There is also a large collection of period advertising, posters and enamel signs.

Open: Daily April to October 11am to 4pm; November to March: Sundays 1pm to 3pm or by special appointment.

Directions: Off A198 near Aberlady. Two miles from A1.

FHG PUBLICATIONS, ABBEY MILL BUSINESS CENTRE, PAISLEY PA1 1TJ

Highland croft open to visitors for "hands-on" experience with over 30 different breeds of farm animals "stroke the goats and scratch the pigs". Farm information centre and old farm implements. For all ages, cloud or shine!

Open: July and August 10am to 5pm.

Directions: On A835 15 miles north of Ullapool

FHG PUBLICATIONS, ABBEY MILL BUSINESS CENTRE, PAISLEY PA1 1TJ

Great day out for all the family. Wild Water Coaster, Microworld exhibition, Forest Trails, Viewing Tower, Climbing Wall*, Tree Top Trail, Steam powered Sawmill*, Clydesdale Horse*. Shop, restaurant and snackbar. (* Easter to October)*

DOGS MUST BE KEPT ON LEADS

Open: Daily (except Christmas Day).

Directions: 20 miles south of Inverness at Carrbridge, just off the A9.

FHG PUBLICATIONS, ABBEY MILL BUSINESS CENTRE, PAISLEY PA1 1TJ

A beautifully restored cotton mill village close to the Falls of Clyde. Explore the fascinating history of the village, try the 'New Millennium Experience', a magical ride which takes you back in time to discover what life used to be like.

Open: 11am to 5pm daily. Closed Christmas Day and New Years Day.

FHG PUBLICATIONS, ABBEY MILL BUSINESS CENTRE, PAISLEY PA1 1TJ

Colourful gardens, imaginative woodland play areas and tumbling waterfalls. The Estate combines history with adventure in a fun day out for all the family, where your dog can run freely. Step back in time and uncover its secrets.

Open: Daily
10.30am to 5pm

Directions: Off A8 west of Langbank.
20 minutes west of Glasgow Airport.

FHG PUBLICATIONS, ABBEY MILL BUSINESS CENTRE, PAISLEY PA1 1TJ

A 60-minute ride along the shores of beautiful Padarn Lake behind a quaint historic steam engine. Magnificent views of the mountains from lakeside picnic spots.

DOGS MUST BE KEPT ON LEAD AT ALL TIMES ON TRAIN

Open: Most days Easter to October.
Free timetable leaflet on request.

Directions: Just off A4086 Caernarfon to Capel Curig road at Llanberis; follow 'Country Park' signs.

FHG PUBLICATIONS, ABBEY MILL BUSINESS CENTRE, PAISLEY PA1 1TJ

Nine rooms in a Georgian house filled with items illustrating the happier times of family life over the past 150 years. Joyful nostalgia unlimited.

Open:
March to end October

Directions:
opposite Beaumaris Castle

FHG PUBLICATIONS, ABBEY MILL BUSINESS CENTRE, PAISLEY PA1 1TJ

Journey through the lanes of cycle history and see bicycles from Boneshakers and Penny Farthings up to modern Raleigh cycles. Over 250 machines on display

PETS MUST BE KEPT ON LEADS

Open: 1st March to 1st November
daily 10am onwards.

Directions: Brown signs to car park.
Town centre attraction.

FHG PUBLICATIONS, ABBEY MILL BUSINESS CENTRE, PAISLEY PA1 1TJ

**Also see page 102 for a list of other attractions which allow pets
(in most cases they must be kept on leads)**

See also Inside Front Cover

The ideal holiday destinations for your pet, be assured of a warm and friendly reception, sit back, close your eyes and soak up the history and atmosphere.

Green Farm Hotel & Restaurant ❖ North Norfolk

For the past 21 years Philip and Dee Dee Lomax have been extending a warm welcome to guests at the Green Farm, to enjoy the relaxed and friendly atmosphere and the highest standards of hospitality.

Enjoy this tranquil backwater of North Norfolk. Green Farm is the ideal base to discover and dip into the hidden delights of Norfolk. The Glorious Norfolk Broads, beautiful beaches, footpaths and bridleways and many National Trust houses.

The charming 16th Century flint-faced Farmhouse Inn offers 14 antique style bedrooms, all en suite, including four-posters. The converted dairy ground floor accommodation is ideal for guests who find stairs difficult. The food enjoys an enviable reputation for quality, presentation and service.

Please telephone for details of our special breaks available all year.

Green Farm Hotel and Restaurant
Thorpe Market, North Walsham, North Norfolk NR11 8TH
Tel: 01263 833602 ❖ Fax: 01263 833163
e-mail: grfarmh@aol.com
website: www.greenfarmhotel.co.uk

New Inn Hotel ❖ Clapham – 'Jewel of the Dales'

A comfortable hotel in the Yorkshire Dales National Park. The New Inn has been lovingly and carefully refurbished during the 16 years of ownership by Keith & Barbara Mannion, with a fine blend of old and new to retain the characteristics of this fine 18th Century Coaching Inn where you can experience a warm and friendly welcome.

The beautiful old Dales village straggles either side of Clapham Beck, one half linked to the other by three bridges, the Church at the top, the New Inn at the bottom. This traditional Village Inn has 20 en suite bedrooms, including ground floor and disabled bedrooms. Resident lounges, Restaurant, two comfortable bars serving a selection of Yorkshire ales, fine wines and a large selection of malt whiskies. Our food offers a mix between traditional and modern cooking.

Truly a 'Yorkshire Inn run by Yorkshire Folk'

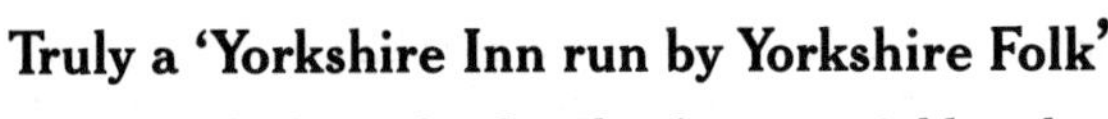

Please telephone for details of our special breaks available all year.

New Inn Hotel
Clapham, Nr Ingleton, North Yorkshire LA2 8HH
Tel: 015242 51203 ❖ Fax: 015242 51496
e-mail: info@newinn-clapham.co.uk
website: www.newinn-clapham.co.uk

See also Colour Advertisement on page 47

Fairhaven Holiday Cottages

Fairhaven offers a wide selection of holiday homes as well as comprehensive local knowledge and a friendly service. We specialise in Kent and Sussex with a few properties in Wiltshire and in Wales. Our directors personally visit all of our properties to ensure quality and up-to-date information. Pets are welcome in many properties and short breaks are available out of season. For full details of all our properties visit our website **www fairhaven-holidays.co.uk**
Alternatively request a colour brochure by telephone, fax or e-mail:
Tel: 08452 304334 • Fax: 01634 570157 • E-mail: enquiries@fairhaven-holidays.co.uk

See also Colour Advertisement on page 58

Holidays your whole family will leap at

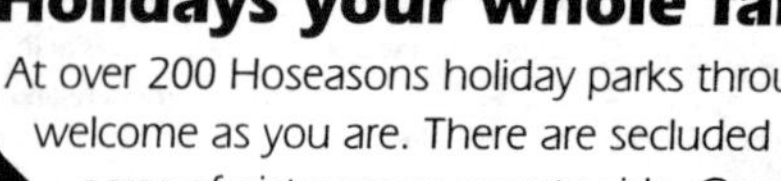

At over 200 Hoseasons holiday parks throughout Britain, your pet is as welcome as you are. There are secluded pine lodges surrounded by acres of picturesque countryside. Or seaside locations with miles of unspoilt coastline to explore. Nearly all offer mid-week and weekend short breaks. Many are open all year round.

01502 502 601 Quote H0004

www.hoseasons.co.uk

Wide choice of cottages & apartments throughout England, Scotland & the Isles. **Pets welcome** in many properties. Quality Cottages in coastal, country and mountain locations. Property finding service. Est. 1980.

Contact: **Mary & Simon Ette,**
Ford Cottage, Thorverton, Exeter EX5 5NT Tel: 01392 860807
Fax: 01392 860552 • E-mail: help@gowithit.co.uk
Website: www.gowithit.co.uk

See also colour advertisement on page 6

Britain's Favourite Cottage Holidays

Country Holidays welcomes you and your pets

None of us likes to leave that important member of the family behind when we go away on holiday. On top of which, there's the hassle and cost of boarding kennels or catteries. So it's great to know that Country Holidays have many properties that welcome your pet. The price is only £16 per pet per week or Short Break, which will save you from those boarding fees and those sad, soulful eyes.

FOR YOUR FREE 2004 BROCHURE CALL
Tel: 0870 4425240
Country Holidays
www.country-holidays.co.uk

See also Colour Advertisement on page 6

Available from most bookshops, the 2004 edition of **THE GOLF GUIDE** covers details of every UK golf course – well over 2800 entries – for holiday or business golf. Hundreds of hotel entries offer convenient accommodation, accompanying details of the courses – the 'pro', par score, length etc.

In association with 'Golf Monthly' and including Holiday Golf in Ireland, France, Portugal, Spain, The USA, South Africa and Thailand .

£9.99 from bookshops or from the publishers (postage charged outside UK) • FHG Publications, Abbey Mill Business Centre, Paisley PA1 1TJ

PLEASE SEND A STAMPED ADDRESSED ENVELOPE WITH ENQUIRIES

RECOMMENDED COTTAGE HOLIDAYS. 1st choice for dream cottages at very competitive prices in all holiday regions of beautiful Britain. All properties inspected. Many accept pets at no extra charge. Full details in our brochure - call 08700 718718.
website: www.recommended-cottages.co.uk

MR P.W. REES, "QUALITY COTTAGES', CERBID, SOLVA, HAVERFORDWEST, PEMBROKESHIRE SA62 6YE (01348 837871). Cottages set in all coastal areas, unashamed luxury, highest residential standards. Dishwashers, microwaves, washing machines. Log fires. Linen supplied. Pets welcome. [pw! 🐕]
website: www.qualitycottages.co.uk

FAIRHAVEN HOLIDAY COTTAGES. (08452 304334; Fax: 01634 570157) Fairhaven offers a wide selection of holiday homes in Kent and Sussex with a few properties in Wiltshire and in Wales. Pets are welcome in many properties and short breaks are available out of season. Please visit our website or request a colour brochure.
e-mail: enquiries@fairhaven-holidays.co.uk website : www.fairhaven-holidays.co.uk

HOSEASONS. At over 200 Hoseasons holiday parks throughout Britain, your pet is as welcome as you are. There are secluded pine lodges surrounded by acres of picturesque countryside. Or seaside locations with miles of unspoilt coastline to explore. Nearly all offer mid-week and weekend short breaks. Many are open all year round. (01502 502 601) Quote H0004.
website: www.hoseasons.co.uk

THE INDEPENDENT TRAVELLER, FORD COTTAGE, THORVERTON, EXETER EX5 5NT (01392 860807 Fax: 01392 860552). For a wide choice of cottages and apartments throughout England, Scotland & the Isles. Pets welcome in many properties. Quality Cottages in coastal, country and mountain location. Property finding service.
e-mail: help@gowithit.co.uk website: www.gowithit.co.uk

COUNTRY HOLIDAYS BROCHURE LINE: 0870 4425240 Many properties welcome pets. (£16 per pet per week/Short Break).
website: www.country-holidays.co.uk

BUCKINGHAMSHIRE

Quainton

Chesham

Town on south side of Chiltern Hills. Ideal walking area.

PAT & GEORGE ORME, 49 LOWNDES AVENUE, CHESHAM HP5 2HH (01494 792647). B&B detached house. 10 minutes from underground. Private bathroom, Tea/coffee. TV. Good walking country - Chiltern Hills (3 minutes). ETC ◆◆◆[🐕]
e-mail: bbormelowndes@tiscali.co.uk

Quainton

Village 6 miles north west of Aylesbury.

MRS H. HOWARD, WOODLANDS FARMHOUSE, QUAINTON, AYLESBURY HP22 4DE (01296 770225). Recently converted stables provide well-equipped, comfortable en suite accommodation. Well placed for Oxford and Waddesdon Manor. Vegetarian and organic food available. Children and well-behaved pets welcome. Open all year

Ely

Magnificent Norman Cathedral dating from 1083. Ideal base for touring the fen country of East Anglia.

MRS C. H. BENNETT, STOCKYARD FARM, WISBECH ROAD, WELNEY PE14 9RQ (01354 610433; Fax: 01354 610422). Comfortable converted farmhouse, rurally situated between Ely and Wisbech. Conservatory breakfast room, TV lounge. Free range produce. Miles of riverside walks. No smoking. B&B from £18. [🐕 pw!]

St Ives

Town on the River Ouse 5 miles east of Huntingdon.

ST IVES MOTEL, LONDON ROAD, ST IVES, HUNTINGDON PE27 5EX (Tel & Fax: 01480 463857). 16 rooms, all en suite, overlooking orchards and garden. Close to Cambridge and A14. Licensed bar and restaurant. AA/RAC ★★[Pets £2-£5 per night depending on type of animal].
e-mail: mail@stives-motel.co.uk website: www.stives-motel.co.uk

Wood Walton

Village 6 miles north of Huntingdon. Wood Walton Fen Nature Reserve to north east.

ELEPHANT & CASTLE MOTEL AND FREEHOUSE, THE GREEN, WOOD WALTON, HUNTINGDON PE 28 5YN (Tel & Fax: 01487 773337). Family-run establishment in tranquil surroundings. 13 en suite motel rooms with shower, TV, tea/coffee making, electric heating and radio. Caravan hook-ups. Bar meals available. Large garden, close to country walks. [Pets £3 per night].

Balterley Green Farm

Deans Lane, Balterley, Near Crewe CW2 5QJ
Tel: 01270 820214 ETC ◆◆◆◆

Jo and Pete Hollins offer guests a friendly welcome to their home on a 145-acre dairy farm in quiet and peaceful surroundings. Situated on the Cheshire/Staffordshire border within easy reach of Junction 16 on the M6. Pets' corner for young children. Within easy reach of Chester, Alton Towers and the Potteries. One family room en suite, one single & one twin (suitable for disabled) all en suite. Bed and Breakfast from £23pp. Caravans and tents welcome.

THE EATON HOTEL

CITY ROAD, CHESTER CH1 3AE

AA ★★ **TEL: 01244 320840 • FAX: 01244 320850**

The Eaton Hotel is the perfect location for sightseeing in Chester. Not only is it convenient for the River Dee, Roman Walls and main shopping areas, all of which are only a few minutes' walk away, but also its canal-side position makes walking your dog the pleasure it should be. All this, complemented by good food and a very friendly atmosphere makes the Eaton Hotel the obvious choice for your stay in Chester. Secure parking on the premises.

website: www.eatonhotelchester.co.uk

Balterley

Small village two miles west of Audley.

MR & MRS HOLLINS, BALTERLEY GREEN FARM, DEANS LANE, BALTERLEY, NEAR CREWE CW2 5QJ (01270 820214). 145-acre dairy farm in quiet and peaceful surroundings. Within easy reach of Junction 16 on the M6. Bed and Breakfast from £23pp. ETC ◆◆◆◆. Caravans and tents welcome. [pw! Pets £2 per night]

Chester

Former Roman city on the River Dee, with well-preserved walls and beautiful 14th century Cathedral. Liverpool 25 miles

THE EATON HOTEL, CITY ROAD, CHESTER CH1 3AE (01244 320840; Fax: 01244 320850). In a perfect central location. All rooms have bath or shower, colour TV, radio, telephone, hair dryer and tea making facilities. [ ]
website: www.eatonhotelchester.co.uk

FREE or REDUCED RATE entry to Holiday Visits and Attractions – see our READERS' OFFER VOUCHERS on pages 103-118

Please mention *Pets Welcome*
when enquiring about accommodation featured in these pages.

See also Colour Advertisement on page 6

Please mention Pets Welcome when writing to enquire about accommodation

Bodmin

Willow Valley Holiday Park

Bush, Bude EX23 9LB • Tel: 01288 353104

Four wooden lodges equipped to high standard. Each has 2 bedrooms, sofa bed in lounge, colour TV, bathroom, fully equipped kitchen. Two miles from town and sandy surfing beaches. Brochure on request. Open 1st March to 31st December. Write or telephone for brochure and price list.

HENTERVENE HOLIDAY PARK

Crackington Haven, Near Bude EX23 0LF **Tel: 01840 230365**

Two miles from unspoilt sandy beach in an Area of Outstanding Natural Beauty. Luxury caravans and pine lodge to let with first class facilities for families and pets. Caravans for sale. Open all year. Short breaks available. Camping £4.50 pppn. Caravan Sales and Tourer Storage.

e-mail: contact@hentervene.co.uk **website: www.hentervene.co.uk**

Five 18th Century converted barns, beamed ceilings, log fires and secluded rural setting. Ideal touring base. Five miles to coast at Crackington Haven. Sleep 2/6. Pets welcome. Open all year. From £75 short breaks, £130 per week. **ETC ★★★**.

Lorraine Harrison, Trenannick Cottages, Warbstow, Launceston, Cornwall PL15 8RP • Tel: 01566 781443

e-mail: lorraine.trenannick@i12.com • website: www.trenannickcottages.co.uk

A 14th Century Country Hotel

Crafthole, Near Torpoint, Cornwall PL11 3BD

Tel: 01503 230863 • Fax: 01503 230675

e-mail: enquiries@liscawn.co.uk • website: www.liscawn.co.uk

Charming, family-run 14th Century Hotel in 'The Forgotten Corner of Cornwall'.

A few minutes walk from the Cornish Coastal Path.
The perfect site for Fishing and Bird-watching.

Central to 3 golf courses, Whitsand Bay, Looe and St Mellion.

En suite accommodation with colour TV and coffee and tea making facilities in every room.

Self-Catering Suites available. Family and Pets welcome.

Bar meals available and cask ales a speciality.

Extensive Grounds and Beer garden with beautiful views over to Dartmoor.

A useful Index of Towns/Villages and Counties appears on page 427 – please also refer to Contents Page 3.

Cusgarne (near Truro)

A cosy, single storey, clean, detached dwelling within grounds of Saffron Meadow. In a quiet hamlet five miles west of Truro. Own enclosed garden, secluded and surrounded by wooded pastureland. Bedroom (double bed) with twin vanity unit. Fully tiled shower/WC and L.B. Comprehensively equipped kitchen/diner. Compact TV room. Storage room. Hot water galore and gas included. Metered electricity. Automatic external safety lighting. Your own ample parking space in drive. Inn, good food, a short walk. Central to Truro, Falmouth and North and South Coast. £170 - £230 per week.

Joyce and George Clench, Saffron Meadow, Cusgarne, Truro TR4 8RW Tel: 01872 863171

AA ★★★

• 3 Star Country House Hotel and self-catering courtyard cottages • Situated in 6 acres of mature gardens and woodland • Ideal for visiting Cornwall's superb gardens • Well behaved dogs welcome • Close to Falmouth and Coastal Paths • Ground floor bedrooms for easy pet access • Ample car parking

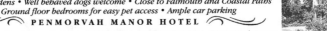

PENMORVAH MANOR HOTEL

Budock Water, Near Falmouth, Cornwall TR11 5ED • Tel: 01326 250277 • Fax: 01326 250509
e-mail: reception@penmorvah.co.uk • web: www.penmorvah.co.uk

See also Colour Advertisement on page 7

TREGILDRY HOTEL

Spectacular seaviews from this elegant and relaxing Hotel in away from it all surroundings. The Which? Hotel Guide comments, *"Top marks for the rooms, the food, the service and the views".*

10 pretty en suite rooms. Excellent cuisine in stylish restaurant. Wonderful uncrowded coastal path walks from the grounds.

Gillan, Manaccan, Cornwall TR12 6HG
Tel: 01326 231378
e-mail: trgildry@globalnet.co.uk • www.tregildryhotel.co.uk

AA ★★ 80%

Silver — Silver Award

"An AA Top 200 Hotel"

WHICH? *The Good Food Guide*

BOSCREGE

CAMPING & CARAVAN PARK
ASHTON, HELSTON, CORNWALL, TR13 9TG

★ Award winning quiet family rural park close to local beaches and attractions with no bar or clubs
★ Free showers ★ Microwave facilities ★ Games room ★ Childs play area ★ Laundry ★ Pets welcome

Phone/Fax 01736 762231 for colour brochure

www.caravanparkcornwall.com - enquires@caravanparkcornwall.com

ROSECRADDOC HOLIDAYS, Rosecraddoc Lodge, Cornwall
"Ducks Ditty", "Mallards" and "Watery Fowls". Three comfortable and well-equipped bungalows on a purpose built holiday estate with beautiful, peaceful open gardens in a woodland setting on the outskirts of Liskeard. One bungalow specially adapted for wheelchairs. PETS VERY WELCOME. Ideal centre for touring North and South coasts, visiting Eden, National Maritime Museum and the Tate Galley St Ives.
Mrs N. Arthur, Rosecraddoc Lodge, Liskeard PL14 5BU • Tel or Fax: 01579 346768

Mrs Northcott, Pendower House, East Taphouse, Liskeard, Cornwall, PL14 4NH. Tel: 01579 320332

Bed and Breakfast ***Central for Cornwall***

H/C in all rooms. Good touring area. Television. All comforts. Central heating. Ground floor suite. Good food. Main Road. Open all year. Moderate terms.

Cutkive Wood Holiday Lodges

Six Cedarwood Chalets in 41 acres own Bluebell Woods with nature trails. Dogs welcome. Pets' corner. Children welcome to help milk goats, feed poultry etc. Three hole practice golf course. Resident owner retired PGA professional golfer. Tuition available. Ideal touring. From £120 to £370 per week March to October.

St Ive, Liskeard PL14 3ND • Tel: 01579 362216
E-mail: cutkwood@hotmail.com • www.cutkivewood.co.uk

Country Caradon Cottages

Luxury cottages in the heart of the Cornish countryside. Ideal centre for exploring Devon and Cornwall, coast and moor. Just east of the Eden Project. Central heating and log burners for cosy off-season breaks. Every comfort for you and your pets.

Celia Hutchinson, Caradon Country Cottages
East Taphouse, Near Liskeard, Cornwall PL14 4NH
Telephone & Fax: 01579 320355
Website: www.caradoncottages.co.uk

RIVERMEAD FARM

Twowatersfoot, Liskeard, Cornwall PL14 6HT
Telephone: 01208 821 464

Self Catering Apartments and Farm Cottage

Set in beautiful wooded Glynn Valley, amidst 30 acres of meadows and water meadows.

- River and lakeside walks.
- Convenient for both Coasts and Moors.
- A mile of Sea Trout and Salmon fishing on the River Fowey.
- Pets welcome.

Brochure on request to Alan & Kathleen Hunstone at Rivermead Farm.
Website: www.zednet.co.uk/rivermead

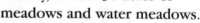

An **award winning Holiday Park** near Helston, in an area of outstanding natural beauty and close to safe sandy beaches. Dogs Welcome!

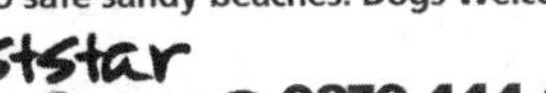

Quote: WP

☎ 0870 444 0080

book online: www.weststarholidays.co.uk/pw

Parc Brawse House

Penmenner Road, The Lizard
TR12 7NR • Tel: 01326 290466

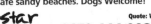

Quality late 19th century Cornish Guesthouse overlooking Lizard Point. Stunning location.

e-mail: benjocharity@aol.com
website: www.cornwall-online.co.uk
***RAC* ◆◆◆◆**

An award winning Holiday Park near Looe, in an area of outstanding natural beauty and close to safe sandy beaches. Dogs Welcome!

Weststar HOLIDAY PARKS

Quote: WP

☎ 0870 444 0080

book online: www.weststarholidays.co.uk/pw

TREWITH HOLIDAY COTTAGES • Self Catering Accommodation Open All Year

Situated in a superb elevated position of outstanding natural beauty. Just 1½ miles from Looe. Choice of 4 refurbished cottages with 1-3 bedrooms. Fully equipped and tastefully furnished with full central heating. Use of laundry room. Peaceful location with delightful walks. Many beaches, coves, fishing, shopping close by.. Because of ponds young children need supervision. Well behaved dogs welcome.

Paul & Barbie Higgins Trewith, Duloe, near Liskeard, Cornwall PL14 4PR • Tel: 01503 262184
mobile: 07968 262184 • E-mail: holiday-cottages@trewith.freeserve.co.uk • www.trewith.freeserve.co.uk

See also Colour Advertisement on page 7

Valleybrook

Peakswater, Lansallos, Looe, Cornwall PL13 2QE

LODGES • COTTAGES • CARAVANS

Small peaceful secluded country site near Looe & Polperro, just 10 miles from the Eden Project.

• High quality scandinavian pine lodges
• Olde - worlde charm cottages
• Short Breaks Available • Dogs Welcome
• Open all year • No club or swimming pool

Contact Denise, Keith & Brian Holder

01503 220493

www.valleybrookholidays.co.uk

Secluded country cottages set in idyllic grounds of historic estate in the enchanting Looe Valley. Each has its own charming garden with a further third of an acre of manicured lawn. They are individually furnished with antiques and country furnishings. Although steeped in character, we offer all modern conveniences such as washer dryers, dishwashers, microwaves, linen, colour TV, video, telephone and much more. Open log fires and inclusive heating for warm cosy breaks off season. Guests and dogs are welcome to walk or stroll in the immediate parkland and grounds. Countryside and coastal walking all nearby. Looe 1½ miles with beaches and excellent restaurants. Delicious home-cooked meals service delivered to your door.

For details contact:* *Mrs E.M. Chapman, Trenant Lodge, Sandplace, Looe, Cornwall PL13 1PH
Tel: 01503 263639/262241
e-mail: Liz@holiday-cottage.com
For on-line Colour Brochure: www.holiday-cottage.com

POLPERRO CORNWALL

Spectacularly situated holiday cottages in picturesque Cornish fishing village.

Sleeping from 2 to 8 persons - £175 to £450 per cottage per week.

With terraced gardens and fabulous outlook over harbour, encompassing 15 mile sea views. Private parking, two minutes shops, beach, quay and National Trust cliff walks. Open all year. Children and pets most welcome. All cottages are fully furnished and equipped to include a colour television, microwave, electric oven, refrigerator, duvets and pillows. **Graham Wright, Guardian House, Liskeard, PL14 6AD**

01579 344080

Talehay Holiday Cottages

Pelynt, Near Looe PL13 2LT

A Quiet Haven in the Countryside near the sea

Cosy, traditional cottages with many original features retained provide superb holiday accommodation on 17C non-working farmstead. Set in 4 acres of unspoilt countryside offering peace and tranquillity with breathtaking coastal and country walks on your doorstep. This is an ideal location for dogs and their owners alike. C.T.B. approved. Close to the Eden Project.

Let our brochure convince you – Tel/Fax Mrs Ann Brumpton 01503 220252
E-mail: pr.brumpton@ukonline.co.uk Website: www.talehay.co.uk

PLEASE NOTE

All the information in this book is given in good faith in the belief that it is correct. However, the publishers cannot guarantee the facts given in these pages, neither are they responsible for changes in policy, ownership or terms that may take place after the date of going to press. Readers should always satisfy themselves that the facilities they require are available and that the terms, if quoted, still apply.

When making enquiries or bookings, a stamped addressed envelope is always appreciated

Cottages for Romantics
Old world charm, log fires, antiques, beautifully furnished with the comforts of home. Private gardens, spectacular views, peace ~ for families, friends and couples to enjoy. Nestling on a south-facing hillside, near coast ~ heated pool, tennis, badminton, lake, shire horses, etc. Enchanting 70 acre estate with bluebell wood, walking and wildlife. Delicious fare also available by candlelight 'at home' or in our tiny inn.
O. Slaughter, Trefanny Hill, Duloe, Near Liskeard, Cornwall, PL14 4QF
Tel: 01503 220 622
e-mail: enq@trefanny.co.uk
website: www.trefanny.co.uk
A Country Lover's Paradise ~ with an abundance of country walks from your garden gate and coastal walks only 4 miles away.
'relax in a little bit of heaven'
THE COTTAGES AT Trefanny Hill Nr. LOOE
'views from your garden gate'
Discover the magic of Trefanny Hill

Cornish Dream

"For those who enjoy the comfort of a high quality hotel but prefer the freedom of a cottage"

...The Good Holiday Cottage Guide

Idyllic 18th Century Country Cottages for romantics and animal lovers, near the sea in the beautiful Looe River valley. Your own delightful private garden with roses around the door and breathtaking views.

Exclusively furnished, antiques, crackling log fires, candlelit meals, dishwashers, videos, four-poster beds, crisp white linen and towels. Riding, heated swimming pool & tennis court. Wonderful walks from your cottage gate.

Golf, fishing, sea, coastal walks all nearby. Looe 3 miles. The cottages are heated and really warm and cosy in winter.Pets are welcome.

Personal attention and colour brochure from:

B.Wright, Treworgey Cottages, Duloe, Liskeard, Cornwall PL14 4PP

Tel: 01503 262730 or 263757

website: www.cornishdreamcottages.co.uk

St Anthony – Helford River

Enchanting creekside cottages in a timeless and tranquil hamlet. Springtime bluebell woods and hedgerows banked with primroses, reflections of multi-coloured sails off sandy beaches, the solitary blue flash of a Kingfisher in autumn, smoke grey herons and shining white egrets standing patiently by the shoreline all evoke the atmosphere of this truly beautiful corner of Cornwall.

- Stunning coastal and riverside walks
- Great country inns and local food
- Warm and comfortable with cosy log fires
- Our own sailing dinghies and fishing boats
- Moorings and easy launching
- National Trust and private gardens nearby
- Short breaks, open all year including Christmas

St Anthony Holidays, Manaccan, Helston, Cornwall TR12 6JW

Tel: 01326 231 357 • E-mail; info@StAnthony.co.uk • www.StAnthony.co.uk

Have your pet's photo featured in Pets Welcome! and receive a FREE Live-a-Lot Pack

As the sponsor of **Pets Welcome! 2004** Winalot is offering readers the chance to win a **Live-a-Lot Pack** for every picture featured.
The special packs include a rucksack, fold away bowl, water bottle, frisbee and dog towel – an essential kit for everyday doggie outings.

SEE PAGE 81 FOR FULL DETAILS

White Lodge Hotel

Mawgan Porth Bay, Near Newquay, Cornwall TR8 4BN
Tel: St Mawgan (STD 01637) 860512
E-mail: adogfriendly@aol.com Website: www.dogfriendlyhotel.co.uk

GIVE YOURSELVES & YOUR DOGS A BREAK

at our family-run White Lodge Hotel overlooking beautiful Mawgan Porth Bay, near Newquay, Cornwall

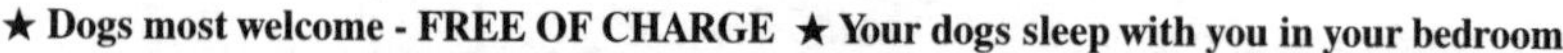

★ Dogs most welcome - FREE OF CHARGE ★ Your dogs sleep with you in your bedroom ★ Direct access to sandy beach and coastal path ★ Dog loving proprietors with 20 years' experience in catering for dog owners on holiday with their dogs ★ ALL bedrooms with colour TV, tea/coffee makers, alarm clocks, radios, heaters etc. ★ Fantastic sea views from most rooms ★ Well-stocked residents' lounge bar, dining room & sun patio with outstanding sea views across the bay ★ Large free car park within hotel grounds

SPECIAL 6 DAYS (5 NIGHTS) CHRISTMAS BREAK ONLY £305 *Half Board*	SPECIAL 6 DAYS (5 NIGHTS) NEW YEAR BREAK ONLY £260 *Half Board*	SPECIAL 6 DAYS (5 NIGHTS) BREAKS ONLY £200-£212.50 *BB & Evening Meal*	WEEKLY TERMS FROM £280-£297.50 FOR 5-COURSE EVENING DINNER, BED AND 4-COURSE BREAKFAST WITH CHOICE OF MENU

This hotel is now open all year – Winter Break packages available
Phone Patsy Powell for free colour brochure
ALL PRICES INCLUDE VAT AT 17½%

See also Colour Advertisement on page 11

The MALMAR Hotel

Trenance, Mawgan Porth, Cornwall TR8 4DA
malmarhotel@supanet.com • www.malmarhotel.com

- Beautifully situated in tranquil location, panoramic sea views. Close to beach, coastal path and lovely valley walks.
- Licensed family hotel, highly commended for our service, friendly atmosphere and home cooking.
- Any number of pets are welcome, may sleep with you and are allowed on the beach all year.
- TV lounge, darts, board games, cards, library available for guests' use.
- Family, double, single rooms, most en suite, majority ground floor. Colour TVs.
- BB&EM from £232 per week.

SPECIAL BREAKS
Four nights for the price of ***three***
PETS **FREE** **FREE** colour brochure
See us @ malmarhotel.com

Malcolm & Marylyn Ward: Newquay (01637) 860324

Dewolf Guest House **100 Henver Road, Newquay TR7 3BL**

The amenities of Newquay are close at hand, Porth Beach only a short walk from the guest house. Double or family rooms including two chalets situated in the rear garden. Downstairs bedroom & chalet - ideal for pets. All rooms non-smoking with en suite facilities, colour TV and tea/coffee making facilities. B&B from £20 per person based on two sharing or from £126 weekly per person. Special Christmas/ New Year Breaks. Off-road car parking available. Open all year.

Tel: 01637 874746 • e-mail: holidays@dewolfguesthouse.com • www.dewolfguesthouse.com

QUARRYFIELD Caravan & Camping Park, Crantock, Near Newquay.

Superbly situated overlooking beautiful Crantock Bay and the River Gannel estuary, park with fully equipped modern caravans for hire, and separate level camping field. Bar, pool, children's play area.

Contact: MRS WINN, TRETHERRRAS, NEWQUAY, CORNWALL TR7 2RE • Tel: 01637 872792

Trethiggey Touring Park, Quintrell Downs, Newquay TR8 4QR

Tel: 01637 877672 *Website: www.trethiggey.co.uk*

Two miles from Newquay and sandy surfing beaches. Beautiful and secluded, landscaped park with panoramic views over countryside. Family-owned site open from March to Jan 2nd. Christmas breaks. Shop and off-licence on park (take away food peak season). Children's play area. Games room, laundry facilities and modern toilet and shower block. Large recreation field. Three pubs and restaurants within walking distance. Park runs evening minibus service to and from Newquay. **e-mail: enquiries@trethiggey.co.uk** ETC ★★★★

Golden Bay Hotel

Unwind and relax in this small and surprisingly affordable quality hotel. Overlooking Fistral beach with the Gannel River and National Trust countryside at the rear. All rooms private facilities, some deluxe four poster rooms. Lovely coastal and countryside walks, also close to golf. B&B £20 - £34. Close to Eden Project, bus pick-up point opposite hotel. Good doggies very welcome and free of charge. ***ETC*** ◆◆◆

Pentire, Newquay, TR7 1PD • Tel: 01637 873318

e-mail: enquiries@goldenbayhotel.co.uk • website: www.goldenbayhotel.co.uk

Raintree House Holidays

A range of well equipped houses and bungalows near Trevose Golf Club, sandy beaches, scenic walks.

Mrs Watts, "WHISTLERS", Treyarnon Bay, Padstow PL28 8JR

e-mail: gill@raintreehouse.co.uk **Tel: 01841 520228/520130** ***web: www.raintreehouse.co.uk***

Cornwall near Perranporth

Greenmeadow Cottages Highly praised luxury cottages, sleep six, superbly clean, comfortable and spacious. Open all year. Short breaks out of season. Pets welcome in two of the cottages. Non-smoking available. Ample off road parking.

For brochure and bookings tel: 01872 540483

See also Colour Advertisement on page 8

CLASSY COTTAGES ~POLPERRO TO FOWEY~ ETC ★★★★/★★★★★ SELF CATERING

We are the proud owners of 4 SUPERB coastal cottage locations. Our cottages are of the highest standard

★ 2 cottages just feet from the sea in Polperro ★ 2 isolated cottages overlooking the sea near Lansallos ★ 10 wonderful cottages where our indoor swimming pool is situated ★ Open fires and heating ★ Telephone/e-mail available ★ Eden Project close by ★ Babysitting and dog sitting

YOU ARE VERY WELCOME TO ARRANGE TO BRING YOUR PETS ★ WE HAVE A LIST OF PET FRIENDLY BEACHES ★ VISIT US ON www.classycottages.co.uk ★ *Contact FIONA and MARTIN NICOLLE on 07000 423000*

When making enquiries or bookings, a stamped addressed envelope is always appreciated

GULLROCK COTTAGES

Port Gaverne Port Isaac North Cornwall

Personal attention from resident owner ensures your home from home comfort in a tranquil setting just yards from the sea at bygone Port Gaverne. **Tel: Malcolm Lee (01208) 880106**

CHIMNEYS

Port Gaverne, Port Isaac, Cornwall PL29 3SQ.
Tel & Fax: 01208 880254

A charming 18th Century Cottage just 10 metres from the beach making it a wonderful venue for pets and their owners. Four bedrooms, two bathrooms, lounge, dining room and kitchen. Good size garden. Close to Eden Project. Brochure available from **Mrs Holmes.**

Step onto the Coastal Path...

Escape the pressures of life. Relax! explore the Cornish Coast from Green Door Cottages in Port Gaverne.

8 comfortable, restored 18th Century cottages set around a sheltered courtyard, plus 2 prestigious apartments with panoramic sea views beside a picturesque cove, directly on the Coastal path, less than half a mile from Port Isaac.
An ideal location for your holiday and short breaks. Well behaved dogs are very welcome.

Call now for a brochure on:
01208 880293

Green Door Cottages
PORT GAVERNE
email: enquiries@greendoorcottages.co.uk
web: www.greendoorcottages.co.uk

See also Colour Advertisement on page 8

CARN AWN

PORT GAVERNE • PORT ISAAC

Carn Awn stands on its own in the Hamlet of Port Gaverne and overlooks the cove. Fishing, swimming, boating and delightful rock pools for the children. Magnificent coastline where you can walk for miles along coastal paths. Many beaches within reach. Plenty of shopping facilities. Car essential. Accommodation for six people in three double bedrooms, bathroom, separate toilet downstairs. Sitting / diningroom. Fully fitted kitchen. Sky TV. Well behaved dogs welcome. Open all year. ETC ★★★

For terms contact: Mrs S. A. May, Orcades House, Port Gaverne, Port Isaac, Cornwall PL29 3SQ Telephone or Fax: 01208 880716 e-mail: jimmay@orcades.u-net.com website: www.orcades.u-net.com

Trewince Manor

Portscatho, St. Mawes TR2 5ET

Peter and Liz Heywood invite you to take your self-catering or touring holiday at their Georgian Manor House Estate in this undiscovered and peaceful corner of Cornwall.

Luxury lodges and manor house apartments available.
Spectacular sea views; our own quay and moorings.

• Relaxing lounge bar and restaurant • Games rooms • Indoor pool • Sauna & Spa bath • • Superb walking and sailing • Abundance of wildlife • DOGS WELCOME

Please write or telephone for further information.

01872 580289 • E-mail: bookings@trewince.co.uk • Web: www.trewince.co.uk

See also Colour Advertisement on page 13

Friesian Valley Cottages

Mawla, Redruth, Cornwall TR16 5DW
Telephone: 01209 890901

Atlantic coast, between Newquay and St Ives. Luxury cottages. Sleep 2 to 6. Peaceful rural hamlet. Beaches and National Trust coastal footpath. Launderette, games room. Ample parking. Colour brochure.

Jasmine and Two Ways, Praa Sands, Near Penzance

Well appointed bungalows. One chalet-bungalow sleeps 9+ in 4 bedrooms. Lovely peaceful countryside with very large garden, not overlooked. 2 miles inland. One three bedroomed, sleeps 6+, overlooking sea, with large garden. Beach 5 mins. Both fully equipped. Dogs very welcome.

MRS JANE LAITY, CHYRASE FARM, GOLDSITHNEY, PENZANCE TR20 9JD
TEL: 01736 763301

GLOBE VALE HOLIDAY PARK

CARAVANS • STATIC CARAVANS • TOURERS • TENTS

In The Countryside Near The Sea

Perfect for pets and owners. Unlimited trails to explore and near "Dogs Allowed" beaches. Also small shop, Children's Play Area, Launderette, Bar and Games Room.

Radnor • Redruth • Cornwall • TR16 4BH • Tel: 01209 891183

Penkerris

A creeper clad Edwardian residence with lawned garden in unspoilt Cornish village. A home from home offering real food. Comfortable bedrooms with facilities (TV, radio, kettle, H & C). Dining room serving breakfast with dinner available by arrangement. Bright cosy lounge with a log fire in winter - colour TV, video & piano. Licensed. Ample parking. Dramatic cliff walks & beaches with good surfing nearby. Easy to find on B3277 road from big roundabout on A30 just by the village sign.

ETC/AA/RAC◆◆

B & B from £17.50 to £25. Dinner from £12.50.

Contact Dorothy Gill-Carey, Penkerris, Penwinnick Road, St Agnes TR5 0PA Tel & Fax: 01872 552262

E-mail: info@penkerris.co.uk *Website: www.penkerris.co.uk*

★★

The Sunholme Hotel

ETC ★★

Goonvrea Road, St Agnes, Cornwall TR5 0NW

Wonderful countryside and coastal views and a warm welcome await visitors to this country house hotel, standing in its own extensive grounds with ample parking on the southern slope of St Agnes Beacon. Excellent home cooked meals complement the luxurious en-suite accommodation. Children and pets welcome. Open all year. Non-smoking

For brochure write or phone: 01872 552318
e-mail: info@sunholme.co.uk
website: www.sunholme.co.uk

Please mention Pets Welcome when writing to enquire about accommodation

Caravan & Touring Holidays

Magnificent Walks • Short Drives to Superb Beaches

Can I?

- expect a quiet, spacious park ....YES
- park by my holiday caravan ....YES
- bring my dog ....YES
- caravans with all amenities ....YES
- children's play area & games room ....YES
- laundry and shop ....YES

NO CLUB, NO BAR, NO DISCO

Chiverton Park, Blackwater, Truro, Cornwall TR4 8HS
Brochure 01872 560667 • www.chivertonpark.co.uk

See also Colour Advertisement on page 8

Within the sound of the sea at Trevaunance Cove...

Delightful old inn with enormous beams

- Log fires
- Real Ale
- Malt Whisky
- Upstairs Eating Areas

The **Driftwood Spars** Hotel

Walkies Country

All bedrooms have excellent facilities, some with wonderful views

OPEN ALL YEAR • AMPLE PARKING

The Driftwood Spars Hotel, Trevaunance Cove,
St Agnes, Cornwall TR5 0RT

Tel: 01872 552428 • www.driftwoodspars.com

See also Colour Advertisement on page 10

BOSINVER HOLIDAY COTTAGES

Nestling in a hidden valley near the sea, the Eden Project and Lost Gardens of Heligan, our small farm has friendly animals and ponies. Choose from our 16th century thatched farmhouse or cottages privately set in their own gardens surrounded by wildflower meadows. Wander down to the fishing lake or village pub, swim in the pool, play tennis, or relax and listen to the birdsong. No pets during Summer School holidays. ETC ★★★★ **Brochure: Pat Smith, Bosinver Farm, St Mewan, St Austell, Cornwall.**

Tel: 01726 72128 • E-mail: reception@bosinver.co.uk • Internet: www.bosinver.co.uk

See also Colour Advertisement on page 10

TRENCREEK FARM HOLIDAY PARK

Hewaswater, St Austell PL26 7JG • Tel: 01726 882540
website: www.trencreek.co.uk

Visiting the Eden Project in Cornwall? We may be able to help with accommodation! Self-catering and camping facilities available. Heated outdoor swimming pool, tennis court and fishing lakes. Children and pets welcome. Self-catering available from £50 for two nights.

See also Colour Advertisement on page 13

HOLIDAY COTTAGE - ST BREWARD

Sleeps 4. Warm and lovely cottage sleeping four in great comfort and utter peace. Log fires, large garden with stream. Glorious walking. Available all year. Terms from £120 to £350 per week, depending on season. Dogs welcome, £6 per week. St Breward is a picturesque village high on Bodmin Moor and within easy reach of both coasts. Situated four miles from the A30.

For further details please contact Mrs Paddy Powell (01208 850186)
website: www.vacation-cornwall.com

The Links Holiday Flats

Lelant, St Ives, Cornwall TR26 3HY

If it's views you want, this is the place for you!

Magnificent location alongside and overlooking West Cornwall Golf Course, Hayle Estuary and St Ives Bay. Both flats have lovely views. Wonderful spot for walking. We are five minutes from the beach and dogs are allowed there all year round. Two well-equipped flats which are open all year.

Your hosts are Bob and Jacky Pontefract • Phone or fax 01736 753326

SANDBANK HOLIDAYS

St Ives Bay, Hayle, Cornwall. TR27 5BL
Website: www.sandbank-holidays.co.uk

High quality Apartments and Bungalows for 2-6 persons. Peaceful garden setting close to miles of sandy beach, acres of grassy dunes and SW Coastal Path. Open all year. Dogs Welcome. Fully equipped for your self-catering holiday. Heated, Colour TV Microwave etc: Spotlessly clean.

*** Short breaks From £90 * Weekly From £120 * Tel: 01736 752594**

See also Colour Advertisement on page 6

The Rosevine Hotel **Porthcurnick Beach, St Mawes, Truro TR2 5EW**

Tel: 01872 580206 • Fax: 01872 580230

Cornwall's new luxury hotel. De luxe bedrooms and suites. Award-winning cuisine. Beautiful sub-tropical gardens facing directly over the safe sandy beach fronting the National Trust coastline. Warm heated indoor pool. Children and pets most welcome.

CORNWALL'S ONLY RAC 3 DINING AWARDS & BLUE RIBBON HOTEL RAC ★★★ AA 80% Red Star

e-mail: info@rosevine.co.uk • website: www.rosevine.co.uk

See also Colour Advertisement on page 10

DALSWINTON HOUSE

e-mail: dalswinton@bigwig.net
website: www.dalswinton.com

A Victorian stone built Cornish house of character in a glorious rural setting. Standing in ten acres of gardens and meadowland, the house overlooks the Vale of Lanherne and the village of St Mawgan with views to the sea at the dog friendly beach of Mawgan Porth. Our hotel offers a comfortable, friendly atmosphere and great food prepared with fresh local produce. Regret no children under 16.

● DOGS FREE OF CHARGE AND ALLOWED EVERYWHERE EXCEPT THE DINING ROOM ● EIGHT ACRES OF PRIVATELY OWNED MEADOWLAND FOR DOG EXERCISE ● BED AND BREAKFAST FROM £32 PER PERSON PER NIGHT ● SHORT BREAK AND WEEKLY RATES AVAILABLE ● AMPLE CAR PARKING AND HEATED OUTDOOR POOL ● TEA / COFFEE & COLOUR TV IN ALL ROOMS ● LICENSED BAR & A RESTAURANT SERVING 3 COURSE DINNER ● GARDEN CHALET FOR SELF-CATERING OR INCLUSIVE TERMS ● EASY ACCESS TO NEWQUAY AIRPORT & THE EDEN PROJECT ●

DALSWINTON HOUSE HOTEL, ST MAWGAN-IN-PYDAR, CORNWALL TR8 4EZ. TEL/FAX: (01637) 860385

See also Colour Advertisement on page 9

TRETHEVY MANOR - TINTAGEL

Mrs Lynda Spring, Trethevy Manor, Trethevy Tintagel, Cornwall PL34 0BG * *Tel/Fax: 01840 770636*
E-mail: manor1151@talk21.com * Website: www.trethevy-manor.co.uk

2 comfortable well equipped self-contained stone built cottages adjoining 12th century Manor House. Exposed beams, interesting history, thoughtfully chosen furnishings. An area of outstanding natural beauty, the dramatic Rocky Valley and St Nectans Glen waterfall are nearby. Lovely beaches, spectacular coastal walks. Wonderful gardens and traditional country inns within easy reach.

Willapark Manor Hotel

Bossiney, Near Tintagel,
Cornwall PL34 0BA
Telephone: 01840 770782

One of the most beautifully situated Country House Hotels in England

website: www.willapark.co.uk ETC ★★

See also Colour Advertisement on page 12

BOSSINEY FARM CARAVAN & CAMPING PARK
TINTAGEL, CORNWALL PL34 0AY

Tel: 01840 770481 **ETC ★★★★**

★ Family-run Park renowned for cleanliness and hospitality ★ 20 Luxury Letting Vans ★ Fully serviced, H&C with shower, room heater ★ All with TV ★ On the coast at Tintagel ★ Ideal for touring ★ Superb value for money

SEND FOR OUR COLOUR BROCHURE TODAY!

www.bossineyfarm.co.uk

Whitsand Bay Hotel, Golf & Country Club

• Character 40 Bedroom Hotel • Set in an area of outstanding natural beauty
• Adjacent to its own 18 hole golf course • Magnificent panoramic sea views
• Good food, wines and service • Health & Fitness facilities • Indoor heated pool

Tel: 01503 230276 • Fax: 01503 230329
www.whitsandbayhotel.co.uk • E-mail: info@whitsandbayhotel.co.uk

See also Colour Advertisement on page 12

Two comfortable well-equipped cottages set in an Area of Outstanding Natural Beauty, each with its own charming garden. Individually furnished with co-ordinating furnishings. Full central heating and double glazed. Microwave, colour TV and Video, telephone, washing machine, fridge and all bed linen. We also offer use of our boat during your stay. All these included in the price. Pets are welcome. Beautiful woodland walks for you to stroll through. Perfect for fishing and bird watching.

King Harry Ferry Cottages

Tel: 01872 861915

High Quality Cottages to Let near Truro

www.kingharry-info.co.uk • E-mail: jean@kingharry.f9.co.uk

See also Colour Advertisement on page 13

FREE or REDUCED RATE entry to Holiday Visits and Attractions — see our READERS' OFFER VOUCHERS on pages 103-118

TOAD HALL COTTAGES (08700 777345. Over 200 outstanding waterside and rural properties in truly beautiful locations in Devon, Cornwall and Exmoor. Call for our highly acclaimed brochure. Pets welcome.
e-mail: thc@toadhallcottages.com website: www.toadhallcottages.com

POWELLS COTTAGE HOLIDAYS, 51 HIGH STREET, SAUNDERSFOOT, PEMBROKESHIRE SA69 9EJ. Many of our top quality holiday properties accept pets. Cottages in Devon, Cornwall, Cotswolds, Pembrokeshire and Heart of England. For colour brochure FREEPHONE 0800 378771 (24 hours).
website: www.powells.co.uk

CLASSIC COTTAGES (01326 565 555). Featuring 500 hand selected coastal and country holiday homes throughout the West Country.
website: www.classic.co.uk

CORNISH HOME HOLIDAYS, WEST CORNWALL (01736 368575). Coastal and country cottages, town houses and apartments. Pets with well behaved owners welcome in many of our properties.
website: www.chh.co.uk

CLASSY COTTAGES – Four superb coastal cottage locations between Polperro and Fowey. Two cottages just feet from the sea on Polperro's harbour wall, two isolated cottages near Lansallos and 10 cottages near our swimming pool. ETC ★★★★ - ★★★★★. Contact FIONA & MARTIN NICOLLE (07000 423000). [pw! Pets £12 per week]
website: www.classycottages.co.uk

A fine selection of Self-catering and similar Cottages on both coasts of Cornwall and on Scilly. Pets welcome in many cottages. Free colour brochure from: CORNISH TRADITIONAL COTTAGES, BLISLAND, BODMIN PL30 4HS (01208 821666; Fax: 01208 821766). [Pets £12 per week]
website: www.corncott.com

Bodmin

Quaint county town of Cornwall, standing steeply on the edge of Bodmin Moor. Pretty market town and touring centre. Plymouth 31 miles, Newquay 20, Wadebridge 7.

MRS JOAN HARRISON, WILBURY, SUNNYBANKS LANE, FLETCHERS BRIDGE, BODMIN PL30 4AN (01208 74001). Spacious house, centrally situated. Three double bedrooms. Optional evening meal. The surrounding area is breathtakingly beautiful, especially in springtime. Short walks from the house will take you to some of the county's best beauty spots like Cardinham Woods which is ideal for dog walking. B&B £18, £15 for stays of more than one night. Stannah Stair Lift.

PENROSE BURDEN, ST BREWARD, BODMIN PL30 4LZ (01208 850277 & 850617; Fax: 01208 850915). Holiday Care Award Winning Cottages featured on TV. Open all year. Outstanding views over wooded valley. Free Salmon and Trout fishing. Daily meal service. Superb walking area. Dogs welcome, wheelchair accessible. [Pets £15 per week]
website: www.penroseburden.co.uk

COOMBE MILL, ST BREWARD, BODMIN PL30 4LZ (01208 850344). An idyllic Cornish hamlet of quiet riverside cottages set amidst a glorious 30 acre estate. Gardens, wildlife, fishing lakes and river fishing. Four posters, log burners, BBQs, home cooking and groceries delivered. Well behaved dogs welcome.
e-mail: mail@coombemill.com website: www.coombemill.com

Boscastle

Picturesque village in tiny harbour, with rocky beach, some sand, and fine scenery. Tintagel 4 miles.

BOSCASTLE/CRACKINGTON-HAVEN AREA. Modern bungalow sleeping 2-6, heating; microwave; TV; Near sandy beaches, spectacular coastal path. Beautiful scenery, walking distance local store and Inn. Just off A39 and central to most tourist attractions. Spring and Autumn £90-£200 per week. Pets welcome. MRS PROUT (01840 250289). [🐕]

Bude

Popular seaside resort overlooking a wide bay of golden sand and flanked by spectacular cliffs. Ideal for surfing; sea water swimming pool for safe bathing.

MINESHOP, CRACKINGTON HAVEN, BUDE EX23 0NR. Cornish Character Cottages, sleeps 1 to 8, in tranquil location. Footpath leads through fields/woods to beach/pub. Excellent walking, breathtaking scenery. Open all year. Proud to be inspected and featured in The Good Holiday Cottage Guide. For more details phone CHARLIE or JANE (01840 230338). [£11 per pet per week.]
e-mail: tippett@mineshop.freeserve.co.uk website: www.crackingtoncottages.co.uk

WILLOW VALLEY HOLIDAY PARK, BUSH, BUDE EX23 9LB (01288 353104). Two bedroom lodges equipped to high standard. Colour TV, bathroom, fully equipped kitchen. Two miles from beach and town. Brochure on request.

Cawsand

Quaint fishing village with bathing beach; sand at low tide. Ideal for watersports. Plymouth (car ferry) 11 miles, (foot ferry 3 miles.

MRS DOLAN, RAME BARTON, RAME, CAWSAND PL10 1LG (01752 822789). Self-contained apartments set in two acres of grounds on beautiful Rame peninsula, enjoy stunning views and wonderful sunsets, coastal walks, birdwatching, fishing and surfing. Whitsand Bay, picturesque Cawsand, Kingsand and Mount Edgecumbe Park close by. Pets welcome. [🐕]
e-mail: joanandbarrie@hotmail.com website: www.ramebarton.co.uk

Crackington Haven

Small coastal village in North Cornwall set amidst fine cliff scenery. Small sandy beach, Launceston 18 miles, Bude 10, Camelford 10.

HENTERVENE PINE LODGE CARAVAN AND CAMPING PARK, CRACKINGTON HAVEN, NEAR BUDE EX23 0LF (01840 230365). Luxury caravans to let. First-class facilities for families and pets. Caravans for sale. Open all year. Short breaks. Camping £4.50 pppn, child Half 4-14 years. Caravan Sales and Tourer Storage. [Pets £15 per week, £1 per night camping].
e-mail: contact@hentervene.co.uk website: www.hentervene.co.uk

Five 18th century converted barns, beamed ceilings, log fires and secluded rural setting. Ideal touring base. Five miles to coast at Crackington Haven. Sleep 2/6. Pets welcome. Open all year. From £75 short breaks, £130 per week. ETC ★★★. APPLY: LORRAINE HARRISON, TRENANNICK COTTAGES, WARBSTOW, LAUNCESTON PL15 8RP (01566 781443). [pw! Pets £10 per stay]
e-mail: lorraine.trenannick@i12.com website: www.trenannickcottages.co.uk

Crafthole

Village near sea at Portwrinkle. Fine views over Whitsand Bay and River Lynner. Golf course nearby. Torpoint 6 miles.

THE LISCAWN INN, CRAFTHOLE, NEAR TORPOINT PL11 3BD (01503 230863; Fax: 01503 230675). Charming, Family-run 14th Century Hotel. Close to Coastal Path in the forgotten corner of Cornwall. En suite accommodation; bar meals available; cask ales a speciality. Open all year. Self-catering suites available. [🐕]
e-mail: enquiries@liscawn.co.uk website: www.liscawn.co.uk

PLEASE MENTION THIS GUIDE WHEN YOU WRITE OR PHONE

TO ENQUIRE ABOUT ACCOMMODATION.

IF YOU ARE WRITING, A STAMPED, ADDRESSED ENVELOPE IS

ALWAYS APPRECIATED.

Cusgarne (near Truro)

Located four miles east of Redruth.

CUSGARNE (NEAR TRURO), JOYCE & GEORGE CLENCH, SAFFRON MEADOW, CUSGARNE, TRURO TR4 8RW (01872 863171). A cosy, single storey, clean, detached dwelling within grounds of Saffron Meadow. Own enclosed garden, secluded and surrounded by wooded pastureland, five miles west of Truro.

Delabole

Village 2 miles west of Camelford.

JOHN AND SUE THEOBALD, TOLCARNE, TREBARWITH ROAD, DELABOLE PL33 9DB. Quiet, comfortable guesthouse in beautiful North Cornwall close to coast path, beaches and surfing. Private bathroom, TV lounge. Kennel and covered run for pets left home during the day. Woodturning courses available. Ample parking. For free brochure call 01840 213558. [pw! 🐕]

Falmouth

Well-known port and resort on Fal estuary, ideal for boating, sailing and fishing; safe bathing from sandy beaches. Of interest is Pendennis Castle (18th century). Newquay 26 miles, Penzance 26, Truro 11.

SELF-CATERING BUNGALOW. Sleeps 6. Walking distance of harbour and town. Dogs welcome. Low Season: £190 to £240; High Season: £280 to £390. ETC ★★★. Apply MRS J. A. SIMMONS, 215A PERRY STREET, BILLERICAY, ESSEX CM12 0NZ (01277 654425). [Pets £5 weekly.]

PENMORVAH MANOR HOTEL, BUDOCK WATER, NEAR FALMOUTH TR11 5ED (01326 250277; Fax: 01326 250509). Situated in 6 acres of mature gardens and woodland. Ideal for visiting Cornwall's superb gardens.Close to Falmouth and Coastal Paths. Well behaved dogs welcome. AA ★★★, ETC ★★★ [Pets £5 per night.]
e-mail: reception@penmorvah.co.uk website: www.penmorvah.co.uk

PETER WATSON, CREEKSIDE HOLIDAY HOUSES, RESTRONGUET, FALMOUTH TR11 5ST (Tel & Fax: 01326 372722). Spacious houses sleep 2/4/6/8. Peaceful, picturesque water's edge hamlet. Boating facilities. Use of boat. Own quay, beach. Secluded gardens. Near Pandora Inn. Friday bookings. Dogs welcome. [£10 per week]

Gorran Haven

Coastal village, 3 miles from Mevagissey.

MRS M.R. BULLED, MENAGWINS, GORRAN, ST AUSTELL PL26 6HP (01726 843517). Traditional cottage, sleeps two to five. Linen, towels, electricity supplied. Beach one mile. Large garden. Central for touring/walking. Near Eden Project. Pets welcome. [🐕]

Helford River

One of the loveliest and most unspoilt rivers in Cornwall, with some of the best sailing waters in the country.

TREGILDRY HOTEL, GILLAN, MANACCAN, CORNWALL TR12 6HG (01326 231378). Spectacular seaviews, 10 pretty en suite rooms. Excellent cuisine, uncrowded coastal path walks. ETC ★★ Silver Award, AA ★★ 80%. "An AA Top 200 Hotel", 2 Rosettes for Food. Good Food Guide. [🐕]
e-mail: trgildry@globalnet.co.uk website: www.tregildryhotel.co.uk

Helston

Ancient Stannary town and excellent touring centre, noted for the annual "Furry Dance". Nearby is Loe Pool, separated from the sea by a bar. Truro 17 miles, St Ives 15, Redruth 11.

BOSCREGE CAMPING & CARAVAN PARK, ASHTON, HELSTON, CORNWALL TR13 9TG. (Tel & Fax: 01736 762231) Award-winning, quiet, rural family park close to beaches and attractions. Colour brochure available. Pets welcome. [🐕]
e-mail: enquires@caravanparkcornwall.com website: www.caravanparkcornwall.com

Liskeard

Pleasant market town and good centre for exploring East Cornwall. Bodmin Moor and the quaint fishing villages of Looe and Polperro are near at hand. Plymouth 19 miles, St Austell 19 miles, Launceston 16, Fowey (via ferry) 15, Bodmin 13, Looe 9.

SUE JEWELL, BOTURNELL FARM COTTAGES, ST PINNOCK, LISKEARD PL14 4QS (01579 320880; Fax: 01579 320375). Cosy character cottages set in 25 acres of fields and woodland between Looe and Bodmin. Linen, electricity included. Well equipped. Dog creche. Pets welcome free. [🐕]
website: www.dogs-holiday.co.uk/

ROSECRADDOC HOLIDAYS, ROSE CRADDOC LODGE, LISKEARD PL14 5BU (Tel & Fax: 01579 346768). Three comfortable, well-equipped bungalows on purpose built holiday estate. Peaceful open gardens in woodland setting. One bungalow adapted for wheelchair use. Ideal centre for touring. Contact: Mrs N. Arthur.

MRS V.M. NORTHCOTT, "PENDOWER HOUSE", EAST TAPHOUSE, LISKEARD PL14 4NH (01579 320332). All comforts. Open all year. Main road, Good food. Moderate terms. Ground floor suite. Central for Cornwall. [🐕]

MRS E. COLES, CUTKIVE WOOD HOLIDAY LODGES, ST IVE, LISKEARD PL14 3ND (01579 362216). Self-catering Chalets in 41 acres of woodland. 2/3 bedrooms; fully equipped inc. linen, colour TV, fridge, cooker and microwave. Pets corner for children. Dogs welcome. [pw! Pets £5 per week]
e-mail: cutkwood@hotmail.com website: www.cutkivewood.co.uk

CELIA HUTCHINSON, CARADON COUNTRY COTTAGES, EAST TAPHOUSE, NEAR LISKEARD, CORNWALL PL14 4NH (Tel & Fax: 01579 320355). Luxury cottages in the heart of the Cornish countryside. Ideal centre for exploring Devon and Cornwall, coast and moor and Eden Project. Meadow and paddock (enclosed). Central heating and log burners for cosy off-season breaks. [Pets £10 per week.]
website: www.caradoncottages.co.uk

MR AND MRS HUNSTONE, RIVERMEAD FARM, TWOWATERSFOOT, LISKEARD PL14 6HT (01208 821464). Self-catering Apartments and Farm Cottage convenient for both coasts and moors. Fishing on River Fowey. Pets welcome at a charge.
website: www.zednet.co.uk/rivermead

Lizard

The most southerly point in England, with fine coastal scenery and secluded coves. Sandy beach at Housel Bay. Truro 28 miles, Helston 11.

MULLION HOLIDAY PARK, WESTSTAR HOLIDAYS (0870 444 0080). Award-winning holiday park near Helston in an Area of Outstanding Natural Beauty, close to safe sandy beaches. Dogs welcome! Quote WP. ETC ★★★★ [Pets £35 per week]
website: www.weststarholidays.co.uk/pw

PARC BRAWSE HOUSE, PENMENNER ROAD, THE LIZARD TR12 7NR (01326 290466). A warm welcome awaits you in this 19th century Cornish house with sea views towards the most southerly point. Comfortable rooms with CTV, most en suite. Close to cliff tops and stunning walks. Relax and unwind and enjoy our home-cooked food. Licensed. Dogs welcome. RAC ◆◆◆◆ [Dogs £4 per night].
e-mail: benjocharity@aol.com website: www.cornwall-online.co.uk

SYMBOLS

- 🐕 **Indicates that pets are welcome free of charge.**
- £ **Indicates that a charge is made for pets: nightly or weekly.**
- pw! **Shows some special provision for pets; exercise facility, feeding or accommodation arrangement.**
- ⌂ **Indicates separate pets accommodation.**

Looe

Twin towns linked by a bridge over the River Looe. Capital of the shark fishing industry; nearby Monkey Sanctuary is well worth a visit.

LOOE BAY, LOOE BAY HOLIDAY PARK, WESTSTAR HOLIDAYS (0870 444 0080). Award-winning holiday park near Looe in an Area of Outstanding Natural Beauty, close to safe sandy beaches. Dogs welcome! Quote WP ETC ★★★★ [Pets £35 per week].
website: www.weststarholidays.co.uk/pw

VALLEYBROOK, PEAKSWATER, LANSALLOS, LOOE PL13 2QE. Small secluded site near Looe and Polperro, just 10 miles from the Eden Project. High quality Scandinavian pine lodges, cottages. Short breaks available. Open all year. Dogs welcome. Contact DENISE, KEITH or BRIAN HOLDER (01503 220493).
website: www.valleybrookholidays.co.uk

MRS BARBIE HIGGINS, TREWITH HOLIDAY COTTAGES, Trewith, Duloe, Cornwall PL14 4PR (01503 262184; mobile: 07968 262184). Four refurbished cottages in peaceful location with panoramic views near Looe. Fully equipped, 1-3 bedrooms, tastefully furnished. Full central heating. Well-behaved dogs welcome. [pets from £12 per week]
e-mail: holiday-cottages@trewith.freeserve.co.uk website: www.trewith.freeserve.co.uk

TRENANT PARK COTTAGES. Four delightful cottages sleep from 2 to 5 persons. Each has spacious lounge with colour TV, fully equipped kitchen, private garden. Ample room to relax. APPLY: MRS E. CHAPMAN, TRENANT LODGE, SANDPLACE, LOOE PL13 1PH (01503 263639/262241). [Pets £15 per week, pw!]
e-mail: Liz@holiday-cottage.com website: www.holiday-cottage.com

NEAR LOOE. In picturesque Cornish fishing village of Polperro, one of the finest on the South Cornish coast, spectacularly situated holiday cottages sleeping from two to eight persons at a charge of £175 to £450 per cottage per week. With terraced gardens and fabulous outlook over harbour encompassing 15 mile sea views. Excellent selection of quality restaurants and olde worlde pubs nearby, and on offer delicious pasties and locally made ice-cream. Private parking, two minutes shops, beach, quay and National Trust cliff walks. Open all year, children and pets most welcome. All cottages are fully furnished and equipped, to include a colour television, microwave, electric oven, refrigerator, duvets and pillows. GRAHAM WRIGHT, GUARDIAN HOUSE, LISKEARD, CORNWALL PL14 6AD 01579 344080. [🐕]

MRS ANN BRUMPTON, TALEHAY HOLIDAY COTTAGES, PELYNT, NEAR LOOE PL13 2LT (Tel & Fax: 01503 220252). Cosy, traditional cottages set in four acres of unspoilt countryside offering peace and tranquillity. Breathtaking coastal and country walks. An ideal location for dogs and their owners. Non-smoking. Close to the Eden Project. C.T.B. approved. ETC ★★★★ [Pets £2 per night, £10 per week]
e-mail: pr.brumpton@ukonline.co.uk website: www.talehay.co.uk

TREMAINE GREEN COUNTRY COTTAGES, PELYNT, NEAR LOOE PL13 2LT (01503 220333). A beautiful hamlet of 11 traditional cosy craftsmen's cottages. Clean, comfortable and well equipped. Set in lovely grounds with country/coastal walks and The Eden Project nearby. ETC ★★★ [Pets £16 per week]
e-mail: stay@tremainegreen.co.uk website: www.tremainegreen.co.uk

WELL MEADOW COTTAGE, DULOE, NEAR LISKEARD. Attractively converted barn set in a large secluded garden. Excellent locality for walking and relaxing. Sleeps 2/4 people. Ideal place for families and dogs alike. ETC ★★★★. Opening Spring 2004 – Rose cottage, sleeps 2/5. For a brochure contact BILL AND KAYE CHAPMAN, COLDRINNICK FARM, DULOE, LISKEARD PL14 4QF (01503 220251). [Pets £10 per week, pw!]
website: www.cornishcottage.net

TALLAND CARAVAN PARK, TALLAND BAY, LOOE PL13 2JA (01503 272715). Fully equipped two and three bedroom caravans. Direct access to coastal path and beach. Shop, clubroom, laundry, play area and swimming pool. Short Breaks off-season. Pets welcome. [Pets £30 per week, pw!]

O. SLAUGHTER, TREFANNY HILL, DULOE, NEAR LISKEARD PL14 4QF (01503 220622). Nestling on a south-facing hillside, near coast. Delicious food. Heated pool, tennis, badminton, lake, shire horses. Enchanting 70 acre estate with bluebell wood, walking and wildlife.
e-mail: enq@trefanny.co.uk website: www.trefanny.co.uk

Idyllic 18th century country cottages for romantics and animal lovers. Looe three miles. Wonderful walks from your gate. Cottages warm and cosy in winter. Personal attention and colour brochure from: B. WRIGHT, TREWORGEY COTTAGES, DULOE, LISKEARD PL14 4PP (01503 262730). [Pets £13.50 per week.]
website: www.cornishdreamcottages.co.uk

Manaccan

Vilage 7 miles east of Helston.

Enchanting creekside cottages in a timeless and tranquil hamlet. Stunning coastal and riverside walks, country inns, local food, warm and comfortable with cosy log fires. Dinghies, moorings. Short breaks. Open all year. ST ANTHONY HOLIDAYS, MANACCAN, HELSTON, CORNWALL TR12 6JW (01326 231 357). [Pets £21 per week].
e-mail; inf1@StAnthony.co.uk website: www.StAnthony.co.uk

Mawgan Porth

Modern village on small sandy bay. Good surfing. Inland stretches the beautiful Vale of Lanherne. Rock formation of Bedruthan Steps is nearby. Newquay 6 miles west.

WHITE LODGE HOTEL, MAWGAN PORTH BAY, NEAR NEWQUAY TR8 4BN (01637 860512). Give yourselves and your dogs a quality holiday break at this family-run hotel overlooking beautiful Mawgan Porth Bay. Lounge bar, sun patio, dining room. Car park. 20 years' experience.This hotel is open all year–Winter Break packages. Phone for free brochure. [🐕 pw!]
e-mail: adogfriendly@aol.com website: www.dogfriendlyhotel.co.uk

THE MALMAR HOTEL, TRENANCE, MAWGAN PORTH TR8 4DA (01637 860324). Small Licensed Hotel. Close to beach and coastal path. Two good golf courses nearby. Good English cooking. Rooms with tea making facilities, colour TV, most ground floor/en suite. [🐕]
e-mail: malmarhotel@supanet.com website: www.malmarhotel.com

Mousehole

Picturesque fishing village with sand and shingle beach. Penzance 3 miles.

In Mousehole, a quaint and unspoilt fishing village, are three personally supervised and fully equipped self-catering flats, two with full sea views. All have microwave, cooker, fridge, TV, all bedding and towels provided. Open all year from £80 per week. Apply: MR A.G. WRIGHT, 164 PORTLAND ROAD, SELSTON, NOTTINGHAM NG16 6AN (01773 775347) [🐕]
e-mail: alang23@hotmail.com

Mullion

Peaceful village and old-world harbour, 5 miles south of Helston; much of surrounding area owned by National Trust.

RUSS & JAN STANLAND, MEAVER FARM, MULLION TR12 7DN (01326 240128; Fax: 01326 240011). Luxury B&B in 300 year-old traditional Cornish Farmhouse in quiet valley on the beautiful Lizard Peninsula. Pretty bedrooms with en suite bathrooms. Exposed beams, log fire, Aga breakfasts. Fenced acre field for run-away humans! Children over 12 welcome. ETC ◆◆◆◆ Silver Award. [🐕]
e-mail: meaverfarm@eclipse.co.uk website: www.meaverfarmhouse.co.uk

Newlyn

Bustling harbour popular with artists - local art gallery with exhibitions of modern paintings and sculptures.

Panoramic views across Mount's Bay. Spacious, comfortable house, sleeps 4. Bedlinen and electricity included. Garden. Garage. No smoking. Owner supervised. From £210. Open all year. ETC ★★★ SHIRLEY AND GRAHAM KEENE, 2 CREEPING LANE, PENZANCE TR18 4PB (01736 366697) [pw! Pets £10 per week]
e-mail: chynessa@netscape.net

Newquay

Popular family holiday resort surrounded by miles of golden beaches. Semi-tropical gardens, zoo and museum. Ideal for exploring all of Cornwall.

MRS DEWOLFREYS, DEWOLF GUEST HOUSE, 100 HENVER ROAD, NEWQUAY TR7 3BL (01637 874746). Double or family rooms, two chalets in rear garden. All rooms non-smoking with en suite facilities, colour TV and tea/coffee making facilities. Ideal for pets. [🐕]
e-mail: holidays@dewolfguesthouse.com website: www.dewolfguesthouse.com

QUARRYFIELD CARAVAN & CAMPING PARK, CRANTOCK, NEWQUAY. Fully equipped modern caravans overlooking beautiful Crantock Bay. Separate camping field. Bar, pool, children's play area. Contact: MRS WINN, TRETHERRAS, NEWQUAY TR7 2RE (01637 872792). [Pets £1.50 per night; £15 per week]

TRETHIGGEY TOURING PARK, QUINTRELL DOWNS, NEWQUAY TR8 4QR (01637 877672).Open 1st March to 2nd January. Toilets, hot showers, disabled toilet, shaver points, hairdryers, dishwashing facilities, launderette, shop, freezer packs, telephone, chemical toilet disposal point, electric hook-ups, games room, TV/off-licence. Static and touring caravans to let. ETC ★★★★ [Pets £1.50 to £1.95 per night]
e-mail: enquiries@trethiggey.co.uk website: www.trethiggey.co.uk

GOLDEN BAY HOTEL, PENTIRE, NEWQUAY TR7 1PD (01637 873318). Affordable quality hotel. Overlooking Fistral beach with the Gannel River and National Trust countryside at rear. All rooms private facilities, some deluxe four poster rooms. Lovely coastal and countryside walks, also close to golf. Close to Eden Project. B&B £20 - £34. ETC ◆◆◆ [🐕]
e-mail: enquiries@goldenbayhotel.co.uk website: www.goldenbayhotel.co.uk

Padstow

Bright little resort with pretty harbour on Camel estuary. Extensive sands. Nearby is Elizabethan Prideaux Place. Newquay 15 miles, Wadebridge 8.

RAINTREE HOUSE HOLIDAYS, WHISTLERS, TREYARNON BAY, PADSTOW PL28 8JR (01841 520228/520130). We have a varied selection of accommodation. Small or large, houses and apartments, some by the sea. All in easy reach of our lovely beaches. Please write or phone for brochure. [🐕]
e-mail: gill@raintreehouse.co.uk website: www.raintreehouse.co.uk

Penzance

Well-known resort and port for Scilly Isles, with sand and shingle beaches. Truro 27 miles, Helston 13, Land's End 10, St Ives 8.

GEORGIAN HOUSE HOTEL, 20 CHAPEL STREET, PENZANCE TR18 4AW (01736 365664). Friendly comfortable hotel near to ferry, public transport and beaches. Spacious en suite rooms with TV and hospitality trays. Some parking. Full menu for breakfast and evening meals, special diets, no problem.Open all year. B&B from £23. Two-bedroomed holiday cottage also available. AA ◆◆◆◆ [🐕]
e-mail: georgianhouse@btopenworld.com

TORWOOD HOUSE HOTEL, ALEXANDRA ROAD, PENZANCE TR18 4LZ. Torwood is a small, licensed, family-run hotel, situated in a beautiful tree-lined avenue 500 metres from the seafront. All rooms en suite, with TV/DVD, tea/coffee makers and radios. Dinner available on request. For further details telephone LYNDA SOWERBY on 01736 360063.
e-mail: Lyndasowerby@aol.com website: www.torwoodhousehotel.co.uk

GLENCREE HOUSE, 2 MENNAYE ROAD, PENZANCE TR18 4NG. Large Victorian Guesthouse just off seafront. Spacious en suite rooms, some with sea views. All with colour TVs and tea/coffee making facilities. Open fires. Unrestricted parking. Excellent breakfast choices. Ideal location for beaches, SW coastal path, Scilly Isles. Open all year. B & B from £19 pppn. Please contact HELEN CAHALANE (01736 362026) [Pets £1 per night]
website: www.glencreehouse.co.uk

Perranporth

North coast resort 6 miles south west of Newquay.

GREENMEADOW COTTAGES, NEAR PERRANPORTH. Spacious, clean luxury cottages. Sleep six. Open all year. Short breaks out of season. Non-smoking available. Ample off road parking. Pets welcome in two of the cottages. For brochure and bookings tel: 01872 540483.

Polperro

Picturesque and quaint little fishing village and harbour. Of interest is the "House of the Props". Fowey 9 miles, Looe 5..

POLPERRO. In picturesque Cornish fishing village, of Polperro, one of the finest on the South Cornish coast, spectacularly situated holiday cottages sleeping from two to eight persons at a charge of £175 to £450 per cottage per week. With terraced gardens and fabulous outlook over harbour encompassing 15 mile sea views. Excellent selection of quality restaurants and olde worlde pubs nearby, and on offer delicious pasties and locally made ice-cream. Private parking, two minutes shops, beach, quay and National Trust cliff walks. Open all year, children and pets most welcome. All cottages are fully furnished and equipped, to include a colour television, microwave, electric oven, refrigerator, duvets and pillows. GRAHAM WRIGHT. GUARDIAN HOUSE, LISKEARD, CORNWALL PL14 6AD 01579 344080. []

CLASSY COTTAGES – Four superb coastal cottage locations between Polperro and Fowey. Two cottages just feet from the sea on Polperro's harbour wall, two isolated cottages near Lansallos and 10 cottages near our swimming pool. ETC ★★★★ - ★★★★★. Contact FIONA & MARTIN NICOLLE (07000 423000). [pw! Pets £12 per week]

Port Gaverne

Hamlet on east side of Port Isaac, near Camel Estuary.

Homes from home around our peaceful courtyard garden 100 yds from sea in bygone fishing hamlet. Each sleeps six and has full CH, fridge-freezer, washer-dryer, dishwasher, microwave, video. £160 (February), £680 (August) weekly. Daily rates off-season. Resident owner. APPLY:- MALCOLM LEE, GULLROCK, PORT GAVERNE, PORT ISAAC PL29 3SQ (01208 880106). []

CHIMNEYS, PORT GAVERNE, PORT ISAAC PL29 3SQ (Tel & Fax: 01208 880254). A charming 18th Century Cottage only 10 metres from beach. Four bedrooms, two bathrooms, lounge, dining room and kitchen. Good size garden. Brochure from Mrs. Holmes. []

GREEN DOOR COTTAGES. PORT GAVERNE. 8 comfortable, restored 18th Century cottages set around a sheltered courtyard, plus 2 prestigious apartments with panoramic sea views beside a picturesque cove, directly on the Coastal path. An ideal location for your holiday and short breaks. Well behaved dogs are very welcome. ETC ★★★/★★★★ For brochure: (01208 880293) []
e-mail: enquiries@greendoorcottages.co.uk website: www.greendoorcottages.co.uk

Porthleven

Small town with surprisingly big harbour. Grand woodland walks. 2 miles SW of Helston.

GREYSTONES GUEST HOUSE, 40 WEST END, PORTHLEVEN, HELSTON TR13 9JL (Tel & Fax: 01326 565583). Picturesque fishing village ideal for touring. Dogs/children welcome. Overlooking sea, near harbour, beaches, shops, pubs and restaurants. Tea and coffee facilities, colour TV. En suite facilities. From £20 pppn. []
e-mail: mawbb@tiscali.co.uk

Please mention ***PETS WELCOME*** when making enquiries about accommodation featured in these pages.

Port Isaac

Attractive fishing village with harbour. Much of the attractive coastline is protected by the National Trust. Camelford 9 miles. Wadebridge 9.

LONG CROSS HOTEL & VICTORIAN GARDENS, TRELIGHTS, PORT ISAAC PL29 3TF (01208 880243). Set in magnificent gardens in an Area of Outstanding Natural Beauty. Tavern in the grounds for your enjoyment. Spacious en suite rooms. Pets' corner. Perfect base for touring. Children's adventure play area. Excellent food served all day. Bargain Spring/Autumn Breaks. [Pets £2.00 per night.]
website: www.longcrosshotel.co.uk

CARN AWN, PORT GAVERNE, PORT ISAAC. Fishing, swimming, boating and delightful rock pools for the children. Many beaches within reach. Car essential. Fully fitted kitchen. Open all year. Well behaved dogs welcome. For terms contact: MRS S.A. MAY, ORCADES HOUSE, PORT GAVERNE, PORT ISAAC, CORNWALL PL29 3SQ (Tel & Fax: 01208 880716) ETC★★★ [🐕].
e-mail: jimmay@orcades.u-net.com website: www.orcades.u-net.com

Portreath

Coastal village 4 miles north west of Redruth.

Charming elegantly furnished self catering cottages between Newquay and St Ives. Sleep 2 to 6. Fully equipped including linen. Beautiful beaches. Laundry and games room. Ample parking. Colour brochure – FRIESIAN VALLEY COTTAGES, MAWLA, CORNWALL TR16 5DW (01209 890901) [🐕]

Portscatho

Tiny cliff-top resort on Roseland Peninsula overlooking beach or rocks and sand. Harbour and splendid views. Falmouth 5 miles.

PETER AND LIZ HEYWOOD, TREWINCE MANOR, PORTSCATHO, NEAR TRURO TR2 5ET (01872 580289). Georgian Manor house estate with luxury lodges and manor house apartments. Lounge bar and restaurant. Superb walking and sailing. Dogs welcome. [pw! Pets £24 per week]
e–mail: bookings@trewince.co.uk website: www.trewince.co.uk

Praa Sands

Magnificent stretch of sands and dunes. Nearby is picturesque Prussia Cove. Penzance 7½ miles, Helston 6..

Well appointed Bungalows. One chalet bungalow sleeps 9 plus in 4 bedrooms. Lovely peaceful countryside with large garden not overlooked. 2 miles inland. One 3 bedroomed sleeps 6 plus. Overlooking sea. Large garden. Both fully equipped. Dogs very welcome. APPLY – MRS J. LAITY, CHYRASE FARM, GOLDSITHNEY, PENZANCE TR20 9JD (01736 763301). [Pets £14 per week]

Redruth

Market town 8 miles west of Truro.

GLOBE VALE HOLIDAY PARK, RADNOR, REDRUTH TR16 4BH (01209 891183). "In the Countryside, near the Sea." Perfect for pets and owners, with unlimited trails to explore and near "Dogs Allowed" beaches. Small shop, play area, launderette, bar and games room. Caravans, static caravans, tourers and tents welcome. [Pets £10 per week] Contact Ron and Lesley Baxter on 01209 891183
e-mail: globe@ukgo.com website: www.globe.ukgo.com

SYMBOLS

- **🐕 Indicates that pets are welcome free of charge.**
- **£ Indicates that a charge is made for pets: nightly or weekly.**
- **pw! Shows some special provision for pets; exercise facility, feeding or accommodation arrangement.**
- **⌂ Indicates separate pets accommodation.**

St Agnes

Patchwork of fields dotted with remains of local mining industry. Watch for grey seals swimming off St. Agnes Head.

PENKERRIS, PENWINNICK ROAD, ST AGNES TR5 0PA (01872 552262). An attractive B&B Hotel (dinner by arrangement) with garden. Lounge with TV, video, piano, and log fires in Winter. Open all year. ETC/AA/RAC ◆◆. [🐕 One dog free]
e-mail: info@penkerris.co.uk website: www.penkerris.co.uk

SUNHOLME HOTEL, GOONVREA ROAD, ST AGNES TR5 0NW (01872 552318). Wonderful countryside and coastal views and a warm welcome await visitors to this country house hotel. Excellent home cooked meals, en-suite accommodation. Children and pets welcome. Open all year. Non-smoking. [🐕]
e-mail: info@sunholme.co.uk website: www.sunholme.co.uk

CHIVERTON PARK, BLACKWATER, TRURO TR4 8HS (01872 560667). Caravan and touring holidays only a short drive from magnificent beaches. Quiet, spacious; laundry, shop, play area and games room. All amenities. No club, bar or disco. [1 dog £15 pw, extra dog £10]
e-mail: info@chivertonpark.co.uk website: www.chivertonpark.co.uk

THE DRIFTWOOD SPARS HOTEL, TREVAUNANCE COVE, ST AGNES TR5 0RT (01872 552428/553323). Take a deep breath of Cornish fresh air at this comfortable Hotel ideally situated for a perfect seaside holiday. Dogs allowed on beach. Miles of footpaths for 'walkies'. Children and pets welcome. [Pets £2 per night]
website: www.driftwoodspars.com

St Austell

Old Cornish town and china clay centre with small port at Charlestown (1½ miles). Excellent touring centre. Newquay 16 miles, Truro 14, Bodmin 12, Fowey 9, Mevagissey 6.

BOSINVER HOLIDAY COTTAGES (01726 72128). Individual cottages and lodges in peaceful garden surroundings. Close to major holiday attractions. Short walk to shop and pub. Phone for brochure. No pets during Summer School holidays. [Pets £20 per week].
e-mail: reception@bosinver.co.uk website: www.bosinver.co.uk

TRENCREEK FARM HOLIDAY PARK, HEWASWATER, ST AUSTELL PL26 7JG (01726 8824540). Self-catering and camping with country views and within easy reach of the sea. Tennis court, heated swimming pool and fishing lakes etc.
website: www.trencreek.co.uk

St Breward

North Cornwall Village 4 miles south of Camelford, edge Bodmin Moor, 12 miles from coast.

Warm and lovely cottage sleeps four in great comfort and utter peace. Log fires, large garden with stream, glorious moorland and coastal walking. Available all year. £120 - £350 per week depending on season. Contact MRS PADDY POWELL (01208 850186). [Dogs £6 per week].
website: www.vacation-cornwall.com

St Ives

Picturesque resort, popular with artists, with cobbled streets and intriguing little shops. Wide stretches of sand.

BOB AND JACKY PONTEFRACT, THE LINKS HOLIDAY FLATS, LELANT, ST IVES TR26 3HY (Tel & Fax: 01736 753326). Magnificent location overlooking golf course and beach. Wonderful spot for walking. Five minutes from beach where dogs allowed all year. Two well-equipped flats open all year.

SANDBANK HOLIDAYS, ST IVES BAY, HAYLE (01736 752594). High quality Apartments and Bungalows for 2-6 persons. Heated, Colour TV, Microwave etc. Open all year. Short Breaks and weekly rates. Dogs welcome. [Pets £12 p.w]
website: www.sandbank-holidays.co.uk

St Mawes

Friendly little harbour town on north bank of Percuil River.

THE ROSEVINE HOTEL, PORTHCURNICK BEACH, PORTSCATHO, ST MAWES TR2 5EW (01872 580206; Fax: 01872 580230). Cornwall's "AA TOP 200" luxury hotel. De luxe bedrooms and suites. Award-winning cuisine. Beautiful sub-tropical gardens facing directly over the safe sandy beach fronting the National Trust coastline. Warm heated indoor pool. AA/RAC ★★★ [🐕]
e-mail: info@rosevine.co.uk website: www.rosevine.co.uk

St Mawgan

Delightful village in wooded river valley. Ancient church has fine carvings.

DALSWINTON HOUSE HOTEL, ST MAWGAN, NR NEWQUAY TR8 4EZ (01637 860385). Old Cornish house standing in ten acres of secluded grounds. All rooms en suite, colour TV, tea/coffee facilities. Solar heated outdoor swimming pool. Restaurant and bar. Out-of-season breaks. No children under 16. [🐕 pw!]
e-mail: dalswinton@bigwig.net website: www.dalswinton.com

St Tudy

Village 5 miles north east of Wadebridge.

Comfortable end of terrace cottage in picturesque and friendly village. Enclosed garden and parking. Ideal location for exploring all Cornwall. Short Breaks and brochure available. Contact: MRS R REEVES, POLSTRAUL, TREWALDER, DELABOLE, CORNWALL PL33 9ET (Tel & Fax: 01840 213120). [🐕]
e-mail: aandr.reeves@virgin.net website: www.uk-holiday-cottages.co.uk/maymear

Tintagel

Attractively situated amidst fine cliff scenery; small rocky beach. Famous for associations with King Arthur, whose ruined castle on Tintagel Head is of interest. Bude 19 miles, Camelford 6.

SANDY AND DAVE WILSON, SALUTATIONS, ATLANTIC ROAD, TINTAGEL PL34 0DE (01840 770287). Comfortable, well-equipped, centrally heated cottages sleeping two. Ideal for touring, walking and relaxing. Close to coastal path and village amenities. Private parking. Ring for brochure. Pets Free. [🐕]
website: www.salutationstintagel.co.uk

MRS LYNDA SPRING, TRETHEVY MANOR, TRETHEVY, TINTAGEL, CORNWALL PL34 0BG (Tel & Fax: 01840 770636). Two comfortable, well-equipped, Self-contained Cottages adjoining historical 12th Century Manor House. One-and-a-half miles from Tintagel. Sandy beaches, spectacular coastal and country walks. [🐕]
e-mail: manor1151@talk21.com website: www.trethevy-manor.co.uk

WILLAPARK MANOR HOTEL, BOSSINEY, TINTAGEL PL34 0BA (01840 770782). Beautiful character house amidst 14 acres and only minutes from the beach. All en suite rooms. Children and pets welcome. Open all year. SAE for brochure. ETC ★★ [🐕]
website: www.willapark.co.uk

BOSSINEY FARM CARAVAN AND CAMPING PARK, TINTAGEL PL34 0AY (01840 770481). Family-run Park. 20 Luxury Letting Vans; fully serviced, H&C with shower, room heater, TV. On the coast at Tintagel. Colour brochure available. BGHP ★★★★ [Pets welcome: 1st pet free, charge for subsequent pets, £10 per week]
website: www.bossineyfarm.co.uk

PLEASE SEND A STAMPED ADDRESSED ENVELOPE WITH ENQUIRIES

Torpoint

Busy and pleasant little town on the Hamoaze facing Devonport from and to which runs a car ferry. Plymouth (via ferry) 3 miles.

WHITSAND BAY HOTEL, GOLF & COUNTRY CLUB, (01503 230276 ; Fax: 01503 230329) Character 40 Bedroom Hotel set in an area of outstanding natural beauty. Adjacent to its own 18 hole golf course. Magnificent panoramic sea views. Good food, wines and service. Health & Fitness facilities. Indoor heated pool.
e-mail: info@whitsandbay hotel.co.uk www.whitsandbayhotel.co.uk

Truro

Bustling Cathedral City with something for everyone. Museum and Art Gallery with interesting shop and cafe is well worth a visit.

KING HARRY FERRY COTTAGES, FEOCK, TRURO TR3 6QJ (01872 861915) Two comfortable well equipped cottages in own charming gardens. Pets welcome. Beautiful woodland walks. Perfect for fishing and bird watching.
e-mail: jean@kingharry.f9.co.uk website: www.kingharry-info.co.uk

Wadebridge

Town on River Camel, 6 miles north-west of Bodmin

Two converted barn luxury self-catering cottages near Wadebridge. Found along a leafy drive, with wonderful views, beside the lazy twisting Camel River with its "Trail" for walking and cycling. Sleep 2-7 plus cot. Two dogs per cottage welcome. CORNWALL TOURISM AWARD 2002 - Self Catering Establishment of the Year - "Highly Commended". . MRS SUE ZAMARIA, COLESENT COTTAGES, ST TUDY, WADEBRIDGE, CORNWALL PL30 4QX (Tel & Fax: 01208 850112). [pw! Pets £15 per week]
e-mail: welcome@colesent.co.uk website: www.colesent.co.uk

ISLES OF SCILLY

St Mary's

Largest of group of granite islands and islets off Cornish Coast. Terminus for air and sea services from mainland. Main income from flower-growing. Seabirds, dolphins and seals abound.

MRS PAMELA MUMFORD, SALLAKEE FARM, ST MARY'S TR21 0NZ (01720 422391). Self-catering farm cottage, available all year round. Sleeps 5. Woodburner. Near beach and coastal paths. Pets welcome. Write or phone for details.

SELECTED COTTAGES THROUGHOUT YORKSHIRE
Northumbria, Lakes & Peak District
Pets Welcome • Low Prices
FREE BROCHURE 08700 718 718
www.recommended-cottages.co.uk

The LAKE DISTRICT and CUMBRIA

Dales Holiday Cottages

Superb, personally inspected, self catering holiday properties in beautiful rural and coastal locations from Beatrix Potter and Wordsworth country to the Borders. Cosy cottages to country houses, many welcome pets and most are open all year.

01756 799821 & 790919
www.dalesholcot.com

See also Colour Advertisement on page 5

Alston, Ambleside

Mrs Clare Le Marie, Brownside House, Leadgate, Alston CA9 3EL
Tel: 01434 382169/ 382100 ◆◆◆

A warm welcome awaits you in the unspoilt North Pennines. Country situation, superb views, large fenced garden for "walkies". Sittingroom with log fire and TV.
Bed & Breakfast £20.00. Dinner, Bed &Breakfast £27.50.

Skelwith Bridge Hotel

NEAR AMBLESIDE, CUMBRIA LA22 9NJ

Former 17th century hotel set in a wooded hamlet in the heart of the Lake District. Excellent location for walking, exploring or simply relaxing. Very attractive seasonal breaks. Children and dogs welcome
Also 2-bedroom riverside self-catering cottage available for weekly hire.

Tel: 015394 32115 • Fax: 015394 34254
e-mail: skelwithbr@aol.com • www.skelwithbridgehotel.co.uk

ETC ★★

Smallwood House Hotel • *No Compromise on Quality*
Ambleside, Central Lake District LA22 9DJ • 015394 32330
Anthony & Christine look forward to welcoming customers old and new.
Now in our 16th year.
www.smallwoodhotel.co.uk • enq@smallwoodhotel.co.uk

See also Colour Advertisement on page 20

PLEASE SEND A STAMPED ADDRESSED ENVELOPE WITH ENQUIRIES

AMBLESIDE

Superior Cottage & Apartment Complex, set in peaceful gardens adjoining the Lakeland Fells & Village centre. Luxury Bathrooms & Fully Fitted Kitchens

ETC FOUR & FIVE STAR RATING
AMONGST THE BEST IN BRITAIN
PETS WELCOME IN MANY UNITS

Brochures & Reservations Tel: 015394 32232
Kirkstone Pass Rd, Ambleside, Cumbria LA22 9EH
website: www.kirkstonefoot.co.uk

'Rest awhile in style'

Quality B&B. Tranquil settings in the heart of the village. Own grounds. Car park. All ensuite. Kettle, clock/radio, TV, Fridge, CD & Video players. Heated indoor pool, sauna, hot tub, sun lounge and rooftop terrace. Special breaks. Friendly service where pets are welcome. **www.oldvicarageambleside.co.uk**

Contact Ian, Helen or Liana
The Old Vicarage,
Vicarage Road,
Ambleside LA22 9DH
Tel: **015394 33364**

IVY HOUSE HOTEL & RESTAURANT

Hawkshead, Near Ambleside, Cumbria LA22 0HS
Telephone: 015394 36204 • Website: www.ivyhousehotel.com

Family-run Listed Georgian hotel, full of great charm and character, 11 en suite bedrooms with colour television and equipped with hot drink trays.

Contact Rob or Julia Treeby for Brochure.

Greenhowe Caravan Park
Great Langdale, English Lakeland.

Greenhowe is a permanent Caravan Park with Self Contained Holiday Accommodation, situated in the heart of the Lake District. It is an ideal centre for Climbing, Fell Walking, Riding, Swimming, Water Skiing or just a lazy holiday. *ETC Grading* ★★★★. Please ask about Short Breaks.

Greenhowe Caravan Park, Great Langdale, Ambleside, Cumbria LA22 9JU
For free colour brochure: Telephone: (015394) 37231 • Fax: (015394) 37464 • Freephone: 0800 0717231

See also Colour Advertisement on page 15

A Luxury Break in Cumbria at Superb Value Prices!

When you fancy pampering yourself and your pet with a touch of luxury, enjoy the relaxing comfort and superb value of the award-winning Appleby Manor Country House Hotel. Excellent restaurant, relaxing lounges, indoor leisure club and breathtaking scenery all around.

★★★ 77%

Phone 017 683 51571 or e-mail now for a full-colour brochure and a free interactive CD-ROM

Appleby-in-Westmorland, Cumbria CA16 6JB
E-mail: reception@applebymanor.co.uk
www.applebymanor.co.uk

Best Western
APPLEBY MANOR
COUNTRY HOUSE HOTEL

SKIDDAW VIEW HOLIDAY HOME PARK

SKIDDAW VIEW HOLIDAY HOME PARK

Bothel, Near Bassenthwaite CA7 2JG. Tel: 016973 20919
E-mail: office@skiddawview.com Web: www.skiddawview.co.uk

We have quality Lodge, Cottage and Holiday Home accommodation for 2-5 persons. Short breaks available. Peaceful, relaxing surroundings with panoramic views, pets warmly welcome. Please telephone for brochure and prices.

NEW HOUSE FARM

BUTTERMERE/LORTON VALLEY, COCKERMOUTH, CUMBRIA CA13 9UU
web: www.newhouse-farm.co.uk
e-mail: hazel@newhouse-farm.co.uk
Tel: 01900 85404 • Fax: 01900 85478

Situated in the quietest and most beautiful part of the lakes, New House Farm has 15 acres of open fields, ponds, streams and woods which guests and dogs may wander around at leisure and there is easy access to nearby lakes and fells. All bedrooms are en-suite. There is a cosy dining room and three comfortable sitting rooms with open log fires. The food served is fine traditional fare. *Bed & Breakfast from £46, Dinner, Bed & Breakfast from £68.*

"THE LORTON VALE - A PLACE FOR ALL SEASONS"

Which? Hotel Guide Award Winner Good Hotel Guide AA ◆◆◆◆◆

See also Colour Advertisement on page 14

Buttermere – Beautiful at any time of the year.
A leading, award-winning, privately-owned Three Star Lakeland hotel
A jewel in the heart of the Lake District

- 21 Refurbished En Suite Bedrooms
- NON SMOKING ACCOMMODATION AVAILABLE
- Traditional Four Posters
- Direct-Dial Telephones
- Drying Room
- Daily Changing Menus
- Carefully Chosen Wines
- Two Fully Licensed BARS and PATIO
- REAL ALES - Expertly Kept
- SELF CATERING ACCOMMODATION
- Maid Service
- Dogs Welcome
- CAMRA, Which?, Les Routiers & Good Hotel Guide Recommended
- AA/ETC Highly Rated Three Star Status
- RAC Dining/Gold Key Awards

BRIDGE HOTEL

Buttermere, Lake District,
Cumbria CA13 9UZ
Tel: (017687) 70252
Fax: (017687) 70215

E-mail: enquiries@bridge-hotel.com
Website: www.bridge-hotel.com

SPECIAL BREAKS ALL YEAR
Superb Unrestricted Walking
Painting – Photography
Fishing – Birdwatching

See also Colour Advertisement on page 14

GRAHAM ARMS HOTEL

Longtown, Near Carlisle, Cumbria CA6 5SE

A warm welcome awaits at this 180-year-old former Coaching Inn. Situated six miles from the M6 (J44) and Gretna Green, The Graham Arms makes an ideal overnight stop or perfect touring base for the Scottish Borders, English Lakes, Hadrian's Wall and much more. 15 comfortable en suite bedrooms, including four-poster and family rooms with TV, radio etc. Meals and snacks served throughout the day. Friendly 'local's bar' serving real ale and a fine selection of malt whiskies. Secure courtyard parking for cars, cycles and motorcycles. Pets welcome with well behaved owners!

Visit our website on www.cumbria.com/hotel • Tel & Fax: 01228 791213
Email: office@grahamarms.com • Website: www.grahamarms.com
Bed and full traditional breakfast £27.50– £34. Special rates for weekend and midweek breaks. RAC ★★

ETC ◆◆◆◆ Tel: 01228 577308 ETC ★★★★

NEW PALLYARDS, HETHERSGILL, CARLISLE CA6 6HZ

One modern bungalow, 3/4 bedrooms, sleeps 8. 2 lovely cottages on farm. Bed and Breakfast, Half Board. En suite double/family, twin/single rooms. Disabled welcome. Won the National Award for the Best Breakfast in Britain and have been filmed for BBC TV.

B&B from £25.00, Dinner £13.00 DB&B weekly rate £160.00 - £170.00. Self Catering £120.00 - £672.00.
E-mail: info@newpallyards.freeserve.co.uk Website: www.newpallyards.freeserve.co.uk

LOWESWATER HOLIDAY COTTAGES

Scale Hill
Loweswater, Cockermouth,
Cumbria CA13 9UX
Tel/Fax: 01900 85232

Nestling among the magnificent Loweswater/ Buttermere fells and lakes, luxury cottages available all year. Open fires, central heating, en suite bathrooms, modern kitchens, gardens. Four country inns with good food within 3 miles, one only ½ mile. Crummock Water 10 minutes walk through National Trust woods. Children and pets welcome. Family-run. Colour brochure. Pets £20 per week. Abandon the car, walks are from the doorstep.

www.loweswaterholidaycottages.co.uk

ETC
★★★★ / ★★★★★

Rose Cottage **Lorton Road, Cockermouth CA13 9DX**

Family-run guest house on the outskirts of Cockermouth. Warm, friendly atmosphere. Ample off-road parking. All rooms en suite with colour TV, tea/coffee, central heating and most have double glazing. Pets most welcome in the house (excluding dining room), and there are short walks nearby. Ideal base for visiting both Lakes and coast. ETC ◆◆◆◆

Tel & Fax: 01900 822189 website: www.rosecottageguest.co.uk

See also Colour Advertisement on page 16

The
Coppermines
& Coniston Lakes Cottages
ETC ★★ - ★★★★★

Unique Lakeland cottages for 2 – 30 of quality and character in stunning mountain scenery. Log fires, exposed beams. Pets welcome!
Tel: 015394 41765
Book online
www.coppermines.co.uk

See also Colour Advertisement on page 16

"Your own country house in the Lakes"

Routen House is a beautiful old farmhouse set in 4 acres in an outstanding position with fabulous views over Ennerdale Lake. Fully modernised while retaining the character of the old farmhouse, it has been furnished to a very high standard. Sleeps 12 plus cot. The house is non-smoking but pets are very welcome. Please contact: **Mrs J. Green.**
Tel & Fax: 01604 626383 • e-mail: joanne@routenhouse.co.uk • www.routenhouse.co.uk

See also Colour Advertisement on page 16

FREE or REDUCED RATE entry to Holiday Visits and Attractions – see our READERS' OFFER VOUCHERS on pages 103-118

THE BURNMOOR INN

Boot, Eskdale,
Cumbria CA19 1TG

Resident proprietors:

Harry and Paddington Berger

Situated in this stunning valley close to amazing walks, including Scafell, Harter and Gable. Both you and your well-behaved hounds can stay in one of our nine en suite bedrooms, or our two bed self-catering cottage (let on short stays in Winter and Spring, or weekly lets all year). We offer excellent home-produced food served in the bar, restaurant or conservatory, where you can enjoy one of our fine real ales (Cask Mark Award 2001, 2002 & 2003) and plan your next day's assault. Dogs are most welcome to be in the bar with you for lunch and dinner. Special Breaks available all year.

Call for a brochure
Tel: 019467 23224 Fax: 019467 23337
e-mail: enquiries@burnmoor.co.uk
website: www.burnmoor.co.uk

Fishergound Farm Eskdale, Cumbria

ETC ★★★

Fisherground is a lovely traditional hill farm, offering accommodation in a stone cottage and three pine lodges, which share an acre of orchard. Ideal for walkers, nature lovers, dogs and children, there is space, freedom, peace and tranquillity here. Eskdale is walking country, with scores of riverside, fell or high mountain walks straight from the farm. Good pubs nearby serve excellent bar meals.

Phone for a colour brochure:
01946 723319 or try our website
e-mail: holidays@fisherground.co.uk
website: www.fisherground.co.uk

HOLLIN HEAD COTTAGE

Situated in the heart of Eskdale, one of the most tranquil valleys of the Lake District, Hollin Head sleeps 2-8 people and has fully equipped kitchen, dining room and large sitting room with a coal fire.

A large walled garden leads out to hundreds of walks – both along the valley bottom or up on the high fells. There are three good pubs within walking distance.

Tel: 01768 776 836 www.hollinhead.co.uk

"Your own country house in the Lakes"

LITTLE PARROCK is an elegant Victorian Lakeland stone house with large rooms and a wealth of period features. Lovely private garden. Fully modernised to a very high standard plus real log fires. Sleeps 10 plus cot. The house is non-smoking but pets are very welcome. Please contact: **Mrs J. Green • Tel & Fax: 01604 626383**
e-mail: joanne@routenhouse.co.uk • www.routenhouse.co.uk

See also Colour Advertisement on page 16

RUSSELL FARM

Burton-in-Kendal, Carnforth, Lancs. LA6 1NN

Tel: 01524 781334

Email: miktaylor@farming.co.uk

Bed, Breakfast and Evening Meal offered. Ideal centre for touring Lakes and Yorkshire Dales, or as a stopover for Scotland or the South. Good food, friendly atmosphere on working dairy farm. Modernised farmhouse. Guests' own lounge.

Contact Anne Taylor for details.

Lakeside Studio Apartments, Derwent Water Marina

Portinscale, Keswick CA12 5RF Tel: 017687 72912

Three self catering apartments only yards from the water, with superb views over Derwentwater and the surrounding fells. Each apartment sleeps 2 plus bed settee. Colour TV, heating and bed linen all included. Non-smoking. Telephone or see our website for details.

website: www.derwentwatermarina.co.uk

Overwater Hall

Hosts: Stephen Bore
Adrian & Angela Hyde

Overwater, Ireby, Near Keswick,
Cumbria CA7 1HH
Tel: 017687 76566
e-mail: welcome@overwaterhall.co.uk
website: www.overwaterhall.co.uk

Our elegant, family-run Country House Hotel offers you the best in traditional comforts, award-winning food and friendly hospitality. Peacefully secluded yet within only a short drive of the popular centres of the Lake District, this is the ideal place for a real break.

Dogs genuinely welcome in your room, in one of the lounges and in our 18 acres of grounds.

Special four night breaks available all year from £240.00 per person, inclusive of Dinner, Room and Breakfast.

Please telephone us for a brochure, or refer to our website for further information.

Cragside

A quiet, comfortable guest house with beautiful views of the surrounding fells yet close to the centre of Keswick. All rooms are en suite, tastefully decorated and centrally heated and have clock radio, colour TV and tea/coffee making facilities. Rest assured you will have a comfortable and relaxed stay with us. Bed and Breakfast from £20. £130 per week en suite. Children from three years welcome. Pets welcome.

39 Blencathra Street, Keswick CA12 4HX Tel: 017687 73344; Minicom: 017687 80410

Lakeland Cottage Holidays

Warm Comfortable Houses and Cottages

in Keswick and Beautiful Borrowdale

Tel: 017687 76065

Wonderful Walks Waiting@lakelandcottages.co.uk

Orchard House Holidays
Applethwaite, Keswick

ETC ★★★

Three superb detached family houses forming their own little hamlet on the edge of Applethwaite, a quiet little backwater just two miles from Keswick and Lake Derwentwater. All have large private gardens and fabulous views. Central heating, laundry, freezer, video, etc. One sleeps up to twelve in six bedrooms, the others up to eight in four bedrooms. Each has two reception rooms, fully equipped kitchen and two bathrooms. Pets welcome. Ideal for combined families or walking groups.

Ring for a colour brochure or try our website:
www.orchardhouseholidays.co.uk
Tel: Mrs Jennifer Hall 01946 723319
e-mail: holidays@fisherground.co.uk

Luxury Lakeland Holiday Cottages and Apartments ETC ★★★★

Former gentleman's residence refurbished to provide quality apartments. Many extras, Sunday Lunch, entry to local leisure club, pets welcome, lake on your doorstep, 16 acres of conservation grounds to explore.

Derwent Manor, Portinscale, Keswick, Cumbria CA12 5RD
Call now for a full colour brochure 017687 72538
e-mail: info@derwent-manor.co.uk • website: www.derwent-manor.co.uk

See also Colour Advertisement on page 17

Derwentwater Hotel AA/RAC/ETC ★★★

In 16 acres of conservation grounds on the shores of Derwentwater. Providing high standards of accommodation. Award-winning hospitality, pets welcome, entry to local leisure club, the perfect Lakeland retreat.

Derwentwater Hotel, Portinscale, Keswick, Cumbria CA12 5RE
Call now for a full colour brochure 017687 72538
e-mail: info@derwentwater-hotel.co.uk • web: www.derwentwater-hotel.co.uk

See also Colour Advertisement on page 17

Rickerby Grange

AA/ETC◆◆◆◆
RAC ◆◆◆◆ SPARKLING AWARD

Portinscale, Keswick, Cumbria CA12 5RH

Set within its own garden with private car parking, in the picturesque village of Portinscale near the shores of Lake Derwentwater within walking distance of the market town of Keswick. Ideally situated for exploring all parts of the Lakes. Offering comfort, friendly service, these being the essential qualities provided by the resident proprietor. A well-stocked bar offering draught beers; comfortable lounge and elegant dining room where a four course dinner can be enjoyed with a varied selection of wines. A la carte also available. Three ground floor bedrooms, all rooms en suite with tea and coffee making facilities, colour TV, direct dial telephone.

DB&B from £49, Winter Rates Available (Special Breaks).
Open all Year, including Christmas and New Year.

Brochure on request, Contact Val or Lynn on 017687 72344
e-mail: val@ricor.co.uk web: www.ricor.co.uk

Thwaite Howe Hotel

-Small friendly country house hotel situated in its own grounds, with magnificent mountain views to Skiddaw. Within easy reach of all the Lake District's attractions and also the Cumbrian coast. Specialising in delicious home cooking, complemented by an excellent selection of fine wines. All eight bedrooms have en suite bathrooms. Residents lounge and well stocked bar. Well behaved dogs welcome, Subject to hotel conditions. Non-smoking rooms. ETC ★★ AA ★★.

Thornthwaite, Near Keswick CA12 5SA Tel: 017687 78281; Fax: 017687 78529

See also Colour Advertisement on page 16

KESWICK COTTAGES **Kentmere, How Lane, Keswick CA12 5RS**

Superb selection of cottages and apartments in and around Keswick. All of our properties are well maintained and thoroughly clean. From a one bedroom cottage to a four bedroom house we have something for everyone. Children and pets welcome. Contact us for a free colour brochure. **Tel: 017687 73895**

e-mail: info@keswickcottages.co.uk • website: www.keswickcottages.co.uk

MIDTOWN COTTAGES, High Lorton

Two well equipped cottages, both with central heating, furnished to a high standard, all with dishwashers & freezers. Overlooking the Fells, at the north end of Lorton Vale. Pets welcome. Non-smoking. Short breaks from £160. Contact Mr & Mrs M. Burrell:

Telephone: 01264 710165 • e-mail: info@midtown-cottages.com
website: www.midtown-cottages.com • ETC ★★★★

See also Colour Advertisement on page 18

A warm welcome awaits you at TOSSBECK, a working farm situated in the unspoilt Lune Valley. The farmhouse is a 17th century Listed building featuring oak panelling and mullioned windows. B&B from £19 with reductions for children. Short break offers. One double en suite and a family/double/twin room with adjoining private facilities, both with TV and drink making facilities. Refreshments served on arrival. An ideal touring base for Lakes and Dales or as a stopover point as situated between M6 junctions. Non-smoking. ETC ◆◆◆

Brochure from: **Pauline Bainbridge, Tossbeck Farm, Middleton, Kirkby Lonsdale LA6 2LZ**
Tel: 015242 76214. • e-mail: postmaster@tossbeck.f9.co.uk • website: www.tossbeck.co.uk

Tossbeck Farm

Bed and Breakfast

Terms quoted in this publication may be subject to increase if rises in costs necessitate

NEAR HOWE HOTEL & COTTAGES

is the ideal answer for a quiet away from-it-all holiday or a break when travelling North or South. Bar with log fire on colder nights and homely dining room with home cooked food.
3 self-catering cottages sleep up to 4 persons, Saddle Back Barn sleeping up to 7 with 3 bedrooms en suite. B&B £20 to £25 per person. *ETC ★★★★ SELF-CATERING.*

Mungrisdale, Penrith CA11 0SH • Tel/Fax: Threlkeld (017687) 79678
E-mail: nearhowe@btopenworld.com • Website: www.nearhowe.co.uk

ETC ◆◆◆

Sawrey House

Elegant Country House Hotel; stunning lake views in peaceful surroundings; superb location for walking, fishing, water sports, riding and touring. Open Christmas and New Year.

AA ◆◆◆◆◆ RAC ◆◆◆◆◆ ETC ◆◆◆◆◆

❧ Beautiful En Suite Rooms ❧ Excellent Cuisine ❧ Elegant Lounge and Bar ❧ Midweek Special Breaks ❧ AA Two Rosettes ❧ Log Fire ❧ Non-smoking Hotel ❧ Pets most welcome ❧ **website: www.sawreyhouse.com**

Sawrey House Country Hotel & Restaurant, Near Sawrey, Hawkshead, Cumbria LA22 0LF
Telephone: 015394 36387 Facsimile: 015394 36010

Your Stepping Stone to the Cumbrian Lake District

ETC ★★★★

Carrock Cottages are three recently renovated stone built cottages set on the fringe of the Lakeland Fells. A quiet rural location near the lovely villages of Hesket Newmarket with its award winning brewery, Caldbeck and Greystoke.
Explore the beauty of the Lake District National Park or head North to historic Carlisle and on to Hadrians Wall.
Fell walking & other activities close to hand as well as excellent restaurants.
A warm welcome guaranteed.
Accommodation for 1 to 12 people.

Carrock House, Hutton Roof, Penrith, Cumbria CA11 0XY
Tel: Malcolm or Gillian on 01768 484 111 or Fax: 017684 888 50

WWW.CARROCKCOTTAGES.CO.UK

See also Colour Advertisement on page 18

ETC ★★★

SECLUDED COTTAGES with Private Fishing
Crossfield Cottages, Kirkoswald, Penrith, Cumbria CA10 1EU
24 hour Brochure line: 01768 898711 (manned most Saturdays)

Tranquil quality cottages overlooking lake amid Lakeland's beautiful Eden Valley countryside, only 30 minutes' drive from Ullswater, North Pennines, Hadrian's Wall and Scottish Borders. Residents' coarse fishing on doorstep. Cottages sleep 2—6, well equipped and maintained. **PETS VERY WELCOME.**

e-mail: info@crossfieldcottages.co.uk **website: www.crossfieldcottages.co.uk**

Elm Tree Barn Tastefully converted sandstone barn in quiet village with magnificent views, offering a warm and friendly welcome. Accommodation is available in one en suite bedroom with comfortable beds, colour TV and tea/coffee making facilities. Full English breakfast is provided. Open all year. B&B from £18 per person.

Mrs Marion Barritt, Elm Tree Barn, Culgaith, Penrith CA10 1QW Tel: 01768 88789
e-mail: marion@elmtreebarn.co.uk • website: www.elmtreebarn.co.uk

---

All pets free of charge at **Tanglewood Caravan Park**

CAUSEWAY HEAD, SILLOTH-ON-SOLWAY, CUMBRIA CA7 4PE

e-mail: tanglewoodcaravanpark@hotmail.com •• website: www. tanglewoodcaravanpark.co.uk

Friendly, quiet tree-sheltered site just a mile inland from beautiful coastline and this charming harbour town. Friendly pub/club with adjacent children's games room. Large clean modern holiday homes for hire, electric hook-ups available

"The ideal holiday for you and your pet" **Write or phone for colour brochure TEL: 016973 31253**

See also Colour Advertisement on page 19

HOLBECK GHYLL LODGE

• Tel: 01484 684605 •

Extremely comfortable traditional Lakeland stone lodge with enclosed garden at rear. Two twin-bedded bedrooms. Dining/livingroom with open fire and sofa bed. Fully equipped oak fitted kitchen. Bathroom with bath and shower. One double bedroom with en suite shower and toilet. Antique pine furniture throughout. Well situated for local walks, lake and pubs. Secure covered way for bikes. Ample parking. Available Easter to end of October. Saturday change over. • ETC ★★★★

Mrs Kaye, Holmdene, Stoney Bank Road, Holmfirth HD9 7SL • FAX: 01484 689051 • e -mail: maggiekaye@hotmail.com

See also Colour Advertisement on page 18

Land Ends Cabins, Watermillock, Near Ullswater CA11 0NB

Tel: 017684 86438 • Only one mile from Ullswater, our four detached log cabins have a peaceful fellside location in 25-acre grounds with two pretty lakes. Ducks, moorhens, red squirrels and wonderful birdlife. Doggy heaven! Sleep 2-5. **e-mail: infolandends@btinternet.com • www.landends.co.uk**

LONSDALE HOUSE HOTEL

11 Daltongate, Ulverston Cumbria LA12 7BD

Family-run Hotel situated right in the heart of Ulverston (South Lakes festival town) offers friendly service, great food and comfortable accommodation. Dogs are most welcome, provided they are accompanied by well-behaved owners, and can stay in the rooms. A short walk from the hotel, on the edge of the National Park, overlooking Ulverston is Sir John Barrow's Monument on Hoad Hill. A popular place for walking with superb views of the Lake District peaks and panoramic view of Morecambe Bay. There are also some good walks along the bay coast a short drive from the hotel. Lonsdale House Hotel is an excellent base to explore the Lake District because we are about 15 minutes from Lake Windermere and about 30 minutes from Windermere village, Coniston and Cartmel.

Phone ***01229 582598*** *for a brochure and find out about our special breaks.*

www.lonsdalehousehotel.co.uk

See also Colour Advertisement on page 19

BURNSIDE PARK – *The Lake District's Complete Resort*

– Pets most welcome!

THE BURNSIDE HOTEL

Set in the heart of the beautiful Lake District National Park, in mature gardens with views of Lake Windermere, situated just 300 metres from the Steamer Piers and bustling village centre of Bowness-on-Windermere, the Burnside Hotel offers you one of the very finest holiday locations.

You can enjoy a wide choice of en suite bedrooms and lake-view suites with the added benefit of smoking or non-smoking rooms and two that are specially adapted for our disabled guests. Our widely acclaimed restaurant, well stocked bars, spacious lounges and the incomparable Parklands Country Club all combine to make your stay in Lakeland a truly memorable one.

The Burnside Hotel offers Full Conference Facilities and is licensed for Civil Wedding Ceremonies. Christmas and New Year Programmes are available.

BURNSIDE PARK

For those who like the freedom of self-catering whilst maintaining high standards of accommodation, Burnside Cottages and Apartments have been traditionally designed to the highest standards and equipped with all the modern amenities you are ever likely to need. Sleeping 2-6 persons there is no need to bring linen or items other than of a personal nature.

For pets wishing to accompany their owners –

You are most welcome throughout the resort except of course in the restaurants and leisure club. There are many walks around the area where you may take your owners for their daily exercise!

N.B. Pets will incur a small charge.

PARKLANDS COUNTRY CLUB

Our all-weather leisure environment has something for everyone. Enjoy a dip in the swimming pool - incorporating children's area; relax in the spa-bath, sauna or steam room. Have a workout in the gym, a game of badminton or squash. Top up your tan on our sunbed or pamper yourself in the beauty salon. A children's soft play area is available and two full size snooker tables are situated in the Club lounge bar which overlooks the pool.

Our Children's PlayPark keeps our 2-10 year old guests entertained!

FOR A COLOUR BROCHURE PLEASE RING FREE ON 0800 220 688

THE BURNSIDE HOTEL, BOWNESS, WINDERMERE, CUMBRIA LA23 3EP
Hotel telephone: 015394 42211 Cottages Telephone: 015394 46624 Fax: 015394 43824
E-mail: stay@burnsidehotel.com Website: www.burnsidehotel.com

Applethwaite House

ETC ◆◆◆

Situated in a quiet cul-de-sac just minutes from the village centre, shops, public transport and local park. We promise you a warm welcome and clean comfortable accommodation with a relaxed and friendly atmosphere. All rooms en suite with colour TV and complimentary hot drinks. Vegetarians catered for and families very welcome. Pets stay FREE but owners must pay. Prices from £19.00 depending on season. Non-smoking.

1 Upper Oak Street, Windermere, Cumbria LA23 2LB
Telephone: 015394 44689
E-mail: info@applethwaitehouse.co.uk
Website: www.applethwaitehouse.co.uk

Prince's Road, Windermere LA23 2DD

KIRKWOOD occupies a quiet spot between Windermere and Bowness, offering a warm and friendly atmosphere with an individual personal service. Rooms are large, en suite with TV and tea/coffee making facilities; some have four-poster beds. Your hosts will be pleased to help plan tours or walks with maps provided. Three-night special breaks available. B&B £25 -£30. Tel/Fax: 015394 43907

e-mail: info@kirkwood51.co.uk website: www.kirkwood51.co.uk

See also Colour Advertisement on page 20

ETC ◆◆◆

Props: Anne & Peter Watson

All rooms are fully en suite and have colour TV, shaver points, central heating and tea/coffee making facilities. There is a choice of Full English, Continental or Vegetarian breakfast. Only two minutes from Bus and Rail Station, very close to town centre and amenities. Pets Welcome. Terms from £18 pp per night, depending on month. Open all year. Short Break terms available.

DENE CREST GUEST HOUSE • Woodland Road, Windermere LA23 2AE
Tel: 015394 44979 • e-mail: denecrest@btinternet.com • www.denecrest.com

See also Colour Advertisement on page 20

Over 200 ETC inspected and graded properties throughout the southern and central Lake District. Lakelovers are sure to have a property to meet your needs. Tel: 015394 88855; Fax: 015394 88857.

E-mail: bookings@lakelovers.co.uk; Website: www.lakelovers.co.uk ETC ★★★/★★★★★

Lakelovers, Belmont House, Lake Road, Bowness-on-Windermere, Cumbria LA23 3BJ

See also Colour Advertisement on page 13

Visit the FHG website

www.holidayguides.com

for details of the wide choice of accommodation featured in the full range of FHG titles

PLEASE SEND A STAMPED ADDRESSED ENVELOPE WITH ENQUIRIES

RECOMMENDED COTTAGES. First choice for dream cottages at very competitive prices in all holiday regions of beautiful Britain. Pets welcome. Low Prices. Free brochure (08700 718 718).
website: www.recommended-cottages.co.uk

DALES HOLIDAY COTTAGES offer a choice of over 100 superb, personally inspected holiday properties, in beautiful rural and coastal locations. Including Wordsworth and Beatrix Potter country. Cosy cottages to Country houses, many open all year. FREE brochure on request. DALES HOLIDAY COTTAGES, CARLETON BUSINESS PARK, SKIPTON, NORTH YORKSHIRE BD23 2AA (01756 799821 & 790919).
website: www.dalesholcot.com

Alston

Small market town 16 miles north-east of Penrith.

MRS CLARE LE MARIE, BROWNSIDE HOUSE, LEADGATE, ALSTON CA9 3EL (01434 382169/ 382100). A warm welcome awaits you in the unspoilt North Pennines. Country situation, superb views, large fenced garden for "walkies". Sitting room with log fire and TV. [🐕]

Ambleside

Popular centre for exploring Lake District at northern end of Lake Windermere. Picturesque Stock Ghyll waterfall nearby, lovely walks. Associations with Wordsworth. Penrith 30 miles, Keswick 17, Windermere 5.

2 LOWFIELD, OLD LAKE ROAD, AMBLESIDE. Ground floor garden flat half a mile from town centre; sleeps 4. Lounge/diningroom, kitchen, bathroom/WC, two bedrooms. Linen supplied. Children and pets welcome. Parking for one car. Bookings Saturday to Saturday. Terms from £130 to £200 per week. Contact: MR P. F. QUARMBY, 3 LOWFIELD, OLD LAKE ROAD, AMBLESIDE LA22 0DH (Tel & Fax: 015394 32326). [🐕]

SKELWITH BRIDGE HOTEL, NEAR AMBLESIDE LA22 9NJ (015394 32115; Fax: 015394 34254). Former 17th century hotel in the heart of the Lake District. Excellent location for walking, exploring or simply relaxing. Also 2-bedroom riverside self-catering cottage available for weekly hire. AA ★★★ [Pets £5 per night].
e-mail: skelwithbr@aol.com website: www.skelwithbridgehotel.co.uk

SMALLWOOD HOUSE HOTEL, COMPSTON ROAD, AMBLESIDE LA22 9DJ (015394 32330) Dogs recommend us, they love the walks from here. Their owners love the rooms and the informality and enjoy their dinners. Car park. Residential licence. [Pets £1 per night. Minimum charge £3]
e-mail: enq@smallwoodhotel.co.uk website: www.smallwoodhotel.co.uk

KIRKSTONE FOOT, KIRKSTONE PASS ROAD, AMBLESIDE LA22 9EH (015394 32232; Fax: 015394 32805). Country house with luxury self-catering Cottages and Apartments sleeping 2/6. Set in peaceful and secluded grounds. Adjoining lovely Lakeland fells, great for walking. Special winter breaks. **ETC** ★★★★ [pw! Pets £3.00 per night.]
e-mail: kirkstone@breathemail.net website: www.kirkstonefoot.co.uk

THE OLD VICARAGE, VICARAGE ROAD, AMBLESIDE LA22 9DH (015394 33364). 'Rest a while in style'. Quality B&B set in tranquil wooded grounds in the heart of the village. Car park. All rooms en suite. Kettle, clock/radio, TV. Heated indoor pool, sauna, hot tub, sun lounge and rooftop terrace. Special breaks. Friendly service where your pets are welcome. Telephone IAN OR HELEN BURT.
website: www.oldvicarageambleside.co.uk

IVY HOUSE HOTEL AND RESTAURANT, HAWKSHEAD, NEAR AMBLESIDE LA22 0HS (015394 36204 Family-run listed Georgian hotel. 11 en suite bedrooms with colour TV and equipped with hot drinks trays. No charge for dogs. Children most welcome. Write or telephone Rob or Julia Treeby for brochure. ETC ◆◆◆◆ [🐕]
website: www.ivyhousehotel.com

GREENHOWE CARAVAN PARK, GREAT LANGDALE, AMBLESIDE LA22 9JU (015394 37231; Fax: 015394 37464; Freephone: 0800 0717231). Permanent Caravan Park with Self Contained Holiday Accommodation. An ideal centre for Climbing, Fell Walking, Riding, Swimming, Water Skiing or just a lazy holiday. ETC ★★★★ [Pets £5 per night, £25 per week]

Appleby-in-Westmorland

Pleasant touring centre on River Eden, between Pennines and Lake District. Castle and Moot Hall of historic interest. Trout fishing, swimming pool, tennis, bowls. Kendal 24 miles, Penrith 13.

APPLEBY MANOR COUNTRY HOUSE HOTEL, ROMAN ROAD, APPLEBY-IN-WESTMORLAND CA16 6JB (017683 51571; Fax: 017683 52888). Enjoy the comfort of Cumbria's award-winning Country House Hotel with superb meals, relaxing lounges, indoor leisure club and breathtaking scenery all around. Phone for a full colour brochure and interactive CD-ROM. [🐕 pw!]
e-mail: reception@applebymanor.co.uk website: www.applebymanor.co.uk

Bassenthwaite

Village on Bassenthwaite Lake with traces of Norse and Roman settlements.

SKIDDAW VIEW HOLIDAY HOME PARK, BOTHEL, NEAR BASSENTHWAITE CA7 2JG (016973 20919). Quality lodge, cottage and holiday home accommodation for 2-5 in peaceful, relaxing surroundings. Please telephone for brochure and prices.[pw!🐕]
e-mail: office@skiddawview.com website: www.skiddawview.co.uk

Borrowdale

Scenic valley of River Derwent, splendid walking and climbing country.

HILTON KESWICK LODORE HOTEL, BORROWDALE, NEAR KESWICK CA12 5UX (017687 77285; Fax: 017687 77343). Luxury Hotel with fabulous views overlooking Derwentwater and fells. Facilities include 71 bedrooms, restaurant and lounge, bar and leisure club. [Pets £2 per night, £14 per week.]

MARY MOUNT HOTEL, BORROWDALE, NEAR KESWICK CA12 5UU (017687 77223). Set in 4½ acres of gardens and woodlands on the shores of Derwentwater. 2½ miles from Keswick in picturesque Borrowdale. Superb walking and touring. All rooms en suite with colour TV and tea/coffee making facilities. Licensed. Brochure on request. ETC ★★ [pw!🐕]
e-mail: mawdsley1@aol.com website: www.marymounthotel.co.uk

Brampton

Market town with cobbled streets. Octagonal Moat Hall with exterior staircases and iron stocks.

IRTHING VALE CARAVAN PARK, OLD CHURCH LANE, BRAMPTON, NEAR CARLISLE CA8 2AA (01697 73600). Cleanliness, peace and quiet, personal attention. 4½ acre site with pitches for 20 caravans plus space for camping. Modern amenities. Ideal for walking, fishing, touring and golf. AA 3 Pennants.
website: www.ukparks.com

Buttermere

Between lake of same name and Crummock Water. Magnificent scenery. Of special note is Sour Milk Ghyll waterfall and steep and impressive Honister Pass. Keswick 15 miles, Cockermouth 10.

NEW HOUSE FARM, BUTTERMERE/LORTON VALLEY, COCKERMOUTH CA13 9UU (01900 85404; Fax: 01900 85478). New House Farm has 15 acres of fields, woods, streams and ponds which guests and dogs can wander around. Comfortable en suite accommodation and fine traditional food. Off season breaks. AA ◆◆◆◆◆. [🐕 ⌂]
e-mail: hazel@newhouse-farm.co.uk website: www.newhouse-farm.co.uk

BRIDGE HOTEL, BUTTERMERE, LAKE DISTRICT CA13 9UZ (017687 70252; Fax: 017687 70215). 21 bedrooms, all with private bathrooms; four-posters available. Daily freshly prepared menus, large selection wines; real ales. Superb walking and fishing. Dogs welcome. Self catering apartments available. [Pets £4 per night]
e-mail: enquiries@bridge-hotel.com website: www.bridge-hotel.com

Carlisle

Important Border city and former Roman station on River Eden. Castle is of historic interest, also Tullie House Museum and Art Gallery. Good sports facilities inc. football and racecourse. Kendal 45 miles, Dumfries 33, Penrith 18.

GRAHAM ARMS HOTEL, ENGLISH STREET, LONGTOWN, CARLISLE CA6 5SE (Tel & Fax: 01228 791213). 15 bedrooms, most en suite, including four-poster and family rooms, all with tea/coffee facilities, TV and radio. Secure courtyard locked overnight. Pets welcome with well-behaved owners. RAC ★★. [🐕]
e-mail: office@grahamarms.com website: www.grahamarms.com

NEW PALLYARDS, HETHERSGILL, CARLISLE CA6 6HZ (01228 577308). Relax and see beautiful North Cumbria and the Borders. Self-catering accommodation in one Bungalow, 3/4 bedrooms; two lovely Cottages on farm. Also Bed and Breakfast or Half Board – en suite rooms. ETC ◆◆◆◆/★★★★ [Pets from £7 per week]
e-mail: info@newpallyards.freeserve.co.uk website: www.newpallyards.freeserve.co.uk

Cockermouth

Market town and popular touring centre for Lake District and quiet Cumbrian coast. On Rivers Derwent and Cocker. Penrith 30 miles, Carlisle 26, Whitehaven 14, Keswick 12.

LOWESWATER HOLIDAY COTTAGES, SCALE HILL, LOWESWATER, COCKERMOUTH CA13 9UX (01900 85232). Nestling among the fells and lakes, luxury cottages available all year. Open fires, central heating, en suite bathrooms, modern kitchens, gardens. Country Inn ½ mile away. Crummock Water 10 minutes' walk through woods. ETC ★★★★/★★★★★. See also advert on p000. [Pets £20 per week].
website: www.loweswaterholidaycottages.co.uk

ROSE COTTAGE GUEST HOUSE, LORTON ROAD, COCKERMOUTH CA13 9DX (Tel & Fax: 01900 822189). Family-run guest house on the outskirts of Cockermouth. Warm, friendly atmosphere. Parking. All rooms en suite with colour TV, tea/coffee, central heating. Pets welcome. Ideal base for visiting both Lakes and coast. ETC ◆◆◆◆
website: www.rosecottageguest.co.uk

Coniston

Village 8 miles south-west of Ambleside, dominated by Old Man of Coniston (2635ft).

THE COPPERMINES AND CONISTON LAKES COTTAGES. Unique Lakeland cottages for 2 – 30 of quality and character in stunning mountain scenery. Log fires, exposed beams. Pets welcome! ETC ★★ - ★★★★★(015394 41765) Book online. [Pets £20 per week]
website: www.coppermines.co.uk

Ennerdale Lake

Wild and remote Lake with footpaths round the shore.

ROUTEN HOUSE. Beautiful old farmhouse set in four acres with fabulous views. Fully modernised and furnished to a very high standard. Sleeps 12 plus cot. Non-smoking. Pets are very welcome. Please contact: MRS J. GREEN (Tel & Fax: 01604 626383).
e-mail: joanne@routenhouse.co.uk website: www.routenhouse.co.uk

Eskdale

Lakeless valley, noted for waterfalls and ascended by a light-gauge railway. Tremendous views. Roman fort. Keswick 35 miles, Broughton-in-Furness 10 miles.

THE BURNMOOR INN, BOOT, ESKDALE, CUMBRIA CA19 1TG (019467 23224; Fax: 019467 23337). Nine en suite bedrooms plus two bed self-catering cottage to let. Dogs welcome to be in the bar with you for lunch and dinner. We do not make a charge for well behaved dogs. Special breaks available all year. Call for a brochure. [🐕]
e-mail: enquiries@burnmoor.co.uk website: www.burnmoor.co.uk

MRS J. P . HALL, FISHERGROUND FARM, ESKDALE CA19 1TF (01946 723319). Self-catering to suit everyone. Scandinavian pine lodges and a stone cottage – on a delightful traditional farm. Adventure playground. Raft pool and games room. Pets' and children's paradise. Brochures available. ETC ★★★ [🐕]
e-mail: holidays@fisherground.co.uk website: www.fisherground.co.uk

HOLLIN HEAD, ESKDALE. With hundreds of walks right from the door, Hollin Head is a comfortable Lakeland cottage sleeping 2-8 people. Coal fire, modern kitchen, walled garden, pets welcome. Contact: RIVENDELL, BASSENTHWAITE, KESWICK, CUMBRIA CA12 4QP (01768 776836; mobile: 07811 211666). [🐕]
e-mail: sally@hollinhead.co.uk website: www.hollinhead.co.uk

Grange-over-Sands

Quiet resort at the north of Morecambe Bay, convenient centre for Lake District. Fine gardens; golf, boating, fishing, tennis and bowls. Lancaster 25 miles, Windermere 16.

HAMPSFELL HOUSE HOTEL, HAMPSFELL ROAD, GRANGE-OVER-SANDS LA11 6BG (015395 32567). Peaceful country house hotel is set in two acres of mature woodland. The fell is ideal for walking dogs. All rooms en suite with colour TV and tea/coffee making facilities. Excellent food and wines. Ample safe parking. ETC/AA ★★ [🐕]
website: www.hampsfellhotel.com

Grasmere

Village famous for Wordsworth associations; the poet lived in Dove Cottage (preserved as it was), and is buried in the churchyard. Museum has manuscripts and relics.

GRASMERE HOTEL, BROADGATE, GRASMERE LA22 9TA (015394 35277). A family-run 13 bedroomed Country House Hotel. Quietly situated in the village with ample parking and a licensed lounge. All rooms en suite. Award-winning restaurant overlooking large secluded gardens, river and surrounding hills. Superb five-course dinners and carefully chosen wine list. Special breaks throughout the year. [Pets £5 per stay].
website: www.grasmerehotel.co.uk

LAKE VIEW COUNTRY HOUSE & SELF-CATERING APARTMENTS, GRASMERE LA22 9TD (015394 35384/35167). Luxury B&B or 3 Star Self-Catering accommodation in unrivalled location near to village yet secluded with wonderful views and lakeshore access. All B&B rooms en suite, some with whirlpool baths. Ground floor accommodation available. No smoking. Featured in "Which?" Good B&B Guide. [Pets £2.50 per night].

LITTLE PARROCK. Elegant Victorian Lakeland stone house with large rooms and a wealth of period features. Lovely private garden. Fully modernised; full central heating and real log fires. Sleeps 10 plus cot. Please contact: MRS J. GREEN (Tel & Fax: 01604 626383).
e-mail: joanne@routenhouse.co.uk website: www.routenhouse.co.uk

SYMBOLS

- **🐕 Indicates that pets are welcome free of charge.**
- **£ Indicates that a charge is made for pets: nightly or weekly.**
- **pw! Shows some special provision for pets; exercise facility, feeding or accommodation arrangement.**
- **⌂ Indicates separate pets accommodation.**

Hawkshead

Quaint village in Lake District between Coniston Water and Windermere. The 16th century Church and Grammar School, which Wordsworth attended, are of interest. Ambleside 5 miles.

ANN TYSON'S GUEST HOUSE. En suite, B&B family accommodation, village situation. Also two self-catering cottages, adjoining B&B, open fires (coal provided), central heating. Sleep 4/5. Excellent walking. Open all year. Contact: MRS L.R. WALTON (01539 436405).
website: www.anntysons.co.uk

HIDEAWAYS, THE MINSTRELS' GALLERY, THE SQUARE, HAWKSHEAD LA22 0NZ (015394 42435; Fax: 015394 36178). Cosy barns and cottages, log fires, stunning views, great walking from doorstep, free fishing and pets welcome in most. Some 5 star, with whirlpool baths!
e-mail: bookings@lakeland-hideaways.co.uk website: www.lakeland-hideaways.co.uk

Kendal

Market town and popular centre for touring the Lake District. Of historic interest is the Norman castle, birthplace of Catherine Parr. Penrith 25 miles, Lancaster 22, Ambleside 13.

MRS HELEN JONES, PRIMROSE COTTAGE, ORTON ROAD, TEBAY CA10 3TL (015396 24791). Adjacent M6 J38 (10 miles north of Kendal). Excellent rural location for North Lakes and Yorkshire Dales. Superb facilities include jacuzzi bath and four-poster bed. One acre garden. Self-contained ground floor flat and self-catering bungalow, disabled friendly, also available. Pets welcome, very friendly. ETC ◆◆◆◆ [🐕]
e-mail: info@primrosecottage.co.uk website: www.primrosecottagecumbria.co.uk

ANNE TAYLOR, RUSSELL FARM, BURTON-IN-KENDAL, CARNFORTH, LANCS. LA6 1NN (01524 781334). Bed, Breakfast and Evening Meal offered. Ideal centre for touring Lakes and Yorkshire Dales. Good food, friendly atmosphere on working dairy farm. Modernised farmhouse. Guests' own lounge. [🐕]
E-mail: miktaylor@farming.co.uk

Keswick

Famous Lake District resort at north end of Derwentwater with Pencil Museum and Cars of the Stars Motor Museum. Carlisle 30 miles, Ambleside 17, Cockermouth 12.

ROYAL OAK HOTEL, BORROWDALE, KESWICK CA12 5XB (017687 77214). Traditional Lakeland hotel with friendly atmosphere. Home cooking, cosy bar, comfortable lounge and some riverside rooms. Winter and Summer discount rates. Brochure and Tariff available. AA ★ Hotel. [🐕]
e-mail: info@royaloakhotel.co.uk website: www.royaloakhotel.co.uk

DERWENT WATER MARINA, PORTINSCALE, KESWICK CA12 5RF – Lakeside Studio Apartments. Self catering apartments sleep 2 plus bed settee with superb views over the lake and fells. Includes colour TV, heating and bed linen. Non-smoking. (017687 72912) for brochure. [🐕 pw!]
website: www.derwentwatermarina.co.uk

WOODSIDE GUEST HOUSE, PENRITH ROAD, KESWICK CA12 4LJ (01768 773522). Friendly family-run establishment. All our rooms are en suite. We have ample private parking and large gardens. Non-smoking. [🐕]
e-mail: ann@pretswell.freeserve.co.uk website: www.woodside.uk.net

OVERWATER HALL, OVERWATER, NEAR IREBY, KESWICK CA7 1HH (017687 76566). Elegant Country House Hotel in spacious grounds. Dogs very welcome in your room. 4 night mid-week breaks from £240 per person, inclusive of Dinner, Room and Breakfast. Mini breaks also available all year. Award-winning restaurant. See also advertisement on page 162. [🐕]
e-mail: welcome@overwaterhall.co.uk website: www.overwaterhall.co.uk

CRAGSIDE GUEST HOUSE, 39 BLENCATHRA STREET, KESWICK CA12 4HX (017687 73344; Minicom: 017687 80410). Quiet, comfortable guest house close to the centre of Keswick. All rooms en suite, tastefully decorated, centrally heated and have clock radio, colour TV and tea/coffee making facilities. AA ◆◆◆. [🐕]

Warm, comfortable houses and cottages in Keswick and beautiful Borrowdale, welcoming your dog. Inspected and quality graded. LAKELAND COTTAGE HOLIDAYS, KESWICK CA12 4QX (017687 76065; Fax: 017687 76869). [Pets £15 per week]
e-mail: info@lakelandcottages.co.uk website: www.lakelandcottages.co.uk

ORCHARD HOUSE, APPLETHWAITE, NEAR KESWICK. Three superb detached family houses two miles from Keswick and Lake Derwentwater. All have large private gardens and fabulous views. Central heating, laundry, freezer, video, etc. One sleeps up to twelve in six bedrooms, the others up to eight in four bedrooms. Pets welcome. Booking and brochure telephone (01946 723319). ETC ★★★ [🐕]
e-mail: holidays@fisherground.co.uk website: www.orchardhouseholidays.co.uk

MIDTOWN COTTAGES, HIGH LORTON. Two well equipped cottages, both with central heating, furnished to a high standard. All cottages have dishwashers & freezers. Overlooking Fells, at north end of Lorton Vale. Pets welcome. Non- smoking. For details contact MR & MRS BURRELL (01264 710165). ETC ★★★★ [🐕]
e-mail: info@midtown-cottages.com website: www.midtown-cottages.com

THWAITE HOWE HOTEL, THORNTHWAITE, NEAR KESWICK CA12 5SA (017687 78281; Fax: 017687 78529). Small friendly country house hotel specialising in delicious home cooking and fine wines. Eight en suite bedrooms. Residents lounge and bar. Well behaved dogs welcome - subject to conditions available from the hotel. Non-smoking rooms. ETC ★★ AA ★★. [Pets £3 per night per pet.]

DERWENTWATER HOTEL. In 16 acres of conservation grounds on the shores of Derwentwater. Providing high standards of accommodation. Award winning hospitality, entry to local leisure club, the perfect Lakeland retreat. DERWENTWATER HOTEL, PORTINSCALE, KESWICK CA12 5RE (017687 72538). [Pets £5 per night]. ETC/AA/RAC ★★★
e-mail: info@derwentwater-hotel.co.uk website: www.derwentwater-hotel.co.uk

VAL BRADLEY, RICKERBY GRANGE, PORTINSCALE, KESWICK CA12 5RH (017687 72344). Delightfully situated in quiet village. Licensed. Imaginative home-cooked food, attractively served. Open all year. ETC/AA ◆◆◆◆ RAC ◆◆◆◆ Sparkling Award. [Pets £2.50 per night, £15 per week]
e-mail: val@ricor.co.uk website: www.ricor.co.uk

LUXURY LAKELAND HOLIDAY COTTAGES AND APARTMENTS. Former gentleman's residence refurbished to provide quality apartments. Many extras. Sunday lunch, entry to local leisure club, lake on your doorstep, 16 acres of conservation grounds to explore. ETC ★★★★ Call now for full colour brochure. DERWENT MANOR, PORTINSCALE, KESWICK CA12 5RD (017687 72538). [Pets £5 per night]
e-mail: info@derwent-manor.co.uk website: www.derwent-manor.co.uk

KESWICK COTTAGES, KENTMERE, HOW LANE, KESWICK CA12 5RS (017687 73895). Cottages and apartments in and around Keswick. Properties are well maintained and clean. From a one bedroom cottage to a four bedroom house. Children and pets welcome. [Pets £10 per week]
e-mail: info@keswickcottages.co.uk website: www.keswickcottages.co.uk

Kirkby-in-Furness

Small coastal village (A595). 10 minutes to Ulverston, Lakes within easy reach. Ideal base for walking and touring.

MRS C. ENGLEFIELD, 1 FRIARS GROUND, KIRKBY-IN-FURNESS LA17 7YB (01229 889601). "Sunset Cottage." Self catering 17th century two-bedroom character cottage with garden. Panoramic views over sea/mountains; Coniston/Windermere 20 minutes. Terms from £115. Open all year. [🐕]
e-mail: chrisngeoff@friarpress.totalserve.co.uk

Please mention ***PETS WELCOME*** when making enquiries about accommodation featured in these pages.

Kirkby Lonsdale

Georgian buildings and quaint cottages. Riverside walks from medieval Devil's Bridge.

MRS PAULINE BAINBRIDGE, TOSSBECK FARM, MIDDLETON, KIRKBY LONSDALE LA6 2LZ (015242 76214). 17th Century Listed farmhouse on a working farm situated in the Lune Valley. B&B from £19. Children and well-behaved pets welcome. Non-smoking. Brochure available. ETC ◆◆◆ [🐕]
e-mail: postmaster@tossbeck.f9.co.uk website: www.tossbeck.co.uk

Kirkby Stephen

5 miles south on B6259 Kirkby Stephen to Hawes road.

COCKLAKE HOUSE, MALLERSTANG CA17 4JT (017683 72080). Charming, High Pennine Country House B&B in unique position above Pendragon Castle in Upper Mallerstang Dale offering good food and exceptional comfort to a small number of guests. Two double rooms with large private bathrooms. Three acres riverside grounds. Dogs welcome.

Kirkoswald

Village in the Cumbrian hills, lying north west of the Lake District. Ideal for touring. Penrith 7 miles.

SECLUDED COTTAGES WITH PRIVATE FISHING, KIRKOSWALD CA10 1EU (24 hour brochure line 01768 898711, manned most Saturdays). Quality cottages, clean, well equipped and maintained. Centrally located for Lakes, Pennines, Hadrian's Wall, Borderland. Enjoy the Good Life in comfort. Pets' paradise. Guests' coarse fishing. Bookings/enquiries 01768 898711. ETC ★★★ [pw! £2 per pet per night].
e-mail: info@crossfieldcottages.co.uk website: www.crossfieldcottages.co.uk

Lake District

North-west corner of England between A6/M6 and the Cumbrian Coast. Fells. valleys and 16 lakes, the largest being Lake Windermere.

BOWNESS LAKELAND HOLIDAYS. Traditional Lakeland cottages, well-equipped and furnished to a high standard, set in Bowness-on-Windermere and the surrounding scenic South Lakes. Ideal setting from which to explore the Lake District. Pets welcome in many properties. Brochure available. Winter Short Breaks. Contact: 131 RADCLIFFE NEW ROAD, WHITEFIELD, MANCHESTER M45 7RP (0161 796 3896; Fax: 0161 272 1841).
e-mail: info@bownesslakelandholidays.co.uk website: www.bownesslakelandholidays.co.uk

Langdale

Dramatic valley area to the west of Ambleside, in the very heart of the National Park.

THE BRITANNIA INN, ELTERWATER, AMBLESIDE LA22 9HP (015394 37210; FaxL 015394 37311). The very picture of a traditional inn, the Britannia overlooks the green in the delightful village of Elterwater in the heart of the Lake District. Home cooked meals and real ales are served in cosy bars with oak beams and log fires. ETC ★★ [🐕]
e-mail: info@britinn.co.uk website: www.britinn.co.uk

Little Langdale

Hamlet 2 miles west of Skelwith Bridge. To west is Little Langdale Tarn, a small lake.

HIGHFOLD COTTAGE, LITTLE LANGDALE. Very comfortable Lakeland cottage, ideally situated for walking and touring. Superb mountain views. Sleeps 5. Personally maintained. Pets welcome. Weekly £210 - £350. ETC ★★★. MRS C.E. BLAIR, 8 THE GLEBE, CHAPEL STILE, AMBLESIDE LA22 9JT (015394 37686). [🐕]

Lowick

Delightful small village in Lake District National Park, 3 miles from Coniston Water and ideal for exploring the southern and western isles.

MRS JENNY WICKENS, GARTH ROW, LOWICK GREEN, ULVERSTON LA12 8EB (01229 885633). Traditional cottage standing alone amidst farmland and common. Quality accommodation, good food, excellent walking, no smoking. Ideal for children and pets. B&B from £20.00. Brochure available. ETC ◆◆◆ [🐕]
e-mail: B&B@garthrow.freeserve.co.uk website: www.garthrow.co.uk

Mungrisdale

Small village ideal for touring. Keswick 8 miles.

NEAR HOWE FARM HOTEL AND COTTAGES, MUNGRISDALE, PENRITH CA11 0SH (Tel & Fax: 017687 79678). Quiet, away from-it-all. Within easy reach of Lakes, walking. Good food. Bar, log fire in cold weather. 5 Bedrooms en suite. B&B from £20 to £25 per person. ETC ◆◆◆/★★★★ *SELF-CATERING*. [Pets – Hotel £2 per day. Cottages £10 per week.]
e-mail: nearhowe@btopenworld.com website: www.nearhowe.co.uk

Near Sawrey

This beautiful village on the west side of Windermere has many old cottages set among trees and beautiful gardens with flowers. The world-famous writer Beattrix Potter lived at Hill Top Farm. A ferry travels across the lake to Hawkshead (2 miles). Far Sawrey ½ mile.

SAWREY HOUSE COUNTRY HOTEL & RESTAURANT, NEAR SAWREY, HAWKSHEAD LA22 0LF (015394 36387; Fax: 015394 36010). Elegant family-run hotel in three acres of peaceful gardens with magnificent views across Esthwaite Water. Excellent food, warm friendly atmosphere. Lounge, Bar. Children and pets welcome. Non-Smoking. AA 2 Rosettes for food. ETC/RAC/AA ◆◆◆◆◆. [Pets £6 per night.]
website: www.sawreyhouse.com

Penrith

Market town and centre for touring Lake District. Of interest are 14th century castle, Gloucester Arms (1477) and Tudor House. Excellent sporting facilities. Windermere 27 miles, Keswick 18.

CARROCK COTTAGES. Three recently renovated stone built cottages set on the fringe of the Lakeland Fells. Ideal for fell walking. Excellent restaurants nearby. A warm welcome guaranteed. Contact MALCOLM OR GILLIAN (01768 484111; Fax: 01768 488850). [Pets £10 per week].
website: www.carrockcottages.co.uk

SECLUDED COTTAGES WITH PRIVATE FISHING, KIRKOSWALD CA10 1EU (24 hour brochure line 01768 898711, manned most Saturdays). Quality cottages, clean, well equipped and maintained. Centrally located for Lakes, Pennines, Hadrian's Wall, Borderland. Enjoy the Good Life in comfort. Pets' paradise. Guests' coarse fishing. Bookings/enquiries 01768 898711. ETC ★★★ [pw! £2 per pet per night].
e-mail: info@crossfieldcottages.co.uk website: www.crossfieldcottages.co.uk

MRS MARION BARRITT, ELM TREE BARN, CULGAITH, PENRITH CA10 1QW (01768 88789). Tastefully converted sandstone barn in quiet village with magnificent views, offering a warm and friendly welcome. Open all year. En suite facilities. B&B from £18. [🐕]
e-mail: marion@elmtreebarn.co.uk website: www.elmtreebarn.co.uk

Silloth-on-Solway

Solway Firth resort with harbour and fine sandy beach. Mountain views. Golf, fishing. Penrith 33 miles, Carlisle 23, Cockermouth 17.

MR AND MRS G.E. BOWMAN, TANGLEWOOD CARAVAN PARK, CAUSEWAY HEAD, SILLOTH CA5 4PE (016973 31253). Friendly country site, excellent toilet and laundry facilities. Tourers welcome or hire a luxury caravan. Telephone or send stamp for colour brochure. [🐕]
e-mail: tanglewoodcaravanpark@hotmail.com website: www.tanglewoodcaravanpark.co.uk

Troutbeck

Village north of Lake Windermere, Church has east window by Burne-Jones.

HOLBECK GHYLL LODGE, TROUTBECK. Lakeland stone lodge. Two twin-bedded bedrooms. Dining/livingroom with open fire and sofa bed. One double bedroom with en suite shower and toilet. Secure covered way for bikes. Ample parking Available Easter to end of October. Saturday change over. ETC ★★★★. MRS KAYE, HOLMDENE, STONEY BANK ROAD, HOLMFIRTH HD9 7SL (01484 684605; Fax: 01484 689051). [🐕]
e-mail: maggiekaye@hotmail.com

Ullswater

Lake stretching for 7 miles with attractive Lakeside walks.

MR & MRS BURNETT, (FELL VIEW HOLIDAYS), FELL VIEW, GLENRIDDING, PENRITH CA11 0PJ (Tel & Fax: 017684 82342; Evenings 01768 867420). Sleep 2-6. Our comfortable well-equipped cottages/apartments/static holiday home have only a field between them and the lake, and have magnificent views of the mountains. Our gardens and grounds are full of birds and flowers which everyone can enjoy. ETC ★★★★ [🐕 pw!]
e-mail: enquiries@fellviewholidays.com website: www.fellviewholidays.com

LAND ENDS CABINS, WATERMILLOCK, NEAR ULLSWATER CA11 0NB (017684 86438). Only one mile from Ullswater, our four detached log cabins have a peaceful fellside location in 25-acre grounds with two pretty lakes. Doggy heaven! Sleep 2-5. [🐕]
e-mail: infolandends@btinternet.com website: www.landends.co.uk

Ulverston

Old town and port with cobbled streets and market square. Laurel and Hardy Museum worth a visit.

LONSDALE HOUSE HOTEL, 11 DALTONGATE, ULVERSTON LA12 7BD (01229 582598). Situated in the heart of Ulverston. Friendly service, great food and comfortable accommodation. Pets welcome. Brochure available. [Pets £2 per night]
website: www.lonsdalehousehotel.co.uk

A useful Index of Towns/Villages and Counties appears on page 427 – please also refer to Contents Page 3.

Windermere

Famous resort on lake of same name, the largest in England. Magnificent scenery. Car ferry from Bowness, one mile distant. Kendal 9 miles.

WATERMILL INN, INGS, NEAR STAVELEY, KENDAL LA8 9PY (01539 821309; Fax: 01539 822309). Misty & Shelly (Dogs) welcome you to the award-winning inn. 16 real ales. Cosy fires, en suite rooms, excellent bar meals. Doggie water and biscuits served in the bar. Good doorstep dog walking. ETC ◆◆◆. [Pets £2 per night].
e-mail: all@watermillinn.co.uk website: www.watermillinn.co.uk

LOW SPRINGWOOD HOTEL, THORNBARROW ROAD, WINDERMERE LA23 2DF (015394 46383) Millie and Lottie (Boxers) would like to welcome you to their peaceful Hotel in its own secluded gardens. Lovely views of Lakes and Fells. All rooms en suite with colour TV etc. Some four-posters. Brochure available. [🐕 pw!]

BURNSIDE HOTEL, KENDAL ROAD, BOWNESS, WINDERMERE LA23 3EP (015394 42211; Fax: 015394 43824). Set in mature gardens with views of Lake Windermere. Choose either luxurious hotel or self-catering cottages and apartments. Full leisure facilities. Pets welcome. Freephone: 0800 220688 [🐕 Hotel, £5 per night, £25 per week S/C]..
e-mail: stay@burnsidehotel.com website: www.burnsidehotel.com

APPLETHWAITE HOUSE, 1 UPPER OAK STREET, WINDERMERE LA23 2LB (015394 44689). A warm welcome, clean, comfortable rooms and a hearty breakfast awaits you in our family-run guest house. Quiet yet convenient location. All rooms have colour TV and complimentary hot drinks. Non-smoking. B&B from £19 per person. Pets stay free. [🐕]
e-mail: info@applethwaitehouse.co.uk website: www.applethwaitehouse.co.uk

KIRKWOOD GUEST HOUSE, PRINCE'S ROAD, WINDERMERE LA23 2DD. (Tel & Fax: 015394 43907). Situated between Windermere and Bowness. Warm and friendly atmosphere. Large en suite rooms with TV and tea/coffee making facilities. Three-night special breaks. ETC ◆◆◆◆ [🐕]
e-mail: info@kirkwood51.co.uk website:www.kirkwood51.co.uk

DENE CREST GUEST HOUSE, WOODLAND ROAD, WINDERMERE LA23 2AE (015394 44979). Comfortable, tastefully furnished Guesthouse. All rooms en suite, colour TV, central heating, tea/coffee making. Open all year. Short Break terms available. Pets Welcome. [pw!, Pets £3 per stay]
e-mail: denecrest@btinternet.com website: www.denecrest.com

Many attractive self-catering holiday homes in a variety of wonderful locations, all well equipped and managed by our caring staff. Pets welcome. Free leisure club membership. For brochure, contact: LAKELOVERS, BELMONT HOUSE, LAKE ROAD, BOWNESS-ON-WINDERMERE LA23 3BJ. (015394 88855; Fax: 015394 88857). ETC ★★★ - ★★★★★ [Pets £15.00 per week.]
e-mail: bookings@lakelovers.co.uk website: www.lakelovers.co.uk

Belper Road, Bradley, Ashbourne DE6 3EN

A small, peaceful, rural, family-run touring caravan park and camping/rally site. Licensed for 34 vans, seasonal rates available. Electric hook-ups, hardstandings, toilets and showers. Pets welcome. Close to Peak District and Derbyshire Dales, Alton Towers, Chatsworth House, National Trust Properties (discounts available for members), Matlock and Bakewell. Two miles from Carsington Water with its sailing, windsurfing, fishing, walking, cycling, play area and shops. Golf, horse riding and swimming - all close by.

Tel: 01335 370855 • e-mail: wattsjulie@talk21.com • www.jinglerscaravanpark.co.uk

NEW HOUSE ORGANIC FARM

Kniveton, Ashbourne DE6 1JL Tel: 01335 342429

Organic family farm in the Derbyshire Dales, near Matlock, Bakewell, Dove Dale; one mile from Carsington Watersports Centre. B&B or self-catering in the holiday cottage, also self-catering in six berth mobile home, gypsy caravan sleeping two/four, two small caravans sleeping two/four, space for tourers and camping. Free working holidays can be arranged. Bed and Breakfast from £10; self-catering from £80 per week.

Pets, horses, bicycles and children welcome.

ETC/AA/RAC ★★

DOG AND PARTRIDGE COUNTRY INN

Swinscoe, Ashbourne DE6 2HS

Tel: 01335 343183

Mary and Martin Stelfox welcome you to a family-run 17th century Inn and Motel set in five acres, five miles from Alton Towers and close to Dovedale and Ashbourne. We specialise in family breaks, and special diets and vegetarians are catered for. All rooms have private bathrooms, colour TV, direct-dial telephone, tea-making facilities and baby listening service. Ideal for touring Stoke Potteries, Derbyshire Dales and Staffordshire Moorlands. Open Christmas and New Year.

Restaurant open all day, non-residents welcome.

e-mail: info@dogandpartridge.co.uk website: www.dogandpartridge.co.uk

Derbyshire Cottages

Tel: 01335 300202

Derbyshire Cottages are set in the grounds of our 17th century Inn, overlooking the Staffordshire Moorlands. Very close to the Peak District, Dovedale, Alton Towers and the quaint town of Ashbourne. Each cottage is built of stone and has its own patio with tables and chairs overlooking open countryside. Fully fitted kitchen, including fridge and split-level cooker. Colour TV, radio and direct-dial telephone with baby listening. Children and pets welcome. Open Christmas and New Year

Call Mary for further details. Website: www.dogandpartridge.co.uk

NOTE

All the information in this book is given in good faith in the belief that it is correct. However, the publishers cannot guarantee the facts given in these pages, neither are they responsible for changes in policy, ownership or terms that may take place after the date of going to press. Readers should always satisfy themselves that the facilities they require are available and that the terms, if quoted, still apply.

The Kings at Ivy House

Georgian Grade II Listed Guest House with many original features including log fires, flagstone floors and listed barns.
Spectacular views.
All rooms en suite with baths.
Ideally situated in Peak Park.
Superb home-cooked evening meals.
Lovely relaxed atmosphere.
Non-smoking. Dogs Welcome.
B&B £37. Dinner £17. Open all year.
Winter Breaks available.

Mervyn & Debbie King,
The Kings at Ivy House,
Biggin-by-Hartington, Newhaven,
Buxton, Derbyshire SK17 0DT
Tel: 01298 84709
E-mail: kings.ivyhouse@lineone.net

Hargate Hall, Wormhill, Near Buxton, Derbyshire SK17 8TA
Tel/Fax: 01298 872591 • www.hargate-hall.co.uk

Twelve Luxury Apartments in a fine country house set in over 5 acres of parkland within the Peak District National Park. Sleep 2-9. All equipped to the highest standard, with satellite TV, hi-fi and video. Open all year. Facilities include:
• mountain bikes • full-size snooker table • games room • adventure playground

ETC ★★★ **Well-behaved pets permitted**

See also Colour Advertisement on page 20

PRIORY LEA HOLIDAY FLATS

Beautiful situation adjoining woodland walks and meadows. Cleanliness assured; comfortably furnished and well-equipped. Colour TV. Bed linen available. Sleep 2/6. Ample private parking. Close to Poole's Cavern Country Park. Brochure available from resident owner. Open all year.
Terms from £90 to £240. Short Breaks available. ETC ★★/★★★.

Mrs Gill Taylor, 50 White Knowle Road, Buxton SK17 9NH. Tel: 01298 23737

THE CHARLES COTTON HOTEL

Hartington, Near Buxton SK17 0AL **Tel: 01298 84229 Fax: 01298 84301**
e-mail: info@charlescotton.co.uk
Website: www.charlescotton.co.uk

ETC ★★

The Charles Cotton is a small comfortable hotel in the heart of the Derbyshire Dales, pleasantly situated in the village square of Hartington, with nearby shops catering for all needs. It is renowned throughout the area for its hospitality and good home cooking. Pets and children are welcome; special diets catered for. The Charles Cotton makes the perfect centre to relax and explore the area, whether walking, cycling, brass rubbing, pony trekking or even hang-gliding. Open Christmas and New Year.

The Devonshire Arms *Peak Forest Nr. Buxton, Derbyshire SK17 8EJ*

Traditional inn in the heart of the Peak District. Close to all main attractions. Excellent walking country. All rooms refurbished to a high standard. En suite, TV, tea/coffee facilities. Excellent meals and traditional ales. Warm welcome to all. Dogs and Kids free. Prices from £23.

Contact: **Nick & Fiona Clough Tel:01298 23875 www.devarms.com** ETC ◆◆◆

BIGGIN HALL

Biggin-by-Hartington, Buxton SK17 ODH

Tel: 01298 84451 • Fax: 01298 84681

www.bigginhall.co.uk **ETC ★★**

Tranquilly set 1,000 ft up in the White Peak District National Park, 17th century Grade II* Listed Biggin Hall - now one of the 'World's Best Loved Hotels' where guests experience the full benefits of the legendary Biggin Air - has been sympathetically restored, keeping its character while giving house room to contemporary comforts. Rooms are centrally heated with bathrooms, en-suite, colour TV, tea-making facilities, silent fridge and telephone. Those in the main house have stone arched mullioned windows, others are in converted 18th century outbuildings. Centrally situated for stately homes and for exploring the natural beauty of the area. Return at the end of the day to enjoy your freshly cooked dinner alongside log fires and personally selected wines.

Well behaved pets are welcome by prior arrangement

Ashbourne

Market town on River Henmore, close to its junction with River Dove. Several interesting old buildings. Birmingham 42 miles, Nottingham 29, Derby 13.

JINGLERS CARAVAN PARK, BELPER ROAD, BRADLEY, ASHBOURNE DE6 3EN (01335 370855). Small family-run touring caravan park and camping/rally site. Licensed for 34 vans, seasonal rates available. Plenty of activities and attractions close by to visit. [pw! 🐕]
e-mail: wattsjulie@talk21.com website: www.jinglerscaravanpark.co.uk

NEW HOUSE ORGANIC FARM, KNIVETON, ASHBOURNE DE6 1JL (01335 342429). Organic family farm in the Derbyshire Dales serving organic, free-range & fair-traded foods. Vegetarian & other diets welcome. B&B/Self-catering holiday cottage, self-catering mobile home 3 caravans, space for tourers and camping. [pw! 🐕]

MRS M.M. STELFOX, DOG AND PARTRIDGE COUNTRY INN, SWINSCOE, ASHBOURNE DE6 2HS (01335 343183). 17th century Inn offering ideal holiday accommodation. Many leisure activities available. All bedrooms with washbasins, colour TV, telephone and private facilities. ETC/AA/RAC ★★[🐕, pw!]
e-mail: info@dogandpartridge.co.uk website: www.dogandpartridge.co.uk

DERBYSHIRE COTTAGES. In the grounds of a 17th century Inn, close to Peak District, Alton Towers and Ashbourne. Each has own patio, fully fitted kitchen, colour TV. Children and pets welcome. Phone MARY (01335 300202) for further details. [pw! 🐕]
website: www.dogandpartridge.co.uk

FREE or REDUCED RATE entry to Holiday Visits and Attractions – see our READERS' OFFER VOUCHERS on pages 103-118

Biggin

Situated 8 miles north of Ashbourne

THE KINGS AT IVY HOUSE, BIGGIN-BY-HARTINGTON, NEWHAVEN, BUXTON, SK17 0DT (01298 84709). Georgian Grade II Listed Guest House with many original features. Spectacular views. All rooms en suite with baths. B&B £37, Dinner £17. Open all year. Dogs Welcome. ETC ◆◆◆◆ and Gold Award. [🐕]
e-mail: kings.ivyhouse@lineone.net

Buxton

Well-known spa and centre for the Peak District. Beautiful scenery and good sporting amenities. Leeds 50 miles, Matlock 20, Macclesfield 12.

BUCKINGHAM HOTEL, 1 BURLINGTON ROAD, BUXTON SK17 9AS (01298 70481; Fax: 01298 72186). Prime location opposite beautiful Pavilion Gardens, yet minutes from centre and attractions. The 37 bedroom Buckingham is the perfect venue from which to discover Buxton and Peak District. Four legs most welcome. Great food, comforts and smiling staff. Visit our website to read our guests' comments. ETC/AA/RAC ★★★
e-mail: frontdesk@buckinghamhotel.co.uk website: www.buckinghamhotel.co.uk

HARGATE HALL, WORMHILL, NEAR BUXTON SK17 8TA (Tel/Fax: 01298 872591) Twelve luxury apartments in a fine country house set in over five acres of parkland within the Peak District National Park. Sleep 2-9. All equipped to the highest standard, with satellite TV, hi-fi and video. ETC ★★★. [🐕]
e-mail: info@hargate-hall.co.uk website: www.hargate-hall.co.uk

PRIORY LEA HOLIDAY FLATS. Close to Poole's Cavern Country Park. Fully equipped. Sleep 2/6. Cleanliness assured. Terms from £90 - £240. Open all year. Short Breaks available. ETC ★★/★★★. MRS GILL TAYLOR, 50 WHITE KNOWLE ROAD, BUXTON SK17 9NH (01298 23737). [pw! Pets £1 per night.]

THE CHARLES COTTON HOTEL, HARTINGTON, NEAR BUXTON SK17 0AL (01298 84229; Fax: 01298 84301). Small hotel. Good home cooking and hospitality. In heart of Derbyshire Dales. Special diets catered for. Ideal for relaxing, walking, cycling, hang-gliding. ETC ★★[🐕]
e-mail: info@charlescotton.co.uk website: www.charlescotton.co.uk

NICK & FIONA CLOUGH, THE DEVONSHIRE ARMS, PEAK FOREST, NEAR BUXTON SK17 8EJ (01298 23875) Situated in a village location in the heart of the Peak District. All rooms en suite with tea/coffee and colour TV. Meals served every day. Excellent walking area. ETC ◆◆◆ [🐕]
website: www.devarms.com

Peak District National Park

A green and unspoilt area at the southern end of the Pennines, covering 555 square miles.

SHEFFIELD/HATHERSAGE. Sleeps 4. Well-equipped converted barn, fenced garden, in open countryside, ideal for Peak Park and Sheffield. For brochure phone 0114 2301949. ETC ★★★★. [Pets £10 per week].

BIGGIN HALL, PEAK PARK (01298 84451). Close Dove Dale. 17th century hall sympathetically restored. Bathrooms en suite, log fires, C/H comfort, warmth and quiet. Fresh home cooking. Beautiful uncrowded footpaths. Brochure on request. ETC ★★
website: www.bigginhall.co.uk

WHEELDON TREES FARM, EARL STERNDALE, BUXTON SK17 0AA (Tel & Fax: 01298 83219). Sleep 2-6. 18th century barn conversion offers seven cosy self-catering holiday cottages. Laundry, payphone and games room. ETC ★★★★[🐕]

When making enquiries please mention FHG Publications

See also Colour Advertisement on page 21

See also Colour Advertisement on page 33

See also Colour Advertisement on page 22

Parkers Farm Holiday Park

Come and stay on a real 400-acre farm in South Devon

FARM COTTAGES • CARAVANS • TOURING SITE

All very clean, with 2 fully tiled toilet/shower blocks (no meters). Electric hook-ups. Views across Dartmoor, 12 miles Torquay; central for touring Devon and Cornwall. Terms from £90 Low Season to £480 High Season. Discounts for couples. Small shop, family bar and restaurant takeaway main season. Games room, laundry, pay phone, etc.

How to find us from Exeter: Take A38 to Plymouth. When you see the sign "26 miles Plymouth", take the second left at Alston Cross signposted to Woodland and Denbury

British Farm Tourist Award, AA ✓✓✓✓, 2002 Gold Award for Quality and Service, Silver David Bellamy Conservation Award, Practical Caravan 2002 Top 100 Parks, West Country Tourist Board ★★★

HIGHER MEAD FARM, ASHBURTON, NEWTON ABBOT, DEVON TQ13 7LJ
Tel: (01364 652598) • Fax: (01364 654004)
e-mail: parkersfarm@btconnect.com • website: www.parkersfarm.co.uk

PETS WELCOME

ETC ★★★

Mrs Angela Bell
Wooder Manor, Widecombe in the Moor, Near Ashburton TQ13 7TR
Tel & Fax: (01364) 621391
website: www.woodermanor.com
e-mail: angela@woodermanor.com

Cottages and converted coach house on 160-acre working family farm nestled in the picturesque valley of Widecombe, surrounded by unspoilt woodland moors and granite tors. Half a mile from village with post office, general stores, inn with dining room, church and National Trust Information Centre. Excellent centre for touring Devon with a variety of places to visit and exploring Dartmoor by foot or on horseback. Accommodation is clean and well-equipped with colour TV, central heating, laundry room. Children welcome. Large gardens and courtyard for easy parking. Open all year, so take advantage of off-season reduced rates. Short Breaks also available. Two properties suitable for disabled visitors. Brochure available.

The Church House Inn ◆ Holne, Near Ashburton, Devon TQ13 7SJ
Tel: 01364 631208 ◆ Fax: 01364 631525
Website: www.churchhouse-holne.co.uk

14th century Inn within the Dartmoor National Park. Standard and en suite rooms available. Bars and restaurant with good fresh food, real ales and fine wines. Dogs welcome FREE OF CHARGE. Great walks!

See also Colour Advertisement on page 24

Blagdon Manor Hotel and Restaurant

Ashwater, North Devon
EX21 5DF

Tel: 01409 211224
Fax: 01409 211634

AA ★★ 84%

Restaurant

Enjoy excellent cuisine using locally sourced produce. Dinner available every night for residents. 2 courses - £21, 3 courses - £25.

Accommodation

7 en suite bedrooms. Panoramic views of the Devon countryside and Dartmoor. A beautifully restored Grade II Listed building, enjoys a peaceful location halfway between Dartmoor and Exmoor and only 20 minutes from the North Cornish coast at Bude. 3 Acres of Gardens and 17 acres of fields. Dogs Welcome. Children over the age of 12. Double/twin rooms are £90 per night, based on 2 people sharing, inclusive of full English breakfast. Single occupancy £72. We make a small charge of £5 per night for dogs.

Liz and Steve along with our 2 chocolate Labradors, Nutmeg and Cassia, look forward to welcoming you to Blagdon Manor.

Website: www.blagdon.com • Email: stay@blagdon.com

See also Colour Advertisement on page 22

LILAC COTTAGE

Smallridge, Axminster

Lilac Cottage is a very pretty rose and vine covered detached cottage in the middle of charming Smallridge. It has been carefully renovated, retaining the inglenook fireplace, oak beams, floors and doors. Oil-fired central heating, colour TV, fully-equipped all-electric kitchen. Furnished to a high standard, sleeps six plus cot. Tenants return year after year. Children and pets are welcome. Walled garden and garage. West Country Tourist Board Registered. The villages and surrounding countryside are beautiful on the borders of Devon, Dorset, and Somerset. Many seaside towns within a seven to ten mile radius, e.g. Lyme Regis, Charmouth and Seaton. Telephone or SAE to:

Mrs J.M. Stuart, Manor Farm House, Deane, Basingstoke, Hants RG25 3AS
Tel & Fax: 01256 782961 or Mrs Young: 01386 840341
E-mail: joanna.sb@free.fr

See also Colour Advertisement on page 24

LEA HILL Membury, Axminster EX13 7AQ

***Tel: 01404 881881* • *Fax: 01404 881890* • AA/ETC ★★★★★**

Historic building. Comfortable en suite rooms. Extensive, delightful gardens and grounds. Many footpaths. Six hole golf course. Stunning views. Evening meals by arrangement. Dogs come free.

e-mail: reception@leahill.co.uk • website: www.leahill.co.uk

MRS V.M. CHUGG **VALLEY VIEW** TEL: 01271 343458

Guineaford, Marwood, Near Barnstaple, Devon EX1 4EA

Friendly Bed and Breakfast accommodation in bungalow situated on 300-acre farm. Near Marwood Hill Gardens and Arlington Court. Colour television and video. Children most welcome, free babysitting. Evening Meal available if required. Bedtime drink at no extra charge. Open all year round. Dogs by arrangement.

Terms from £16.

"Easily the best choice of cottages in Devon... ...and comfortably the best value."

Contact us now for a free colour guide and unbiased recommendation service to the 400 best value cottages around Exmoor and Devon's unspoilt National Trust Coast.

North Devon Holiday Homes
19 Cross Street, Barnstaple EX31 1BD
Tel:(01271) 376322 (24 hrs) Fax:(01271) 346544
E-mail: info@northdevonholidays.co.uk
Website: www.northdevonholidays.co.uk

See also Colour Advertisement on page 23

YOUR PET STAYS FREE

Sandy Cove Hotel stands in 20 acres of cliff, coast and garden. The Hotel Restaurant overlooks the sea and cliffs with spectacular views of the bay. You will probably wonder how we can do it for the price when we offer a FIVE-COURSE MEAL including seafood platters with lobster, smoked salmon and steak. Every Saturday a Swedish Smorgasbord and Carvery carved by the Chef, and followed by dancing till late. Live entertainment weekly from Whitsun until September. All bedrooms have colour TV, telephone, tea making and are en suite. The cocktail bar overlooks the bay and you have the use of the hotel's 80º heated indoor pool and recreation centre with sauna, sunbed, gym equipment and whirlpool, ALL FREE OF CHARGE.

Please return this advertisement to qualify for "Pets Stay Free" offer. Bargain Breaks and weekly rates available all year. Includes 5-course Evening Meal and coffee. Children— free accommodation. Please send for free brochure pack. Children under 5 years completely free, including meals.

Indoor pool heated to 80°F with roll-back sides to enjoy the sun

Sandy Cove Hotel
Combe Martin Bay, Devon, EX34 9SR
Tel: (01271) 882243 & 882888
e-mail: rg14003483@aol.com

ETC ★★★

See also Colour Advertisement on page 26

The Pines at Eastleigh

Hotel & Cottages
Eastleigh, Near Bideford,
North Devon EX39 4PA
Tel: 01271 860561

AA ◆◆◆◆

A Georgian country house set in 7 hilltop acres with magnificent views over the Torridge estuary to Lundy Island. Log-fires, king-size beds, garden room bar with library, maps and a warm welcome await our guests.

Breakfasts use home produced and prize-winning locally sourced ingredients.

There are ground floor rooms set around the courtyard garden with easy access. All rooms are en suite and have teletext television, well-stocked hospitality tray with tea and coffee making facilities, telephones and hairdryers.

Selected by the AA as "One of Britain's Best in 2004."

Bed & Breakfast from £29. Self-catering from £206 for 4. No Smoking.

website: www.thepinesateastleigh.co.uk
e-mail:pirrie@thepinesateastleigh.co.uk

Waterside is a small riverside cottage right on the edge of the Torridge Estuary. The main bedroom, livingroom and back garden all have magnificent views over the water, and there is a mooring below the garden wall for a boat. 2 bedrooms, 2 wcs, own parking, riverside walk adjacent. Half a mile along river walk to centre of Bideford. **01237 473801** for prices and dates. Send SAE to **P.W. Barnes, 140 Bay View Road, Northam, Devon EX39 1BJ** for brochure.

The Edgemoor Country House Hotel

Haytor Road, Lowerdown Cross, Bovey Tracey, Devon TQ13 9LE

Charming AA ★★★ Country House Hotel in peaceful wooded setting adjacent Dartmoor National Park. Many lovely walks close by. All rooms en suite. Good Food. Dogs (with well-behaved owners) welcome. For more information, photographs, current menus and general information about the area - see our website:

website: www.edgemoor.co.uk or e-mail: edgemoor@btinternet.com Tel: 01626 832466

Lake House Cottages and B&B

North Devon/Cornwall Border

Lake Villa, Bradworthy, Devon EX22 7SQ

ETC ★★★

Come and stay in one of four cosy, character cottages in peaceful countryside, half-a-mile from Bradworthy village square in this hidden corner of Devon. Perfectly situated to explore the spectacular coastline of North Devon and Cornwall as well as the West Country moors. There are also several gardens within reach (Rosemoor, Eden Project) and other places of interest. The cottages sleep six, four, three and two and are well furnished and fitted with everything you will need for a great cottage holiday for you and your pet. There are also two en suite B&B rooms available in our own home. Tennis court and gardens.

Brochure: Peter & Lesley Lewin on 01409 241962 • e-mail: info@lakevilla.co.uk • website: www.lakevilla.co.uk

A HAVEN OF PEACE AND TRANQUILLITY

At Little Comfort Farm, Braunton, North Devon *ETC★★★*

Five spacious self-catering cottages with secluded gardens on organic family farm. Just minutes from golden sandy beaches where dogs are allowed. Well-stocked coarse fishing lake. Private 1½ km walk. Wood fires for cosy winter breaks. Pets very welcome. Tel: 01271 812 414 Fax: 01271 817 975

E-mail: jackie.milsom@btclick.com **www.littlecomfortfarm.co.uk**

Woodlands Guest House

Parkham Road, Brixham, South Devon TQ5 9BU.

Overlooking the beautiful Brixham Harbour and Torbay - The English Riviera.

Dogs most welcome – free of charge • Your dogs sleep with you in your bedroom • Near dog-friendly parks and beaches • Most bedrooms en suite • All bedrooms with colour TV, tea/coffee making facilities, mini-fridge etc. • Fantastic panoramic views over Brixham, Harbour, Marina, the Sea and Torbay • Ideal holiday base from which to explore Glorious South Devon • Car park within grounds and unrestricted on-road parking outside.

BED & 4-COURSE BREAKFAST WITH CHOICE OF MENU - EN SUITE ROOMS - ONE NIGHT FROM ONLY £24 TO £26 PER PERSON INCLUSIVE - REDUCTIONS FOR LONGER STAYS. PHONE 01803 852040 JOHN OR DIANE PARRY FOR FREE COLOUR BROCHURE.

e-mail: Dogfriendly2@aol.com website: www.dogfriendlyguesthouse.co.uk

See also Colour Advertisement on page 25

Please mention *Pets Welcome*

when enquiring about accommodation featured in these pages.

Devoncourt is a development of 24 self-contained flats, occupying one of the finest positions in Torbay, with unsurpassed views. At night the lights of Torbay are like a fairyland to be enjoyed from your very own balcony. EACH FLAT HAS:

Marina views	**Heating**	**Sea Views over Torbay**
Private balcony	**Own front door**	**Separate bathroom and toilet**
Separate bedroom	**Bed-settee in lounge**	**Lounge sea views over Marina**
Kitchenette - all electric	**Private car park**	**Opposite beach**
Colour television	**Overlooks lifeboat**	**Short walk to town centre**
Double glazing	**Open all year**	**Mini Breaks October to April**

DEVONCOURT HOLIDAY FLATS
BERRYHEAD ROAD, BRIXHAM, DEVON TQ5 9AB
Tel: 01803 853748 (or 07050 338889 after office hours)
website: www.devoncourt.net

SNAPDOWN FARM CARAVANS

Chittlehamholt, Umberleigh, North Devon EX37 9PF (01769) 540708

12 ONLY – 6 berth CARAVANS with all facilities in beautiful, peaceful, unspoilt country setting - down our quiet lane, on the farm, well away from busy roads. Each with outside seats and picnic table. Field and woodland walks, abundant wildlife, help feed and milk the goats. Easy reach sea and moors. Well behaved pets welcome.
£90 to £245 and £100 to £270 inc. gas and electricity in caravans. Illustrated brochure available. (Discount for couples early/late season.)

Northcott Barton Farm Cottage ETC ★★★★

Beautifully equipped, spotlessly clean three bedroom cottage with large enclosed garden. A walker's and country lover's ideal: for a couple seeking peace and quiet or a family holiday. Very special rates for low season holidays, couples and short breaks. Near golf, riding, Tarka trail and R.H.S. Rosemoor. Character, comfort, beams, log fire, ***"Perfick"***. Pets Welcome, no charge. **For availability please contact Sandra Gay, Northcott Barton, Ashreigney, Chulmleigh, Devon EX18 7PR • Tel/Fax: 01769 520259 • e-mail: sandra@northcottbarton.co.uk • website: www.northcottbarton.co.uk**

See also Colour Advertisement on page 24

2 Thorn Cottages,
Combeinteignhead,
South Devon.
TQ12 4RB
Tel: 01626 872779
mobile: 07786023407

THORN COTTAGE

Ideally located 17th century cottage in peaceful village with inn serving excellent food one minutes' walk away. Log fire, Inglenook fireplace. Original beamed ceilings. Colour TV/video. Garden. Washing machine. Parking. Sleeps 4/5. Non-smokers only. One well-behaved dog welcome. Available all year.

Email: debbie@saunders17.freeserve.co.uk • Website: visitwestcountry.com/thorncottage

Graded ★★★★

Combe Martin Devon

Chalets and caravans on our quiet, private site set in beautiful countryside, near village, beaches, rocky coves and Exmoor. Also Bungalow available this year. No Club or Disco. Swimming Pool. Laundry.

SCENIC DOG WALK

Colour brochure: Mr M. J. Hughes

www.manleighpark.co.uk

e-mail: info@manleighpark.co.uk

(01271) 883353

Oburnford Farm

Cullompton, Devon. EX15 1LZ

Mrs Margaret Chumbley Tel & Fax: 01884 32292

e-mail: margaretchumbley@amserve.com

Treat yourself to a "special break" and enjoy our welcoming friendly family atmosphere. Listed Georgian Farmhouse set in large gardens. Pets most welcome. Ideal National Trust, coasts, moors and M5 (J28).

Bed and Breakfast with Evening meals and "Free Wine" £32 per night.

FOREST GLADE

FOREST GLADE International Caravan & Camping Park

A small country estate surrounded by forest in which deer roam.
Situated in an area of outstanding natural beauty.
Large, flat, sheltered camping/touring pitches. Modern facilities building, luxury 2/6 berth full service holiday homes, also self contained flat for 2 persons.
Colour brochure on request.

FREE Indoor Heated Pool

AA DELUXE

GOLD

FOREST GLADE HOLIDAY PARK (PW), CULLOMPTON, DEVON EX15 2DT

Motor caravans welcome - Facilities for the disabled. Dogs welcome. Tourers please book in advance. ETC ★★★★

Tel: 01404 841381 (Evenings to 8pm) Fax: 01404 841593; E-mail: enquiries@forest-glade.co.uk; Website: www.forest-glade.co.uk

See also Colour Advertisement on page 28

Hills to climb and streams to cross,
Fir and oak all clothed in moss,
Walkers' paradise, tourists' dreams,
Pets are welcome too, it seems.
Local produce on the table,
Pleased to see you when you're able.
Home from home without the cooking,
Phone me now to make a booking.

Mrs J. Colton,
Peek Hill Farm, Dousland,
Yelverton, Devon PL20 6PD
(01822 854808)
www.peekhill.freeserve.co.uk

En suite

Dartmoor Tourist Association inspected

GET AWAY FROM IT ALL

There will always be times when you wish there was somewhere you could go to get away from it all, relax in beautiful surroundings, and sample delicious food.

THE CHERRYBROOK HOTEL

is an ideal choice

Set in the heart of Dartmoor National Park, Cherrybrook is an excellent base for walking, touring or simply enjoying the breathtaking scenery. Warmest welcome.

To find out more, telephone or fax Margaret or Andy Duncan on: 01822 880260

CHERRYBROOK HOTEL, TWO BRIDGES, YELVERTON, DEVON PL20 6SP

e-mail: info@cherrybrook-hotel.co.uk • website: www.cherrybrook-hotel.com

ETC ◆◆◆◆ **See also Colour Advertisement on Page 38**

Peaceful woodland setting next to the River Walkham in the Dartmoor National Park. Ideally placed to explore the beauty of Devon. Purpose - built lodges available all year round, sleeping 2-7, tastefully blending into the surroundings. Interior specification and furnishings to a high standard - including fully-fitted kitchen with oven, microwave and dishwasher.

Free brochure: Dept PW, Dartmoor Country Holidays,
Magpie Leisure Park, Horrabridge, Yelverton, Devon PL20 7RY.
Tel:01822 852651

See also Colour Advertisement on page 38

See also Colour Advertisement on page 27

BADGER'S HOLT • Dartmoor National Park Luxury self catering holiday accommodation nestling by the River Dart at the foot of Yar Tor adjacent to the famous Badger's Holt tea rooms - a traditional Devonshire cream tea not to be missed! Home cooked lunches. Two purpose-built apartments all fully equipped and maintained to the highest standard. Accommodation available all year • Pets welcome • Tea rooms open March to October

• "Bench Tor" - 2 bedroom sleeps 4 • "Yar Tor" - 3 bedroom, 2 bathrooms sleeps 6-8 •

Enquiries to Badger's Holt, Dartmeet, Dartmoor PL20 6SG • Tel: 01364 631213 • Fax: 01364 631475

See also Colour Advertisement on page 28

Apartments at Dartmouth, Devon

Comfortable holiday apartments with private balconies – superb river and harbour views. Sailing, boating, fishing, coastal walks within easy reach. Available all year round with colour TV, linen and parking. From £99 per week.

SAE or phone for FREE colour brochure

RIVERSIDE COURT, SOUTH EMBANKMENT, DARTMOUTH TQ6 9BH

Tel: 01803 832093 • Fax: 01803 835135 • Website: www.dartsideholidays.com

Member South West Tourism

The Old Bakehouse

ETC ★★★

Mrs S.R. Ridalls, 7 Broadstone, Dartmouth TQ6 9NR • Tel & Fax: 01803 834585

Character cottages with beams and old stone fireplaces, one with four-poster bed. In conservation area, 2 minutes from historic town centre and river. Blackpool sands 15 minute drive. Baby-sitting. Free parking. Open all year. Autumn/Winter/Spring breaks • website: www.oldbakehousedartmouth.co.uk • e-mail: PioneerParker@aol.com

Torcross Apartments Situated directly on the beach in the unspoilt countryside of the South Hams between the blue waters of Start Bay and the Slapton Ley Nature Reserve. Seven miles to Dartmouth. Central heating. Ground floor apartments and lift to all floors.
In-house bar, restaurant and take-away food service. Lovely walks. Brochure with pleasure or visit our **website: www.torcross.com e-mail: enquiries@torcross.net**

Torcross, South Devon TQ7 2TQ. Tel: 01548 580206 Fax: 01548 580996

West Country Tourist Board MEMBER

see also colour advertisement on page 37

Watermill Cottages, *Hansel, Dartmouth TQ6 0LN*

Comfortable, well equipped, stone cottages in peaceful riverside setting. Wonderful walks in and around our idyllic valley near dog-friendly Slapton Sands and coastal path. Sleep 3-6. Wood fires. Winter Breaks from £95.

Brochure: 01803 770219 or e-mail: graham@hanselpg.freeserve.co.uk
Pam and Graham Spittle **website: www.watermillcottages.co.uk**

See also Colour Advertisement on page 28

THE ROYAL OAK INN

Dunsford, Near Exeter EX6 7DA

Tel: 01647 252256

Enjoy a friendly welcome in our traditional Country Pub in the picturesque thatched village of Dunsford. Quiet en suite bedrooms are available in the tastefully converted cob barn. Ideal base for touring Dartmoor, Exeter and the coast, and the beautiful Teign Valley. Real Ale and home-made meals are served. Well-behaved children and dogs are welcome.

Please ring Mark or Judy Harrison for further details.

See also Colour Advertisement on page 28

See also Colour Advertisement on page 31

FREE or REDUCED RATE entry to Holiday Visits and Attractions – see our READERS' OFFER VOUCHERS on pages 103-118

LOWER LUXTON FARM

Upottery, Honiton EX14 9PB

Tel & Fax: 01823 601269

If you are looking for a quiet, peaceful and relaxing holiday, come to Lower Luxton Farm, where a warm and friendly welcome awaits you. Situated in an Area of Outstanding Natural Beauty in the centre of the Blackdown Hills, overlooking the Otter Valley. Carp, tench and rudd fishing in our farm pond. Olde worlde farmhouse with inglenook and beams. Private or en suite rooms with tea/coffee making and TV. Good home cooking assured and plenty of it. Open all year. SAE or telephone Mrs Elizabeth Tucker for details.

Bed and Breakfast from £18 per night. Weekly Bed and Breakfast and six Evening Dinners from £140 per week.

HOPE BARTON BARNS

Tel: 01548 561393
www.hopebarton.co.uk
★★★★
Open All Year

Nestling in its own valley close to the sandy cove, Hope Barton Barns is an exclusive group of 17 stone barns in two courtyards and 3 luxury apartments in the converted farmhouse. Heated indoor pool, sauna, gym, lounge bar, tennis court, trout lake and a children's play barn. We have 35 acres of pastures and streams with sheep, goats, pigs, chickens, ducks and rabbits. Superbly furnished and fully equipped, each cottage is unique, and vary from a studio to four bedrooms, sleeping 2 to 10. Farmhouse meals. Ample parking. Golf, sailing and coastal walking nearby. A perfect setting for family summer holidays, walking in Spring/Autumn or just a "get away from it all" break. Free-range children and well behaved dogs welcome. For full colour brochure please contact: ***Mike or Judy Tromans.***

Hope Cove - Near Salcombe - South Devon - TQ7 3HT

Blue Bay Apartments • Hope Cove, Near Salcombe

Tel: 01548 511400 • website: www.blue-bay-apartments.co.uk

- Four sunny apartments ~ Sleep 2-6 people
- Beach and Cliff Walks 300 yards • Lovely Sea and Country Views
- Children and Pets Very Welcome

ETC ★★★

See also Colour Advertisement on page 35

St Brannocks House

Come and see me sometime!

Hi! I'm Sam the Daxi and my friends can come and stay here *free*. Look forward to seeing you.

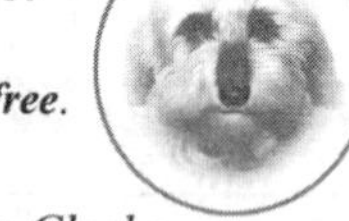

Phone or write to Barbara Clarke

Tel/Fax: 01271 863873 **ETC/RAC ★★**

email: stbrannocks@aol.com

www.stbrannockshotel.co.uk

St Brannocks Road, Ilfracombe EX34 8EQ

See also Colour Advertisement on page 30

WIDMOUTH FARM

ETC ★★★

Watermouth, Near Ilfracombe, Devon EX34 9RX

Comfortable, well equipped cottages in 35 acres of gardens, pasture, woodland and private beach. Wonderful scenery. Ideal for birdwatching, painting, sea fishing & golf. Dogs welcome. **Tel: 01271 863743 • Fax: 01271 866479**

E-mail:holiday@widmouthfarmcottages.co.uk • www.widmouthfarmcottages.co.uk

See also Colour Advertisement on page 30

Varley House, Chambercombe Park, Ilfracombe EX34 9QW

Tel: 01271 863927; Fax: 01271 879299; E-mail: info@varleyhouse.co.uk; www.varleyhouse.co.uk

Built at the turn of the 20th century for returning officers from the Boer War, Varley generates a feeling of warmth and relaxation, combined with an enviable position overlooking Hillsborough Nature Reserve. Winding paths lead to the Harbour and several secluded coves. Our attractive, spacious, fully en suite, non-smoking bedrooms all have colour TV, central heating, generous beverage tray, hairdryer and clock radio alarm. Superb food, beautiful surroundings and that special friendly atmosphere so essential to a relaxing holiday. Cosy separate bar. Car Park. Children over 5 years of age. Dogs by arrangement. Bed and Breakfast from £26 per person. Weekly from £170 per person. Dinner available £15.

Westwell Hall Hotel

Torrs Park, Ilfracombe EX34 8AZ Tel & Fax: 01271 862792

Elegant Victorian Licensed Hotel set in own grounds. Elevated position with fine views of sea and countryside. Ample car parking. All rooms en suite.

B&B £25 pppn. **RAC ★★ AA Associated Hotel**

Instow **Tides Reach Cottage**

Seafront cottage - photo shows view from garden of sandy beach and sea. Parking by the cottage. Instow is a quiet seaside village; shops, pubs and restaurants serving meals overlooking the water. Cottage has 3 bedrooms, enclosed garden, many sea views. Colour TV, washing machine, coastal walks. Dogs welcome. Other sea front cottages available.

Ring 01237 473801 for prices and vacancies only or send SAE for brochure to Mrs P.T. BARNES, 140 Bay View Road, Northam, Bideford, Devon EX39 1BJ

See also Colour Advertisement on page 24

TEIGN VALLEY FOREST

HALDON LODGE FARM, KENNFORD

NEAR EXETER, DEVON EX6 7YG Tel: 01392 832312

Attractive private grounds in peaceful surroundings.

Delightful modern 34ft Caravan only five miles from Exeter and short distance Dawlish, Teignmouth and Torbay, from £70 per week. Lounge (TV), two bedrooms, kitchen, bathroom (H&C) and toilet. Tourers and campers welcome. Famous village inn and farm shop nearby. Three private, well-stocked coarse fishing lakes close to the park. Horse riding at a nearby farm.

Pets Welcome ● Open all year ● Enquiries to D. L. Salter

PLEASE MENTION THIS GUIDE WHEN YOU WRITE OR PHONE TO ENQUIRE ABOUT ACCOMMODATION.

IF YOU ARE WRITING, A STAMPED, ADDRESSED ENVELOPE IS ALWAYS APPRECIATED.

See also Colour Advertisement on page 32

Dittiscombe Holiday Cottages, South Devon

Relax and unwind in the tranquil wildlife valley of Dittiscombe.
We are perfectly situated to explore the many delights of South Devon, with walking, golfing, riding, and beautiful beaches nearby.
There are six individual traditional stone cottages to choose from, all are well-equipped and have private gardens with country views.

Dogs Welcome. Open all year. Short Breaks.

Dittiscombe Holiday Cottages, Slapton, Kingsbridge, Devon TQ7 2QF

Tel: 01548 521272

e-mail: info@dittiscombe.co.uk

www.dittiscombe.co.uk

See also Colour Advertisement on page 30

BRITISH HORSE SOCIETY
APPROVED RIDING ESTABLISHMENT

COLLACOTT FARM

Quality Country Cottages

Eight delightful country cottages sleeping 2-12 set around a large cobbled courtyard, amidst twenty acres of tranquil Devon countryside. All are well equipped with wood-burning stove, dishwashers, heating, bed linen, and their own individual patio and garden. A tennis court, heated swimming pool, games room, children's play area, trampoline room and BHS approved riding centre makes Collacott an ideal holiday for the whole family.

Jane & Chris Cromey-Hawke, Collacott Farm, King's Nympton, Umberleigh, North Devon EX37 9TP
Telephone: S.Molton 01769 572491
website: www.collacott.co.uk
e-mail: jane@collacott.co.uk

Rudge Farm

House built in the 14th Century. Listed as of special historical and architectural interest. Set in beautiful grounds with pond, orchard and woods. Trout fishing and almost 200 acres to wander in. Much wildlife and perfect for watching buzzards and badgers. House very tastefully furnished and fully-equipped. Will sleep up to 8. No charge for dogs, linen or fuel. David and Marion Mills look forward to meeting you. Send for our brochure.

LAPFORD • CREDITON • DEVON • EX17 6NG
TEL: 01363 83268

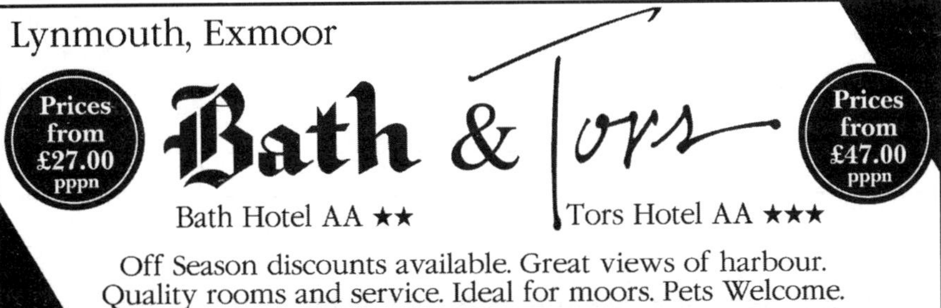

Lynmouth, Exmoor
Prices from £27.00 pppn
Bath & Tors
Prices from £47.00 pppn
Bath Hotel AA ★★
Tors Hotel AA ★★★
Off Season discounts available. Great views of harbour.
Quality rooms and service. Ideal for moors. Pets Welcome.
01598 752238 www.torslynmouth.co.uk 01598 753236

Please mention ***PETS WELCOME*** when making enquiries about accommodation featured in these pages.

See also Colour Advertisement on page 32

Readers are requested to mention this guidebook when seeking accommodation (and please enclose a stamped addressed envelope).

Brendon House

A charming 18th century licensed Country House, nestling in the delightful wooded Lyn Valley on Exmoor. Brendon House offers fully equipped en suite bedrooms, a comfortable residents' lounge, dining room and spacious gardens bordering onto the Lyn salmon and trout river, all this against a backdrop of stunning Exmoor scenery.

For dinner you can choose from our menu of delicious Devon country fare, our Exmoor Game Selection and local seafood dishes. Vegetarian dishes are also available.

B&B from £24 • Four-course dinner £16 • Pets stay FREE

For reservations or a colour brochure:

Ian & Sandra Rigby, Brendon House Hotel, Brendon, Lynton EX35 6PS

website: www.brendonvalley.co.uk/Brendon_House.htm

e-mail: brendonhouse4u@aol.com • Tel: 01598 741206

See also Colour Advertisement on page 32

WEST AISH FARM

Morchard Bishop

Two self-catering cottages.
(See classified ad under Morchard Bishop)

Contact:
Molly & Jeff Kingaby for brochure.
Tel: 01363 877427
e-mail: westaish@eclipse.co.uk
website: www. eclipse.co.uk/westaish

33% of our guests have stayed with us at least once before

Situated in the pretty village of Mortehoe, The Smugglers offers luxury accommodation from twin rooms to family suites. Treat yourselves and your pets to beautiful coastal walks and golden beaches, before you sample our delicious home-cooked meals, real ales and warm, year round hospitality.

The Smugglers, North Morte Road, Mortehoe, N. Devon EX34 7DR Tel/Fax: 01271 870891

See also Colour Advertisement on page 33

Quality en suite accommodation in small, friendly hotel magnificently situated on cliff-side above secluded cove with spectacular sea views. Superb food, well-stocked licensed bar lounge. TV and tea-making facilities in all rooms. Please write or telephone for full details.

LUNDY HOUSE HOTEL

Mortehoe, North Devon EX34 7DZ • Tel: 01271 870372

e-mail: info@lundyhousehotel.co.uk • website: www.lundyhousehotel.co.uk

See also Colour Advertisement on page 33

Pets are always welcome at

Roselands Holiday Chalets.

Situated between Newton Abbot and Totnes, this accommodation is within easy reach of all South Devon attractions, beaches and Dartmoor. The detached, fully equipped, chalets sleep from two to five persons and are situated in a peaceful, enclosed garden, with free parking. One chalet has access for wheelchair users. Pets really are very welcome at Roselands.

And sociable dogs have the freedom of the garden.

Open all year. From October to March we offer special rates for winter breaks.

For more information just telephone us on 01803 812701

or email to: enquiries@roselands.net

or visit our website: www.roselands.net

THE DARNLEY HOTEL **The best of Ilfracombe, North Devon...**

The Darnley Hotel,3 Belmont Road,
Ilfracombe,Devon EX34 8DR
Tel: 01271 863955, Fax: 01271 864076
Email: info@darnleyhotel.co.uk
Web: www.darnleyhotel.co.uk

The Darnley Hotel is a small family run hotel with a warm and friendly atmosphere. The distinctive Victorian building is set within attractive gardens
Pets are welcome free of charge

FLUXTON FARM
Ottery St Mary, Devon EX11 1RJ

Cat lovers' paradise in charming 16th century farmhouse set in lovely Otter Valley. Two acres of beautiful gardens with pond and stream. Five miles from beach at Sidmouth. All rooms en suite, TV and Teasmaids. Central heating. Peace and quiet. Pets welcome free of charge. Plenty of dog walking space. Brochure available. Terms from: B&B £25 per person per day .

Tel: 01404 812818 **AA ◆◆**

SOUTH DEVON • NEAR TORBAY

Luxury 6-berth all electric caravans new in 2000/2002 and other 4,6 and 8 berths to let. All with toilets and showers. All with electricity, colour TV and fridges. Dogs on lead welcome.

Tourist Board graded park ★★★★.

Launderette, shop and payphone. Also separate area for tourers, motor caravans and tents with new toilet/shower block opened in 2001 with family rooms. Electric hook-ups and hard standings.

J. & E. BALL, Dept PW, Higher Well Farm Holiday Park Stoke Gabriel, Totnes, S. Devon TQ9 6RN Tel: 01803 782289

AMBER HOUSE HOTEL ***6 Roundham Road, Paignton, TQ4 6EZ***
Val & James Banks ***Tel: 01803 558372***

✱ Family-run Hotel. ✱ Colour TVs, tea/coffee making facilities. ✱ En-suite facilities and ground floor rooms. ✱ Restricted smoking. ✱ Good food, highly recommended. ✱ Large car park. ✱ Spacious garden and patio. ✱ Park and beach 5 minutes' walk. ✱ Warm welcome to pets and their families. ✱ B&B from £18 per night. ✱ PETS FREE.

See also Colour Advertisement on page 33

Wake Up to Nature!

at Churchwood Valley

Seven Times David Bellamy Gold Award Winner.

Give your pets a holiday, while you relax in one of our comfortable log cabins, set in a peaceful wooded valley near the beach. Enjoy wonderful walks in woods and along the coast. Abundance of birds and wildlife. Up to two pets per cabin. Open April to January.

Wembury Bay, South Devon

e-mail: Churchwoodvalley@btinternet.com

Tel: 01752 862382

See also Colour Advertisement on page 34

Avalon Guest House, **167 Citadel Road, The Hoe, Plymouth PL1 2HU**

Joe and Louise McShane extend a warm welcome to their family-run guest house situated on Plymouth Hoe. Close to the sea front, historic Barbican, ferry port, theatre, pavilions and city centre. All rooms have full central heating, colour TV and tea/coffee facilities. En suite available. Access to rooms at all times. Open all year round. Tel: 01752 668127

Cranbourne Hotel

278/282 Citadel Road, The Hoe, Plymouth PL1 2PZ
Tel: 01752 263858/661400/224646 Fax: 01752 263858

E-Mail: cran.hotel@virgin.net **Web: www.cranbournehotel.co.uk**

* Equidistant City Centre and Hoe Promenade * All bedrooms beautifully decorated, heated, with colour TV, tea/coffee facilities
* 3/4 mile Ferry Terminal * Keys for access at all times * Licensed Bar
* Pets by prior arrangement (No charge) * Large secure car park

Under the personal supervision of The Williams Family

The Lamplighter Hotel

103 Citadel Road, The Hoe, Plymouth PL1 2RN
Tel: 01752 663855; Tel/Fax: 01752 228139
e-mail: lamplighterhotel@ukonline.co.uk

Lamplighter Hotel is family-run and situated on Plymouth Hoe, close to the seafront, Barbican and city centre. All rooms provide full English breakfast; tea, coffee and biscuits; TV. Car park. Reductions for children. Pets by arrangement. *B&B from £19pp.* ETC/AA ◆◆◆ BRITTANY FERRIES *Mastercard and Visa accepted.*

Bolberry Farm Cottages ❖ ***Bolberry, Near Salcombe, Devon TQ7 3DY***

Luxury two and three bedroom Barn conversion cottages • Private gardens • Shared orchard • Views across valley • Parking • Finished to a very high standard • Linen and towels included • Central heating • Close to coastal path and pet friendly beaches • No charge for pets • Dog wash • Short Breaks out of season • Special couples rate • Discount on meals taken at our nearby Port Light Hotel • Credit/Debit cards accepted • The Pets Holiday Specialist

Tel: 01548 561384 • e-mail: info@portlight-salcombe.co.uk • www.bolberryfarmcottages.co.uk

See also Colour Advertisement on page 34

HOPE BARTON BARNS Tel: 01548 561393. An exclusive group of 17 barns & 3 luxury apartments in converted farmhouse. Indoor pool, sauna, gym, lounge bar, tennis court, lake & children's play barn. 35 acres of pastures & streams with sheep, goats, pigs, chickens, ducks & rabbits. Superbly equipped, the accommodation varies from a studio to 4 bedrooms, sleeping 2 - 10. Ample parking. Golf, sailing & coastal walking. Children & well behaved dogs welcome. For colour brochure contact Mike or Judy Tromans.
Hope Cove, Near Salcombe, South Devon TQ7 3HT www.hopebarton.co.uk Open All Year. ★★★★

SALCOMBE HOUSEBOAT HOLIDAYS

SALCOMBE BOAT & MARINE Co. Ltd.
Strand Court, Whitestrand, Devon TQ8 8ET

Relax on Salcombe's beautiful tranquil estuary. Well equipped Houseboats for self catering. Motor boat & rowing dinghy incl. Children & pets very welcome. For our brochure please telephone: 01548 843730

see also colour advertisement on page 35

Seamark

Six 2/3 bedroom Cottages set in two acres of gardens. Indoor swimming pool. Sauna. Games room. Beach. Golf and Windsurfing close by.
Thurlestone Sands, Near Salcombe, Devon TQ7 3JY
Tel/Fax: 01548 561300 • www.seamarkdevon.co.uk

See also Colour Advertisement on page 35

Sand Pebbles Hotel

Sand Pebbles stands in its own grounds with twelve en suite rooms overlooking the sea or countryside with colour televisions, radios and beverage trays. Our lovely restaurant has an enviable reputation for serving superb food. We are just 300 yards from the safe, sandy beaches that Hope Cove is renowned for, and the coastal walks which give some of the most spectacular views in the south west. Hope Cove has a timeless quality all of its own and is one of England's most delightful places to retreat for a short break or a long holiday. There's nowhere else quiet like it. Well behaved children and dogs are welcome. Please call Steve or Lorraine for a brochure.

Sand Pebbles Hotel & Restaurant, Hope Cove, Devon TQ7 3HF Tel: 01548 561673
Website: www.sandpebbleshotel.co.uk

See also Colour Display Advertisement on page 35

MILKBERE HOLIDAYS

COTTAGES, BUNGALOWS, APARTMENTS
Coast and Country on Devon/Dorset border
Free colour Brochure

3 Fore Street, Seaton, Devon EX12 2LE
Telephone: 01297 22925 (brochure)
e-mail: info@milkberehols.com
website: www.milkberehols.com
PETS WELCOME

See also Colour Advertisement on page 36

GLENSIDE House ETC/AA ◆◆◆

Ringmore Road, Shaldon, South Devon TQ14 0EP Tel: 01626 872448

Charming waterside cottage hotel. Doggy walks on foreshore to beach. Garden, car park. B&B from £23.00; DB&B from £36.00. Telephone for brochure.

e-mail: glensidehouse@amserve.com

website: www.tuckedup.com/glensidehouse.html

ETC ★★★★

Boswell Farm Cottages

17th century farmhouse with seven individual cottages, lovingly converted from period farm buildings, each with its enclosed, delightful garden. Idyllic walks in Area of Outstanding Natural Beauty, two miles from beach and World Heritage coastline.

Mr & Mrs B. P. Dillon, Boswell Farm, Sidford, Sidmouth EX10 0PP • Tel &Fax: 01395 514162
e-mail: dillon@boswell-farm.co.uk • website: www.boswell-farm.co.uk

See also Colour Advertisement on page 36

SELF-CATERING COTTAGES AND LODGES

Brochures & Reservations
FREECALL 0808 145 2700

Otterfalls, New Road,
Upottery, Devon EX14 9QD

website: www.otterfalls.co.uk
e-mail: hols@otterfalls.fsnet.co.uk

- ★ Beautiful scenery in peaceful surroundings
- ★ 18 luxurious stone cottages
- ★ 9 Finnish lodges
- ★ 3 fishing lakes
- ★ Heated indoor swimming pool
- ★ Tennis court, pitch & putt, games room
- ★ Bar/Bistro May to September
- ★ Children and pets welcome
- ★ Open all year
- ★ Log fires

Oakdown

SIDMOUTH'S MULTI AWARD WINNING TOURING & HOLIDAY HOME PARK
Weston - Sidmouth - Devon - EX10 0PH
Telephone: Park/Reservations 01297 680387 • Fax: 01297 680541
e-mail: oakdown@btinternet.com
www.bestcaravanpark.co.uk

Welcome to Oakdown "Caravan Holiday Park of the Year" in the Excellence in England Awards 2003 – Sidmouth's multi award winning park. Set within the East Devon World Heritage Coast, Oakdown is level, sheltered and landscaped into groves to give privacy. Our luxurious amenities include aids for the disabled. Enjoy our Field Trail to the famous Donkey Sanctuary.

Free colour brochure with pleasure.

See also Colour Advertisement on page 36

LEIGH FARM SELF-CATERING HOLIDAYS
WESTON, SIDMOUTH, DEVON EX10 0PH

Cottage & Bungalows 150 yards from National Trust Valley leading to Coastal Path & Beach. Lovely cliff-top walks and level walks around nearby Donkey Sanctuary fields.

Contact: Geoff & Gill Davis • Tel: 01395 516065 • Fax: 01395 579582 • e-mail: leigh.farm@virgin.net
website: www.streets-ahead.com/leighfarm ETC ★★★★

TAVISTOCK - EDGE OF DARTMOOR

Comfortably furnished studio cottage five miles from the market town of Tavistock. Ideal for two. Private walled garden. Pets welcome. Private parking, free coal for open fire. All linen provided. Wonderful walking, riding, fishing country with excellent local pubs. Terms £195 per week.

Higher Quither, Milton Abbot, Tavistock, Devon PL19 0PZ
Contact: Mrs P.G.C. Quinton. Tel: 01822 860284.

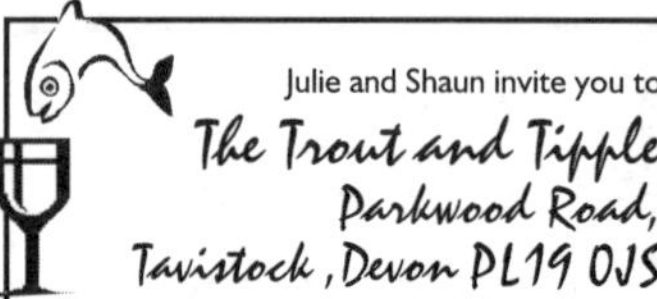

Dogs welcome, bowls of water and treats available on request.
Children welcome.
Non-smoking dining room and games room.
Real Ales include locally brewed Jail Ale and Dartmoor Best.
Lunch every Sunday.
Tel: 01822 618886 Web: www.troutandtipple.co.uk

A warm welcome awaits you at Silver Birches, a comfortable riverside bungalow on the edge of Dartmoor. Good centre for bird-watching, forest walks, golf, riding; free salmon/trout fishing for residents. All rooms en suite. Guest lounge with TV, dining room, sun lounge. Two self-catering caravans in garden from £135 per week. Dogs welcome FREE. *Bed and Full English Breakfast from £25 pppn.*

Silver Birches, Teign Valley, Trusham, Newton Abbot, Devon TQ13 0NJ Tel: 01626 852172

Cutaway Cottage
Thurlestone, Kingsbridge, Devon TQ7 3NF

Self-catering cottage within fenced garden in the middle of the village, on private road. • 5 minutes to pub & shop. • 20 minutes to beaches & sea • Ideal for children, dog walkers & bird watchers.

Phone ***Pat*** on 01548 560688

PETITOR HOUSE • ST MARYCHURCH, TORQUAY

Beautiful, spacious, attractively furnished, Victorian House with panoramic sea views. Sleeps six in three bedrooms (1 double, 2 twin). Large walled garden with access to coastal path. Croquet lawn. South-facing sun terrace overlooking the sea.

Colour Brochure: Les & Ann Shaw Telephone 01803 327943 E-mail: annshaw101@hotmail.com

---

Simply Perfection

Derwent Hill is a gracious Victorian Villa set in an acre of secluded gardens with its own outdoor heated swimming pool. There are 5 spacious fully equipped self-contained holiday flats, some with sea views. Beautiful Cockington Country Park is only ½ a mile away with Torquay's beaches, Riveria Centre and Harbour side attractions all within 1 mile.

* **Dogs welcome FREE**
* **Central Heating, electricity & bed linen all inclusive**
* **Flats for 1 – 6 people**
* **Open all year**
* **Short breaks available Sept – June**
* **Pubs & Restaurants nearby**

PHONE: 01803 606793
Email:info@derwent-hill.co.uk

GREENWAY ROAD, CHELSTON, TORQUAY, TQ2 6JE

Regional Tourist Board southwesttourism MEMBER

See also Colour Advertisement on page 37

PLEASE MENTION THIS GUIDE WHEN YOU WRITE OR PHONE TO ENQUIRE ABOUT ACCOMMODATION.

IF YOU ARE WRITING, A STAMPED, ADDRESSED ENVELOPE IS ALWAYS APPRECIATED.

See also Colour Advertisement on page 29

Sunnymeade Country Hotel

West Down, Near Woolacombe, North Devon EX34 8NT
01271 863668; Fax: 01271 866061
website: www.sunnymeade.co.uk

Small, friendly, comfortable country hotel with our own large enclosed garden set in beautiful countryside.

** A few minutes away from Ilfracombe, Exmoor and Woolacombe's Blue Flag Beach, (where dogs are allowed).*
** Award-winning home cooked traditional English food, using fresh local produce.*
** Special diets can be accommodated, Vegetarian choice always available*
**Licensed Bar *Deaf accessible*
** 10 en suite rooms, 4 on the ground floor. Open all year including Christmas. Pets Welcome – dogs are free*
** Lots of lovely walks accessible right from the door.*

See also Colour Advertisement on page 37

Chichester House

The Esplanade, Woolacombe, North Devon EX34 7DJ
HOLIDAY APARTMENTS ON SEA FRONT

Quiet, relaxing, fully furnished apartments. Uninterrupted sea and coastal views. Watch the sun go down into the sea from your own balcony. Open all year. Free parking.

"WOOLACOMBE IS THE 7th BEST BEACH IN THE WORLD" – DAILY MAIL

SAE Resident Proprietor: Mrs Joyce Bagnall Tel: 01271 870761

See also Colour Advertisement on page 38

FARM & COTTAGE HOLIDAYS (01237 479698). 450 superb cottages. The widest selection of farm cottages throughout Devon, Cornwall & Somerset in rural and coastal locations.
website: www.farmcott.co.uk

HOLIDAY HOMES & COTTAGES S.W, 365A TORQUAY ROAD, PAIGNTON TQ3 2BT (01803 663650; Fax: 01803 664037). Hundreds of Self-Catering Holiday Cottages, Houses, Bungalows, Apartments, Chalets and Caravans in Devon and Cornwall. Please write or phone for free colour brochure.
e-mail: holcotts@aol.com website: www.swcottages.co.uk

SWEETCOMBE COTTAGE HOLIDAYS, ROSEMARY COTTAGE, WESTON, NEAR SIDMOUTH EX10 0PH (01395 512130; Fax: 01395 515680). Selection of Cottages, Farmhouses and Flats in Sidmouth and East Devon, all personally selected and very well-equipped. Gardens. Pets welcome. Please ask for our colour brochure. [🐕]
e-mail: enquiries@sweetcombe-ch.co.uk website: www.sweetcombe-ch.co.uk

CLASSIC COTTAGES (01326 565 555). Featuring 500 hand selected coastal and country holiday homes throughout the West Country.
website: www.classic.co.uk

POWELLS COTTAGE HOLIDAYS, 51 HIGH STREET, SAUNDERSFOOT, PEMBROKESHIRE SA69 9EJ. Many of our top quality holiday properties accept pets. Cottages in Devon, Cornwall, Cotswolds, Pembrokeshire and Heart of England. For colour brochure FREEPHONE 0800 378771 (24 hours).
website: www.powells.co.uk

MARSDENS COTTAGE HOLIDAYS, DEPT 14, 2 THE SQUARE, BRAUNTON EX33 2JB (01271 813777; Fax: 01271 813664). Experience the charms of a North Devon holiday from the comfort and luxury of a Marsdens holiday cottage. Write or phone today for your free colour brochure. [Pets £15 per week].
e-mail: holidays@marsdens.co.uk website: www.marsdens.co.uk

RECOMMENDED COTTAGES. First choice for dream cottages at very competitive prices in all holiday regions of beautiful Britain. Pets welcome. Low Prices. Free brochure (08700 718 718).
website: www.recommended-cottages.co.uk

TOAD HALL COTTAGES (08700 777345. Over 200 outstanding waterside and rural properties in truly beautiful locations in Devon, Cornwall and Exmoor. Call for our highly acclaimed brochure. Pets welcome.
e-mail: thc@toadhallcottages.com website: www.toadhallcottages.com

FREE or REDUCED RATE entry to Holiday Visits and Attractions – see our READERS' OFFER VOUCHERS on pages 103-118

Ashburton

Delightful little town on southern fringe of Dartmoor. Centrally placed for touring and the Torbay resorts. Plymouth 24 miles, Exeter 20, Kingsbridge 20, Tavistock 20, Teignmouth 14, Torquay 14, Totnes 8, Newton Abbot 7.

PARKERS FARM HOLIDAY PARK, HIGHER MEAD FARM, ASHBURTON, NEWTON ABBOT TQ13 7LJ (01364 652598; Fax: 01364 654004). Farm Cottages and Caravans to let, also level touring site with two toilet/shower blocks and electric hook-ups. Central for touring; 12 miles Torquay. WCTB ★★★ [pw!]
e-mail: parkersfarm@btconnect.com website: www.parkersfarm.co.uk

MRS A. BELL, WOODER MANOR, WIDECOMBE IN THE MOOR, NEAR ASHBURTON TQ13 7TR (Tel & Fax: 01364 621391). Cottages nestled in picturesque valley. Surrounded by unspoilt woodland and moors. Clean and well equipped, colour TV, central heating, laundry room. Two properties suitable for disabled visitors. Colour brochure available. ETC ★★★ [pw! £15 per week for first dog; £10 per week for others. ⌂]
e-mail: angela@woodermanor.com website: www.woodermanor.com

THE CHURCH HOUSE INN, HOLNE, NEAR ASHBURTON TQ13 7SJ (01364 631208; Fax: 01364 631525). 14th Century inn within Dartmoor National Park. En suite rooms available. Bars and restaurant; real ales. Great walks. [🐕]
website: www.churchhouse-holne.co.uk

Ashwater

Village 6 miles south-east of Holsworthy.

BLAGDON MANOR HOTEL AND RESTAURANT, ASHWATER, NORTH DEVON EX21 5DF (01409 211224 Fax: 01409 211634) Beautifully restored Grade II Listed building in peaceful location 20 minutes from Bude. 7 en suite bedrooms, three-acre gardens. No children under 12 years. AA ★★ 84% [pw! Dogs £5 per night]
email: stay@blagdon.com website: www.blagdon.com

Axminster

Small friendly market town, full of old world charm, set in the beautiful Axe Valley. Excellent centre for touring Devon, Somerset and Dorset. 5 miles from coast.

LILAC COTTAGE. A beautifully renovated cottage. Oil-fired central heating. All electric kitchen. Inglenook fireplace; beamed ceiling. Sleeps six plus cot. Colour TV. Garden. Garage. SAE please. APPLY – MRS J.M. STUART, MANOR FARM HOUSE, DEANE, BASINGSTOKE, HANTS RG25 3AS (Tel & Fax: 01256 782961) or Mrs Young (01386 840341). [Pets £6 per week.]
e-mail: joanna.sb@free.fr

LEA HILL, MEMBURY, NEAR AXMINSTER EX13 7AQ (01404 881881; Fax: 01404 881890). Tranquil location. Wonderful scenery. Close to World Heritage Coast. Eight acres including six hole golf course. Luxuriously appointed rooms. Evening meals by arrangement. AA/ETC ★★★★★ [🐕]
e-mail: reception@leahill.co.uk website: www.leahill.co.uk

Barnstaple

The largest town in Devon, once an important centre for the wool trade, now a lively shopping centre with thrice weekly market, modern leisure centre, etc.

MRS V.M. CHUGG, VALLEY VIEW, MARWOOD, BARNSTAPLE EX31 4EA (01271 343458). Bungalow on 300 acre farm. Bed and Breakfast accommodation. Near Marwood Hill Gardens and Arlington Court. Children most welcome, free baby-sitting. Dogs by arrangement. Terms from £16. [pw!]

NORTH DEVON HOLIDAY HOMES, 19 CROSS STREET, BARNSTAPLE EX31 1BD (01271 376322; Fax: 01271 346544). Free colour guide to the 400 best value cottages around Exmoor and Devon's National Trust Coast. [Pets £10 per week.]
e-mail: info@northdevonholidays.co.uk website: www.northdevonholidays.co.uk

Berrynarbor

This peaceful village overlooking the beautiful Sterridge valley has a 17th century pub and even older church, and is half-a-mile from the coast road between Combe Martin and Ilfracombe.

SANDY COVE HOTEL, BERRYNARBOR EX34 9SR (01271 882243 or 882888). Hotel set amidst acres of gardens and woods. Heated swimming pool. Children and pets welcome. A la carte restaurant. All rooms en suite with colour TV, tea-making. Free colour brochure on application. ETC ★★★ [🐕 one dog]
e-mail: rg14003483@aol.com

Bideford

Neat port and resort on River Torridge. Attractive, many-arched stone bridge, wooded hills. Boat trips from quay. The sea is 3 miles distant at Westward Ho! Exeter 43 miles, Launceston 32, Bude 26, Ilfracombe21, Barnstaple 9, Torrington 7.

THE PINES AT EASTLEIGH, NEAR BIDEFORD EX39 4PA (01271 860561). Luxury cottages also B&B. Log-fires, king-size beds, garden room bar with library, maps and a warm welcome await our guests. Children welcome. B&B from £29; Cottages from £206 for 4 persons. No smoking. AA ◆◆◆◆ [pw! £2 per night, £10 per week]
e–mail: pirrie@thepinesateastleigh.co.uk website: www.thepinesateastleigh.co.uk

WATERSIDE. Small riverside cottage on the edge of Torridge Estuary. Magnificent views over the water, mooring below the garden wall for a boat. For prices and dates call (01237 473801). Send SAE to P.W.BARNES, 140 BAY VIEW ROAD, NORTHAM, DEVON EX39 1BJ.

Bigbury-on-Sea

A scattered village overlooking superb coastal scenery and wide expanses of sand.

MR SCARTERFIELD, HENLEY HOTEL, FOLLY HILL, BIGBURY-ON-SEA TQ7 4AR (01548 810240). Edwardian cottage-style hotel, spectacular sea views. Overlooking beach, dog walking. En suite rooms with telephone, tea making, TV etc. Home cooking. No smoking establishment. Licensed. ETC ★★ HOTEL and SILVER AWARD. AA ★★ 72%, GOOD HOTEL GUIDE, CAESAR AWARD WINNER 2003, "WHICH?" GUIDE, COASTAL CORKER 2003. [Pets £2.00 per night.]

MRS J. TUCKER, MOUNT FOLLY FARM, BIGBURY-ON-SEA, KINGSBRIDGE TQ7 4AR (01548 810267). Cliff top position, with outstanding views of Bigbury Bay. Spacious, self catering wing of farmhouse, attractively furnished. Farm adjoins golf course and River Avon. Lovely coastal walks, ideal centre for South Hams and Dartmoor. No smoking. Always a warm welcome, pets too!

Bovey Tracey

Little town nestling on southern fringe of Dartmoor. Fine scenery including Haytor Rocks (4 miles) and Becky Falls (3½ miles). Exeter 14 miles, Torquay 13, Newton Abbot 6, Chudleigh 4.

THE EDGEMOOR COUNTRY HOUSE HOTEL, HAYTOR ROAD, LOWERDOWN CROSS, BOVEY TRACEY TQ13 9LE (01626 832466; Fax: 01626 834760). Country House Hotel in peaceful wooded setting adjacent Dartmoor National Park. Many lovely walks close by. All rooms en suite. Dogs welcome. See our website for further details. AA ★★★, Rosettes for Excellent Food [🐕]
e-mail: edgemoor@btinternet.com website: www.edgemoor.co.uk

Bradworthy

Village to the north of Holsworthy. Well placed for North Devon and North Cornish coasts.

PETER & LESLEY LEWIN, LAKE HOUSE COTTAGES AND B&B (01409 241962). Four well equipped cottages sleeping two to six. Quiet rural position; one acre gardens and tennis court. Half-a-mile from village shops and pub. Spectacular coast eight miles. Also two lovely en suite B&B rooms, all facilities, from £20. ETC ★★★. [🐕]
e-mail: info@lakevilla.co.uk website: www.lakevilla.co.uk

When making enquiries please mention FHG Publications

Braunton

5 miles north west of Barnstaple. To the south west are Braunton Burrows nature reserve, a lunar landscape of sand dunes noted for rare plants, and the 3 mile stretch of Saunton Sands.

LITTLE COMFORT FARM, BRAUNTON, NORTH DEVON EX33 2NJ (01271 812 414; Fax: 01271 817 975). Five spacious self-catering cottages sleeping 2-10 on organic family farm, just minutes from golden sandy beaches where dogs are allowed. Well-stocked coarse fishing lake. Private 1½km farm trail. Wood fires for cosy winter breaks. PETS VERY WELCOME [Pets £16 per week].
e-mail: jackie.milsom@btclick.com website: www.littlecomfortfarm.co.uk

Brixham

Lively resort and fishing port, with quaint houses and narrow winding streets. Ample opportunities for fishing and boat trips.

DEVONCOURT HOLIDAY FLATS, BERRYHEAD ROAD, BRIXHAM TQ5 9AB (01803 853748 or 07050 338889 after office hours). 24 self-contained flats with private balcony, colour television, heating, private car park, all-electric kitchenette, separate bathroom and toilet. Open all year. [Pets £10 per week.]
e-mail: devoncourt@devoncoast.com website: www.devoncourt.net

BRIXHAM HOLIDAY PARK, FISHCOMBE COVE, BRIXHAM (01803 853324). Situated on coastal path. Choice of one and two-bedroomed chalets. Indoor heated pool, free club membership, comfortable bar offering meals and takeaway service, launderette. 150 yards from beach with lovely walks through woods beyond. ETC ★★★★. [Pets £25 per week]
e-mail: enquiries@brixhamholpk.fsnet.co.uk website: www.brixhamholidaypark.co.uk

WOODLANDS GUEST HOUSE. Dogs most welcome free of charge, they sleep with you in your bedroom. Dog-friendly parks and beaches nearby. Most rooms en suite with TV, tea/coffee facilities, mini-fridge etc. Overlooking the beautiful Brixham Harbour and Torbay - The English Riviera. Prices range from £24 to £26 pppn. Phone JOHN OR DIANE PARRY (01803 852040) for a brochure. [🐕]
e-mail: Dogfriendly2@aol.com website: www.dogfriendlyguesthouse.co.uk

Chittlehamholt

Standing in beautiful countryside in the Taw Valley and just off the B3227. Barnstaple 9 miles, South Molton 5.

SNAPDOWN FARM CARAVANS, CHITTLEHAMHOLT, UMBERLEIGH, NORTH DEVON EX37 9PF (01769 540708). 12 only – 6 berth caravans with flush toilets, showers, colour TV, fridges, cookers and fires. Laundry room. Picnic tables. Unspoilt countryside. Field and woodland walks. Terms £90 to £245 and £100 to £270 inc. gas and electricity in caravans. [Pets £8.75 per week.]

Chulmleigh

Mid-Devon village set in lovely countryside, just off A377 Exeter to Barnstaple road. Exeter 23 miles, Tiverton 19, Barnstaple 18.

SANDRA GAY, NORTHCOTT BARTON FARM COTTAGE, NORTHCOTT BARTON, ASHREIGNEY, CHULMLEIGH EX18 7PR (Tel & Fax: 01769 520259). Three bedroom character cottage, large enclosed garden, log fire. Special rates low season, couples and short breaks. Near golf, riding, Tarka Trail and RHS Rosemoor. ETC ★★★★ [🐕]
e-mail: sandra@northcottbarton.co.uk website: www.northcottbarton.co.uk

Combeinteignhead

Pretty village of cob, slate and thatch. Easy access to fine beaches, coastal and moorland walks. Situated between Shaldon and Newton Abbot.

MRS DEBBIE SAUNDERS, 2 THORN COTTAGES, COMBEINTEIGNHEAD, SOUTH DEVON TQ12 4RB (01626 872779; mobile: 077860 23407). Log fire, inglenook fireplace. Original beamed ceilings. Colour TV/video. Garden. Washing machine. Parking. Sleeps 4/5. Non-smokers only. One well-behaved dog welcome. Available all year. [🐕]
e-mail: debbie@saunders17.freeserve.co.uk website: visitwestcountry.com/thorncottage

Combe Martin

Coastal village with harbour set in sandy bay. Good cliff and rock scenery. Of interest is the Church and "Pack of Cards" Inn. Barnstaple 14 miles, Lynton 12, Ilfracombe 6.

MR M. J. HUGHES, MANLEIGH HOLIDAY PARK, RECTORY ROAD, COMBE MARTIN EX34 0NS (01271 883353). Holiday Chalets, accommodate 4/6 persons. lSet in 6 acres. Free use of swimming pool. Dogs welcome provided they are kept under control. Also 12 Caravans to let. Graded ★★★★. [Pets £18 per week. pw!]
e-mail: info@manleighpark.co.uk website: www.manleighpark.co.uk

Cullompton

Small market town off the main A38 Taunton - Exeter road. Good touring centre. Noted for apple orchards which supply the local cider industry. Taunton 19 miles, Exeter 13, Honiton 11, Tiverton 9.

MRS M. CHUMBLEY, OBURNFORD FARM, CULLOMPTON EX15 1LZ (Tel & Fax: 01884 32292). Listed Georgian Farmhouse set in large gardens. Ideal National Trust, coasts, moors and M5 (J28). Bed, Breakfast and Evening meal and "Free Wine" £32 per night. Pets most welcome. [🐕]
e-mail: margaretchumbley@amserve.com

FOREST GLADE HOLIDAY PARK (PW), KENTISBEARE, CULLOMPTON EX15 2DT (01404 841381; Fax: 01404 841593). Country estate with deluxe 2/4/6 berth caravans. All superbly equipped. Many amenities on site. Mother and Baby Room. Campers and tourers welcome. SAE for colour brochure. ETC ★★★★, AA Four Pennants De Luxe, David Bellamy Gold Award. [Pets 50p/£1 per night, pw!]
e-mail: enquiries@forest-glade.co.uk website: www.forest-glade.co.uk

Dartmoor

365 square miles of National Park with spectacular unspoiled scenery, fringed by picturesque villages.

MRS J. COLTON, PEEK HILL FARM, DOUSLAND, YELVERTON PL20 6PD (01822 854808). Good breakfast and comfy beds; TV, kettle in rooms. Views from Dartmoor to Bodmin. Picnics can be provided. Good walking. Pleasant stay guaranteed. Open all year except Christmas. [🐕]
website: www.peekhill.freeserve.co.uk

CHERRYBROOK HOTEL, TWO BRIDGES, YELVERTON PL20 6SP (01822 880260). Set in the heart of Dartmoor National Park. Seven comfortably furnished en suite bedrooms. Good quality home-cooked food with menu choice. Ideal for touring. Warmest welcome. ETC ◆◆◆◆ [🐕]
e-mail: info@cherrybrook-hotel.co.uk website: www.cherrybrook-hotel.co.uk

DARTMOOR COUNTRY HOLIDAYS, MAGPIE LEISURE PARK, DEPT PW, BEDFORD BRIDGE, HORRABRIDGE, YELVERTON PL20 7RY (01822 852651). Purpose-built pine lodges in peaceful woodland setting. Sleep 2-7. Furnished to very high standard (microwave, dishwasher etc). Easy walk to village and shops. Launderette. Dogs permitted. [Pets £15.00 per week]

PRINCE HALL HOTEL, TWO BRIDGES, DARTMOOR PL20 6SA (01822 890403; Fax: 01822 890676). Small, friendly, relaxed country house hotel with glorious views onto open moorland. Walks in all directions. Nine en suite bedrooms. Log fires. Gourmet cooking. Excellent wine list. Fishing, riding, golf nearby. Three Day Break from £247 per person. AA/ETC ★★ [🐕]
e-mail: petsgofree@princehall.co.uk

BADGER'S HOLT, DARTMEET, DARTMOOR PL20 6SG (01364 631213; Fax: 01364 631475). Luxury self catering holiday accommodation by the River Dart. Three apartments, fully maintained "Bench Tor" and."Yar Tor" has three bedrooms, two bathrooms (sleeps 6/8). Accommodation available all year. [Pets welcome £16 per week].

SYMBOLS

🐕 Indicates that pets are welcome free of charge.

£ Indicates that a charge is made for pets: nightly or weekly.

pw! Shows some special provision for pets; exercise facility, feeding or accommodation arrangement.

⌂ Indicates separate pets accommodation.

Dartmouth

Historic port and resort on the estuary of the River Dart, with sandy coves and pleasure boat trips up the river. Car ferry to Kingswear.

DARTSIDE HOLIDAYS, RIVERSIDE COURT, SOUTH EMBANKMENT, DARTMOUTH TQ6 9BH (01803 832093; Fax: 01803 835135). Comfortable holiday apartments with private balconies and superb river and harbour views. Available all year with colour TV, linen and parking. From £99 per week. Free Colour Brochure on request. [Pets £10 per week.]
website: www.dartsideholidays.com

MRS S.R. RIDALLS, THE OLD BAKEHOUSE, 7 BROADSTONE, DARTMOUTH TQ6 9NR (Tel & Fax: 01803 834585). Five cottages (one with four-poster bed). Sleep 2–6. Near river, shops, restaurants. Blackpool Sands 15 minutes' drive. TV, linen free, baby-sitting. Open all year. Free parking. ETC ★★★ [🐕]
e-mail: PioneerParker@aol.com website: www.oldbakehousedartmouth.co.uk

TORCROSS APARTMENTS, SLAPTON SANDS, TORCROSS VILLAGE, NEAR KINGSBRIDGE, SOUTH DEVON TQ7 2TQ (01548 580206). Fully equipped self-catering apartments with lovely lake and sea views. Resident owners and spotlessly clean. Brochure with pleasure or visit our website. WCTB. [Pets £7 to £24 per week]
e-mail: enquiries@torcross.net website: www.torcross.com

PAM & GRAHAM SPITTLE, WATERMILL COTTAGES, HANSEL, DARTMOUTH TQ6 0LN (01803 770219). Comfortable, well equipped, old stone cottages in peaceful riverside setting. Wonderful walks in and around our idyllic valley near Slapton Sands and coastal paths. Sleep 3-6. Open all year. Telephone for brochure. [Pets £15 per week]
e-mail: graham@hanselpg.freeserve.co.uk website: www.watermillcottages.co.uk

Dawlish

Bright resort with sandy beach and sandstone cliffs. Lovely gardens with streams, waterfalls and famous black swans. Exeter 13 miles, Torquay 12.

MRS F. E. WINSTON, "STURWOOD", 1 OAK PARK VILLAS, DAWLISH EX7 0DE (01626 862660). Holiday flats. Comfortable, self-contained, accommodating 2-6. Own bathroom, 1/2 bedrooms. Colour television. Garden. Parking. Full Fire Certificate. Leisure centre and beach close by. Pets welcome. [🐕]

Dunsford

Attractive village in upper Teign valley with Dartmoor to the west. Plymouth 35 miles, Okehampton 16, Newton Abbot 13, Crediton 9, Exeter 8.

ROYAL OAK INN, DUNSFORD, NEAR EXETER EX6 7DA (01647 252256). Welcome to our Victorian country inn with real ales and home-made food. All en suite rooms are in a 300-year-old converted barn. Well behaved children and dogs welcome. [🐕]

Exeter

Chief city of the South-West with a cathedral and university. Ample shopping, sports and leisure facilities.

MRS SALLY GLANVILL, RYDON FARM, WOODBURY, EXETER EX5 1LB (Tel & Fax: 01395 232341). 16th Century Devon Longhouse on working dairy farm. Bedrooms with private or en suite bathrooms, hairdryers, tea/coffee facilities. Romantic 4-poster. Open all year. ETC/AA ◆◆◆◆. From £26 to £35. [🐕]

THE LORD HALDON COUNTRY HOUSE HOTEL, DUNCHIDEOCK, NEAR EXETER EX6 7YF (01392 832483, Fax: 01392 833765). Extensive gardens amid miles of rolling Devon countryside. ETC ★★★, AA ★★★ and 2 Rosettes. [Pets £5 per week.]
e-mail: enquiries@lordhaldonhotel.co.uk website: www.lordhaldonhotel.co.uk

Exmoor

265 square miles of unspoiled heather moorland with deep wooded valleys and rivers, ideal for a walking, pony trekking or fishing holiday.

HEDDON VALLEY MILL, NEAR LYNTON AND LYNMOUTH. Seven Cottages in converted mill. River walks in private 50 acres in beautiful Heddon valley for your dog's safety. Log fires. Four-posters. Heated indoor pool/jacuzzi. Breaks from £98, weeks from £248. ETC ★★★/★★★★. Contact: COASTAL EXMOOR HIDEAWAYS (08717 170772).
website: www.coastalexmoorhideaways.co.uk

EXMOOR SANDPIPER INN, COUNTISBURY, LYNMOUTH EX35 6AG (01598 741263). Romantic coaching inn on Exmoor. 16 en suite bedrooms, extensive menus with daily specials, good wines. Horse riding, walking. No charge for dogs. [🐕]
e-mail: info@exmoor-sandpiper.co.uk

JAYE JONES AND HELEN ASHER, TWITCHEN FARM, CHALLACOMBE, BARNSTAPLE EX31 4TT (01598 763568). Comfort for country lovers in Exmoor National Park. All rooms en suite with TV. Meals prepared with local and some organic produce. Stabling £50 per week. Dogs no charge. B&B £22–£30, DB&B £39.50–£47.50. ETC ◆◆◆◆ [🐕, ⌂]
e-mail: holidays@twitchen.co.uk website: www.twitchen.co.uk

Holsworthy

Town 9 miles east of Bude.

MRS S. PLUMMER, LONG CROSS HOUSE, BLACK TORRINGTON, NEAR HOLSWORTHY EX21 5QG (01409 231219). Long Cross House is situated at the edge of the delightful village of Black Torrington, midway between the market towns of Holsworthy and Hatherleigh in rural North Devon. Rooms are en suite with central heating and have tea/coffee making facilities and TV. Children, dogs and horses welcome. Bed and Breakfast from £17.50 per person. Evening Meal by arrangement.

Honiton/Taunton

Busy South Devon town now happily by-passed. Noted for lace and pottery. Excellent touring centre. Newton Abbott 31 miles, Exmouth 18, Taunton 18, Exeter 17, Budleigh Salterton 16, Lyme Regis 15, Chard 13, Sidmouth 10.

LOWER LUXTON FARM, UPOTTERY, HONITON EX14 9PB (Tel & Fax: 01823 601269). Quiet, peaceful and relaxing in area of outstanding natural beauty in the centre of the Blackdown Hills. Fishing in our farm pond. Olde worlde farmhouse. Rooms en suite or private bathroom. Open all year. SAE or telephone Mrs Elizabeth Tucker for details. [🐕]

Hope Cove

Attractive fishing village, flat sandy beach and safe bathing. Fine views towards Rame Head; cliffs. Kingsbridge 6 miles.

HOPE BARTON BARNS, HOPE COVE, NEAR SALCOMBE TQ7 3HT (01548 561393). 17 stone barns in two courtyards and three luxury apartments in farmhouse. Farmhouse meals. Free range children and well behaved dogs welcome. For full colour brochure please contact: Mike or Judy Tromans. ★★★★ [pw! 🐕]
website: www.hopebarton.co.uk

BLUE BAY APARTMENTS, HOPE COVE (01548 511400). Four sunny apartments, sleep 2-6 people. Fully equipped. Beach and cliff walks 300 yards. Lovely sea and country views. Children and pets very welcome. ETC ★★★
website: www.blue-bay-apartments.co.uk

Ilfracombe

This popular seaside resort clusters round a busy harbour. The surrounding area is ideal for coastal walks.

ST BRANNOCKS HOUSE, ST BRANNOCKS ROAD, ILFRACOMBE EX34 8EQ (01271 863873). Good food and excellent accommodation guaranteed at this friendly Hotel. All rooms TV, tea making; en suite. Licensed bar. Parking. Children and pets welcome. RAC/ETC ★★ [🐕]
e-mail: stbrannocks@aol.com website: www.stbrannockshotel.co.uk

WIDMOUTH FARM, NEAR ILFRACOMBE, DEVON EX34 9RX. (01271 863743; Fax: 01271 866479). Comfortable, well equipped cottages in 35 acres of gardens, pasture, woodland and private beach. Wonderful scenery. Ideal for birdwatching, painting, sea fishing & golf. Dogs welcome. ETC ★★★. [pw! Pets £15 per week].
e-mail: holiday@widmouthfarmcottages.co.uk website: www.widmouthfarmcottages.co.uk

VARLEY HOUSE, CHAMBERCOMBE PARK, ILFRACOMBE EX34 9QW (01271 863927; Fax: 01271 879299). Relax with your dog, fabulous walks nearby. Fully en suite non-smoking rooms with lots of thoughtful extras. Superb food, beautiful surroundings. Bar. Car Park. Children welcome over five years. ETC ◆◆◆◆ AA ◆◆◆◆ Selected Award. [🐕] WE WANT YOU TO WANT TO RETURN.
e-mail: info@varleyhouse.co.uk website: www.varleyhouse.co.uk

WESTWELL HALL HOTEL, TORRS PARK, ILFRACOMBE EX34 8AZ (Tel & Fax: 01271 862792). Elegant Victorian Licensed Hotel set in own grounds, adjacent to National Trust coastal walks. All spacious rooms en suite with colour TV and tea/coffee making facilities. B&B £25pp. RAC ★★. AA Associated Hotel [🐕]

Instow

On estuaries of Taw and Torridge, very popular with boating enthusiasts. Barnstaple 6 miles, Bideford 3.

TIDES REACH COTTAGE, INSTOW. Seafront cottage with extensive beach and sea views. 3 bedrooms, enclosed garden, own parking. Central heating, colour TV, coastal walks. Dogs welcome. For colour brochure send SAE to Mrs P.T. BARNES, 140 BAY VIEW ROAD, NORTHAM, BIDEFORD EX39 1BJ (01237 473801). [Dog £10 per week]

Kennford

Village 4 miles south of Exeter.

MRS D.L. SALTER, HALDON LODGE FARM, KENNFORD, NEAR EXETER EX6 7YG (01392 832312). Private grounds near Teign Valley Forest. Modern Holiday Caravan. Two bedrooms, kitchen, lounge, bathroom/toilet, TV. Farm shop, famous village Inn nearby.Sea short distance. Coarse fishing lake locally. Pets welcome. [pw! 🐕]

Kingsbridge

Pleasant town at head of picturesque Kingsbridge estuary. Centre for South Hams disrict with its lush scenery and quiet coves.

JOURNEY'S END INN, RINGMORE, NEAR KINGSBRIDGE TQ7 4HL (01548 810205). Historic inn in unspoilt setting. Extensive food menu served in bar and dining room; wide range of real ales. Comfortable en suite bedrooms with colour TV. Golf, fishing nearby. [Pets £2.50 per night]

BEACHDOWN, CHALLABOROUGH BAY, KINGSBRIDGE TQ7 4JB. Comfortable, fully-equipped chalets on private, level and secluded site in beautiful South Hams. 150 yards from beach and South West Coastal Path. Contact: NIGEL or GARETH (01548 810089). [pw! Pets £15.00 per week].
e-mail: enquires@beachdown.co.uk website: www.beachdown.co.uk

THE SLOOP INN, BANTHAM, NEAR KINGSBRIDGE TQ7 3AJ (01548 560489/560215; Fax: 01548 561940). Five en suite bedrooms, four luxury self-catering apartments. Pet friendly. Bed & Breakfast from £34 per person. Self-catering from £245 inclusive. Short breaks available.[🐕]

MRS B. KELLY, BLACKWELL PARK, LODDISWELL, KINGSBRIDGE TQ7 4EA (01548 821230). 17th century Farmhouse, five miles from Kingsbridge. Ideal centre for Dartmoor, Plymouth, Torbay, Dartmouth and many beaches. Some bedrooms en suite. Bed, Breakfast and Evening Meal or Bed and Breakfast. Pets welcome free of charge. [pw! 🐕]

DITTISCOMBE HOLIDAY COTTAGES, SLAPTON, KINGSBRIDGE, DEVON TQ7 2QF (01548 521272). Relax and unwind in the tranquil wildlife valley of Dittiscombe. We are perfectly situated to explore the many delights of South Devon, with walking, golfing, riding, and beautiful beaches nearby. There are six individual traditional stone cottages to choose from, all are well-equipped and have private gardens with country views. ETC 3-4 stars. Green Tourism Silver Medallist. Colour brochure available or please visit our website to find out more. [Pets £15 per week].
e-mail: info@dittiscombe.co.uk website: www.dittiscombe.co.uk

King's Nympton

3 miles north of Chulmleigh. Winner of CPRE Award for Devon Village of the year 1999.

JANE & CHRIS CROMEY-HAWKE, COLLACOTT FARM, KING'S NYMPTON, UMBERLEIGH, NORTH DEVON EX37 9TP (01769 572491). Eight Country Cottages sleeping from 2 to 12 in rural area; lovely views, private patios and gardens. Well furnished and equipped. Heated pool, tennis court, BHS approved riding school. Laundry room. Open all year. [Pets £3 per night, £20 per week]
e-mail: jane@collacott.co.uk website: www.collacott.co.uk

Lapford

Village 5 miles south east of Chulmleigh.

MRS M. MILLS, RUDGE FARM, LAPFORD, CREDITON EX17 6NG (01363 83268). Set in beautiful grounds with pond, orchard and woods. Trout fishing and almost 200 acres to wander in. Much wildlife and perfect for watching buzzards and badgers. House very tastefully furnished and fully-equipped. Will sleep up to 8. No charge for dogs, linen or fuel. David and Marion Mills look forward to meeting you. Send for our brochure. [🐕]

Lynmouth/Exmoor

Small resort with Harbour at foot of cliff below Lynton, on Lynmouth Bay.

TORS HOTEL, TORS PARK, LYNMOUTH, NORTH DEVON EX35 6NA (01598 753236; Fax: 01598 752544). Great views of harbour. Quality rooms and service. Ideal for moors. Pets welcome. Prices from £47.00 pppn. Off season discounts available. AA ★★★
e-mail: torshotel@torslynmouth.co.uk website: www.torslynmouth.co.uk

BATH HOTEL, TORS PARK, LYNMOUTH, EXMOOR, NORTH DEVON EX35 6NA (01598 752238). Great views of harbour. Quality rooms and service. Ideal for moors. Pets welcome. Prices from £27.00 pppn. Off season discounts available. AA ★★
website: www.torslynmouth.co.uk

FREE or REDUCED RATE entry to Holiday Visits and Attractions – see our READERS' OFFER VOUCHERS on pages 103-118

Lynton/Lynmouth

Picturesque twin villages joined by a unique cliff railway (vertical height 500 ft). Lynmouth has a quaint harbour and Lynton enjoys superb views over the rugged coastline.

COUNTISBURY LODGE HOTEL, COUNTISBURY HILL, LYNMOUTH EX35 6NB (01598 752388). Former Victorian vicarage, peacefully secluded yet only 5 minutes to Lynmouth village. En suite rooms, central heating. Ideal for birdwatching and moors. Parking. Short Breaks. Also available S/C cottage and apartment. AA ◆◆◆◆ [🐕]

R.S. BINGHAM, NEW MILL FARM, BARBROOK, LYNTON EX35 6JR (01598 753341). Exmoor Valley. Two delightful genuine modernised XVII century cottages by stream on 100-acre farm with A.B.R.S. Approved riding stables. Free fishing. ETC ★★★★. SAE for brochure. [pw! Pets £15 per week.]

MOORLANDS. Where countryside and comfort combine. Two self-contained apartments within a family-run guesthouse, close to Exmoor countryside. Hotel amenities available for guests use. Contact: MR I. CORDEROY, MOORLANDS, WOODY BAY, PARRACOMBE, NEAR LYNTON, DEVON EX31 4RA (01598 763224).
website: www.moorlandshotel.co.uk

MR AND MRS I RIGBY, BRENDON HOUSE, BRENDON, LYNTON EX35 6PS (01598 741206). Charming country house in beautiful Lyn Valley. Ideal walking. Restaurant serving country fare, seafood and good wines. Doggy bags! ETC ◆◆◆◆ [🐕]
e-mail: brendonhouse4u@aol.com website: www.brendonvalley.co.uk/Brendon_House.htm

Morchard Bishop

An old traditional Devon village almost equal distances from both moors and both coasts.

MOLLY AND JEFF KINGABY, WEST AISH FARM, MORCHARD BISHOP, NEAR CREDITON EX17 6RX (01363 877427). Two Self-Catering Cottages set in a former cobbled farmyard on a southerly slope overlooking Dartmoor. One cottage sleeps 5. Bungalow sleeps 4. £148 – £350. Short Breaks (3 nights) £110. If you have forgotten what peace and quietness is like, come and stay with us! [🐕 pw!]
e-mail: westaish@eclipse.co.uk website: www.eclipse.co.uk/westaish

Mortehoe

Adjoining Woolacombe with cliffs and wide sands. Interesting rock scenery beyond Morte Point. Barnstaple 15 miles.

THE SMUGGLERS, NORTH MORTE ROAD, MORTEHOE EX34 7DR (Tel & Fax: 01271 870891). In the pretty village of Mortehoe. The Smugglers offers luxury accommodation from twin rooms to family suites. En suite rooms, Satellite TV, Full English Breakfast, Licensed Bar, Beer Garden, Home-cooked Meals. Well trained pets welcome.

LUNDY HOUSE HOTEL, MORTEHOE, NORTH DEVON EX34 7DZ (01271 870372). Quality en suite accommodation in small, friendly hotel. Superb food, licensed bar lounge, restaurant. TV & tea-making facilities in all rooms. Write or phone for full details. [🐕]
e-mail: info@lundyhousehotel.co.uk website: www.lundyhousehotel.co.uk

Newton Abbot

Known as the Gateway to Dartmoor and the coast, this lively market town has many fine buildings, parks and a racecourse.

ROSELANDS HOLIDAY CHALETS, TOTNES ROAD, IPPLEPEN, NEWTON ABBOT TQ12 5TD (01803 812701). Within easy reach of all South Devon attractions, detached, fully equipped chalets sleeping 2-5 persons; one suitable for wheelchairs. Sociable dogs have freedom of garden. Telephone for details. [pw! 1st pet free, extra pets £5 per week.]
e-mail: enquiries@roselands.net website: www.roselands.net

When making enquiries or bookings,
a stamped addressed envelope is always appreciated

North Devon (Ilfracombe)

This popular seaside resort clusters round a busy harbour. The surrounding area is ideal for coastal walks.

THE DARNLEY HOTEL, 3 BELMONT ROAD, ILFRACOMBE EX34 8DR (01271 863955; Fax: 01271 864076). A small family-run hotel with a warm and friendly atmosphere. The distinctive Victorian building is set within attractive gardens. Pets are welcome free of charge. ETC/RAC ★★ [🐕]
e-mail: info@darnleyhotel.co.uk website: www.darnleyhotel.co.uk

Okehampton

Market town on edge of Dartmoor.

BOB & SUE ANNEAR, BEER FARM, OKEHAMPTON EX20 1SG (01837 840265; Fax: 01837 840245). Barn conversions, now four comfortable cottages. Each sleep 4-6. TV/video, microwave, dishwasher, CH. Games room. Children welcome. Horses by arrangement. Excellent mid-Devon base for walking/touring. ETC ★★★★ *SELF-CATERING*. [Dogs £15 per week[.
e-mail: beerfarm.oke@which.net website: www.beerfarm.co.uk

MRS PAM JEFFERY, NORTHLAKE, EXETER ROAD, OKEHAMPTON EX20 1QH (01837 53100). A warm welcome awaits at this friendly bed and breakfast with views across Dartmoor. Superbly sited for walking, cycling, riding and touring. Day kennelling available. [🐕] [pw!]
e-mail: pamjeffery@northlakedevon.co.uk website: www.northlakedevon.co.uk

Ottery St Mary

Pleasant little town in East Devon, within easy reach of the sea. Many interesting little buildings including 11th century parish church. Birthplace of the poet Coleridge.

MRS A. FORTH, FLUXTON FARM, OTTERY ST MARY EX11 1RJ (01404 812818). Charming 16th-Century farmhouse with large garden. Good food. Peace and quiet. Cat lovers' paradise. AA ◆◆ [🐕 pw!]

Paignton

Popular family resort on Torbay with long, safe sandy beaches and small harbour.
Exeter 25 miles, Newton Abbott 9, Torquay 3.

J. AND E. BALL, DEPARTMENT P.W., HIGHER WELL FARM HOLIDAY PARK, STOKE GABRIEL, TOTNES TQ9 6RN (01803 782289). Within 4 miles Torbay beaches and 1 mile of River Dart. Central for touring. Dogs on leads. Tourist Board Graded Park ★★★★. [Pets £2 per night, £14 per week in statics, free in tents and tourers, pw!]

VAL & JAMES BANKS, AMBER HOUSE HOTEL, 6 ROUNDHAM ROAD, PAIGNTON TQ4 6EZ (01803 558372). Family-run licensed hotel. En suite facilities and ground floor rooms. Good food. Highly recommended. Restricted smoking. A warm welcome assured to pets and their families. [🐕]

Plymouth

Historic port and resort, immpressively rebuilt after severe war damage. large naval docks at Devonport. Beach of pebble and sand.

CHURCHWOOD VALLEY, WEMBURY BAY, NEAR PLYMOUTH PL9 0DZ (01752 862382). Relax in one of our comfortable log cabins, set in a peaceful wooded valley near the beach. Enjoy wonderful walks in woods and along the coast. Abundance of birds and wildlife. Up to two pets per cabin. [Pets £5 per week]
e-mail: churchwoodvalley@btinternet.com

AVALON GUEST HOUSE, 167 CITADEL ROAD, THE HOE, PLYMOUTH PL1 2HU (01752 668127). Family-run guest house, close to the sea front. All rooms have full central heating, colour TV and tea/coffee facilities. En suite available. Open all year round. [🐕]

CRANBOURNE HOTEL, 278/282 CITADEL ROAD, THE HOE, PLYMOUTH PL1 2PZ (01752 263858/661400/224646; Fax: 01752 263858). Convenient for Ferry Terminal and City Centre. All bedrooms with colour TV and tea/coffee. Licensed bar. Keys provided for access at all times. Under personal supervision. Pets by arrangement. ◆◆◆◆ [🐕]
e-mail: cran.hotel@virgin.net website: www.cranbournehotel.co.uk

LAMPLIGHTER HOTEL, 103 CITADEL ROAD, THE HOE, PLYMOUTH PL1 2RN (01752 663855; Tel & Fax: 01752 228139). Family-run hotel situated close to seafront, Barbican and city centre. All rooms with tea/coffee making facilities and TV. Car park. Pets by arrangement. Mastercard and Visa accepted. ETC/AA ◆◆◆ BRITTANY FERRIES. [🐕]
e-mail: lamplighterhotel@ukonline.co.uk

Salcombe

Fishing and sailing centre in sheltered position. Fine beaches and coastal walks nearby.

SALCOMBE COAST & COUNTRY COTTAGES, CHURCH STREET, SALCOMBE TQ8 8DH (01548 843773). Over 200 self-catering properties in and around Salcombe and the South Hams, the ideal destination for a holiday or short break with your dog all year round. [Pets £15 per week].
website: www.coastandcountry.co.uk

HAZEL AND SEAN HASSALL, BOLBERRY FARM COTTAGES, BOLBERRY, NEAR SALCOMBE, DEVON TQ7 3DY (01548 561384). Luxury Barn conversion cottages. Private gardens. Close to coastal path and pet friendly beaches. Dog wash. Short Breaks out of season. The Pets Holiday Specialist. [🐕]
e-mail: info@portlight-salcombe.co.uk website: www.bolberryfarmcottages.co.uk

HOPE BARTON BARNS, HOPE COVE, NEAR SALCOMBE TQ7 3HT (01548 561393). 17 stone barns in two courtyards and three luxury apartments in farmhouse. Farmhouse meals. Free range children and well behaved dogs welcome. For full colour brochure please contact: Mike or Judy Tromans. ★★★★ [pw! 🐕]
website: www.hopebarton.co.uk

THE SALCOMBE BOAT MARINE COMPANY LTD, WHITESTRAND, SALCOMBE TQ8 8ET (Tel & Fax: 01548 843730, Mobile:07976 962239). A holiday with a difference. Unwind with a houseboat holiday on Salcombe's tranquil estuary. Write or phone for brochure. [Pets £20 weekly.]

SEAMARK, THURLESTONE SANDS, NEAR SALCOMBE TQ7 3JY (01548 561300). 6 lovely cottages adjoining coastal path. Beach close by, golf one mile. Indoor heated swimming pool, sauna and games room. Laundry room. Pay phone. Colour brochure. [pets £25 per week]
website: www.seamarkdevon.co.uk

SAND PEBBLES HOTEL, HOPE COVE, NEAR KINGSBRIDGE TQ7 3HF (01548 561673). In own grounds overlooking sea and countryside. Tastefully furnished en suite rooms, TV, beverage facilities. Excellent restaurant. Golf, tennis, riding, within easy reach. [Pets £3 per night].
website: www.sandpebbleshotel.co.uk

Seaton

Bright East Devon resort near Axe estuary. Shingle beach and chalk cliffs; good bathing, many lovely walks in vicinity. Exeter 23 miles, Sidmouth 11.

MILKBERE HOLIDAYS, 3 FORE STREET, SEATON EX12 2LE (01297 22925 – brochure/01297 20729 – bookings). Attractive self-catering Cottages, Bungalows, Apartments. Coast and Country on Devon/Dorset border. Free colour brochure. Pets welcome. [Pets £20 per week].
e-mail: info@milkberehols.com website: www.milkberehols.com

Shaldon

Delightful little resort facing Teignmouth across the Teign estuary. Sheltered by the lofty prominence of Shaldon Ness, beach side activities are largely concerned with boats and sailing; beaches are mainly of sand. Mini golf course. The attractions of Teignmouth are reached by a long road bridge or passenger ferry.

GLENSIDE HOUSE, RINGMORE ROAD, SHALDON TQ14 0EP (Tel & Fax: 01626 872448). Charming, waterside cottage hotel. Level river walks to beach. En suite available. Garden, car park. B&B from £23.00; DB&B from £36.00. Telephone for brochure. ETC/AA ◆◆◆. [Pets £3.50 daily, £15 weekly.]
e-mail: glensidehouse@amserve.com website: www.tuckedup.com/glensidehouse.html

Sidmouth

Sheltered resort, winner of many awards for its floral displays. Good sands at Jacob's Ladder beach.

BOSWELL FARM COTTAGES, SIDFORD, SIDMOUTH EX10 0PP (Tel & Fax: 01395 514162) 17th century farmhouse with seven individual cottages, lovingly converted from period farm buildings, each with its enclosed, delightful garden. Facilities available - art studio, tennis court and trout pond. Idyllic walks in Area of Outstanding Natural Beauty, two miles from beach and World Heritage coastline. ETC ★★★★ [pw! Pets £18 per week.]
e-mail: dillon@boswell-farm.co.uk website: www.boswell-farm.co.uk

OTTERFALLS AND OTTERS RISE, NEW ROAD, UPOTTERY EX14 9QD (FREECALL 0808 145 2700; Fax: 01404 861706). 27 luxurious fully equipped self-catering cottages and lodges set in 130 acres. Fishing lakes, heated indoor pool, bar/bistro. Wonderful walking, including special pet "off-lead" walkways. [Pets £25 per week, pw!]
e-mail: hols@otterfalls.fsnet.co.uk website: www.otterfalls.co.uk

OAKDOWN TOURING AND HOLIDAY HOME PARK, WESTON, SIDMOUTH EX10 0PH (01297 680387; Fax: 01297 680541). Privately owned park set in East Devon Heritage Coast. Level and sheltered; luxury holiday homes to hire, pitches for touring units. Colour brochure. Pets are charged for. ETC ★★★★★ [pw! varied prices.]
e-mail: oakdown@btinternet.com website: www.bestcaravanpark.co.uk

LEIGH FARM SELF-CATERING HOLIDAYS, WESTON, SIDMOUTH EX10 0PH. Cottage & Bungalows 150 yards from National Trust Valley leading to Coastal Path and beach. Lovely cliff top walks and level walks around nearby Donkey Sanctuary fields. ETC ★★★★ Contact: Geoff & Gill Davis (01395 516065; Fax: 01395 579582). [pw! Pets £16 per week]
e-mail: leigh.farm@virgin.net website: www.streets-ahead.com/leighfarm

Tavistock

Birthplace of Sir Francis Drake and site of a fine ruined Benedictine Abbey. On edge of Dartmoor, 13 miles north of Plymouth

MRS P.G.C. QUINTON, HIGHER QUITHER, MILTON ABBOT, TAVISTOCK PL19 0PZ (01822 860284). Modern self-contained barn conversion. Own private garden. Terms from £195 inc. linen, coal and logs. Electricity metered. [pw! 🐕]

THE TROUT AND TIPPLE, PARKWOOD ROAD, TAVISTOCK, DEVON PL19 0JS (01822 61886). (A386 - Tavistock to Okehampton road). Non-smoking dining room and games room. Real Ales including locally brewed Jail Ale and Dartmoor Best. Lunch every Sunday. Children and dogs welcome.
website: www.troutandtipple.co.uk

Teign Valley

Picturesque area on edge of Dartmoor. The River Teign flows into the English Channel at Teignmouth.

S. & G. HARRISON-CRAWFORD, SILVER BIRCHES, TEIGN VALLEY, TRUSHAM, NEWTON ABBOT TQ13 0NJ (01626 852172). Comfortable riverside bungalow on the edge of Dartmoor. Good centre for bird-watching, forest walks, golf, riding; fishing. All rooms en suite. Two self-catering caravans in garden from £135 per week. B&B from £25.00 nightly. [🐕]

Thurlestone

Village resort above the cliffs to the north of Bolt Tail, 4 miles west of Kingsbridge.

CUTAWAY COTTAGE, THURLESTONE, KINGSBRIDGE TQ7 3NF. Self-catering cottage within a fenced garden in the middle of the village. Private road, 5 minutes to pub & shop, 20 minutes to beaches & sea, Ideal for children, dog walkers & bird watchers. Phone PAT on 01548 560688

Terms quoted in this publication may be subject to increase if rises in costs necessitate

---

Torquay

Popular resort on the English Riviera with a wide range of attractions and entertainments. Yachting and watersports centre with 10 superb beaches and coves.

PETITOR HOUSE, TORQUAY. Beautiful Victorian House. Panoramic sea views. Unique quiet idyllic clifftop position. House sleeps six in three bedrooms and is well-furnished and equipped. Pets welcome. Colour brochure from: LES & ANN SHAW, 52 PETITOR ROAD, ST MARYCHURCH, TORQUAY TQ1 4QF (01803 327943) [🐕]
e-mail: annshaw101@hotmail.com

DERWENT HILL HOLIDAY FLATS, GREENWAY ROAD, CHELSTON, TORQUAY TQ2 6JE (01803 606793). Five spacious, fully equipped, self-contained, centrally heated holiday flats in Victorian villa. Secluded gardens. Heated pool. Beaches, Riviera Centre within one mile. Short breaks available. ETC ★★★ [pw! 🐕]
e-mail: info@derwent-hill.co.uk website: www.derwent-hill.co.uk

FAIRMOUNT HOUSE HOTEL, HERBERT ROAD, CHELSTON, TORQUAY TQ2 6RW (01803 605446). Somewhere special – a small licensed hotel with comfortable en suite bedrooms, cosy bar, delicious home cooking. Peaceful setting. One mile town centre. B&B from £28 per person. Bargain Breaks available. ETC ◆◆◆◆ [Pets £3 per night, £21 per week]

RED HOUSE HOTEL AND MAXTON LODGE HOLIDAY APARTMENTS, ROUSDOWN ROAD, CHELSTON, TORQUAY TQ2 6PB (01803 607811; Fax: 01803 605357). Choose either the friendly service and facilities of a hotel or the privacy and freedom of self-catering apartments. The best of both worlds!, AA/ETC ★★ Hotel & ★★★ Self-catering. [🐕 in flats; £3 per night in hotel]
e-mail: stay@redhouse-hotel.co.uk website: www.redhouse-hotel.co.uk

Torrington

Pleasant market town on River Torridge. Good centre for moors and sea. Exeter 36 miles, Okehampton 20, Barnstaple 12, Bideford 7.

SALLY MILSOM, STOWFORD LODGE, LANGTREE, NEAR TORRINGTON EX38 8NU (01805 601540). Sleep 4/6. Away from the crowds. Four delightful cottages with heated indoor pool, and two secluded period farm cottages. Peaceful countryside, convenient North Devon coast and moors. Magnificent views and walks. Phone for brochure. ETC ★★★. [Pets £10 per week, pw!]
e-mail: stowford@dial.pipex.com website: www.stowford.dial.pipex.com

Totnes

Town at tidal estuary of River Dart, 7 miles west of Torquay

SEA TROUT INN, STAVERTON, NEAR TOTNES, DEVON TQ9 6PA (01803 762274; Fax: 01803 762506). Hidden away in the tranquil Dart Valley but conveniently placed for Dartmoor, Torbay and the South Devon coast. Delightful cottage style bedrooms, two traditional English bars and elegant restaurant.

FLEAR FARM COTTAGES, EAST ALLINGTON, TOTNES, SOUTH DEVON TQ9 7RF (01548 521227; Fax: 01548 521600). Superb cottages, indoor heated swimming pool, sauna, all weather tennis court, large indoor and outdoor play areas. Non-smokers only. Log fires and full central heating. ETC ★★★★/★★★★★ [Pets £15 per week].
website: www.flearfarm.co.uk

Woolacombe

Favorite resort with long, wide stretches of sand. Barnstaple 15 miles, Ilfracombe 6.

EUROPA PARK, STATION ROAD, WOOLACOMBE (01271 870159). Luxury bungalows, superb views. Touring caravans and tents. Full facilities. Pets welcome, 6-acre dog park. Indoor heated swimming pool. [pw! £5 per week.]

PEBBLES HOTEL, COMBESGATE BEACH, WOOLACOMBE EX34 7EA (01271 870426). Family-run Hotel overlooking sea and beaches. All rooms en suite, with colour TV, tea/coffee making etc. Special Short Break packages. Write or phone for colour brochure. ETC ★ [dog symbol]
website: www.pebbleshotel.com

SUNNYMEADE COUNTRY HOTEL, WEST DOWN, NEAR WOOLACOMBE EX34 8NT (01271 863668; 01271 866061). Small country hotel set in beautiful countryside. A few minutes away from Ilfracombe, Exmoor and Woolacombe's Blue Flag Beach. 10 en suite rooms, 4 on the ground floor. Deaf accessible. Pets welcome-dogs are free. ETC ◆◆◆ [dog symbol, pw!]
website: www.sunnymeade.co.uk

MRS JOYCE BAGNALL, CHICHESTER HOUSE, THE ESPLANADE, WOOLACOMBE EX34 7DJ (01271 870761). Holiday apartments on sea front. Fully furnished, sea and coastal views. Watch the sun go down from your balcony. Open all year. SAE Resident Proprietor. [Pets £8 per week, pw!]

• • *Some Useful Guidance for Guests and Hosts* • •

Every year literally thousands of holidays, short breaks and overnight stops are arranged through our guides, the vast majority without any problems at all. In a handful of cases, however, difficulties do arise about bookings, which often could have been prevented from the outset.

It is important to remember that when accommodation has been booked, both parties – guests and hosts – have entered into a form of contract. We hope that the following points will provide helpful guidance.

GUESTS:

- When enquiring about accommodation, be as precise as possible. Give exact dates, numbers in your party and the ages of any children.
- State the number and type of rooms wanted and also what catering you require – bed and breakfast, full board etc. Make sure that the position about evening meals is clear – and about pets, reductions for children or any other special points.
- Read our reviews carefully to ensure that the proprietors you are going to contact can supply what you want. Ask for a letter confirming all arrangements, if possible.
- If you have to cancel, do so as soon as possible. Proprietors do have the right to retain deposits and under certain circumstances to charge for cancelled holidays if adequate notice is not given and they cannot re-let the accommodation.

HOSTS:

- Give details about your facilities and about any special conditions. Explain your deposit system clearly and arrangements for cancellations, charges etc. and whether or not your terms include VAT.
- If for any reason you are unable to fulfil an agreed booking without adequate notice, you may be under an obligation to arrange suitable alternative accommodation or to make some form of compensation.

While every effort is made to ensure accuracy, we regret that FHG Publications cannot accept responsibility for errors, omissions or misrepresentations in our entries or any consequences thereof. Prices in particular should be checked because we go to press early. We will follow up complaints but cannot act as arbiters or agents for either party.

• *Tamarisk Farm* • **West Bexington, Dorchester DT2 9DF**

On slope overlooking Chesil beach, three large (one for wheelchair disabled Cat I - M3) and two small COTTAGES, and two secluded CHALETS (not ETC graded), each standing in own fenced garden. Sleep 4/6. On organic farm with arable, sheep, cattle, horses and market garden (organic vegetables, meat and wholemeal flour available). Good centre for touring, sightseeing, walking. Lovely place for dogs. Very quiet. Sea views. Terms from £105-£650 **ETC ★★★/★★★★**

E-mail: tamarisk@eurolink.ltd.net • www.tamariskfarm.co.uk • Mrs Josephine Pearse Tel: 01308 897784

ANVIL HOTEL & RESTAURANT

Salisbury Road, Pimperne, Blandford, Dorset DT11 8UQ Tel: 01258 453431/480182

A long, low thatched building set in a tiny village deep in the Dorset countryside – what could be more English? This typical Old English hostelry offering good old-fashioned English hospitality, a full à la carte menu with mouthwatering desserts in the charming beamed restaurant with log fire,together with specials of the day and light bites menu in the two bars. All bedrooms with private facilities. Ample parking. **From £60 single, £80 double.**

e-mail: info@anvilhotel.co.uk website: www.anvilhotel.co.uk ***ETC ★★ Hotel***

Langtry Manor

Somewhere Special... for Someone Special

Built by Edward VII as a Lovenest for Lillie Langtry. A rare gem of a hotel where the building, food, service and history blend to form something quite exceptional. Four posters, Jacuzzi's, complimentary leisure club and award-winning restaurant. Midweek and weekend breaks. As featured on BBC Holiday Show. Pets welcome by arrangement.

Derby Road, East Cliff, Bournemouth BH1 3QB

Tel: (01202) 553887 www.langtrymanor.com

See also Colour Advertisement on page 40

TAKE ME WITH YOU TO....

THINKS

WHITE TOPPS

THE **REALLY** DOG FRIENDLY PLACE

Small, friendly and catering only for guests with dogs. In a nice quiet position close to lovely walks on the beach (dogs allowed) and Hengistbury Head. Plus the New Forest isn't far away. There's no charge for me, of course and the proprietor, MARJORIE TITCHEN, just loves dogs.

- CAR PARKING
- RESIDENTIAL LICENCE
- DOG(S) ESSENTIAL - ANY SIZE, ANY NUMBER, ANYWHERE
- GROUND FLOOR ROOM FOR ELDERLY DOGS
- VEGETARIANS WELCOME
- ADULTS ONLY (14yrs +)
- GENEROUS HOME COOKING

WRITE (SAE APPRECIATED) OR PHONE FOR FACT SHEET.

45 CHURCH ROAD, SOUTHBOURNE, BOURNEMOUTH, DORSET BH6 4BB TEL: 01202 428868

e-mail: Thedogplace1@aol.com

IF YOU DON'T LOVE DOGS YOU WON'T LIKE WHITE TOPPS

Alum Dene Hotel

2 Burnaby Road, Alum Chine, Bournemouth BH4 8JF Tel: 01202 764011

Renowned for good old fashioned hospitality and friendly service. Come and be spoilt at our licensed hotel. All rooms en suite, colour TV. Some have sea views. 200 metres sea. Parking. Christmas House party. No charge for pets.

BOURNEMOUTH HOLIDAY APARTMENTS

Recently refurbished to a high standard. Ideally situated close to sea and shops. Sleep one to ten persons. Car parking space for each apartment. Discounts for bookings of over one week. Children and pets welcome. Brochure available from:

Mike & Lyn Lambert, Aaron, 16 Florence Road, Bournemouth BH5 1HF
Tel: 01202 304925 • Fax: 01425 475151 • e-mail: mikelyn_lambert@btinternet.com

HOLIDAY FLATS AND FLATLETS

- A SHORT WALK TO GOLDEN SANDY BEACHES •
- MOST WITH PRIVATE BATHROOMS •
- CLEANLINESS AND COMFORT ASSURED •
- LAUNDRY ROOM • FREE PRIVATE PARKING •
- DOGS WELCOME • COLOUR TV IN ALL UNITS •
- NO VAT CHARGED •

CONTACT: M. DE KMENT, 4 CECIL ROAD,
BOURNEMOUTH BH5 1DU (07788 952384)

THE VINE HOTEL

22 Southern Road, Southbourne
Bournemouth BH6 3SR
Telephone: 01202 428309

A small, family, award-winning Hotel only 3 minutes' walk from sea and shops. All rooms en suite; tea/coffee making facilities and colour TV. Residential licence with attractive bar. Full central heating. Forecourt parking. Open all year.

Pets Welcome – Free of Charge. FHG Diploma STB ◆◆◆

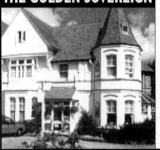

THE GOLDEN SOVEREIGN

Steve Pini,
The Golden Sovereign Hotel, 97 Alumhurst Road, Alum Chine, Bournemouth, Dorset BH4 8HR
Tel & Fax: 01202 762088 • E-mail: scott.p@talk21.com

Charming Victorian Hotel close to award-winning beaches and wooded chine walks. Minutes from Bournemouth/Poole town centres. Experience our unique atmosphere and sample our freshly cooked food. En suite rooms, all with tea/coffee facilities, television, clock/alarm and direct dial telephones with extra point for internet access.

Our priority? – Your comfort and happiness.

Brochure and prices on request. Rates from £25 pppn.

Website: www.goldensovereignhotel.com

English Tourism Council ◆◆◆◆ GUEST ACCOMMODATION

FROGMORE FARM
CHIDEOCK, BRIDPORT
DT6 6HT

Enjoy Bed and Breakfast on a 90-acre grazing farm set in beautiful West Dorset, overlooking Lyme Bay. En suite shower rooms available. Cosy TV lounge with wood fire; guests' dining room, tea making facilities. Children & dogs welcome. OR CHOOSE our lovely self catering Cottage, sleeps 6. Fully equipped, bed linen supplied; lounge with woodburner and colour TV. Car essential. Open all year. Brochure and terms free on request.

Apply MRS S. NORMAN Tel: 01308 456159

Lancombes House ~ Holiday Cottages

ETC ★★★

Four superbly converted cottages, each with its own sitting-out area, barbecue and garden furniture. Some have fenced gardens. Spacious open plan living areas, most with wood burning stoves. Deep in the heart of Hardy country, this is a delightful area to explore whether on foot or horseback. There are many things to do and pets and children are very welcome. Prices start at £120 for mini-breaks; open all the year round.

Mrs Carol Mansfield, Lancombes House, West Milton, Bridport DT6 3TN
Tel: 01308 485375 website: www.lancombeshouse.co.uk

Dolphins River Park

Small, very peaceful park set in beautiful landscaped grounds of mature trees, shrubs and lawns on the banks of the River Char.

Luxury fully self-contained 4 and 6 berth Caravans for hire and sale.

(Facilities include laundry room, local tourist information)

Direct access to footpaths and fields.

One mile from the beach. ***WELL CARED FOR PETS WELCOME.***

Colour Brochure available from:
Dolphins, Berne Lane, Charmouth, Dorset DT6 6RD
FREEPHONE: 0800 0746375

The Street, Charmouth, Dorset DT6 6QF Telephone 01297 560339
Phillip and Carole Mapstone

Former coaching inn built around 1500, oak beams and panelling. Log fires; 11 unique bedrooms, 10 en suite, the other has its own bathroom. Guest lounge, licensed bar and dining room. Vegetarians and Vegans catered for.

An abundance of National Trust land, footpaths and Heritage coastline. Dogs welcome.

ETC 4 Diamond Award **Smoking permitted in guest conservatory only.**

Visit the FHG website
www.holidayguides.com
for details of the wide choice of accommodation featured in the full range of FHG titles

MANOR FARM HOLIDAY CENTRE

Charmouth, Bridport, Dorset DT6 6QL (01297) 560226

Three bedroomed bungalow, two and three bedroomed houses, Luxury caravans. All units for four to six people. Children and pets welcome. Swimming pool and children's pool. Licensed bar with family room. Shop. Launderette. Children's play area. Ten minutes' walk to safe sand and shingle beach. Many fine walks locally. Golf, riding, tennis, fishing and boating all nearby.

SAE TO MR. F. LOOSMORE FOR COLOUR BROCHURE

NEW FOREST

Country Holiday Chalet on small, quiet, secluded woodland park.Sleeps four. Fenced private garden. Dogs welcome. Car parking. £150 to £350 per week. Write enclosing SAE or telephone:

Mrs L.M Bowling, Owlpen Caravans Ltd, Owlpen, 148 Burley Road, Bransgore, Near Christchurch, Dorset BH23 8DB Tel: 01425 672875 Mobile: 07860 547391

ETC ◆◆◆◆ **CHURCHVIEW GUEST HOUSE**

Winterbourne Abbas, Dorchester, Dorset DT2 9LS Tel/Fax: 01305 889296

Our 17th century Guest House, noted for hospitality, delicious breakfasts and evening meals, makes an ideal base for touring beautiful West Dorset. Our character bedrooms are comfortable and well-appointed. Meals, served in our beautiful dining room, feature local produce, with relaxation provided by two attractive lounges and licensed bar. Hosts, Jane and Michael Deller, are pleased to give every assistance, with local information to ensure a memorable stay. Short breaks available. Non-smoking.

Terms: Bed and Breakfast: £27 – £37; Dinner, Bed and Breakfast: £41 – £52.

E-mail: stay@churchview.co.uk • Website: www.churchview.co.uk

THE STABLES

Hyde Crook, Frampton DT2 9NW • 01300 320075

The Stables is a comfortable country house developed around a 1935 cottage overlooking the valley of Frampton. Set in a small area of woodland off the A37, in the heart of Thomas Hardy country, we enjoy uninterrupted views of open countryside. There is unrestricted off-road parking and 20 acres of ground with wild life, ducks, sheep and horses. All guest accommodation is contained in a separate wing of the house and comprises a comfortable sitting room/TV lounge on the ground floor, with private staircase to a twin en suite bedroom, double bedroom, single bedroom and bathroom on the first floor. The twin beds can be converted to a king-size for stays of two nights or more. All rooms are double glazed with central heating, and a log fire is lit in the sitting room in the cooler seasons. Terms from **£21**pppn. The Stables specialises in pet friendly facilities for dogs and horses.

e-mail: cobalangley@aol.com • website: www.framptondorset.com

Eype's Mouth Country Hotel

Eype, Bridport DT6 6AL • Tel: 01308 423300 • Fax: 01308 420033
e-mail: eypehotel@aol.com • website: www.eypehotel.co.uk

Situated in a secret spot, down a leafy lane, just a five minute walk from the sea. All 18 rooms en suite, with colour TV, tea and coffee making facilities and trouser press. Two of the rooms having four-poster beds. Restaurant with views over Lyme Bay. Smugglers Bar serving bar snacks lunchtimes and evenings with patio overlooking the sea. Heidi our Dalmatian looks forward to meeting you and your Fido.

See also Colour Advertisement on page 41

FREE or REDUCED RATE entry to Holiday Visits and Attractions – see our READERS' OFFER VOUCHERS on pages 103-118

Readers are requested to mention this guidebook when seeking accommodation (and please enclose a stamped addressed envelope).

THE KNOLL HOUSE

STUDLAND BAY

ESTABLISHED 1931

A peaceful and relaxing holiday for all ages.
An independent country-house hotel, in an unrivalled position above three miles of golden beach. Dogs are especially welcome and may sleep in your room. Special diets arranged. Our 100 acre grounds offer nice walks; squirrels and rabbits!

~

Good food and a sensible wine list.
Tennis courts; nine acre golf course and outdoor heated pool.
Health spa with Jacuzzi, Sauna, Turkish room, plunge pool and gym.
Many ground-floor and single rooms for older guests.

~

Family suites, of connecting rooms with bathroom, separate young children's dining room.
Playrooms and fabulous SAFE adventure playground.

~

Daily full board terms: £97-£130. Children less, according to age.

~

Open Easter - end October

ONLY 2 HOURS FROM HEATHROW

STUDLAND BAY
DORSET
BH19 3AW

For Colour Brochure
TEL 01929 · 450450 FAX 01929 · 450423
Email: enquiries@knollhouse.co.uk
Website: www.knollhouse.co.uk

See also Colour Advertisement on page 39

• Gothic National Trust Hotel • Set in 20 acres overlooking Studland Bay •

• Superb food & rooms • Sea views & 4 posters • Log fires •

• Tennis, golf, horse-riding • 2 minute walk to beach •

Tel/Fax: 01929 450288

www.themanorhousehotel.com

See also Colour Advertisement on page 41

Fairfields Hotel

'We want all our guests to feel extremely welcome, relaxed and comfortable'

A private hotel, family-owned, at the rural heart of a National Trust Conservation Area and Studland Nature Reserve.

* Home cooked country food * Large garden * Short walk to three miles of sandy beach * Panoramic sea/country views * All rooms en suite, TV, tea/coffee * Children Welcome * Family Rooms * ETC Four Diamonds * Les Routiers Corps d'Elite Wine Award and 2001 Cuisine Award.

Swanage Road, Studland Bay, Dorset BH19 3AE

Tel: (01929) 450 224 for a brochure today

A warm welcome awaits all dogs – and their owners – at the Limes Hotel, only a few hundred yards from wonderful coastal walks and beach, surrounded by the unspoilt Purbeck Hills. En suite rooms with colour TV and hospitality trays. Pets come free!

• Car Park • Licensed Bar • Families Welcome

• Open all Year for Bed and Breakfast

48 Park Road, Swanage, Dorset BH19 2AE

Tel: 01929 422664 Fax: 0870 0548794

info@limeshotel.demon.co.uk

www.limeshotel.demon.co.uk

DORSET COTTAGE HOLIDAYS

PETS GO FREE. Self-catering cottages, town houses, bungalows and apartments. All within 10 miles of Heritage Coastline and sandy beaches. Excellent walking in idyllic countryside. Short breaks from £105, weekly from £135 (per cottage). Open all year.

Free brochure tel: 01929 553443

e-mail: enq@dhcottages.co.uk • www.dhcottages.co.uk

SWANAGE BAY VIEW HOLIDAY PARK

4/5/6 BERTH FULL MAINS CARAVANS

COMFORTABLE AND WELL EQUIPPED

*Colour TV * Launderette * Sea Views * Parking space * Pets welcome*

* Fully licensed club with entertainment. * Indoor swimming pool*

EASTER – OCTOBER, REDUCED TERMS EARLY/LATE HOLIDAYS

SAE: M. Stockley, 17 Moor Road, Swanage, Dorset BH19 1RG • Tel: 01929 424154

Lulworth Cove - Cromwell House Hotel, BH20 5RJ Tel: 01929 400253/400332; Fax: 01929 400566

Catriona and Alistair Miller welcome guests to their comfortable family-run hotel, set in secluded gardens with spectacular sea views. Situated 200 yards from Lulworth Cove, with direct access to the Dorset Coastal Footpath. A heated swimming pool is available for guests' use from May to October. Accommodation is in 17 en suite bedrooms, with TV, direct-dial telephone, and tea/coffee making facilities; most have spectacular sea views. Restaurant, bar wine list. Two nights dinner, bed and breakfast (fully en suite) from £90. Off peak mid week breaks available. Open all year except Christmas. **ETC/AA/RAC ★★**

See also Colour Advertisement on page 41

Dormer Cottage

Woodlands at Hyde, Near Wareham BH20 7NT

Proprietor: Mrs M.J.M Constantinides

Tel: 01929 471239

In the midst of 'Hardy Country', a secluded cottage, sleeping 5, converted from a former barn and forming part of the ex Dower House of Hyde Estate. All linen provided. Golf, pony-trekking, riding nearby. Pets and children most welcome. SAE please for terms and further particulars.

Ideal for a quiet holiday far from the madding crowd.

Gorselands Caravan Park, West Bexington-on-Sea, Dorset DT2 9DJ

Attractive secluded park set in coastal valley overlooking Chesil Beach, part of Dorset's World Heritage Jurassic Coastline. Tourist Board graded. Glorious sea views. Country and seaside walks. An ideal base for discovering Dorset's charming villages and Heritagestline. The beach is a mile either by car or through the meadows, and the fishing is excellent. Pets are most welcome.

Tel: 01308 897232 • Fax: 01308 897239

See also Colour Advertisement on page 42

Double Three Guest House, 33 Rodwell Road, Weymouth, Dorset DT4 8QP

I am Ben, a 5-year-old terrier x and it would be grrreat for you to visit my lovely comfortable non-smoking home. So, bark to your family that this is the ideal place to take a paws and explore Dorset's beautiful beaches and countryside. Howl that they will have an ecstatic welcome from my family (Ron and Kathy). Sing that B&B is from £16 - £25 pppn and finally whine for them to send for free information.

Tel: 01305 786259 e-mail: doublethree16762@aol.com website: www.doublethree.co.uk

Available from most bookshops, the 2004 edition of **THE GOLF GUIDE** covers details of every UK golf course – well over 2800 entries – for holiday or business golf. Hundreds of hotel entries offer convenient accommodation, accompanying details of the courses – the 'pro', par score, length etc.

In association with 'Golf Monthly' and including Holiday Golf in Ireland, France, Portugal, Spain, The USA, South Africa and Thailand .

£9.99 from bookshops or from the publishers (postage charged outside UK) • FHG Publications, Abbey Mill Business Centre, Paisley PA1 1TJ

Abbotsbury

Village of thatched cottages; Benedictine monks created the famous Abbotsbury Swannery.

MRS JOSEPHINE PEARSE, TAMARISK FARM, WEST BEXINGTON, DORCHESTER DT2 9DF (01308 897784). Self Catering properties sleep 4/6. Overlooking Chesil Beach: three large (one for wheelchair disabled Cat 1-M3) and two small Cottages (ETC 3/4 stars) and two secluded Chalets (not ETC graded) on mixed organic farm with arable, sheep, cattle, horses and market garden with vegetables, meat and wholemeal flour available. Good centre for touring, sightseeing, walking. Glorious sea views, very quiet. Lovely place for dogs. Terms from £105 to £650. [🐕]
e-mail: tamarisk@eurolink.ltd.net website: www.tamariskfarm.co.uk

Blandford

Handsome Georgian town that rose from the ashes of 1731 fire; rebuilt with chequered brick and stone. Also known as Blandford Forum.

ANVIL HOTEL & RESTAURANT, PIMPERNE, BLANDFORD DT11 8UQ (01258 453431/480182). A typical Old English hostelry offering good old-fashioned English hospitality. Full à la carte menu with mouthwatering desserts in the charming restaurant with log fire, delicious desserts, bar meals, specials board. All bedrooms with private facilities. Ample parking. ETC ★★ [Pets £2.50 per night]
e-mail: info@anvilhotel.co.uk website: www.anvilhotel.co.uk

Bournemouth

One of Britain's premier holiday resorts with miles of golden sand, excellent shopping and leisure facilities. Lively entertainments include Festival of Lights at the beginning of September.

Three self-contained apartments in quiet avenue, one minute from clean, sandy beaches and five minutes from shops. Sleep 2/6. Fully equipped including linen. All have fridge, toilet and shower room, microwave, colour TV, central heating, electric meter. Parking. Terms from £140. Contact: MRS HAMMOND, STOURCLIFFE COURT, 56 STOURCLIFFE AVENUE, SOUTHBOURNE, BOURNEMOUTH BH6 3PX (01202 420698). [Pets £5 weekly]

LANGTRY MANOR, DERBY ROAD, EAST CLIFF, BOURNEMOUTH (01202 553887). A rare gem of a hotel where the building, food, service and history blend to form something quite exceptional. Midweek and weekend breaks. Pets welcome by arrangement.
website: www.langtrymanor.com

BILL AND MARJORIE TITCHEN, WHITE TOPPS HOTEL, 45 CHURCH ROAD, SOUTHBOURNE, BOURNEMOUTH BH6 4BB (01202 428868). Situated in quiet position close to lovely walks and beach. Dogs essential. Free parking. Residential licence. [🐕 pw!]
e-mail: Thedogplace1@aol.com

ALUM DENE HOTEL, 2 BURNABY ROAD, ALUM CHINE, BOURNEMOUTH BH4 8JF (01202 764011) Renowned for good old fashioned hospitality and friendly service. Come and be spoilt at our licensed hotel. All rooms en suite, colour TV. Some have sea views. 200 metres sea. Parking. Christmas House party. No charge for pets. [🐕]

MIKE AND LYN LAMBERT, AARON, 16 FLORENCE ROAD, BOURNEMOUTH BH5 1HF (01202 304925/01425 474007 Fax: 01425 475151). Modern Holiday Apartments sleeping one to ten persons, close to sea and shops. Recently extensively renovated with new kitchens and bathrooms. Clean well-equipped flats. Car park. Write or phone for colour brochure and terms.
e-mail: mikelyn_lambert@btinternet.com

SYMBOLS

- 🐕 **Indicates that pets are welcome free of charge.**
- £ **Indicates that a charge is made for pets: nightly or weekly.**
- pw! **Shows some special provision for pets; exercise facility, feeding or accommodation arrangement.**
- ⌂ **Indicates separate pets accommodation.**

HOLIDAY FLATS AND FLATLETS a short walk to golden, sandy beaches. Most with private bathrooms. Cleanliness and comfort assured. Dogs welcome. Contact: M DE KMENT, 4 CECIL ROAD, BOURNEMOUTH BH5 1DU (07788 952394). [Pets £20 per week]

ANNE & RICHARD REYNOLDS, THE VINE HOTEL, 22 SOUTHERN ROAD, SOUTHBOURNE, BOURNEMOUTH BH6 3SR (01202 428309). Small, family, Hotel only 3 minutes' walk from sea and shops. All rooms en suite. Residential licence. FHG Diploma, STB ◆◆◆ [🐕]

STEVE PINI, THE GOLDEN SOVEREIGN HOTEL, 97 ALUMHURST ROAD, ALUM CHINE, BOURNEMOUTH BH4 8HR (Tel & Fax: 01202 762088). Charming Victorian Hotel close to award winning beaches and wooded chine walks. Cosy bar, freshly cooked optional evening meals. En suite rooms, all with tea/coffee making facilities, television, clock/radio alarm and direct dial telephones with extra point for internet access. Minutes from Bournmouth/poole town centres. Rates from £25pppn. ETC ◆◆◆◆ [🐕]
e-mail: scott.p@talk21.com website: www.goldensovereignhotel.com

Bridport

Market town of Saxon origin noted for rope and net making. Harbour at West Bay has sheer cliffs rising from the beach.

MRS S. NORMAN, FROGMORE FARM, CHIDEOCK, BRIDPORT DT6 6HT (01308 456159). The choice is yours - Bed and Breakfast in charming farmhouse, OR self-catering Cottage equipped for six, pets welcome. Brochure and terms free on request. [1st dog free, 2nd dog £3.00 per night, £15 per week]

MRS CAROL MANSFIELD, LANCOMBES HOUSE, WEST MILTON, BRIDPORT DT6 3TN (01308 485375). Pretty cottages in converted barns. Panoramic views to sea four miles away. Set in 10 acres, some have fenced gardens. Many walks from our land. ETC ★★★ [🐕]
website: www.lancombeshouse.co.uk

Charmouth

Small resort on Lyme Bay, 3 miles Lyme Regis. Sandy beach backed by undulating cliffs where many fossils are found. Good walks.

DOLPHINS RIVER PARK, BERNE LANE, CHARMOUTH DT6 6RD (FREEPHONE 0800 0746375). Luxury 4 and 6 berth caravans on small, peaceful park. Coin-op laundry. One mile from beach. Colour brochure available. [Pets £2.50 per night, £12 per week]

THE QUEEN'S ARMES HOTEL, THE STREET, CHARMOUTH DT6 6QF (01297 560339). Former coaching inn c.1500. Log fires; 11 unique bedrooms, 10 en suite, one with own bathroom. Lounge, bar and dining room. Vegetarians and vegans catered for. ETC ◆◆◆◆ [🐕]

MR F. LOOSMORE, MANOR FARM HOLIDAY CENTRE, CHARMOUTH, BRIDPORT DT6 6QL (01297 560226). All units for four to six people. Ten minutes' level walk to beach, many fine local walks. Swimming pools, licensed bar with family room, shop, launderette. Sporting facilities nearby. Children and pets welcome. SAE for colour brochure. [Pets from £20 per week]

Christchurch

Residential town near coast. Yachting based on Christchurch harbour and Christchurch Bay.

COUNTRY HOLIDAY CHALET on small, quiet, secluded woodland park. Sleeps four. Fenced private garden. Dogs welcome. Car parking. £150 to £350 per week. BH & HPA Member. Write enclosing SAE or telephone: MRS L.M. BOWLING, OWLPEN CARAVANS LTD, OWLPEN, 148 BURLEY ROAD, BRANSGORE, NEAR CHRISTCHURCH, DORSET BH23 8DB (01425 672875; mobile 07860 547391). [🐕 pw!]

PLEASE SEND A STAMPED ADDRESSED ENVELOPE WITH ENQUIRIES

Dorchester

Busy market town steeped in history. Roman remains include Amphitheatre and villa.

GRACE COTTAGE. Charming cottage with enclosed garden. Lounge/dining room, study/bedroom, two bedrooms, well-equipped kitchen, two bathrooms. Pub nearby. Non-smokers only. Good touring centre. ETC ◆◆◆◆. Apply: MRS WILLIS, LAMPERTS COTTAGE, SYDLING ST NICHOLAS DT2 9NU (01300 341659; Fax: 01300 341699). [🐕]
e-mail: nickywillis@tesco.net

CHURCHVIEW GUEST HOUSE, WINTERBOURNE ABBAS, DORCHESTER DT2 9LS (Tel & Fax: 01305 889296). Beautiful 17th Century Licensed Guest House set in the heart of West Dorset, character bedrooms, delightful period dining room, two lounges and bar. Non-smoking. B&B £27–£37 pp. B&BEM £41–£52. Short breaks available. ETC ◆◆◆◆. [🐕]
e-mail: stay@churchview.co.uk website: www.churchview.co.uk

MRS JACOBINA LANGLEY, THE STABLES B&B, HYDE CROOK (OFF A37), FRAMPTON DT2 9NW (01300 320075; Fax: 01300 321718). Comfortable country house in 20 acres with uninterrupted country views. Guest accommodation in separate wing, fully double-glazed, with central heating. All pets most welcome. [pw! £1.50 per night]
e-mail: cobalangley@aol.com website: www.framptondorset.com

Eype

Village near coast 2km south-west of Bridport.

EYPE'S MOUTH COUNTRY HOTEL, EYPE, BRIDPORT DT6 6AL (01308 423300; Fax: 01308 420033). Experience the tranquillity of Dorset. Situated in a secret spot, down a leafy lane, just a five minute walk from the sea. Restaurant with views over Lyme Bay. [Pets £3.00 per night]
e-mail: eypehotel@aol.com website: www.eypehotel.co.uk

Lyme Regis

Picturesque little resort with harbour, once the haunt of smugglers. Shingle beach with sand at low tide. Fishing, sailing and water ski-ing in Lyme Bay. Taunton 28 miles, Dorchester 24, Seaton 8.

WESTOVER FARM COTTAGES, WOOTTON FITZPAINE, NEAR LYME REGIS DT6 6NE (01297 560451). Within walking distance of the sea. Two beautiful cottages, sleep 6/7, with large secluded gardens. Car parking. Logs, Linen available. 3 bedrooms. Well behaved Pets welcome. ETC ★★★ [Pets £15 per week.]
e-mail: wfcottages@aol.com website: www.lymeregis.com/westover-farm-cottages/

MRS J TEDBURY, LITTLE PADDOCKS, YAWL HILL LANE, LYME REGIS DT7 3RW (01297 443085). A six-berth caravan on Devon/Dorset border overlooking Lyme Bay and surrounding countryside. Situated on a smallholding with animals. Fully equipped. Also fully equipped chalet for two. [🐕]

Milton Abbas

Village 6 miles south-west of Blandford Forum, 1 kilometre north-west of 14/15C Milton Abbey and Milton Abbey boys school.

LITTLE HEWISH BARN, MILTON ABBAS, BLANDFORD FORUM, DORSET DT11 0DP. (01258 881235; Fax: 01258 881393). Converted 150 year old brick and flint barn offering comfortable, very high standard accommodation. Two en suite double bedrooms. Children and well-behaved pets very welcome. ETC ★★★★★ [🐕]
e-mail: terry@littlehewish.co.uk

Piddletrenthide

Village 6 miles north of Dorchester.

THE POACHERS INN, PIDDLETRENTHIDE DT2 7QX (01300 348358; Fax: 01300 348153). On B3143 in lovely Piddle Valley, this delightful Inn offers en suite rooms with colour TV, tea/coffee making, phone. Swimming pool. Restaurant or Bar meals available. Garden – good dog walks! B&B £30.00. ETC/AA ◆◆◆◆. [Pets £2 per night, £10 per week]

Poole

Flourishing port and market town. Three museums with interesting collections and lively displays.

SANDFORD HOLIDAY PARK, WESTSTAR HOLIDAYS (0870 444 0080). Award-winning holiday park near Poole in a beautiful woodland setting and close to safe sandy beaches. Dogs welcome! Quote WP. ETC ★★★★ [Pets £35 per week, pw!]
website: www.weststarholidays.co.uk/pw

Sherborne

Town with abbey and two castles, one of which was built by Sir Walter Raleigh with lakes and gardens by Capability Brown.

WHITE HORSE FARM, MIDDLEMARSH, SHERBORNE DT9 5QN. Toad Hall sleeps 4; Badger's sleeps 2; Ratty's sleeps 2/4; Moley's sleeps 2. Character self-catering holiday cottages in rural location. Well-equipped and comfortable. TV, video, free films. 2 acres of paddock, garden and duck pond. Inn 100 yards. ETC ★★★★. DAVID, HAZEL, MARY AND GERRY WILDING (01963 210222) [🐕]
e-mail: enquiries@whitehorsefarm.co.uk website: www.whitehorsefarm.co.uk

Studland Bay

Unspoilt seaside village at south western end of Poole Bay, 3 miles north of Swanage.

THE KNOLL HOUSE, STUDLAND BH19 3AW (01929 450450; Fax: 01929 450423). Country House Hotel within National Trust reserve. Golden beach. 100 acre grounds. Family suites of connecting rooms, six lounges. Tennis, golf, swimming, games rooms, health spa. Full board terms £97-£130 daily. See our Full Page Advertisement under Studland Bay. [pw! £4 nightly, includes food]
e-mail: enquiries@knollhouse.co.uk website: www.knollhouse.co.uk

THE MANOR HOUSE HOTEL, STUDLAND BAY, DORSET BH19 3AU (Tel & Fax: 01929 450288). National Trust hotel set in 20 acres on cliffs overlooking Studland Bay. Superb food and accommodation. Log fires and four-posters.Tennis, horseriding, golf and walking.
website: www.themanorhousehotel.com

Swanage

Traditional family holiday resort set in a sheltered bay ideal for water sports. Good base for a walking holiday.

FAIRFIELDS HOTEL, STUDLAND BAY, NEAR SWANAGE BH19 3AE (Tel & Fax: 01929 450224). A private hotel, family-owned, at the rural heart of a National Trust Conservation area and Studland Nature Reserve. Short walk to three miles of sandy beach. ETC ◆◆◆◆ [Pets £4 per night].

LIMES HOTEL, 48 PARK ROAD, SWANAGE BH19 2AE (01929 422664; Fax: 0870 0548794). Small friendly Hotel. En suite rooms, TV, tea/coffee making facilities. Licensed bar. Children and pets welcome. Credit cards accepted. Telephone or SAE for brochure. ETC◆◆◆◆ [🐕]
e-mail: info@limeshotel.demon.co.uk website: www.limeshotel.demon.co.uk

DORSET COTTAGE HOLIDAYS. Self-catering cottages, town houses, bungalows and apartments. All within 10 miles of Heritage Coastline and sandy beaches. Excellent walking in idyllic countryside. Short breaks from £105, weekly from £135 (per cottage). Open all year. Free brochure tel: 01929 553443. [🐕]
e-mail: enq@dhcottages.co.uk website: www.dhcottages.co.uk

MRS M. STOCKLEY, SWANAGE BAY VIEW HOLIDAY PARK, 17 MOOR ROAD, SWANAGE BH19 1RG (01929 424154). 4/5/6-berth Caravans. Pets welcome. Easter to October. Colour TV. Shop. Parking space. Rose Award Park [🐕]

Wareham

Picturesque riverside town almost surrounded by earthworks, considered pre-Roman. Nature reserves of great beauty nearby. Weymouth 19 miles, Bournemouth 14, Swanage 10, Poole 6.

MRS L. S. BARNES, LUCKFORD WOOD HOUSE, EAST STOKE, WAREHAM BH20 6AW (01929 463098; Fax: 01929 405715). Spacious, peaceful surroundings, delightful scenery. B&B luxurious farmhouse. Farmhouse breakfast served in conservatory or dining room. Camping facilities include showers, toilets. Near Lulworth Cove, Studland, Tank Museum and Monkey World. Open all year. From £28. [Pets £5 per night, £30 per week]
e-mail: info@luckfordleisure.co.uk website: www.luckfordleisure.co.uk

CATRIONA AND ALISTAIR MILLER, CROMWELL HOUSE HOTEL, LULWORTH COVE BH20 5RJ (01929 400253/400332; Fax: 01929 400566). Comfortable family-run hotel, set in secluded gardens with spectacular sea views. Heated swimming pool, 17 en suite bedrooms. Restaurant, bar wine list. ETC/AA/RAC ★★. [🐕]

DORMER COTTAGE, WOODLANDS AT HYDE, NEAR WAREHAM BH20 7NT (01929 471239). In the midst of Hardy Country, secluded cottage. All linen provided. Golf, pony trekking, riding nearby. Children and pets welcome. Beds ready made. [🐕]

West Bexington

Seaside village with pebble beach. Chesil beach stretches eastwards. Nearby is Abbotsbury with its Benedictine Abbey and famous Swannery. Dorchester 13 miles, Weymouth 13, Bridport 6.

GORSELANDS CARAVAN PARK, DEPT PW, WEST BEXINGTON-ON-SEA DT2 9DJ (01308 897232; Fax: 01308 897239). Holiday Park. Fully serviced and equipped 4/6 berth caravans. Shop and launderette on site. Glorious sea views. Good country and seaside walks. One mile to beach. Holiday apartments with sea views and private garden. Pets most welcome. Colour brochure on request. ETC ★★★★ [🐕]

Weymouth

Set in a beautiful bay with fine beaches and a picturesque 17th-century harbour, Weymouth has a wide range of entertainment and leisure amenities.

DOUBLE THREE GUEST HOUSE, 33 RODWELL ROAD, WEYMOUTH DT4 8QP (01305 786259). Comfortable non-smoking home. Ideal to explore Dorset's beaches and countryside. B&B from £16-£25 pppn. Send for free information. [🐕]
e-mail: doublethree16762@aol.com website: www.doublethree.co.uk

A useful Index of Towns/Villages and Counties appears on page 427 – please also refer to Contents Page 3.

DURHAM

All pets welcome. Plenty of space to exercise pets • 20 en suite rooms including 5 luxury suites Renowned Carvery and A la carte restaurant • Conservatory with games • Licensed bar Mini breaks available all year. • Jersey Farm is family-run by the original owners still with the farm animals in the field. We guarantee a relaxing time in this peaceful and scenic part of England.

Jersey Farm Hotel, Darlington Road, Barnard Castle, Co Durham DL12 8TA
Tel: 01833 638223 Fax: 01833 631988 Website: www.jerseyfarm.co.uk

See also Colour Advertisement on page 42

Low Lands Farm, **Low Lands, Cockfield, Bishop Auckland, County Durham DL13 5AW.**
Tel: 01388 718251 • Mobile: 07745 067754 • e-mail: info@farmholidaysuk.com
website: www.farmholidaysuk.com • Two award-winning, beautifully renovated self-catering cottages on a working family farm. Each cottage sleeps up to four people, plus cot. Beams, log fires, gas BBQ, own gardens and parking. Pets and children most welcome; childminding and equipment available. Terms from £150 to £295, incl. linen, towels, electricity and heating. Call Alison or Keith Tallentire for a brochure. ETC Cat. 3 Disabled Access

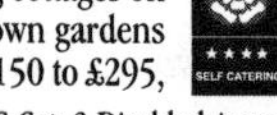

See also Colour Advertisement on page 42

Charming farmhouse with stunning views. You will be most welcome. Ideal for Newcastle, Durham, Beamish etc. Bed and Breakfast;dinner available, licensed. Great for pets.

MELITA & DAVID TURNER, BEE COTTAGE FARMHOUSE, CASTLESIDE, CONSETT DH8 9HW (01207 508224)

e-mail: welcome@beecottagefarmhouse.freeserve.co.uk • web:www.beecottage.co.uk

Ivesley Equestrian Centre

Ivesley, Waterhouses, Durham DH7 9HB. TEL: 0191 373 4324; FAX: 0191 373 4757
e-mail: ivesley@msn.com • website: www.ridingholidays-ivesley.co.uk
Beautifully furnished comfortable country house set in 220 acres in Durham, but very quiet and rural. Excellent dog exercising facilities. En suite bedrooms. Excellent food. Licensed. Fully equipped Equestrian Centre adjacent.

Mrs P. A. Booth

Barnard Castle

Market town with Norman ruins. Bowes museum has forty rooms with paintings by El Greco, Goya and Canaletto

JERSEY FARM HOTEL, DARLINGTON ROAD, BARNARD CASTLE, CO. DURHAM DL12 8TA (01833 638223; Fax: 01833 631988). 20 En suite Rooms, five Luxury Suites. Renowned Carvery Restaurant open seven days. Alternative Menu available. Open all day for meals/drinks. Conservatory with games. Licensed Bar. Mini Breaks available. [pw! Pets £3.50 per night, £15.00 per week]
website: www.jerseyfarm.co.uk

Bishop Auckland

Town on right bank of River Wear, 9 miles south-west of Durham. Castle, of varying dates, residence of the Bishops of Durham.

ALISON & KEITH TALLENTIRE, LOW LANDS FARM, LOW LANDS, COCKFIELD, BISHOP AUCKLAND DL13 5AW (01388 718251; mobile: 07745 067754). Two self-catering cottages on a working livestock farm. Each sleeps up to 4, plus cot. Prices from £150-£295. Call for a brochure. Pets and children most welcome. ETC ★★★★ ETC CATEGORY 3 DISABLED ACCESSIBILITY. [🐕]
e-mail: info@farmholidaysuk.com website: www.farmholidaysuk.com

Please mention Pets Welcome when writing to enquire about accommodation

Castleside

A suburb 2 miles south-west of Consett.

MELITA & DAVID TURNER, BEE COTTAGE FARMOUSE, CASTLESIDE, CONSETT DH8 9HW (01207 508224). Charming farmhouse with stunning views. You will be most welcome. Ideal for Newcastle, Durham, Beamish etc. Bed and Breakfast; dinner available, licensed. Great for pets. ETC ◆◆◆ [🐕]
e-mail: welcome@beecottagefarmhouse.freeserve.co.uk website: www.beecottage.co.uk

Waterhouses

6 miles west of Durham.

MRS P. A. BOOTH, IVESLEY EQUESTRIAN CENTRE, IVESLEY, WATERHOUSES, DURHAM DH7 9HB (0191 373 4324; Fax: 0191 373 4757). Beautifully furnished comfortable country house set in 220 acres in Durham but very quiet and rural. Excellent dog exercising facilities. En suite bedrooms. Excellent food. Licensed. Fully equipped Equestrian Centre adjacent. [Pets £2 per night].
e-mail: ivesley@msn.com website: wwwridingholidays-ivesley.co.uk

ESSEX

Frinton On Sea, Mersea Island, St Lawrence Bay, Weeley (Nr Clacton-on-Sea)

RUSSELL LODGE 47 Hadleigh Road, Frinton on Sea CO13 9HQ • Tel: 01255 675935 • Email: stay@russell-lodge.fsnet.co.uk

Bed and breakfast in Edwardian home, situated near the centre of town, within easy walking of shops, churches, restaurants, inns and the seafront with the famous greensward and Crescent Gardens. Accommodation consists of a double/twin bedroom with en suite facilities. We have a smaller bedroom furnished as a single, however it can be converted to twin or double bed format. This room has private bathroom immediately across landing. Fully-equipped kitchen for self-catering during the day. **Rates £25 per person per night.**

Coopers Beach Holiday Park

ETC★★★

East Mersea, Mersea Island, Near Colchester, Essex CO5 8TN

Charming holiday park on the seafront at Mersea Island. Joined to the mainland by causeway. Modern, well-equipped caravans to hire. Outdoor heated pool, adventure play area, tennis, beach, shop, clubroom with sea views, multi-sports court. Local to park – water sports. Historic Colchester – Zoo, Castle, Shopping.

www.gbholidayparks.co.uk Call **0870 442 9288** for brochure

Waterside Holiday Park

Main Road, St Lawrence Bay, Near Southminster, Essex CM0 7LY

Attractive park situated by the River Blackwater with fine estuary views towards Mersea Island. Modern quality range of hire caravans. Indoor pool, sauna and jacuzzi, outdoor play area, mini-market, café and country club. Local to park – nature reserves, sheltered beach and interesting walks. Tourers and tents welcome.

www.gbholidayparks.co.uk Call **0870 442 9298** for brochure

Weeley Bridge Holiday Park

ETC★★★

Weeley, Near Clacton-on-Sea, Essex CO16 9DH

Small, beautifully maintained park in the heart of Essex Countryside. Modern quality range of hire caravans. Attractive tree-lined fishing lake, mature woodland, outdoor heated pool. Adventure play area, mini-market, restaurant, multi-sports court and licensed bar. Seaside resorts only a short drive away.

www.gbholidayparks.co.uk Call **0870 442 9295** for brochure

Frinton On Sea

Resort adjoining Walton-on-the-Naze to the south west, 5 miles north east of Clacton-on-Sea.

RUSSELL LODGE 47 HADLEIGH ROAD, FRINTON ON SEA CO13 9HQ (01255 675935). Accommodation consists of a double/twin bedroom with en suite facilities. We have a smaller bedroom furnished as a single, however it can be converted to twin or double bed format. Private bathroom. Fully-equipped kitchen. £25 pppns.
e-mail: stay@russell-lodge.fsnet.co.uk

Mersea Island

Winding lanes cross open countryside, joined to mainland by Strood Causeway.

COOPERS BEACH HOLIDAY PARK, EAST MERSEA, MERSEA ISLAND, NEAR COLCHESTER CO5 8TN. Charming seafront holiday park joined to mainland by causeway. Modern, well-equipped caravans to hire. Ideal for water sports – outdoor heated pool, beach, multi-sports court. Call 0870 442 9288 for brochure. ETC ★★★ [🐕]
website: www.gbholidayparks.co.uk

St Lawrence Bay

On the south side of the River Blackmore estuary, 6 miles north of Burnham-on-Crouch.

WATERSIDE HOLIDAY PARK, MAIN ROAD, ST LAWRENCE BAY, NEAR SOUTHMINSTER CM0 7LY. Attractive park with fine estuary views. Modern quality range of hire caravans. Indoor pool; country club; nature reserves; sheltered beach and interesting walks nearby. Tourers and tents welcome. Call 0870 442 9298 for brochure. [🐕]
website: www.gbholidayparks.co.uk

Weeley (Near Clacton-On-Sea)

Village 5 miles north-west of Clacton-on-Sea.

WEELEY BRIDGE HOLIDAY PARK, WEELEY, NEAR CLACTON-ON-SEA CO16 9DH. Small beautifully maintained park in the heart of Essex countryside. Quality range of hire caravans. Fishing lake, outdoor heated pool, adventure play area, restaurant, bar. Short drive to coast. Call 0870 442 9295 for brochure. ETC ★★★ [🐕]
website: www.gbholidayparks.co.uk

Bourton-on-the-Water, Cheltenham

This charming 13th Century farmhouse hotel, in its own extensive grounds (14 acres), is ideal for dog walking. The Hotel is situated in the village of Clearwell in the Forest of Dean and close to the Wye Valley. Twenty-two en suite bedrooms including Four-Posters and Cottage Suite. The award-winning restaurant serves a selection of traditional food and a comprehensive wine list. B&B from £75 per room.

Tudor Farmhouse Hotel & Restaurant, Clearwell, Near Coleford GL16 8JS
• Tel: 01594 833046 • E-mail: info@tudorfarmhousehotel.co.uk • WTB ★★★

See colour advertisement on page 43

ETC ★★

The Bull Hotel

The Market Place, Fairford, Gloucestershire GL7 4AA
Tel: 01285 712535/712217 • Fax: 01285 713782
e-mail: info@thebullhotelfairford.co.uk
website: www.thebullhotelfairford.co.uk

AA ★★

15th century family-run coaching inn. Ideal for touring Cotswolds. A la carte restaurant situated in original stables. Ideal for conferences and weddings. 1½ miles private fishing on River Coln. The hotel has a choice of 22 fully equipped bedrooms with sloping roofs and oak beams. Four-poster beds available. There are good golf courses, squash and tennis courts, sailing facilities and fishing within easy reach of the hotel. Situated in the South Cotswolds. **Tariff: £49.50 - £89.50**

GUNN MILL HOUSE
Forest of Dean
Gloucestershire GL17 OEA

Tel & Fax: 01594 827577

E-mail: info@gunnmillhouse.co.uk Website: www.gunnmillhouse.co.uk

The Lucas family invite you, and your owners, to stay in their Georgian home and 5 acre grounds right in the forest – walks galore! Antiques, a roaring log fire, old-fashioned luxury, with all en suite rooms and suites. First-class home cooked dinners. Licensed. Non-smoking.

Bed & Breakfast £50–£80 per couple. Pets £7.50 per stay.

The Laurels at Inchbrook

Mrs Lesley Williams-Allen, The Laurels at Inchbrook
Nailsworth GL5 5HA Tel & Fax: 01453 834021
e-mail: laurels@inchbrook.fsnet.co.uk

A lovely rambling licensed house and cottage, where dogs and their owners are encouraged to relax and enjoy. All rooms are en suite and include family, twin and double rooms, each with colour TV and hospitality trays. There is wheelchair access and a ground floor room suitable for disabled guests. We have a ground floor panelled lounge full of interesting books and a piano, and on the top floor a games room. Smoking is not allowed (except in the courtyard and garden). The secluded streamside garden with parking backs onto fields and offers a swimming pool and the opportunity to observe wildlife. We are ideally situated for touring all parts of the Cotswolds and West Country, surrounded by a wealth of beautiful countryside, first-class restaurants and pubs, and all kinds of activities. Children and pets welcome. Non-smoking. Bed and Breakfast from £21 per person. Credit cards accepted. Dinner by arrangement. Brochure on request. RAC ♦♦♦

SWAN HOUSE COUNTRY GUEST HOUSE

Tel: 01594 516504
Fax: 01594 516177

Philip and Elaine extend a warm welcome to our family guesthouse in the village of Newnham near the Forest of Dean. Our 17th century house has six bedrooms, all individually decorated and en suite, with many comforts including electric blankets. There is a choice of evening meals; most dietary needs can be catered for. We have a carefully tended garden which we are happy to share with you. Pets are welcome.

High Street, Newnham-on-Severn, Gloucs GL14 1BY AA ♦♦♦♦
e-mail: enquiries@swanhousenewnham.co.uk • website: www.swanhousenewnham.co.uk

Established over 30 years AA/RAC ◆◆◆

Large Country House with attractive garden, overlooking fields. Four minutes to town centre. One four-poster bedroom; double, twin or family rooms, all en suite. Tea/coffee making facilities, colour TV in all rooms. TV lounge. Central heating. Children and pets welcome. Car park. Bed and Full English Breakfast from £20.00 to £25.00 pppn. Open all year except Christmas.

THE LIMES **Evesham Road, Stow-on-the-Wold, GL54 1EN**
Tel: 01451 830034/831056 • e-mail: thelimes@zoom.co.uk

Mr & Mrs J E Taylor, Court Farm, Randwick, Stroud GL6 6HH.
Tel: 01453 764210 Fax: 01453 766428

A 17th Century beamed Farmhouse, with large, en suite rooms, centre of hillside village of Randwick. Beautiful views over Stroud Valleys. A stream divides the fields with a large, pretty garden for guests to enjoy. Village pub food. Tourist attractions are Westonbirt Arboretum, Gloucester Waterways, Berkeley Castle. B & B prices from £20 to £22; Evening meal can be provided. **e-mail: johnetaylor@courfarm.freeserve.co.uk**

Attention All Dog Lovers!

Romantic 18th century Coach House in the heart of the beautiful Cotswold Hills. Sleeps 4 adults and 2 children. Beams, wood-burners, outdoor heated swimming pool, and bubbling Hot Tub. Hillside garden and 20 acres of woodland. Free private kennel facilities (optional). Breaks £115 - £550. Also Pear Tree Cottage close to 600 acres N.T. Common. Sleeps 4 plus child. Luxurious outdoor Jacuzzi. £120 - £300. Colour brochure from Ros Smith.

The Old Coach House, Edgecombe House, Toadsmoor Road, Brimscombe, Stroud GL5 2UE Tel: 01453 883147

See also Colour Advertisement on page 43

Dear Rover, *Well, we've just got back from our holidays – absolute bliss and what a lovely place the Downfield is – we got a really warm welcome from the owners. Great walks in the Cotswolds, comfy rooms, a bar, delicious food and the Joneses I brought with me were really pleased as well. I made lots of new friends – there were even some cats to chase! Why don't you come with me next year and bring your owners with you – Just call Nigel or Maura on the dog and bone on* **01453 764496** **The Downfield Hotel, 134 Cainscross Road,**
Lots of licks, Toby **ETC/AA/RAC ◆◆◆** **Stroud, Gloucestershire GL5 4HN**

See also Colour Advertisement on page 43

SYMONDS YAT ROCK
LODGE

SYMONDS YAT ROCK LODGE

Motel-style accommodation in perfect location for walking and relaxing.
Rural situation with forest tracks directly opposite hotel giving easy access to Wye Valley, Forest of Dean and stunning views from Symonds Yat Rock.
Canoeing, climbing, horse riding and cycle tracks all close by.
Accommodation is comfortable and smart and the welcome is friendly in this small family-run hotel. Rooms are all en suite and on the ground floor, directly accessed from the car park.
6 berth static caravan with wonderful views also on site and available for hire.
4-poster and family rooms available.
Most of our guests come with their dogs and come back time and again.
Come and see for yourself!

HILLERSLAND NEAR COLEFORD GL16 7NY
TEL: 01594 836191
e-mail: info@rocklodge.co.uk
website: www.rocklodge.co.uk

POWELLS COTTAGE HOLIDAYS, 51 HIGH STREET, SAUNDERSFOOT, PEMBROKESHIRE SA69 9EJ. Many of our top quality holiday properties accept pets. Cottages in Devon, Cornwall, Cotswolds, Pembrokeshire and Heart of England. For colour brochure FREEPHONE 0800 378771 (24 hours).
website: www.powells.co.uk

Bourton-on-the-Water

Delightfully situated on the River Windrush which is crossed by minature stone bridges. Stow-on-the-Wold 4 miles.

CHESTER HOUSE HOTEL, VICTORIA STREET, BOURTON-ON-THE-WATER GL54 2BU (01451 820286; FREEPHONE 0800 0199577). Personally supervised by proprietors Clive & Tina Brooks. All rooms en suite, all with central heating, colour TV, phone, tea/coffee making facilities. Wheelchair friendly. Ideal for touring Cotswolds. [🐕]
e-mail: kingsbridgeinn.bourtononthewater@eldridge-pope.co.uk
website: www.chesterhouse.u-net.com or book on-line at www.roomattheinn.info

Cheltenham

Anglo-Saxon market town transformed into elegant Regency resort with the discovery of medicinal springs. 8 miles east of Gloucester.

CHARLTON KINGS HOTEL, LONDON ROAD, CHELTENHAM GL52 6UU (01242 231061; Fax: 01242 241900). Ideal venue for Cheltenham and the Cotswolds. Double en suite room from £47.50 per person for 1 night, £42.50 per person for 3 nights or £38.00 for 5 nights including full English breakfast. All rooms beautifully refurbished, most have views of the Cotswold Hills. We offer a standard of service only a small hotel can provide. [Pets £3 per night]. ETC/AA/RAC ★★★
e-mail: enquiries@charltonkingshotel.co.uk website: www.charltonkingshotel.co.uk

Clearwell (Forest of Dean)

Village 2 miles south of Coleford in the ancient Forest of Dean.

TUDOR FARMHOUSE HOTEL & RESTAURANT, CLEARWELL, NEAR COLEFORD GL16 8JS (Freephone 0800 7835935; Tel: 01594 833046; Fax: 01594 837093). Charming 13th Century farmhouse hotel in extensive grounds, ideal for dog walking. 22 en suite bedrooms including Four Posters and Cottage Suite. Award-winning restaurant. WTB ★★★, AA ★★ and Rosette. [🐕]
e-mail: info@tudorfarmhousehotel.co.uk website: www.tudorfarmhousehotel.co.uk

Fairford

Small town 8 miles east of Cirencester.

THE BULL HOTEL, MARKET PLACE, FAIRFORD GL7 4AA (01285 712535/712217; Fax: 01285 713782). Ideal for holding conferences and wedding receptions. Restaurant offers à la carte menu and fine wines. The hotel has a choice of 22 fully equipped bedrooms with sloping roofs and oak beams. Four-poster beds available. ETC/AA ★★ [Pets £5 per night, £20 per week]
e-mail: info@thebullhotelfairford.co.uk website: www.thebullhotelfairford.co.uk

PLEASE MENTION THIS GUIDE WHEN YOU WRITE OR PHONE TO ENQUIRE ABOUT ACCOMMODATION.

IF YOU ARE WRITING, A STAMPED, ADDRESSED ENVELOPE IS ALWAYS APPRECIATED.

Forest of Dean

Formerly a royal hunting ground, this scenic area lies between the rivers Severn and Wye.

DRYSLADE FARM, ENGLISH BICKNOR, COLEFORD (Tel & Fax: 01594 860259). Daphne and Phil warmly welcome you and your dogs for B&B at their 18th century farmhouse on family working farm. Situated in Royal Forest of Dean and close to Symonds Yat with ample walking. Excellent breakfast. Terms from £22 - £25. ETC ◆◆◆◆, MOBILITY LEVEL 1.
website: www.drysladefarm.co.uk

GUNN MILL HOUSE COUNTRY GUEST HOUSE, LOWER SPOUT LANE, MITCHELDEAN GL17 0EA (Tel & Fax: 01594 827577). Eight individually designed rooms including four-poster and suites with direct access to 5-acre garden and Forest of Dean. All en suite, TV. Fine dining. Licensed. Large gardens and 5 acres of fields. [pw! Pets £7.50 per stay]. SEE DISPLAY ADVERT.
e-mail: info@gunnmillhouse.co.uk website: www.gunnmillhouse.co.uk

Nailsworth

Hilly town 4 miles south of Stroud

LESLEY WILLIAMS-ALLEN, THE LAURELS, INCHBROOK, NAILSWORTH GL5 5HA (Tel & Fax: 01453 834021). A lovely rambling licensed house and cottage, where dogs and their owners are encouraged to relax and enjoy. Ideally situated for touring all parts of the Cotswolds and West Country. Brochure. B&B from £21. Credit cards accepted. RAC ◆◆◆ [🐕]
e-mail: laurels@inchbrook.fsnet.co.uk

Newnham-on-Severn

Town on right bank on River Severn, 10 miles south-west of Gloucester.

PHILIP AND ELAINE SHELDRAKE, SWAN HOUSE COUNTRY GUEST HOUSE, HIGH STREET, NEWNHAM-ON-SEVERN GL14 1BY (01594 516504). Family guest house near Forest of Dean. Six individually decorated bedrooms, all en suite, with many comforts. Choice of evening meal. Garden. Pets welcome. Stabling available in village. AA ◆◆◆◆ [Pets £5 per week]
e-mail: enquiries@swanhousenewnham.co.uk website: www.swanhousenewnham.co.uk

Painswick

Beautiful little Cotswold town with characteristic stone-built houses.

MISS E. COLLETT, HAMBUTTS MYND, EDGE ROAD, PAINSWICK GL6 6UP (01452 812352; Fax: 01452 813862). Bed and Breakfast in an old Converted Corn Mill. Very quiet with superb views. Three minutes to the centre of the village. Central heating. One double room, one twin, one single, all with TV. From £29 to £53 per night per room. ALL ROOMS EN SUITE. RAC/TBC ◆◆◆. [🐕]
e-mail: ewarland@aol.com

Stow-on-the-Wold

Charming Cotswold hill-top market town with several old inns and interesting buildings. Birmingham 45 miles, Gloucester 26, Stratford-upon-Avon 21, Cheltenham 18, Chipping Norton 9.

THE LIMES, EVESHAM ROAD, STOW-ON-THE-WOLD GL54 1EN (01451 830034/831056). Large Country House. Attractive garden, overlooking fields, 4 minutes town centre. Television lounge. Central heating. Car park. Bed and Breakfast from £20 to £25.00 pppn. Twin, double or family rooms, all en suite. Children and pets welcome. AA/RAC ◆◆◆, Tourist Board Listed. [🐕]
e-mail: thelimes@zoom.co.uk

Stroud

Cotswold town on River Frome below picturesque Stroudwater Hills, formerly renowned for cloth making. Bristol 32 miles, Bath 29, Chippenham 25, Cheltenham 14, Gloucester 9.

MRS A. RHOTON, HYDE CREST, CIRENCESTER ROAD, MINCHINHAMPTON GL6 8PE (01453 731631). Beautiful country house with enclosed acre garden. All rooms on ground floor opening on to patios and lawns. 500 acres of commons, plus country walks nearby. AA ◆◆◆◆ [🐕]
e-mail: hydecrest@compuserve.com website: http://www.hydecrest.co.uk

TOM AND LESLEY WILLIAMS, ORCHARDENE, CASTLE ST, KINGS STANLEY, STONEHOUSE GL10 3JA (01453 822684; Fax: 01453 821554). Warm welcome at Cotswold Stone cottage. Seven minutes J13 M5. Ideal location to explore undiscovered Cotswolds and Severn Vale. Glorious walks. B&B from £20. Evening Meal optional. Organic and local food. [🐕]
e-mail: toranda@btopenworld.com

MR & MRS J. E. TAYLOR, COURT FARM, RANDWICK, STROUD GL6 6HH (01453 764210; Fax: 01453 766428). A 17th century beamed Farmhouse on working farm. Much of our food produced organically. Large garden. Abundant wildlife. Children and pets welcome. [🐕]
e-mail: johnetaylor@courfarm.freeserve.co.uk

Enchanting Coach House. Hillside garden and woodlands. Sleeps 4 adults, 2 children. Beams, wood-burners, swimming pool and hot tub. Breaks £115 - £550. Second cottage also available. Sleeps 4 plus child. Colour brochure: MRS R SMITH, EDGECOMBE HOUSE, TOADSMOOR ROAD, STROUD GL5 2UE (01453 883147). [pw!🐕 ⌂]

DOWNFIELD HOTEL, CAINSCROSS ROAD, STROUD GL5 4HN (01453 764496). Easy to find – just 5 miles from M5 – and easy to park. Ideal location for exploring Cotswolds. Comfortable lounges, home-cooked evening meal, cosy bar – all at sensible prices. Dogs and children most welcome. ETC/AA/RAC ◆◆◆. [🐕]
e-mail: info@downfieldhotel.co.uk website: www.downfieldhotel.co.uk

Symonds Yat

Popular beauty spot on River Wye, 4 miles north-east of Monmouth.

SYMONDS YAT ROCK LODGE, HILLERSLAND, NEAR COLEFORD GL16 7NY (01594 836191). Family-run Lodge in Royal Forest of Dean near Wye Valley. All rooms en suite, colour TV. 4 poster and family rooms. Brochure available on request. Dogs welcome. [🐕]
e-mail: info@rocklodge.co.uk website: www.rocklodge.co.uk

SYMBOLS

- **🐕 Indicates that pets are welcome free of charge.**
- **£ Indicates that a charge is made for pets: nightly or weekly.**
- **pw! Shows some special provision for pets; exercise facility, feeding or accommodation arrangement.**
- **⌂ Indicates separate pets accommodation.**

THE WOODLANDS LODGE HOTEL

Bartley Road, Woodlands, New Forest, Hampshire SO40 7GN

AA ✿✿ AA ★★★ **Reservations: (023) 80 292257** ETC ★★★

Fax: (023) 80 293090

e-mail: reception@woodlands-lodge.co.uk • website: www.woodlands-lodge.co.uk

RELAXATION, COMFORT AND TRANQUILLITY

The Woodlands Lodge Hotel is a luxuriously restored Georgian Country House, set within the beautiful New Forest, yet only 15 minutes from Southampton. This former hunting lodge has been totally refurbished and offers guests comfort, peace and tranquillity.

Our attractive gardens, set in three acres, have direct access to the forest, and are ideal for romantic walks. Golf, fishing and horse riding are available nearby and the hotel is perfectly situated for touring the area. Come and unwind from the stress of everyday life and enjoy pure luxury without ostentation.

All bedrooms enjoy full en suite facilities of whirlpool bath and separate shower and have king-size beds, 21" TV with satellite channels, hairdryer, trouser press, tea/coffee making facilities and direct-dial telephone. Some rooms have features including real flame fire, four-poster bed, balcony, and Forest views. The service is friendly, efficient and informal.

Our four-course menu, served in the elegant dining room, is changed seasonally to make use of fresh local produce and has two AA Rosettes for excellence. The menu is complemented by an interesting and reasonably priced wine list.

Woodlands Lodge is dog and cat friendly. The Hotel also has a paddock should you wish to bring your horse.

See also Colour Advertisement on page 43

ETC/AA ★★★ **WHITLEY RIDGE COUNTRY HOUSE HOTEL**

Beaulieu Road, Brockenhurst SO42 7QL Tel: 01590 622354 Fax: 01590 622856

Beautiful Georgian Hotel in 5 acres of secluded grounds with direct access to Forest. Guests with pets can walk freely along the river banks and through woodlands. 14 delightful bedrooms, all en suite; cosy bar, splendid dining room. Superb cuisine, friendly and efficient service. The Ideal Hotel for those who love the freedom to explore the New Forest and the many other interesting attractions in the area.

Efford Cottage

Everton, Lymington, Hampshire SO41 0JD

Tel: 01590 642315 • Fax: 01590 641030

e-mail: effordcottage@aol.com • web: www.effordcottage.co.uk

Guests receive a warm and friendly welcome to our home, which is a spacious Georgian cottage. All rooms are en suite with many extra luxury facilities. We offer a four-course multi-choice breakfast with homemade bread and preserves. Patricia is a qualified chef and uses our home-grown produce. An excellent centre for exploring both the New Forest and the South Coast with sports facilities, fishing, bird watching and horse riding in the near vicinity. Private parking. Dogs welcome. Sorry no children. *Bed and Breakfast from £25–£35 pppn. Mrs Patricia J. Ellis.*

RAC Sparkling Diamond & Warm Welcome Accolades

STB Winner of " England For Excellence 2000"

RAC/AA/STB ◆◆◆◆◆ Gold Award. STB member with Welcome Host. FHG Diploma 1997/1999/2000

AA Nominated Landlady of Year 1998 & nominated Best British Breakfast Award 1999 & 2001.

AA ◆◆◆◆ Guest Accommodation **Harts Lodge** **242 Everton Road, Everton, Lymington, Hampshire S041OHE**

Bungalow (non-smoking), set in three acres. Large garden with small lake. Quiet location. Three miles west of Lymington. Friendly welcome. Double, twin and family en suite rooms, each with tea/coffee making facilities and colour TV. Delicious four-course English breakfast. The sea and forest are five minutes away by car. Horse riding, golf and fishing are nearby. The village pub, ½ mile serves excellent meals. Pets welcome. Bed and Breakfast from £25 per person.

Tel: 01590 645902

"DOLPHINS" is a very caring and homely Victorian cottage in a quiet location, Central Lymington, offering warm hospitality and highest standards of accommodation. Ground floor twin or king-size en suite room available, with small garden and own access leading to beautiful park to exercise pets within 2 minutes' walk. Also single, twin, double/family rooms, all with colour TV and tea/coffee making facilities. Very close to beautiful New Forest and Sea Walks. Just 5 minutes from railway/bus/coach stations and ferry. B&B from £18-£29 pppn; Children half price. Pets FREE. Leisure club facilities, beach chalet & mountain bikes if required. **ETC ◆◆◆◆ Welcome Host.**

Contact: Jane & Mike Finch, "Dolphins", 6 Emsworth Road, Lymington SO41 9BL Tel & Fax: 01590 676108
Mobile 07958 727536 • E-mail: dolphins@easynet.co.uk • Website: www.dolphinsnewforestbandb.co.uk

★★★ CROWN HOTEL • NEW FOREST ★★★

Tired of the same old walks? Enjoy forest, heath and the beach whilst staying at The Crown Hotel. 38 en suite rooms, all individual and recently refurbished. Our Chef of 30 years at The Crown, Stephen Greenhalgh, delights us with his imaginative menus using local produce wherever possible either in the informal bar or the Restaurant overlooking our water featured garden. Dogs are welcome to bring their well behaved owners!

High Street, LYNDHURST, Hampshire SO43 7NF

Tel: 023 8028 2922 • Fax: 023 8028 2751

E-mail: reception@crownhotel-lyndhurst.co.uk • Web: www.crownhotel-lyndhurst.activehotels.com

See also Colour Advertisement on page 44

Readers are requested to mention this guidebook when seeking accommodation (and please enclose a stamped addressed envelope).

AA ★★

ORMONDE HOUSE HOTEL

SOUTHAMPTON ROAD, LYNDHURST, HAMPSHIRE SO43 7BT

TEL: (023) 8028 2806 • FAX: (023) 8028 2004

E-mail: info@ormondehouse.co.uk • Website: www.ormondehouse.co.uk

Elegant luxury at affordable prices in England's historic New Forest. Set back from the road this family run Two Star Hotel is situated opposite the open forest, ideal for easy walking. 19 pretty en suite rooms and four luxury self-contained suites all with colour TV, phone and beverage making. 'Super luxury' rooms and 'suites' have whirlpool baths and super king sized beds; with suites, in addition, having full kitchens with washing/drying machines and dishwashers. Dine with us - our chefs have an excellent reputation amongst regular guests for their freshly prepared dishes, daily changing specials and wickedly tempting puddings. Close to Exbury Gardens and Beaulieu Motor Museum. Special 3 and 4 night breaks available throughout the year.

B&B from £30 pppn; DB&B from £45 pppn.

ST. URSULA ◆◆◆◆

30 Hobart Road, New Milton, Hants. BH25 6EG

Between sea and New Forest, comfortable family home. Excellent facilities & warm welcome for well behaved pets and owners. Ground floor suite suitable for disabled guests plus single and twin rooms.

Mrs Judith Pearce **B&B from £24** **Tel: 01425 613515**

COTTAGE BED & BREAKFAST AT APPLEDORE

Holmsley Road, Wotton, New Milton, Hants, BH25 5TR

Tel: 01425 629506 • Mobile: 07773 527626

This graciously decorated New Forest Cottage is presented by myself, Mariette and my husband Trevor, whose home cooked breakfasts are a veritable joy, served in the conservatory overlooking the garden. Our Cottage is located in the heart of the New Forest where you can enjoy all the verdant tranquil beauty and step back in time as you traverse the leafy glades. Take care to observe the spectacular wildlife in their natural environment. There are many local pubs and restaurants which will happily welcome your pet. For pets and families alike we offer a warm and friendly welcome. All en suite rooms, Tea/Coffee making facilities, TV, Towels and Toiletries.

FREE or REDUCED RATE entry to Holiday Visits and Attractions
– see our READERS' OFFER VOUCHERS on pages 103-118

Ashurst

Three miles north-east of Lyndhurst.

WOODLANDS LODGE HOTEL, BARTLEY ROAD, ASHURST,WOODLANDS SO40 7GN (Tel: (023) 80 292257; Fax: (023) 80 293090). Luxury Hotel offering peace and tranquillity. 16 bedrooms, all en suite with whirlpool bath, TV, hairdryer, telephone etc. AA Award winning Restaurant. Direct access to Forest. Stables available. ETC/AA★★★ [🐕]
e-mail: reception@woodlands-lodge.co.uk website: www.woodlands-lodge.co.uk

Brockenhurst

Popular village surrounded by National Trust land. Southampton 10 miles, Lyndhurst 6.

WHITLEY RIDGE COUNTRY HOUSE HOTEL, BEAULIEU ROAD, BROCKENHURST SO42 7QL (01590 622354; Fax: 01590 622856). Georgian Hotel set in 5 acres of secluded grounds. 14 bedrooms, all en suite, cosy bar and splendid dining room. Superb cuisine, friendly and efficient service. Ideally located for the New Forest. ETC/AA ★★★ [Pets £4 per night, £20 per week]

Lymington

Residential town and yachting centre 15 miles east of Bournemouth.

HONEYSUCKLE HOUSE, 24 CLINTON ROAD, LYMINGTON SO41 9EA (Tel & Fax: 01590 676635). Ground floor double room, en suite, non-smoking. Woodland walk, park, quay and marinas nearby. B&B from £23 pppn. [🐕]
e-mail: derekfarrell1@btow

MRS P. J. ELLIS, EFFORD COTTAGE, EVERTON, LYMINGTON SO41 0JD (Tel & Fax: 01590 642315; Fax: 01590 641030). Friendly, award-winning Georgian cottage standing in grounds of one acre. Excellent centre for New Forest and South Coast. All rooms en suite with luxury facilities. B&B from £25 - £35pppn. No children. RAC/AA/STB ◆◆◆◆◆. [Pets £2 per night.]
e–mail: effordcottage@aol.com website: www.effordcottage.co.uk

MRS R SQUE, HARTS LODGE, 242 EVERTON ROAD, LYMINGTON SO41 0HE (01590 645902). Bungalow (non-smoking), set in three acres. Accommodation comprising double, twin and family en suite rooms, each with tea/coffee making facilities and colour TV. Horse riding, golf and fishing are nearby. Pets welcome. AA ◆◆◆◆. [Pets £2 per night, £10 per week].

MRS J. FINCH, "DOLPHINS", 6 EMSWORTH ROAD, LYMINGTON SO41 9BL (Tel & Fax: 01590 676108; Mobile: 07958 727536). Single, twin, double and family rooms all with colour TV and tea/coffee making facilities; ground floor en suite available. Leisure facilities, beach chalet & mountain bikes. Doggy-bed provided if required. Very close to New Forest and sea walks. Park two minutes' walk. Please write or telephone for brochure. ETC ◆◆◆◆ Welcome Host. [🐕]
e-mail: dolphins@easynet.co.uk website: www.dolphinsnewforestbandb.co.uk

Lyndhurst

Good base for enjoying the fascinating New Forest as well as the Hampshire coastal resorts. Bournemouth 20 miles, Southampton 9.

THE CROWN HOTEL, LYNDHURST, NEW FOREST S043 7NF (023 8028 2922; Fax: 023 8028 2751). A mellow, listed building in the centre of the village, an ideal base for exploring the delights of the New Forest with your canine friend(s). Free parking, quiet garden, three star luxury and animal loving staff. [Pets £5.00 per night].
e-mail: reception@crownhotel-lyndhurst.co.uk
website: www.crownhotel-lyndhurst.activehotels.com

ORMONDE HOUSE HOTEL, SOUTHAMPTON ROAD, LYNDHURST SO43 7BT (023 8028 2806, Fax: 023 8028 2004). Opposite open forest, easy drive to Exbury Gardens and Beaulieu. Pretty en suite rooms with colour TV, phone and beverage making. Super lux rooms and suites with whirlpool baths and kingsize beds. Bar, lounge and delicious dinners available. Free room upgrade on 4-night midweek D, B&B bookings. AA ★★. [Pets £3.50 per night, max. 2 per room]
e-mail: info@ormondehouse.co.uk website: www.ormondehouse.co.uk

New Forest

Area of heath and woodland of nearly 150 square miles, formerly Royal hunting grounds.

Luxury 2-bedroomed residential-type caravan. Sleeps 4/6. Maintained to high standard, full kitchen, bathroom, sitting/diningroom, own garden. Idyllic setting in heart of New Forest. Non-smoking, ample parking. Children over 5 years. £165-£285 Easter to mid-October. Well behaved dogs welcome. MRS E. MATTHEWS, THE ACORNS, OGDENS, NEAR FORDINGBRIDGE SP6 2PY (01425 655552) [Pets £10 per week]
e-mail: acornshols@btopenworld.com website: www.acornshols.btinternet.co.uk

THE WATERSPLASH HOTEL, THE RISE, BROCKENHURST SO42 7ZP. Prestigious New Forest family-run country house hotel set in large garden. Noted for fine personal service, accommodation and traditional English cuisine at its best. All rooms en suite. Luxury 4 poster with double spa bath. Swimming pool. RAC, AA ★★. Colour brochure available (01590 622344).[🐕]
e-mail: bookings@watersplash.co.uk website: www.watersplash.co.uk

MRS J. PEARCE, ST. URSULA, 30 HOBART ROAD, NEW MILTON BH25 6EG (01425 613515). Excellent facilities and warm welcome for well behaved pets and owners! Ground floor suite suitable for disabled guests, plus single and twin rooms. Bed & Breakfast from £24. ◆◆◆◆ [🐕]

GORSE COTTAGE, BALMER LAWN ROAD, BROCKENHURST. Cottage/bungalow on open forest road close to the village in the New Forest. Beautifully decorated and appointed, sleeps 4 in 2 bedrooms. Conservatory, luxury bathroom, log fire, televisions/video, secluded sunny garden. Pets Welcome. Contact: MR J. GILBERT (0870 3210020) or website for details. ETC ★★★★★ [Pets £15 per week]
e-mail: info@gorsecottage.co.uk website: www.gorsecottage.co.uk

New Milton

Located 5 miles west of Lymington.

COTTAGE BED & BREAKFAST, APPLEDORE, HOLMSLEY ROAD, WOOTON, NEW MILTON BH25 5TR (01425 629506; mobile: 07773 527626). Graciously decorated cottage in the heart of New Forest. Enjoy the spectacular wildlife. All rooms en suite with tea/coffee making facilities and TV. [🐕]

Portsmouth

Historic port and naval base, with Nelson's flagship HMS Victory in harbour.

Quality 2-star accommodation with a superb sea front location. Good walking! All rooms en suite, etc. Passenger lift, licensed bar/restaurant, car park. Contact: MARK & JENNY BRUNNING, THE SEACREST HOTEL, 12 SOUTH PARADE, SOUTHSEA, PORTSMOUTH PO5 2JB (02392 733192; Fax: 02392 832523). AA ★★ 70%.
e-mail: seacrest@boltblue.com website: www.seacresthotel.co.uk

PLEASE NOTE

All the information in this book is given in good faith in the belief that it is correct. However, the publishers cannot guarantee the facts given in these pages, neither are they responsible for changes in policy, ownership or terms that may take place after the date of going to press. Readers should always satisfy themselves that the facilities they require are available and that the terms, if quoted, still apply.

Sway

Village in southern part of New Forest and within easy reach of sea. Lymington 4 miles south east.

MRS THELMA ROWE, 9 CRUSE CLOSE, SWAY SO41 6AY (Tel & Fax: 01590 683092). Ground floor and first floor suites. Both en suite with sitting room, tea making facilities, fridge, TV and video. Quiet, very comfortable, friendly accommodation. ETC ◆◆◆ [pets £2 per night]
e-mail: ronrowe@talk21.com website: www.tivertonnewforest.co.uk

MRS H.J. BEALE, HACKNEY PARK, MOUNT PLEASANT LANE, SWAY, LYMINGTON SO41 8LS (01590 682049). Coach House and two apartments in commanding and tranquil setting adjoining the New Forest. Superb walking, riding and driving country. Many interesting places nearby. Excellent stabling/grazing.

Winchester

Site of an old Roman town. Ancient capital of Wessex and of England. Notable cathedral, famous boys' public school, a wealth of old and historic buildings.

THE WINCHESTER ROYAL HOTEL, ST PETER STREET, WINCHESTER SO23 8BS (01962 840840; Fax: 01962 841582). Quality Hotel of character quietly located in the heart of England's Ancient Capital. All rooms en suite with satellite TV, tea and coffee making facilities, direct-dial telephone, etc. Easy access to Hotel's large private walled garden. Two-Day Break, Half Board from £136. AA/RAC ★★★ [Pets £10 per night, including doggy dinner.]

HEREFORDSHIRE

Docklow, Hereford

NICHOLSON FARM HOLIDAYS

DOCKLOW, LEOMINSTER HR6 0SL

Self-catering properties on a working dairy farm. Beautiful views. Wide choice of restaurants and bar meals in the area. Supermarket 10 minutes. Excellent walking, golf, riding, carp fishing available on the farm, swimming and tennis 10 mins. Dogs are welcome but must not remain in during the owner's absence. Non-smoking.

Mrs J. Brooke Tel: 01568 760346

Church Farm

Coddington, Ledbury HR8 1JJ Tel: 01531 640271

Black and White listed farmhouse on working farm in quiet hamlet. Oak beamed accommodation in two double and one twin. Close to Malvern Hills. Ideal touring being equidistant Ross-on-Wye, Hereford, Worcester and Gloucester. Plenty of space and fields for dogs to run. Warm hospitality assured in quiet, relaxed atmosphere. Plenty of good English fare – evening meals if required. Log fires, TV.

website:www.dexta.co.uk

Holly House Farm

Allensmore, Hereford HR2 9BH

Tel: 01432 277294, Fax: 01432 261285

Mrs Diana Sinclair

Our luxury farmhouse is situated in beautiful and peaceful open countryside, yet only five minutes from Hereford city centre. Bedrooms are double or twin ensuite or private bathrooms with central heating, TV, tea and coffee making facilities. All pets are welcome and your dog can either sleep in your bedroom or in a stable. Should you wish to leave your dog here for the day whilst you go out, your dog can be looked after for you. Bridleways and footpaths are close to our house.

e-mail: hollyhousefarm@aol.com • website: www.hollyhousefarm.org.uk

THE STEPPES

Ullingswick, Near Hereford HR1 3JG
Tel: 01432 820424
Fax: 01432 820042
Website: www.steppeshotel.co.uk
E-mail: info@steppeshotel.co.uk

Resident Owners:
Henry and Tricia Howland

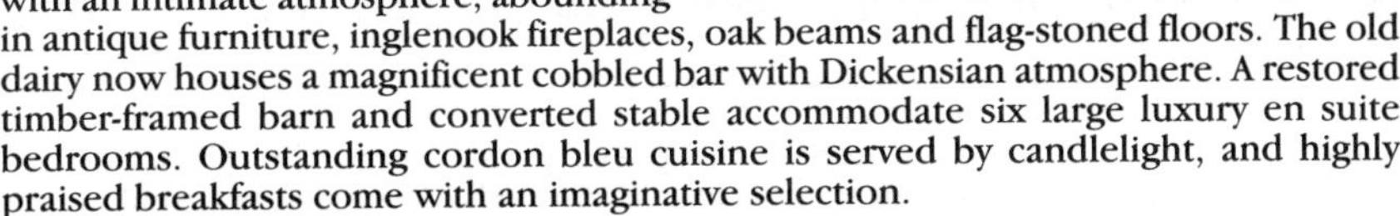

"The Steppes" is an award-winning hotel with an intimate atmosphere, abounding in antique furniture, inglenook fireplaces, oak beams and flag-stoned floors. The old dairy now houses a magnificent cobbled bar with Dickensian atmosphere. A restored timber-framed barn and converted stable accommodate six large luxury en suite bedrooms. Outstanding cordon bleu cuisine is served by candlelight, and highly praised breakfasts come with an imaginative selection.

Set in the tiny hamlet of Ullingswick in the Wye Valley, this is an excellent centre for visiting many areas of natural beauty and points of historic interest. It is ideal walking country being within easy reach of the Malvern Hills and Black Mountains.

Leisure breaks from £60 per person per night to include breakfast, dinner and en suite bedroom. The Steppes is a non-smoking hotel.

ETC ◆◆◆◆◆ Silver Award
"Which" County Hotel of the Year 1994
Johansens Most Excellent Value Hotel 1996.

Mocktree Barns Holiday Cottages

ETC ★★★

A small group of barns offering comfortable self-catering accommodation around sunny courtyard. • Well-equipped, sleeping between two and six. • Friendly owners. • Open all year. • Short breaks available • Pets and children welcome. Lovely views, excellent walks • Direct access to footpaths through farmland and woods. • Hereford, Cider Country, Shropshire Hills, Shrewsbury, Ironbridge and the splendid mid-Wales countryside all an easy drive away. • Beautiful Ludlow seven miles. • Guided Walks/tours arranged. • Golf, fishing, cycling nearby.

Colour brochure from Clive and Cynthia Prior, Mocktree Barns, Leintwardine, Ludlow SY7 OLY
(01547 540441) • e-mail: mocktreebarns@care4free.net • web: www.mocktreeholidays.co.uk

See also Colour Advertisement on page 52

The Grove

Stone building, divided horizontally. Each flat has open plan lounge, fitted kitchen/dining area, bathroom and toilet. Electric storage heating, automatic washing machine, microwave, colour TV, radio, CD & cassette player. The Granary has a wood burner, the Dairy on the ground floor an open fireplace. All linen and towels included. Ideal base for touring beautiful Border country, black and white villages and for walking in some extremely peaceful surroundings. The farm is mixed arable and stock and there are lovely little woodland and riverside walks on the farm itself. Pets welcome under strict control. Friendly farm atmosphere. Sleeps 4. Terms from £140 per week.

ETC ★★★

Mrs N. Owens, Pembridge, Leominster HR6 9HP
Telephone 01544 388268 e-mail:nancy@grovedesign.co.uk

the Inn on the Wye
Quality Food with Excellent Service!
A beautifully restored 18th Century coaching inn with views of Goodrich Castle on the banks of the River Wye. All bedrooms en-suite with colour TV, telephone, & usual facilities. Ala carte & bar snack menus offering home cooked food.
Peaceful country walks - ideal base for touring.
Families welcome. Children's play area and gardens.
Open all day, seven days a week. Large car park.
Pets welcome by arrangement.
Kerne Bridge, Goodrich,
Nr Ross-on-Wye, HR9 5QS
Tel: 01600 890872 Fax: 01600 890594
E-mail: theinnonthewye@kernebridge.freeserve.co.uk
www. theinnonthewye.co.uk
RAC

See also Colour Advertisement on page 44

LEA HOUSE is a former 16th Century Coaching Inn, beautifully refurbished with antiques, an inglenook fireplace and loads of beams. Homemade breads and preserves complement the excellent home-cooked meals. The area is a doggy paradise - The Royal Forest of Dean, Wye Valley and Welsh hills are close by. NO-SMOKING. Dogs £5 per stay.
AA ◆◆◆◆ *In the village of Lea, Ross-on-Wye, HR9 7JZ* *Tel: 01989 750652*
e-mail: enquiries@leahousebandb.com **website: www.leahousebandb.com**

Ye Hostelrie Hotel GOODRICH, ROSS ON WYE, HR9 6HX AA★★ ETC★★
Tel: 01600 890241 • Fax: 01600 890838 • E-mail: info@ye-hostelrie.co.uk • Website: www.ye-hostelrie.co.uk
Fully centrally heated 17th Century Inn. Situated near to Goodrich Castle in the Wye Valley, it affords easy access to the Forest of Dean, rural Herefordshire and Wales. Only a mile from the A40. Dine in the restaurant, or the bar, choosing from our extensive menu. A choice of real ales and fine wines, Morning Coffee and Afternoon Cream Tea is also available. B&B in a double, twin bedded room or family room with en suite facilities, colour television, courtesy tray, clock radio, from: Double £50, Single £32.50. Cot provided. Pets are welcome in the bedrooms and garden.

See also Colour Advertisement on page 44

THE STEPPES
Ullingswick,
Near Hereford HR1 3JG
Tel: 01432 820424
Fax: 01432 820042

"The Steppes" is an award-winning hotel with an intimate atmosphere, abounding in antique furniture, inglenook fireplaces, oak beams and flag-stoned floors. Set in the tiny hamlet of Ullingswick in the Wye Valley, this is an excellent centre for visiting many areas of natural beauty and points of historic interest. Leisure breaks from £60 per person per night to include breakfast, dinner and en suite bedroom. A non-smoking hotel. **ETC** ◆◆◆◆◆ Silver Award
E-mail: info@steppeshotel.co.uk **Website: www.steppeshotel.co.uk**

Docklow

Village 4 miles east of Leominster.

NICHOLSON FARM HOLIDAYS, DOCKLOW, LEOMINSTER HR6 0SL (01568 760346) Self-catering properties on a working dairy farm. Beautiful views, ideal for walking, carp fishing available on the farm, swimming and tennis 10 mins. Dogs are welcome but must not remain in during the owner's absence. Non-smoking. [🐕]

Great Malvern

Fashionable spa town in last century with echoes of that period.

KATE AND DENIS KAVANAGH, WHITEWELLS FARM COTTAGES, RIDGEWAY CROSS, NEAR MALVERN WR13 5JR (01886 880607; Fax: 01886 880360). Charming converted Cottages, sleep 2–6. Fully equipped with colour TV, microwave, barbecue, fridge, iron, etc. Linen, towels also supplied. One cottage suitable for the disabled with full wheelchair access. Short breaks, long lets, large groups. ETC ★★★★ [Pets £10 per week. pw!] Also see adverts under Great Malvern, Worcestershire.
e-mail: info@whitewellsfarm.co.uk website: www.whitewellsfarm.co.uk

Hereford

Well-known touring centre on River Wye. Good sport and entertainment facilities including steeplechasing. Cheltenham 37 miles, Gloucester 28, Ross-on-Wye 15.

DIANA SINCLAIR, HOLLY HOUSE FARM, ALLENSMORE, HEREFORD HR2 9BH (01432 277294; Fax: 01432 261285). Escape with your horse or dog to our spacious luxury farmhouse. Bed and Breakfast from £22.50. Brochure available.[pw! 🐕 ⌂]
e-mail: hollyhousefarm@aol.com website: www.hollyhousefarm.org.uk

CHURCH FARM, CODDINGTON, LEDBURY HR8 IJJ (01531 640271). Black and white 16th-century Farmhouse on a working farm close to the Malvern Hills — ideal for touring and walking. Two double and one twin bedrooms. Excellent home cooking. Warm welcome assured. Open all year. [🐕]
website: www.dexta.co.uk

THE STEPPES, ULLINGSWICK, NEAR HEREFORD HR1 3JG (01432 820424; Fax: 01432 820042). Award-winning hotel with intimate atmosphere. Large luxury en suite bedrooms. Set in Wye Valley within easy reach of Malverns and Black Mountains. Non-smoking. ETC ◆◆◆◆◆ Silver Award, Which? Hotel Guide, Johansens. [Pets £5 per night].
e-mail: info@steppeshotel.co.uk website: www.steppeshotel.co.uk

Kington

Town on River Arrow, close to Welsh border, 12 miles north of Leominster.

MRS C. D. WILLIAMS, RADNOR'S END, HUNTINGTON, KINGTON HR5 3NZ (01544 370289). Tranquil, detached character cottage in the Welsh Borders. Sleeps 4 to 6. Cot. Fully-equipped, washing machine, central heating. Private garden and patio. Parking. Near Offa's Dyke, ideal for walking and wildlife. [🐕]

Pembridge

Tiny medieval village surrounded by meadows and orchards.

MRS N. OWENS, THE GROVE, PEMBRIDGE, LEOMINSTER HR6 9HP (01544 388268). The farm is mixed arable and stock and there are lovely little woodland and riverside walks on the farm itself. Pets welcome under strict control. Friendly farm atmosphere. Sleeps 4. Terms from £140 per week. ETC ★★★. [Pets £5 per week, pw!]
e-mail: nancy@grovedesign.co.uk

Ross-on-Wye

An attractive town standing on a hill rising from the left bank on the Wye. Cardiff 47 miles, Gloucester 17.

THE ARCHES GUEST HOUSE, WALFORD ROAD, ROSS-ON-WYE HR9 5PT (01989 563348). All rooms en suite with colour TV and beverage making facilities. Centrally heated. Bed and Breakfast. Family room available. Pets welcome. AA/ETC ◆◆◆ [🐕]
e-mail: thearches@which.net

THE KING'S HEAD HOTEL, 8 HIGH STREET, ROSS-ON-WYE HR9 5HL (FREEPHONE: 0800 801098). Small coaching inn dating back to the 14th century with all bedrooms offering en suite bathrooms and a full range of modern amenities. Comprehensive menu offers home-cooked food which is served in a warm and friendly atmosphere. Bargain breaks all year round. [🐕]
website: www.kingshead.co.uk

LEA HOUSE, LEA, ROSS-ON-WYE, HR9 7JZ (Tel & Fax: 01989 750652). Double/family en suite; twin/double en suite; twin private bath - all individually styled with TV and beverage tray. Secluded garden. Dogs very welcome. AA ◆◆◆◆ [Dogs £5 per stay]. See Display Advert.
e-mail: enquiries@leahousebandb.com website: www.leahousebandb.com

THE INN ON THE WYE, KERNE BRIDGE, GOODRICH, NEAR ROSS-ON-WYE HR9 5QT (01600 890872; Fax: 01600 890594). Beautifully restored 18th century coaching inn, near Goodrich Castle on the banks of the River Wye. All bedrooms en suite. Peaceful country walks, ideal base for touring.
website: www.theinnonthewye.co.uk

YE HOSTELRIE, GOODRICH, ROSS-ON-WYE HR9 6HX (01600 890241). Enjoy comfort and good food at this fully centrally heated 17th Century Inn. We have a reputation for quality food at a reasonable price. ETC/AA ★★ [🐕]
e-mail: info@ye-hostelrie.co.uk website: www.ye-hostelrie.co.uk

Ullingswick

Village 8 miles north of Hereford

THE STEPPES, ULLINGSWICK, NEAR HEREFORD HR1 3JG (01432 820424; Fax: 01432 820042). Award-winning hotel with intimate atmosphere. Large luxury en suite bedrooms. Set in Wye Valley within easy reach of Malverns and Black Mountains. Non-smoking. ETC ◆◆◆◆◆ Silver Award, Which? Hotel Guide, Johansens. [Pets £5 per night].
e-mail: info@steppeshotel.co.uk website: www.steppeshotel.co.uk

SYMBOLS

🐕 **Indicates that pets are welcome free of charge.**
£ **Indicates that a charge is made for pets: nightly or weekly.**
pw! **Shows some special provision for pets; exercise facility, feeding or accommodation arrangement.**
⌂ **Indicates separate pets accommodation.**

Bonchurch, Cowes, Ryde

Sentry Mead Hotel

MADEIRA ROAD, TOTLAND BAY, ISLE OF WIGHT PO39 0BJ
Tel & Fax: 01983 753212 • e-mail: pets@sentry-mead.co.uk
website: www.sentry-mead.co.uk

Sentry Mead is a tranquil retreat set in its own spacious gardens where well-behaved dogs are welcome throughout the hotel (except in the dining room) and to sleep in guests' bedrooms; our own Labrador and Retriever always make our canine visitors feel at home as soon as they arrive. Personal care and attention to detail make this a very special 3 star hotel for both pets and people for either a short break or a longer stay.

AA ★★★ RAC ★★★ RAC AWARD FOR SERVICE, HOSPITALITY & COMFORT

See also Colour Advertisement on page 45

The *Country Garden Hotel*

Church Hill, Totland Bay, Isle of Wight PO39 0ET
ETC/RAC ◆◆◆◆

Surrounded by lovely walks and hikes. Garden and sea view rooms available. B&B from £41pp/day; DB&B from £55pp/day. Brochure on request. **Phone/Fax: 01983 754521**
e-mail: countrygardeniow@aol.com
www.thecountrygardenhotel.co.uk

See also Colour Advertisement on page 45

Ventnor Holiday Villas **Apartments and Villas on a south facing hillside leading down to a small rocky bay. Views are spectacular & the hillside sheltered but open to all the sunshine that is going. Apartments open all year - villas and caravans open April to October. Three night break per unit from £150. Pets welcome in villas.**
Write or phone for brochure: Wheelers Bay Road, Ventnor PO38 1HR. Tel: 01983 852973
E-mail: sales@ventnorholidayvillas.co.uk website: www.ventnorholidayvillas.co.uk

"TUCKAWAY"

Private, comfortable, self-catering Chalet, within a large secluded garden. Sleeps four. Colour TV, games room, swimming pool and laundry room. Parking. Grassed exercise area available for dogs. Open all year. Apply for colour brochure or telephone:
Mrs R.J. Bayldon, Furzebrake, Cranmore Avenue, Cranmore, Near Yarmouth, Isle of Wight PO41 0XR Tel: (01983) 760082

Other specialised FHG PUBLICATIONS

Published annually: available in all good bookshops or direct from the publisher.

- **Recommended COUNTRY HOTELS OF BRITAIN £6.99**
- **Recommended SHORT BREAK HOLIDAYS IN BRITAIN £6.99**
- **Recommended WAYSIDE INNS OF BRITAIN £6.99**
- **PETS WELCOME £7.99**
- **THE GOLF GUIDE Where to Play / Where to Stay £9.99**

FHG PUBLICATIONS LTD, Abbey Mill Business Centre, Seedhill, Paisley, Renfrewshire PAI ITJ
Tel: 0141-887 0428 • Fax: 0141-889 7204
e-mail: fhg@ipcmedia.com • website: www.holidayguides.com

ISLAND COTTAGE HOLIDAYS. Charming individual cottages in lovely rural surroundings and close to the sea. Over 50 cottages situated throughout the Isle of Wight. Beautiful views, attractive gardens, delightful country walks. All equipped to a high standard and graded for quality by the Tourist Board. For a brochure please telephone 01929 480080; Fax: 01929 481070. ETC ★★★ to ★★★★★.
e-mail: enq@islandcottageholidays.com website: www.islandcottageholidays.com

Bonchurch

One mile north-east of Ventnor.

A. EVANS, "THE WATERFALL", SHORE ROAD, BONCHURCH, VENTNOR PO38 1RN (01983 852246). Spacious, self-contained Flat. Sleeps 3 adults. Colour TV. Sun verandah and garden. The beach, the sea and the downs. [🐕]
e-mail: benbrook.charioteer@virgin.net

MRS J. LINES, ASHCLIFF HOLIDAY APARTMENTS, BONCHURCH PO38 1NT(01983 853919). Three self-contained apartments within Victorian house. Large south-facing gardens. Sea views. Large private car park. Pets welcome to use garden. ETC ★★★★ [🐕]

Cowes

Yachting centre with yearly regatta since 1814. Newport 4 miles.

SUNNYCOTT CARAVAN PARK, COWES PO31 8NN (01983 292859; Fax: 01983 295389). Small, quiet, family-run park close to Cowes. All caravans have full cooker, microwave, fridge and colour TV. Shop and laundry room on site. We welcome pets. Short breaks arranged. ETC ★★★ [Pets £7.50 per week]
website: www.sunnycott.co.uk

Ryde

Popular resort and yachting centre, fine sands, pier. Shanklin 9 miles, Newport 7, Sandown 6.

HILLGROVE PARK, FIELD LANE, ST HELENS, NEAR RYDE PO33 1UT (01983 872802). Family-run Caravan Park. Select site 10 minutes sea, 3 minutes bus stop. Many local walks, heated swimming pool. Phone for brochure. Pets welcome (only one per unit). ETC ★★★★ Holiday Park. [Pets £2.00 per night, £15.00 per week]
website: www.hillgrove.co.uk

Totland Bay

Small resort 3 miles south-west of Yarmouth Bay.

SENTRY MEAD HOTEL, MADEIRA ROAD, TOTLAND BAY PO39 0BJ (01983 753212). Get away from it all at this friendly and comfortable haven, just two minutes from a sandy beach and cliff walks. Bedrooms have en suite bath or shower, colour TV and radio, telephone, hairdryer, beverage tray. Delicious table d'hôte dinners; lunchtime bar menu. AA/RAC ★★★ [Pets £3 per night, £20 per week]
e-mail: pets@sentry-mead.co.uk website: www.sentry-mead.co.uk

COUNTRY GARDEN HOTEL, CHURCH HILL, TOTLAND BAY PO39 OET (Tel & Fax: 01983 754521). All en suite, garden and seaview rooms available; TV, phone, duvets, feather/down pillows, fridge, hairdryer etc. Special winter, spring, autumn rates. ETC/RAC ◆◆◆◆[pw!] pets £3 per day]
e-mail: countrygardeniow@aol.com website: www.thecountrygardenhotel.co.uk

Ventnor

Well-known resort with good sands, downs, popular as a winter holiday resort. Nearby is St Boniface Down, the highest point on the island. Ryde 13 miles, Newport 12, Sandown 7, Shanklin 4.

CASTLEHAVEN CARAVAN SITE, BOX PW, NITON, NEAR VENTNOR, ISLE OF WIGHT PO38 2ND (01983 855556/730461). Island's most southerly six-berth, two-bedroomed caravans, all overlooking the Channel. Small, friendly site. Unspoilt seashore/countryside setting. On the shore. Kiosk serving breakfasts/evening meals by arrangement.
e-mail: caravans@castlehaven.co.uk website: www.castlehaven.co.uk

VENTNOR HOLIDAY VILLAS, WHEELERS BAY ROAD, VENTNOR PO38 1HR. (01983 852973). Apartments and Villas on south facing hillside leading down to a small rocky bay. Apartments open all year, Villas & caravans April to October. Write or phone for a brochure. Pets welcome in villas. ETC ★/★★ [Pets £20 per week]
e-mail: sales@ventnorholidayvillas.co.uk website: www.ventnorholidayvillas.co.uk

Yarmouth

Coastal resort situated 9 miles west of Newport. Castle built by Henry VIII for coastal defence.

THE ORCHARDS HOLIDAY CARAVAN & CAMPING PARK, NEWBRIDGE, YARMOUTH PO41 0TS (Dial-a-brochure 01983 531331; Fax: 01983 531666). Luxury holiday caravans, some with central heating. Excellent facilities including indoor pool with licensed cafe. Dog exercise areas. Coarse fishing; ideal walking, cycling and golf. Open late February to New Year.
e–mail: info@orchards-holiday-park.co.uk website: www.orchards-holiday-park.co.uk

"TUCKAWAY" – Holiday Chalet in private, secluded position. Sleeps four. Swimming pool. Gardens. Dogs welcome. APPLY: R. BAYLDON, FURZEBRAKE, CRANMORE AVENUE, YARMOUTH PO41 OXR (01983 760082). [🐕]

Garden of England
Cottages in Kent & Sussex
Tel: 01732 369168 • Fax: 01732 358817
The Mews Office, 189a High Street,
Tonbridge, Kent TN9 1BX

Accommodation for all seasons
Big paws and little paws are welcome in many of our holiday homes, plus pets go free with every well behaved owner.
All properties ETC quality assessed
e-mail: holidays@gardenofenglandcottages.co.uk
website: www.gardenofenglandcottages.co.uk

See Also Colour Advertisement on page 46

Broadstairs, Dover, Isle of Sheppey, New Romney

HANSON HOTEL **(Lic.)** **41 Belvedere Road, Broadstairs CT10 1PF Tel: (01843) 868936**
A small friendly Georgian hotel with relaxed atmosphere, centrally situated for beach, shops and transport. B/B only or renowned for excellent food, we offer a 5-course Evening Dinner with choice of menu prepared by Chef/Proprietor ★ Attractive Bar ★ Most en suite.
Children and pets welcome.
OPEN ALL YEAR ***S.A.E. or telephone for brochure to Trevor and Jean Webb*** SPRING AND WINTER BREAKS

St Margaret's Holiday Park **ETC★★★★★**
Reach Road, St Margaret's at Cliffe, Near Dover, Kent CT15 6AE
Exclusive park perched high on the White Cliffs and close to the bustling Port of Dover. Modern, well-equipped caravans for hire. Superb facilities – indoor pool, gymnasium, spa pool, sauna and solarium, outdoor play area, Bistro bar and restaurant.
Visit Historic Canterbury. Day trips to France.
www.gbholidayparks.co.uk Call **0870 442 9286** for brochure

Warden Springs Holiday Park **ETC★★★★**
Eastchurch, Isle of Sheppey, Kent ME12 4HF
Situated on Kent's Sunshine Island the park overlooks the sea and is surrounded by picturesque countryside and woodland. Modern, well-equipped caravans for hire. Outdoor heated pool, take away, bar and outdoor play area. Local to park – fine beaches, clifftop walks and sporting opportunities. Tourers and tents welcome.
www.gbholidayparks.co.uk Call **0870 442 9281** for brochure

Romney Sands Holiday Park **ETC★★★★**
The Parade, Greatstone-on-Sea, New Romney, Kent TN28 8RN
Popular park opposite one of the finest sandy beaches on the Kent coast. Great range of caravans and chalets for hire. Indoor pool complex, diner, crazy golf, kids' club, outdoor play area, bowling green, tennis, mini-market, bar and entertainment venues.
See mysterious Romney Marshes~past haunt of smugglers.
www.gbholidayparks.co.uk Call **0870 442 9285** for brochure

PLEASE NOTE

All the information in this book is given in good faith in the belief that it is correct. However, the publishers cannot guarantee the facts given in these pages, neither are they responsible for changes in policy, ownership or terms that may take place after the date of going to press. Readers should always satisfy themselves that the facilities they require are available and that the terms, if quoted, still apply.

GARDEN OF ENGLAND COTTAGES IN KENT & SUSSEX, THE MEWS OFFICE, 189a HIGH STREET, TONBRIDGE, KENT TN9 1BX (01732 369168; Fax: 01732 358817). Pets welcome in many of our holiday homes, pets go free with well-behaved owners. All properties ETC assessed. [🐕]
e-mail: holidays@gardenofenglandcottages.co.uk website: www.gardenofenglandcottages.co.uk

Broadstairs

Quiet resort, once a favourite of Charles Dickens. Good sands and promenade.

HANSON HOTEL, 41 BELVEDERE ROAD, BROADSTAIRS CT10 1PF (01843 868936). Small, friendly licensed Georgian Hotel. Home comforts; children and pets welcome. Attractive bar. SAE. [pw! Pets 50p per night]

Dover (near)

Busy passenger port whose white cliffs are the enduring symbol of island Britain.

ST MARGARET'S HOLIDAY PARK, REACH ROAD, ST MARGARET'S AT CLIFFE, NEAR DOVER, CT15 6AE. Exclusive park perched on the White Cliffs. Modern, well-equipped caravans for hire. Superb facilities – indoor pool, gymnasium, spa pool, bar and restaurant. Day trips to France. Call 0870 442 9286 for brochure. ETC★★★★★ [🐕]
website: www.gbholidayparks.co.uk

Isle of Sheppey

Island off the north coast of Kent, separated from mainland by the Swale and River Medway.

WARDEN SPRINGS HOLIDAY PARK, EASTCHURCH, ISLE OF SHEPPEY ME12 4HF. On Kent's Sunshine Island, overlooking the sea, surrounded by picturesque countryside. Modern, well-equipped caravans for hire. Outdoor heated pool, takeaway, bar. Tourers and tents welcome. Call 0870 442 9281 for brochure. ETC★★★★ [🐕]
website: www.gbholidayparks.co.uk

New Romney

Town 9 miles south west of Hythe and 2km inland from Littlestone-on-Sea on St Mary's Bay.

ROMNEY SANDS HOLIDAY PARK, THE PARADE, GREATSTONE-ON-SEA, NEW ROMNEY TN28 8RN. Opposite one of Kent's finest sandy beaches. Great range of caravans and chalets for hire. Indoor pool complex, kids' club, sports facilities, entertainment venues. Call 0870 442 9285 for brochure. ETC ★★★★ [🐕]
website: www.gbholidayparks.co.uk

St Margaret's Bay

4 miles north-east of Dover.

DEREK AND JACQUI MITCHELL, REACH COURT FARM COTTAGES, REACH COURT FARM, ST MARGARET'S BAY, DOVER CT15 6AQ (01304 852159; Tel & Fax: 01304 853902). Situated in the heart of the Mitchell family farm, surrounded by open countryside, these five luxury self-contained cottages are very special. The cottages are set around the old farmyard, which has been attractively set to lawns and shrubs, with open views of the rural valley both front and back. ETC ★★★★
e-mail: jacmitch2002@yahoo.co.uk

FREE or REDUCED RATE entry to Holiday Visits and Attractions – see our READERS' OFFER VOUCHERS on pages 103-118

SEE PAGE 81 FOR FULL DETAILS

Blackburn

Industrial town on River Darwen and on Leeds and Liverpool Canal.

THE BROWN LEAVES COUNTRY HOTEL, LONGSIGHT ROAD, COPSTER GREEN, NEAR BLACKBURN BB1 9EU (01254 249523; Fax: 01254 245240). Situated on the A59 halfway between Preston and Clitheroe, five miles from Junction 31 on M6 in beautiful Ribble Valley. All rooms ground floor, en suite facilities, TV, tea-making and hairdryer. Guests' lounge and bar lounge. Car parking. Pets by arrangement. All credit cards welcome.
website: www.brownleavescountryhotel.co.uk

Blackpool

Famous resort with fine sands and many attractions and vast variety of entertainments. Blackpool Tower (500ft). Three piers. Manchester 47 miles, Lancaster 26, Preston 17, Fleetwood 8.

MRS C. MOORE, COTSWOLD, 2A HADDON ROAD, NORBRECK, BLACKPOOL FY2 9AH (01253 352227). Quality flatlets fully equipped. Cross road to beach and trams. Terms from £120. Phone or SAE for brochure. [🐕]

THE BRAYTON, 7-8 FINCHLEY ROAD, GYNN SQUARE, BLACKPOOL FY1 2LP (01253 351645). Quiet licensed hotel overlooking Gynn gardens and the promenade. Excellent home-cooked meals served daily. Easy parking. Open all year. ETC ◆◆◆
e-mail: information@the-brayton-hotel.com website: www.the-brayton-hotel.com

Mellor

Village 3 miles north-west of Blackburn

ROSE COTTAGE, LONGSIGHT ROAD, CLAYTON-LE-DALE BB1 9EX (01254 813223; Fax: 01254 813831). Picturesque cottage on A59, five miles from M6, M65. Well-appointed rooms with private facilities. Weekend breaks, excellent stop for travellers to Scotland. Credit Cards accepted. [🐕]
e-mail: bbrose.cott@talk21.co.uk website: www.SmoothHound.co.uk/hotels/rosecott.html

Pilling

Village 3 miles north east of Preesall.

BERYL AND PETER RICHARDSON, BELL FARM, BRADSHAW LANE, SCRONKEY, PILLING, PRESTON PR3 6SN (01253 790324).18th century farmhouse with one family room, one double and one twin. All en suite, and centrally heated. Full English breakfast is served. Open all year except Christmas and New Year. [🐕]

Southport

Elegant seaside resort with Victorian feel. Amusement park, zoo and Birkdale championship golf course.

THE GARDEN COURT, 22 BANK SQUARE, SOUTHPORT PR9 0DG (Tel & Fax: 01704 530219). Victorian town house overlooking Floral Hall, Marine Lake and sea. All attractions within easy walking distance. En suite bedrooms, some four-poster. Licensed bar. Friendly, comfortable accommodation from £19.50 B&B pppn. [🐕]

CRIMOND HOTEL & RESTAURANT, KNOWSLEY ROAD, SOUTHPORT PR9 0HN (01704 536456; Fax: 01704 548643). Situated close to the town centre, this hotel can cater for all your needs with the luxury of an indoor swimming pool. Open all year. Table d'hôte service. Full central heating. [Pets £1 per night].
website: www.crimondhotel.co.uk

***When making enquiries or bookings,
a stamped addressed envelope is always appreciated***

Market Harborough

Town on River Welland 14 miles south-east of Leicester.

BROOK MEADOW HOLIDAYS. Three self-catering chalets, farmhouse Bed and Breakfast, Carp fishing, camping and caravan site with electric hookups. Phone for brochure. ETC ★★★ to ★★★★. MRS MARY HART, WELFORD ROAD, SIBBERTOFT, MARKET HARBOROUGH LE16 9UJ (01858 880886). [camping, £5 per night B&B, £10 Self-catering]
e-mail: brookmeadow@farmline.com website: www.brookmeadow.co.uk

Melton Mowbray

Old market town, centre of hunting country. Large cattle market. Church and Ann of Cleves' House are of interest. Kettering 29 miles, Market Harborough 22, Nottingham 18, Leicester 15.

SYSONBY KNOLL HOTEL, ASFORDBY ROAD, MELTON MOWBRAY LE13 OHP (01664 563563; Fax: 01664 410364.). Family-run 3 star hotel on edge of town, plenty of room for exercise on site and longer walks available. Special weekend breaks, pets genuinely welcome. See website for details. ETC/AA ★★★ []
website: www.sysonby.co.uk

Little London Cottages, Tetford, Horncastle ETC ★★★★/★★★★★

Three very well-equipped properties, each standing in own garden, on our small estate. Lovely walks, fishing, pony trekking nearby. 'The Garth', a single storey conversion of farm buildings with three bedrooms. 'Cornerways', a 19th century, two-bedroomed cottage with log fire. 'Mansion Cottage', a 17th/18th century cottage with two bedrooms, low ceilings and doorways, and steep stairs. Short breaks and special offers. Pets welcome free.

Contact: **Mrs S. D. Sutcliffe, The Mansion House, Little London, Tetford, Horncastle LN9 6QL**
Tel: 01507 533697 or 07767 321213; debbie@sutcliffell.freeserve.co.uk • www.littlelondoncottages.co.uk

Sunnydale Holiday Park ETC★★★
Sea Lane, Saltfleet, Lincolnshire LN11 7RP

Friendly park on the edge of the beautiful Lincolnshire coastline. Modern, well-equipped caravans for hire. Indoor pool, indoor and outdoor play areas, convenience store, bar and spacious beer garden. In the area – picturesque market towns, lively sea resorts and theme parks. Tourers and tents welcome.

www.gbholidayparks.co.uk Call **0870 442 9293** for brochure

Horncastle

Market town once famous for annual horse fairs. 13th Century Church is noted for brasses and Civil War relics.

LITTLE LONDON COTTAGES, TETFORD, HORNCASTLE. Three very well-equipped properties standing in own gardens on our small estate. Lovely walks, fishing, pony trekking nearby. Short breaks and special offers. Contact: MRS S.D. SUTCLIFFE, THE MANSION HOUSE, LITTLE LONDON, TETFORD, HORNCASTLE LN9 6QL (01507 533697; mobile: 07767 321213). [🐕]
e-mail: debbie@sutcliffell.freeserve.co.uk website: www.littlelondoncottages.co.uk

Langton-by-Wragby

Village located south-east of Wragby.

MISS JESSIE SKELLERN, LEA HOLME, LANGTON-BY-WRAGBY, LINCOLN LN8 5PZ (01673 858339). Ground floor accommodation in chalet-type house. Central for Wolds, coast, fens, historic Lincoln. Market towns, Louth, Horncastle, Boston, Spilsby, Alford, Woodhall Spa. Two double bedrooms, washbasin, TV; bathroom, toilet adjoining; lounge with colour TV, separate dining room. Drinks provided. Children welcome reduced rates. Car almost essential, parking. Numerous eating places nearby. B&B from £20 per person. Open all year. Tourist Board Listed [🐕]

Mablethorpe

Coastal resort 11 miles from Louth.

MRS GRAVES, GRANGE FARM, MALTBY-LE-MARSH, ALFORD LN13 0JP (01507 450267; Fax: 01507 450180). Farmhouse B&B and country cottages set in ten idyllic areas of Lincolnshire countryside. Peaceful base for leisure and sightseeing. Private fishing lake. Many farm animals. Brochure available. Pets welcome. [🐕]
website: www.grange-farmhouse.co.uk

Saltfleet

Small, sleepy village overlooked by derelict windmill. Narrow harbour with moorings for small vessels.

SUNNYDALE HOLIDAY PARK, SEA LANE, SALTFLEET LN11 7RP. Friendly coastal park. Well-equipped caravans for hire. Indoor pool, play areas, shop, bar and beer garden. Market towns, sea resorts and theme parks nearby.Tourers and tents welcome. Call 0870 442 9293 for brochure. ETC★★★ [🐕]
website: www.gbholidayparks.co.uk

LONDON

London

Legislative capital and major port. Theatres, shops, museums, places of historic interest. Airports at Heathrow and Gatwick.

ST ATHANS HOTEL, 20 TAVISTOCK PLACE, RUSSELL SQUARE, LONDON WC1H 9RE (Tel: 020-7837 9140; Fax: 020-7833 8352). Family Bed and Breakfast near British Museum, shops, parks and theatres. Russell Square two blocks away, Euston and King's Cross stations ten minutes. LTB LISTED. [🐕]
e-mail: stathans@ukonline.co.uk

NORFOLK

Readers are requested to mention this guidebook when seeking accommodation (and please enclose a stamped addressed envelope).

CASTAWAYS HOLIDAY PARK

BH & HPA approved

Set in the quiet, peaceful village of Bacton, with direct access to fine sandy beach, and ideal for beach fishing and discovering Norfolk and The Broads. Modern Caravans, Pine Lodges and Flats with all amenities. Licensed Club. Entertainment. Amusement Arcade. Children's Play Area.

PETS WELCOME

Enquiries and Bookings to:

Castaways Holiday Park, Paston Road, Bacton-on-Sea, Norfolk NR12 0JB • Tel: (01692) 650436 and 650418
website: www.castawaysholidaypark.co.uk

Red House

Chalet & Caravan Park

Small, family-run coastal site with direct access to sandy beach. Caravans, flats and centrally heated chalets. All accommodation has self-contained facilities including colour television. Some accommodation available with sea view. On site licensed bar. Shop and laundry room. Ideal location for touring the Broads or sightseeing North Norfolk. DOGS VERY WELCOME. Open from March to January.

Red House Chalet and Caravan Park,
Paston Road, Bacton-on-Sea, Norfolk NR12 0JB (01692 650815).

Peacock House Old farmhouse. Lovely countryside with good walks. 3½ miles from Dereham, close for Norwich, NT houses, Sandringham, beaches. All rooms en suite, tea/coffee facilities. TV in all rooms. Own lounge, no smoking. Very warm welcome. B&B from £23.50pp. Open all year. Children and dogs welcome. **ETC ◆◆◆◆ Gold Award.**

Mrs Jenny Bell, Peacock Lane, Old Beetley, Dereham, Norfolk NR20 4DG
Tel: 01362 860371 E-mail: PeackH@aol.com Web: www.SmoothHound.co.uk/hotels/peacockh.html

A useful Index of Towns/Villages and Counties appears on page 427 – please also refer to Contents Page 3.

Owner Paul Whittome with Augustus and Sweep

the hoste

Set in the UK's most beautiful village of Burnham Market, this stylish, fabulous hotel offers a friendly atmosphere with attentive service. Individually designed bedrooms, air conditioned dining rooms, a traditional bar with log fire which attracts many of the locals and is the sort of place where nice dogs like to meet, a sunny patio and garden in which to relax with dogs, and a conservatory.

Beach and woodland walks – 1 mile away.

Amazing value mid-week. Dinner, Bed and Breakfast breaks.

Awards: Johansens, Egon Ronay, GoodHotel Guide, Norfolk Dining Pub of the Year, AA 2 Rosette Restaurant.

Tel: 01328 738777 • Fax: 01328 730103

e-mail: reception@hostearms.co.uk • web: www.hostearms.co.uk

The Hoste Arms, 17th Century Inn, The Green, Burnham Market, Norfolk PE31 8HD

See also colour advertisement on page 46

NOW OPEN MARCH TO JANUARY

Elm Beach is a small, select, 4-star Caravan Park with unique, uninterrupted views of the Sea and Caister's golden, sandy beaches. We offer a range of 6-berth, fully equipped Caravans, many of which overlook the sea or have sea views. We are a quiet, privately-run park with no entertainment facilities, but enjoy, free of charge, entertainment supplied by neighbouring parks, both within easy walking distance. Pets very welcome.

Elm Beach Caravan Park

Manor Road, Caister-on-Sea, Norfolk NR30 5HG

Freephone: 08000 199 360

www.elmbeachcaravanpark.com e-mail: enquiries@elmbeachcaravanpark.com

NOTE

All the information in this book is given in good faith in the belief that it is correct. However, the publishers cannot guarantee the facts given in these pages, neither are they responsible for changes in policy, ownership or terms that may take place after the date of going to press. Readers should always satisfy themselves that the facilities they require are available and that the terms, if quoted, still apply.

ETC ★★ SILVER AWARD

The Norfolk Mead Hotel

Coltishall • Norfolk • NR12 7DN

Privately owned beautiful Georgian Country House Hotel. Located in 12 tranquil riverside acres, six miles from Norwich and 12 miles from the coast. Ten en suite rooms all individually decorated to a high standard. Cottage and Garden suite ideal for dog owners. Fishing lake, boating and birdlife. Renowned restaurant offering superb cuisine and a comprehensive wine list.Well mannered dogs welcome.

Telephone 01603 737531

E-mail: info@norfolkmead.co.uk Website: www.norfolkmead.co.uk

KING'S CHALET PARK

Enquiries to: Stenson Guest House, 32 Overstrand Road, Cromer, Norfolk NR27 0AJ

Families Welcome & Pets Free of Charge

Well-equipped Chalets sleeping 2 to 6; shower/ bathroom, microwave, TV. Tourist Board and NNH/GHA Approved. One Twin, one Double bedroom, bed sofa in lounge. Well-equipped kitchenette. Quiet site adjacent to woods, Golf Club and beach. Local shops nearby or pleasant 10 minutes' walk into town.

Telephone: 01263 511308

CROMER — SELF CATERING COTTAGES

A terrace of four charming almshouses recently modernised and redecorated throughout. Providing **2 & 3 bedroom accommodation for 4/6 persons.**

Central heating is included in the letting fee during the low season, together with duvets, bed linen and towels. **Short breaks available.**

Each cottage has its own enclosed garden, ideal for children and **pets always welcome!** Ample car parking in cottage grounds.

Enjoy a walk with your dog on the miles of open uncrowded beaches in North Norfolk. Cromer has a Cinema and Pier with first-rate live shows.

Also included is membership of Forest Park with its beautiful woodland walks, clubhouse and swimming pool open during the high season.

Detailed brochure and tariff (prices from £195 to £390 p.w.)

Broadgates Cottages, Northrepps,
Forest Park Caravan Site Ltd, Northrepps Road,
Cromer, Norfolk NR27 0JR
Tel: 01263 513290 • Fax: 01263 511992

FOREST PARK
Outstanding Natural Beauty

e-mail: gill@broadgates.co.uk • website: www.broadgates.co.uk

Kings Chalet Park, Cromer, Norfolk • *Sleep 2-4* • *Open March to October*
Comfortable, well-equipped chalets situated on beautiful, landscaped, quiet site. Ideally placed for walks to adjacent woods, cliffs and sandy beaches. 10 minutes' walk to town. Golf course and local shops nearby. Plenty of local places of interest to visit. One twin, one double room, bathroom, colour TV, microwave, well-equipped kitchenette. Children welcome. **DETAILS FROM: MRS I. SCOLTOCK, SHANGRI-LA, LITTLE CAMBRIDGE, DUTON HILL, DUNMOW, ESSEX CM6 3QU • TEL: 01371 870482**

See also Colour Advertisement on page 48

Chalet 49 ~ Kings Chalet Park, Cromer.

Mrs M. Walker, 39 Pauls Lane, Overstrand, Cromer, Norfolk NR27 0PF Tel: 01263 579269

Luxury, well equipped chalet situated on quiet landscaped site, adjacent to sandy beaches, woods, cliff-top walks and golf courses. Ten minutes' walk to town. Local shops nearby. Two bedrooms, bathroom, fitted kitchen, microwave, colour TV, etc. Sleeps four. Cleaned and maintained by owner. Pets welcome. Open March to October.

"Cromer's Premier Clifftop Hotel"

PETS WELCOME

30 en suite bedrooms all with sea views - Executive Suites.
All Day Coffee Shop - à la carte Restaurant - Bolton's Bistro
Special 3 & 4 Night Breaks - 7 nights for the price of 6
The Cliftonville Hotel, Seafront, Cromer, Norfolk NR27 9AS

Tel: 01263 512543 Fax: 01263 515700 e-mail: reservations@cliftonvillehotel.co.uk

BARTLES LODGE

Stay in the peaceful, tranquil heart of Norfolk's most beautiful countryside. All rooms tastefully decorated in country style, with full en suite facilities, TVs, tea/coffee making facilities, etc. Overlooking 12 acres of landscaped meadows with its own private fishing lakes. Bed and Breakfast from £24.

Recommended by "Which?" Good Bed & Breakfast Guide.

Bartles Lodge, Church Street, Elsing, Dereham NR20 3EA Tel: 01362 637177

Scarning Dale

Dale Road, Scarning, East Dereham NR19 2QN
Tel: 01362 687269

A warm welcome awaits you. 16th Century house in 25 acres of landscaped gardens, paddocks and woodland. Excellent home cooking (à la carte and table d'hôte). Indoor heated swimming pool and full size snooker table. Good access Norfolk and Suffolk. Self-catering cottages also available. Dogs welcome in self-catering cottages. Grazing and Stables available.

Tariff: Single £50 – £60; Double £90 – £100.

Holly Farm Cottages, High Common, Cranworth, Norfolk IP25 7SX

Two comfortable, single-storey cottages each sleeping 1-4. Fully equipped, including TV/video, dishwasher, washing machine, central heating. Enclosed garden. Ample car parking. Uninterrupted views of beautiful countryside, peaceful lanes for walking/cycling. Local golf and fishing. Convenient for Norwich, North Norfolk Coast and Broads.

Tel: 01362 821468 **e-mail: jennie.mclaren@btopenworld.com**

Experience the great joy of Norfolk We offer your pets 8 acres of lawns, paddock and woodland, with Norfolk's vast beaches within a few minutes' drive. Superbly equipped cottages, leisure centre with indoor pool; animal farm, children's play area, enchanted wood, grass tennis court, croquet lawn.

Vere Lodge, South Raynham, Fakenham NR21 7HE • 01328 838261

www.idylliccottages.co.uk ***For those who demand the very best***

See also Colour Advertisement on page 48

When making enquiries please mention FHG Publications

Located on a working farm, a courtyard of 2/3 bedroomed SELF CATERING CHALETS & 2 COTTAGES. All fully equipped, and all with central heating which is included in the letting fee. Situated 20 miles from the coast and 15 miles from Norwich and the Broads. 365 acres of mature woodland adjoining owners' farm – ideal for walking. Private fishing on owner's lake. Pets welcome at charge of £10.

ETC ★★/★★★

MOOR FARM STABLE COTTAGES

FOXLEY, NORFOLK NR20 4QN • Tel or Fax: 01362 688523

✧ Sunwright Holiday Chalets ✧

Sundowner holiday park, Newport, Hemsby, near Great Yarmouth. Fully furnished and equipped self catering chalets, sleep up to 6. Two bedrooms, kitchen with all your cooking needs, lounge with TV, bathroom with shower over bath. Close to beach, Norfolk Broads and many attractions. Pets most welcome!

Contact Mrs Michelle Browne, 19 Nile Road, Gorleston, Great Yarmouth, Norfolk NR31 6AS

Tel: 01493 304282, E-mail: sunwrightholiday@aol.com OR visit our website www.sunwrightholidays.co.uk

Debit/Credit cards accepted

A warm welcome for you and your pets. Inexpensive, 'live-as-you-please' self-catering holidays in beautiful Norfolk. Chalets, Bungalows, and Cottages near Great Yarmouth & Norfolk Broads.

SUPERB VALUE FOR 2004 SEASON

Colour Brochure Tel: 01493 732176 7 days a week Find us on the internet: www.carefree-holidays.co.uk

See also Colour Advertisement on page 46

THE OLD STABLES
HOLIDAY COTTAGES

Horningtoft, Dereham, Norfolk NR20 5DX

ETC ★★★★ Self-Catering

Attractive, new brick and flint barn conversions, sleeping 4 - 6 people with all the comforts of home.

Games Room • Cycle Hire Available • Wheel Chair Access • Pets Welcome • Short breaks

Situated in a peaceful, rural village, within easy access of pubs, restaurants, shops, sports centres and the North Norfolk coastline. Also good for fishing, and walking.

For further details please contact: **IVAN on Tel: 01328 700262 Mobile: 07775 707992**

MARINE BAR with accommodation. Pets are very welcome at a small charge of £1 per night. We do not have en suite rooms but every room has its own basin. Bar meals available all day. Colour television in all bedrooms. Most rooms have a view. £20 per person per night. Open all year.

The Marine Bar
HUNSTANTON

10 St Edmonds Terrace, Hunstanton, Norfolk PE36 5EH Tel: 01485 533310

A useful Index of Towns/Villages and Counties appears on page 427 – please also refer to Contents Page 3.

ETC ★★★

HOLMDENE FARM.

BEESTON, KING'S LYNN PE32 2NJ.

17th century farmhouse situated in central Norfolk within easy reach of the coast and Broads. Sporting activities available locally, village pub nearby. One double room, one twin and two singles. Pets welcome. Bed and Breakfast from £20 per person; Evening Meal from £15. Weekly terms available and child reductions. Two self-catering cottages. Sleeping 4/8. Terms on request.

MRS G. DAVIDSON, Tel: 01328 701284

e-mail: holmdenefarm@farmersweekly.net
website: www.northnorfolk.co.uk/holmdenefarm

Pott Row

Detached 2 bedroom bungalow sleeps 4. In quiet rural Norfolk village close to Sandringham and beaches. Facilities include colour TV, video, microwave, fridge/freezer, washing machine, off road parking, dog run. All dogs welcome FREE. Open all year. Please telephone for brochure.

Mrs. J.E. Ford, 129 Leziate Drove, Pott Row, King's Lynn PE32 1DE Tel: 01553 630356

KILN CLIFFS CARAVAN PARK

KILN CLIFFS
MUNDESLEY

Peaceful family-run site with NO clubhouse situated around an historic brick kiln. Luxury six-berth caravans for hire, standing on ten acres of grassy cliff top. Magnificent view out over the sea; private path leads down to extensive stretches of unspoilt sandy beach. All caravans fully equipped (except linen) and price includes all gas and electricity. Caravans always available for sale or for hire. Within easy reach are the Broads, Norwich, the Shire Horse Centre, local markets, nature reserves, bird sanctuaries; nearby golf, riding and fishing. Facilities on site include general store and launderette. Responsible pet owners welcome.

Substantial discounts for off-peak bookings – phone for details.

Call for brochure. Mr R. Easton, Kiln Cliffs Caravan Park, Cromer Road, Mundesley, Norfolk NR11 8DF. Tel: 01263 720449

A warm welcome to all pets and their owners at "Whincliff" by the sea. Family/en suite, twin or single room available. Tea/coffee facilities, TV in all rooms, private parking, sea views, unspoilt beach and coastal walks to enjoy.

WHINCLIFF Bed & Breakfast

Mrs Christine Thrower

CROMER ROAD, MUNDESLEY NR11 8DU • TEL: 01263 721554

http://whincliff.freeuk.com • e-mail: whincliff@freeuk.com

HOLIDAY PROPERTIES (Mundesley) Ltd

Self-catering holiday chalets to let on 3 pretty sites in village on north Norfolk coast, close to lovely sandy beach, and all village's amenities. All chalets are heated with fully equipped kitchens, colour TVs. Sleep 4-6. Senior citizen discount. Pets welcome. For colour brochure **01263 720719**

ETC ★-★★★

e-mail: holidayproperties@tesco.net • www.holidayprops.freeuk.com

ETC ◆◆◆

Dolphin Lodge

Friendly-run bungalow accommodation. B&B in village setting just two-and-a-half miles from beaches. Many rural walks. Easy reach of all Norfolk attractions including Norfolk Broads. All rooms en suite, tea/coffee facilities, TVs, hairdryers etc.

Mrs G. Faulkner, Dolphin Lodge, 3 Knapton Road, Trunch, North Walsham, Norfolk NR28 0QE Tel: 01263 720961

NORFOLK COUNTRY COTTAGES. Norfolk's leading holiday cottage letting agency. For brochure Tel: 01603 871872. CARLTON HOUSE, MARKET PLACE, REEPHAM, NORFOLK NR10 4JJ.
website: www.norfolkcottages.co.uk/pw

Bacton-on-Sea

Village on coast. 5 miles from North Walsham.

CASTAWAYS HOLIDAY PARK, PASTON ROAD, BACTON-ON-SEA NR12 0JB (01692 650436 and 650418). In peaceful village with direct access to sandy beach. Modern caravans, Pine Lodges and Flats, with all amenities. Licensed club, entertainment, children's play area. Ideal for discovering Norfolk. [Pets £17 per week/£3 p.n./£10 per short break]
website: www.castawaysholidaypark.co.uk

RED HOUSE CHALET AND CARAVAN PARK, PASTON ROAD, BACTON-ON-SEA NR12 0JB (01692 650815). Small family-run site, ideal for touring Broads. Chalets, caravans and flats all with showers, fridges and colour TV. Some with sea views. Licensed. Open March–January. [Pets £10 weekly.]

Beetley

Village 4 miles/6 km north of East Dereham, which is notable for old buildings, including the parish church.

MRS JENNY BELL, PEACOCK HOUSE, PEACOCK LANE, OLD BEETLEY, DEREHAM NR20 4DG (01362 860371). Old farmhouse in lovely countryside. All rooms en suite, tea / coffee facilities. TV's in all rooms. Own lounge, B&B from £23.50pp. Open all year. Non-smoking. Children and dogs welcome. ETC ◆◆◆◆ Gold Award. [pw! 🐕]
e-mail: PeackH@aol.com website: www.SmoothHound.co.uk/hotels/peacockh.html

Bradenham

Village 5 miles south-west of East Dereham.

MID NORFOLK - Charming cottage decorated and furnished to high standard. Sleeps two. Has well enclosed private garden. Situated in sleepy hamlet. Lovely walks. Pets welcome. From £100 to £210 per week. MRS ROWNTREE, "FOXLEA", WEST END, BRADENHAM, NORFOLK IP25 7QZ (01760 441733)

Burnham Market

Village 5 miles west of Wells-next-the-Sea.

THE HOSTE ARMS, THE GREEN, BURNHAM MARKET PE31 8HD (01328 738777; Fax: 01328 730103) Fabulous hotel with friendly atmosphere and attentive service. High degree of comfort offered. British brasserie style food served. Traditional bar. AA 2 Rosettes for food.
e-mail: reception@hostearms.co.uk website: www.hostearms.co.uk

SEE PAGE 81 FOR FULL DETAILS

Caister-on-Sea

Historic site with Roman ruins and 15th century Caister Castle with 100 foot tower.

Superior brick-built, tiled roof cottages. Adjacent golf course. Lovely walks on dunes and coast. 2-4 night breaks early/late season, Christmas and New Year. Terms from £69 to £345. SAND DUNE COTTAGES, TAN LANE, CAISTER-ON-SEA, GREAT YARMOUTH NR30 5DT (01493 720352; mobile: 07785 561363).
e-mail: sand.dune.cottages@amserve.net
website: www.eastcoastlive.co.uk/sites/sanddunecottages.php

ELM BEACH CARAVAN PARK, MANOR ROAD, CAISTER-ON-SEA NR30 5HG (Freephone: 08000 199 360). Small, quiet park offering 6-berth, fully equipped caravans, most with sea views. Entertainment supplied free of charge by neighbouring parks. Pets very welcome. [Pets £20 per week]
e-mail: enquiries@elmbeachcaravanpark.com website: elmbeachcaravanpark com

Go BLUE RIBAND for quality inexpensive self-catering holidays where your dog is welcome – choice of locations all in the borough of Great Yarmouth. Detached 3 bedroom bungalows, seafront bungalows, detached Sea-Dell chalets and modern sea front caravans. Free colour brochure: DON WITHERIDGE, BLUE RIBAND HOUSE, PARKLANDS, HEMSBY, GREAT YARMOUTH NR29 4HA (01493 730445). [pw! 🐕].
website: www.BlueRibandHolidays.co.uk

Coltishall

Village to the north east of Norwich.

THE NORFOLK MEAD HOTEL, COLTISHALL, NORWICH, NORFOLK NR12 7DN (01603 737531). Renowned restaurant offering superb cuisine and a comprehensive wine list. Well mannered dogs welcome. Johansens recommended. [Pets £6 per night]
e-mail: info@norfolkmead.co.uk website: www.norfolkmead.co.uk

Cromer

Attractive resort built round old fishing village. Norwich 21 miles.

KINGS CHALET PARK, CROMER NR27 0AJ (01263 511308) . Well-equipped chalets sleeping 2 to 6; shower/bathroom, microwave and TV. 1 Twin, 1 Double bedroom, bed sofa in lounge, well-equipped kitchenette. Quiet site adjacent to woods, golf club and beaches. Local shops nearby. Pleasant 10 minutes' walk to town. Tourist Board and NNH/GHA Approved. Families welcome. [🐕]

All-electric two and three bedroom Holiday Cottages accommodating four to six persons in beautiful surroundings. Sandy beaches, sports facilities, Cinema and Pier (live shows). Parking. Children and pets welcome. ETC ★★-★★★ Brochure: BROADGATES COTTAGES, NORTHREPPS, FOREST PARK CARAVAN SITE LTD, NORTHREPPS ROAD, CROMER, NORFOLK NR27 0JR (01263 513290; Fax: 01263 511992) [Pets £12 weekly].
e-mail: gill@broadgates.co.uk website: www.broadgates.co.uk

KINGS CHALET PARK, CROMER. Comfortable well-equipped chalets on quiet site; ideally placed for woodland and beach walks. 10 minutes' walk to town, shops nearby. Details from MRS I. SCOLTOCK, SHANGRI-LA, LITTLE CAMBRIDGE, DUTON HILL, DUNMOW, ESSEX (01371 870482). [one Pet free]

CHALET 49 ~ KINGS CHALET PARK,CROMER. Luxury, well equipped chalet , adjacent to beaches, woods, cliff-top walks and golf courses. Local shops. Two bedrooms, bathroom, fitted kitchen, microwave, colour TV, etc. Sleeps four to five. Cleaned and maintained by owner. Pets welcome. Open March to October. MRS M. WALKER, 39 PAULS LANE, OVERSTRAND, CROMER, NORFOLK NR27 0PF (01263 579269) [Pets £10 per week]

CLIFTONVILLE HOTEL, SEAFRONT, CROMER NR27 9AS (01263 512543; Fax: 01263 515700). Ideally situated on the Norfolk coast. Beautifully restored Edwardian Hotel. 30 en suite bedrooms all with sea view. Executive suites. Seafood Bistro, à la carte Restaurant. [pw! pets £4 per night]

Dereham

Situated 16 miles west of Norwich. St Nicholas Church has 16th century bell tower.

BARTLES LODGE, CHURCH STREET, ELSING, DEREHAM NR20 3EA (01362 637177). Stay in the peaceful, tranquil heart of Norfolk's most beautiful countryside. All rooms en suite, TVs, tea/coffee making facilities, etc. Recommended by "Which?" Good Bed & Breakfast Guide. [pw! Pets £2 per night, £7 per week]

SCARNING DALE, SCARNING, EAST DEREHAM NR19 2QN (01362 687269). Self-catering cottages (not commercialised) in grounds of owner's house. On-site indoor heated swimming pool and full-size snooker table. B&B for six also available in house (sorry no pets in house). Grazing and Stables available.

East Dereham

Site of 7th Century nunnery. Archaeogical Museum at Bishop Banner's Cottages, with distinctive fruit and flower plaster work.

HOLLY FARM COTTAGES, HIGH COMMON, CRANWORTH, NORFOLK IP25 7SX (01362 821468). 2 single-storey cottages each sleeping 1-4. TV/video, dishwasher, washing machine, central heating. Enclosed garden. Ample car parking. Peaceful lanes for walking/cycling. Local golf and fishing. Use of field for pony/horse. [🐕]
e-mail: jennie.mclaren@btopenworld.com

Fakenham

Agricultural centre on River Wensum 23 miles north-west of Norwich.

VERE LODGE, SOUTH RAYNHAM, NEAR FAKENHAM NR21 7HE (01328 838261; Fax: 01328 838300). 14 superbly equipped cottages with leisure centre and heated indoor pool. 8 acres of lawns, paddock and woodland, with Norfolk's vast beaches nearby. [pw! Pets £23 per week]
e-mail: major@verelodge.co.uk website: www.idylliccottages.co.uk

Foxley

Village 6 miles east of East Dereham.

Self Catering Chalets (2/3 bedrooms) on working farm. All fully equipped, with central heating. 20 miles from coast, 15 from Broads. Mature woodland nearby. Ideal for walking. ETC ★★/★★★. MOOR FARM STABLE COTTAGES, FOXLEY NR20 4QN (01362 688523). [Pets £10 per week]

Great Yarmouth

Traditional lively seaside resort with a wide range of amusements, including the Marina Centre and Sealife Centre.

MRS MICHELLE BROWNE, SUNWRIGHT HOLIDAYS, 19 NILE ROAD, GORLESTON, GREAT YARMOUTH NR31 6AS (01493 304282) Sundowner holiday park, near Great Yarmouth. Fully furnished and equipped self catering chalets, sleep up to 6. Close to beach, Norfolk Broads and many attractions. [Pets £15 per week].
e-mail: sunwrightholiday@aol.com website: www.sunwrightholidays.co.uk

CAREFREE HOLIDAYS, CHAPEL BRIERS, YARMOUTH ROAD, HEMSBY, GREAT YARMOUTH NR29 4NJ (01493 732176). A wide selection of superior chalets for live-as-you-please holidays near Great Yarmouth and Norfolk Broads. All amenities on site. Parking. Children and pets welcome. [Pets £10 per week, £5 on short breaks, 2nd pet free.]

Horningtoft

Village 4 miles south of Fakenham.

MR IVAN BAKER, OLD STABLES HOLIDAY COTTAGES, CHURCH FARM, HORNINGTOFT, DEREHAM, NORFOLK NR20 5DX (Tel: 01328 700262; Mobile: 07775 707992). All the comforts of home in new barn conversions in a peaceful, rural village. Easy access to pubs, restaurants, shops and the north Norfolk coastline. [🐕]

Hunstanton

Neat little resort which faces west across The Wash with many beautiful medieval and Georgian buildings.

MRS E. PRICE, MARINE HOTEL, HUNSTANTON PE36 5EH (01485 533310). Overlooking sea and green. Pets welcome. Colour TV in all bedrooms. Open all year except Christmas period. [Pets £1 per night].

King's Lynn

Ancient market town and port on the Wash with many beautiful medieval and Georgian buildings.

MRS G. DAVIDSON, HOLMDENE FARM, BEESTON, KING'S LYNN PE32 2NJ (01328 701284). 17th century farmhouse situated in central Norfolk within easy reach of the coast and Broads. Sporting activities available locally, village pub nearby. One double room, one twin and one single. Pets welcome. Bed and Breakfast from £20 per person; Evening Meal from £15. Weekly terms available and child reductions. Two self-catering cottages. Sleeping 4/8. Terms on request. ETC ★★★ [🐕]
e-mail: holmdenefarm@farmersweekly.net website: www.northnorfolk.co.uk/holmdenefarm

MRS J. E. FORD, LEZIATE DROVE, POTT ROW, KING'S LYNN PE32 1DE (01553 630356). Detached bungalow sleeps 4. In quiet village close to Sandringham and beaches. Facilities include colour TV, video, microwave, fridge/freezer, washing machine, off road parking, dog run. [🐕]

Mundesley-on-Sea

Small resort backed by low cliffs. Good sands and bathing. Norwich 20 miles, Cromer 7.

47 SEAWARD CREST, MUNDESLEY. West-facing brick built chalet on private site with lawns, flowers and parking. Large lounge/dining room, kitchenette, two bedrooms, bathroom. Beach and shops nearby. Weekly terms from £90. Pets most welcome. SAE please: MRS DOAR, 4 DENBURY ROAD, RAVENSHEAD, NOTTS, NG15 9FQ (01623 798032).

KILN CLIFFS CARAVAN PARK, CROMER ROAD, MUNDESLEY NR11 8DF (01263 720449). Peaceful family-run site situated around an historic brick kiln. Six-berth caravans for hire, standing on ten acres of grassy cliff top. All caravans fully equipped (except linen) and price includes all gas and electricity. [Pets £5 per week].

MRS CHRISTINE THROWER, WHINCLIFF BED & BREAKFAST, CROMER ROAD, MUNDESLEY NR11 8DU (01263 721554). Clifftop house, sea views and sandy beaches. Rooms with colour TV and tea-making. Families and pets welcome. Open all year round. [🐕]
e-mail: whincliff@freeuk.com website: http://whincliff.freeuk.com

HOLIDAY PROPERTIES (MUNDESLEY) LTD, 6a PASTON ROAD, NORWICH, NORFOLK NR11 8BN (01263 720719). Self-catering holiday chalets on three pretty sites in village on North Norfolk coast, close to sandy beach, and village amenities. All chalets are heated with fully equipped kitchens, colour TVs. Sleep 4-6. Pets welcome. Low season short breaks. [Pets £10 per week].
e-mail: holidayproperties@tesco.net website: www.holidayprops.freeuk.com

Neatishead

Ideal for touring East Anglia. Close to Norwich. Aylsham 14 miles, Norwich 10, Wroxham 3.

ALAN AND SUE WRIGLEY, REGENCY GUEST HOUSE, THE STREET, NEATISHEAD, NORFOLK BROADS NR12 8AD (Tel & Fax: 01692 630233). 18th century three-bedroomed guest house renowned for generous English breakfasts. Ideal East Anglian touring base. Accent on personal service. B&B from £22. ETC/AA ◆◆◆◆ Dogs welcome. [Pets £4 per night.]
e-mail: regencywrigley@btopenworld.com website: www.norfolkbroads.com/regency

---

Terms quoted in this publication may be subject to increase if rises in costs necessitate

---

North Walsham

Market town 14 miles north of Norwich, traditional centre of the Norfolk reed thatching industry.

MR P. O'HARA, GEOFFREY THE DYER'S HOUSE, CHURCH PLAIN, WORSTEAD, NORTH WALSHAM NR28 9AL (01692 536562). 17th century Listed weaver's house in centre of conservation village. Close to Broads, Coast, Norwich. Good walking and touring. All rooms en suite. Wholesome, well-cooked food. Dogs welcome. [🐕]
e-mail: valohara@hotmail.com

MRS. G. FAULKNER, DOLPHIN LODGE, 3 KNAPTON ROAD,TRUNCH, NORTH WALSHAM NR28 0QE (01263 720961). Friendly-run bungalow accommodation. B&B in village setting two-and-a-half miles from beaches. Many rural walks. Easy reach of all Norfolk attractions including Norfolk Broads. All rooms en suite, tea/coffee facilities, TVs, hairdryers etc. ETC ◆◆◆

Old Hunstanton

Coastal resort on The Wash 14 miles north east of King's Lynn.

COBBLERS COTTAGE, 3 WODEHOUSE ROAD, OLD HUNSTANTON PE36 6JD (01485 534036). Near Royal Sandringham/Norfolk Lavender. All en suite twin/double rooms. Colour TV and tea-making facilities. Near the beach, golf, bird watching, pubs and restaurants. Also self catering annexe. [Pets free in B&B; one or two dogs £15 per week S/C ground floor]
e-mail: lesley.cobblerscottage@btinternet.com

Thornham

Village 4 miles east of Hunstanton. Site of Roman signal station.

THE LIFEBOAT INN, SHIP LANE, THORNHAM PE36 6LT (01485 512236; Fax: 01485 512323). A welcome sight for the weary traveller for centuries. Dogs welcome. Restaurant (one AA rosette). Bird watching and walking along miles of open beaches. Please ring for brochure and tariff. [🐕]
e-mail: reception@lifeboatinn.co.uk website: www.lifeboatinn.co.uk

Thorpe Market

Village 4 miles south of Cromer.

GREEN FARM HOTEL AND RESTAURANT, THORPE MARKET, NORTH WALSHAM, NORTH NORFOLK NR11 8TH (01263 833602; Fax: 01263 833163). 16th Century flint-faced farmhouse inn. 14 antique style en suite bedrooms. Telephone for details of our special breaks available all year. [Pets £5 per night]
e-mail: grfarmh@aol.com website: www.greenfarmhotel.co.uk

Thurne

Idyllic Broadland village. Great Yarmouth 10 miles.

HEDERA HOUSE AND PLANTATION BUNGALOWS, THURNE, NORFOLK NR29 3BU (01692 670242 or 01493 844568). Adjacent river, seven bedroomed farmhouse, 10 competitively priced bungalows in peaceful gardens. Outdoor heated pool. Enjoy boating, fishing, walking, touring, nearby golf, horseriding, sandy beaches and popular resorts.

Wells-Next-the-Sea

Lovely little resort with interesting harbour, famous for its cockles, whelks and shrimps. A winding creek leads to a beach of fine sands with dunes. Norwich 31 miles, King's Lynn 27, Cromer 19.

MRS J. M. COURT, EASTDENE, NORTHFIELD LANE, WELLS-NEXT-THE-SEA NR23 1LH (01328 710381). Homely Guest House offers warm welcome. Bed and Breakfast from £22. Two double, one twin bedded rooms, all en suite; tea/coffee making facilities and colour TV. Private parking. [Pets £1 per night].

Weybourne

Village 4 miles north-east of Holt.

BOLDING WAY HOLIDAY COTTAGES, WEYBOURNE, HOLT NR25 7SW (0800 0560 996 or 01263 588666). Sleeping 2-8, each with its own garden (2 other cottages available but no pets). 10 minute walk to sea. Free membership of local indoor leisure centre. Open all year. ETC ★★★★ [🐕]
website: www.boldingway.co.uk

Winterton-on-Sea

Good sands and bathing. Great Yarmouth 8 miles.

WINTERTON VALLEY HOLIDAYS. A selection of modern superior fully appointed holiday chalets in a choice of locations near Great Yarmouth. Enjoy panoramic views from WINTERTON, a quiet and picturesque 35-acre estate, while CALIFORNIA has all the usual amenities, with free entry to the pool and clubhouse. Pets are very welcome at both sites. For colour brochure; 15 KINGSTON AVENUE, CAISTER-ON-SEA NR30 5ET (01493 377175).
website: www.wintertonvalleyholidays.co.uk

WINTERTON HOLIDAYS, WINTERTON-ON-SEA, GREAT YARMOUTH. For a peaceful. relaxing holiday. One and two bedroom self-catering chalets, furnished and equipped to a high standard. Quiet, picturesque park overlooking Winterton Valley with panoramic sea views. Miles of walks along the valley, dunes and beach. MRS JUNE HUDSON, 42 LARK WAY, BRADWELL, GREAT YARMOUTH NR31 8SB (01493 444700). [Pets £10 per week]
website: www.wintertonholidays.com

Wroxham

Village 7 miles north east of Norwich.

WROXHAM PARK LODGE, 142 NORWICH ROAD, WROXHAM NR12 8SA (01603 782991). Elegant Victorian House near north Norfolk coast, Great Yarmouth and Norwich. Open all year. All rooms en suite, tea/coffee making facilities, colour TV. Pets by arrangement. Ring for brochure. ETC ◆◆◆◆ [🐕]

THE BROADS HOTEL, STATION ROAD, WROXHAM, NORWICH NR12 8UR (01603 782869; Fax: 01603 784066). Comfortable hotel owned and run by dog-loving family. Ideally situated for boating, fishing and exploring the beautiful Norfolk countryside and coastline. All rooms fully en suite. [🐕]

SYMBOLS

- 🐕 **Indicates that pets are welcome free of charge.**
- £ **Indicates that a charge is made for pets: nightly or weekly.**
- pw! **Shows some special provision for pets; exercise facility, feeding or accommodation arrangement.**
- ⌂ **Indicates separate pets accommodation.**

FREE or REDUCED RATE entry to Holiday Visits and Attractions – see our READERS' OFFER VOUCHERS on pages 103-118

Mount Pleasant Farm

Alnmouth, Alnwick NE66 3BY

Mount Pleasant farm is situated on a hill overlooking seaside village of Alnmouth. Ideal base for beaches, castles, the Farnes, the Cheviots & Holy Island. Farmhouse annexe open plan sleeps 2. Chalet two bedrooms sleeps 4. Caravan is 6 berth. Pets welcome.

Prices on application.

Telephone 01665 830 215 for more details.

The Mizen Head Hotel

En suite bedrooms, a residents' conservatory lounge and non-smoking restaurant. Public bar offers good food and real ales with an open log fire in winter. A la carte restaurant uses local produce. Family rooms are available with listening service and cots if required. Car park. Children and pets welcome. Local attractions include Bamburgh Castle and Holy Isle. For golfers discounts can be arranged.
website: www.mizenheadhotel.co.uk

AA ★★

Bamburgh, Northumberland NE69 7BS
Tel: 01668 214254
Fax: 01668 214104

See also Colour Advertisement on page 51

Hotel Waren Mill, Bamburgh, Northumberland NE70 7EE
Tel: 01668 214581 e-mail: enquires@warenhousehotel.co.uk
web: www.warenhousehotel.co.uk AA ★★★ RAC ★★★ ETC ★★★

Why not let your best friend join you and your partner at our luxurious Country House Hotel. Excellent accommodation, superb food and extensive moderately priced wine list. Rural setting in six acres of grounds on edge of Budle Bay 2 miles from Bamburgh Castle. No children under 14 please.

Etive Cottage, Warenford, Near Belford

Etive is a well-equipped two bedroomed stone cottage with double glazing and central heating. Situated on the outskirts of the hamlet of Warenford with open views to the Bamburgh coast. Fenced garden and secure courtyard parking. Pet and owners welcome pack on arrival - give your pets the holiday they deserve.

For brochure contact Jan Thompson Tel/Fax: 01668 213233

BLUEBELL FARM West Street, Belford, Northumberland NE70 7QE

Sleeps 2/6 plus cot. Traditional stone cottages converted from original farm buildings. An ideal base for Heritage Coast, beaches, Holy Island (Lindisfarne), Farne Islands, Kyloe/Cheviot Hills, Scottish Borders. Excellent pubs/food within walking distance. Berwick/Alnwick each 14 miles. Six self-contained cottages providing accommodation in double/ twin/children's bedrooms with linen/duvets/towels; kitchen with gas cookers/microwaves/fridge-freezers, Colour TVs. Garden/patio with barbecue; children's play area. Short Breaks/weekends. Rates £170 to £230 and £290 to £430.

Please contact Phyl Carruthers for details: Tel: 01668 213362; Mobile: 0770 3335430. E-mail: phyl.carruthers@virgin.net

Cresswell Towers Holiday Park

ETC★★★

Cresswell, Near Morpeth, Northumberland NE61 5JT

Highly attractive park in a natural woodland setting. Modern, well-equipped caravans for hire. Outdoor heated pool, sun terrace, outdoor children's play area, multi-sports court, café, shop and clubhouse. Local to park – spectacular beaches, pleasant walks, golfing and sea fishing.

www.gbholidayparks.co.uk

Call **0870 442 9311** for brochure

Scotchcoulthard • Haltwhistle, Northumberland NE49 9NH

01434 344470 • Fax: 01434 344020 • *Props: A.D. & S.M. Saunders*
e-mail: info@scotchcoulthard.co.uk • www.scotchcoulthard.co.uk

Situated in 178 acres within Northumberland National Park, fully equipped self-catering cottages (sleep 2/7). All bedrooms en suite; open fires. Fridge/freezer, colour TV, microwave; all except one have dishwasher and washing machine. Linen, towels, all fuel incl. Heated indoor pool, games room. Well-behaved dogs and horses welcome.

Sandy Bay Holiday Park

ETC★★★

North Seaton, Ashington, Northumberland NE63 9YD

Charming coastal park with own beach. Pleasant clifftop views and walks along the adjacent River Wansbeck. Modern, well-equipped caravans for hire. Indoor heated pool, outdoor play area, kids' club, cycle paths, multi-sports courts, choice of bars, take away, pitch' n 'putt and entertainment.

www.gbholidayparks.co.uk Call **0870 442 9310** for brochure

BIRLING VALE, WARKWORTH.

Attractive stone built detached house in secluded garden. Fully equipped, two double bedrooms, one twin, cot. Free central heating. Close to sandy beaches, trout and salmon rivers and many places of interest. Well-trained dogs welcome. Weekly rates from £130 (low season) – £440 (high season).

SAE to Mrs J. Brewis, Woodhouse Farm, Shilbottle, Near Alnwick NE66 2HR Tel: 01665 575222

See also Colour Advertisement on page 51

Warkworth House Hotel

Bridge Street, Warkworth Northumberland NE65 OXB

ETC/RAC ★★★

Set at the heart of the small village of Warkworth with its riverside walks, ideal for walking the dog while enjoying the view. Take a walk on the miles of open uncrowded beaches where your pet can roam free out of danger. Enjoy the many beauties that Northumberland can offer to complete a relaxing short break or holiday. Our kitchen will prepare your evening meal, a treat not to be missed. After which you can relax with coffee in the lounge (pets welcome). Please phone for bookings and brochures.

Tel: 01665 711276 Fax: 01665 713323
E-mail: welcome@warkworthhousehotel.co.uk
Website: www.warkworthhousehotel.co.uk

DALES HOLIDAY COTTAGES offer a selection of around 50 superb, personally inspected holiday properties, in beautiful rural and coastal locations. Including Hadrian's Wall country and the Borders. Cosy cottages to Country houses, many open all year. FREE brochure on request. DALES HOLIDAY COTTAGES, CARLETON BUSINESS PARK, SKIPTON, NORTH YORKSHIRE BD23 2AA. (01756) 799821 & 790919.
website: www.dalesholcot.com

Alnmouth

Quiet little resort with wide sands. Alnwick with impressive Alnwick Castle is 5 miles north west.

MRS A. STANTON, MOUNT PLEASANT FARM, ALNMOUTH, ALNWICK NE66 3BY (01665 830215). Situated at top of hill on outskirts of seaside village; convenient for castles and Holy Island. Self-contained annexe sleeps 2 adults; open-plan; shower room. Chalet and 6-berth caravan also available. [Pets £5 per week]

Bamburgh

Village on North Sea coast with magnificent castle. Grace Darling buried in churchyard

THE MIZEN HEAD HOTEL, BAMBURGH NE69 7BS (01668 214254; Fax: 01668 214104). A warm welcome awaits owners and pets alike at the Mizen Head. Close to the beautiful Northumbrian coastline and just a short drive from many lovely walks in the Ingram Valley. The hotel boasts log fires, good food and real ales. AA ★★
website: www.mizenheadhotel.co.uk

MR P. LAVERACK, WAREN HOUSE HOTEL, WAREN MILL, BAMBURGH NE70 7EE (01668 214581). Luxurious Country House Hotel. Excellent accommodation, superb food, moderately priced wine list. Rural setting. No children under 14 please. ETC/ RAC /AA ★★★. [🐕]
e-mail: enquires@warenhousehotel.co.uk website: www.warenhousehotel.co.uk

Belford

Village 14 miles south-east of Berwick-upon-Tweed.

ETIVE COTTAGE, WARENFORD, NEAR BELFORD. Well-equipped two-bedroomed cottage with double glazing, central heating. Open views to coast. Fenced garden; secure parking. Welcome pack. Brochure: JAN THOMPSON (Tel & Fax: 01668 213233). [🐕]

BLUEBELL FARM, WEST STREET, BELFORD NE70 7QE (01668 213362; Mobile: 0770 333 5430) Sleeps 2/6 plus cot. Traditional self-contained stone cottages converted from original farm buildings. Ideal base for Heritage Coast, Holy Island (Lindisfarne), Farne Islands and Scottish Borders. Rates £170 to £230 and £290 to £430. Please contact Phyl Carruthers for details. [Pets £20 per week]
e-mail: phyl.carruthers@virgin.net

Cresswell

Coastal village 4 miles north of Ashington. Beach protected from North Sea by outlying reef.

CRESSWELL TOWERS HOLIDAY PARK, CRESSWELL, NEAR MORPETH NE61 5JT. Highly attractive park in a natural woodland setting. Well-equipped caravans for hire. Outdoor heated pool, multi-sports court, café, shop and clubhouse. Spectacular beaches, golfing nearby. Call 0870 442 9311 for brochure. ETC★★★[🐕]
website: www.gbholidayparks.co.uk

SYMBOLS

- 🐕 **Indicates that pets are welcome free of charge.**
- £ **Indicates that a charge is made for pets: nightly or weekly.**
- pw! **Shows some special provision for pets; exercise facility, feeding or accommodation arrangement.**
- ☖ **Indicates separate pets accommodation.**

Haltwhistle

Small market town about one mile south of Hadrian's Wall.

KATH AND BRAD DOWLE, SAUGHY RIGG FARM, TWICE BREWED, HALTWHISTLE NE49 9PT (01434 344120). Close to the best parts of Hadrian's Wall. A warm welcome and good food. All rooms en suite. Parking. TV. Central heating. Children and pets welcome. Open all year. Prices from £17.50 pppn. ETC ◆◆◆◆
e-mail: kathandbrad@aol.com website: www.saughyrigg.co.uk

A.D. & S.M. SAUNDERS, SCOTCHCOULTHARD, HALTWHISTLE NE49 9NH (01434 344470; Fax: 01434 344020). Situated in 178 acres within Northumberland National Park, fully equipped self-catering cottages (sleep 2/7). Linen, towels, all fuel incl. Heated indoor pool, games room. Well-behaved dogs and horses welcome. [🐕]
e-mail: info@scotchcoulthard.co.uk website: www.scotchcoulthard.co.uk

Newbiggin-on-Sea

Fishing town and resort on the North Sea coast, 2 miles east of Ashington.

SANDY BAY HOLIDAY PARK, NORTH SEATON, ASHINGTON NE63 9YD. Charming coastal park with own beach. Modern, well-equipped caravans for hire. Indoor heated pool, outdoor activities, choice of bars, take away and entertainment. Call 0870 442 9310 for brochure. ETC★★★ [🐕]
website: www.gbholidayparks.co.uk

Warkworth

Village on River Coquet near North Sea coast north-west of Amble with several interesting historic remains.

Birling Vale is an attractive stone built detached house in secluded garden. Fully equipped, two double bedrooms, one twin, cot. Free central heating. Close to sandy beaches, trout and salmon rivers and many places of interest. Well-trained dogs welcome. Weekly rates from £130 Low Season, £250 Mid Season, £440 High Season. SAE to MRS J. BREWIS, WOODHOUSE FARM, SHILBOTTLE, NEAR ALNWICK NE66 2HR (01665 575222). [🐕]

WARKWORTH HOUSE HOTEL, BRIDGE STREET, WARKWORTH NE65 OXB (01665 711276; Fax: 01665 713323). Set in heart of small village, ideal for dog walking. Miles of open uncrowded beaches. Delicious evening meals. Phone for brochure. [🐕]
e-mail: welcome@warkworthhousehotel.co.uk website: www.warkworthhousehotel.co.uk

NOTTINGHAMSHIRE

Burton Joyce

Residential area 4 miles north-east of Nottingham.

MRS V. BAKER, WILLOW HOUSE, 12 WILLOW WONG, BURTON JOYCE, NOTTINGHAM NG14 5FD (0115 931 2070). Large Victorian house in quiet village location, two minutes walk River Trent, four miles city. Attractive accommodation in bright, clean rooms with tea/coffee making facilities, TV. Private parking. From £19 pppn. Reduced rates for children. Good local eating. Please phone first for directions. [🐕]

Readers are requested to mention this guidebook when seeking accommodation (and please enclose a stamped addressed envelope).

Burford

COTTAGE IN THE COUNTRY. Holiday homes in Heart of England. 'Home from Home' quality and comfort. Short breaks available. Brochure (01993 831 495).
e-mail: cottage@cottageinthecountry.co.uk website: www.cottageinthecountry.co.uk

Burford

Small Cotswold Town on River Windrush, 7 miles west of Witney.

THE INN FOR ALL SEASONS, THE BARRINGTONS, NEAR BURFORD, OXFORDSHIRE OX18 4TN (01451 844324). Family-run and owned Hotel based on traditional 16th century English Coaching Inn. Ideal base for touring, walking and garden visiting. From £57 pppn DB&B for a minimum of two nights. [🐕]
e-mail: sharp@innforallseasons.com website: www.innforallseasons.com

Tackley

Village 3 miles north-east of Woodstock.

JUNE AND GEORGE COLLIER, 55 NETHERCOTE ROAD, TACKLEY, KIDLINGTON, OXFORD OX5 3AT (01869 331255; mobile: 07790 338225; Fax: 01869 331670). Bed and Breakfast in Tackley. An ideal base for touring, walking and riding. Central for Oxford, The Cotswolds, Stratford-on-Avon, Blenheim Palace. Woodstock four miles. There is a regular train and bus service with local Hostelries serving excellent food. ETC ◆◆◆ [🐕]
e-mail: colliers.bnb@virgin.net

Woodstock

Old town 8 miles north-west of Oxford. Home to Oxford City and County Museum.

GORSELANDS HALL, BODDINGTON LANE, NORTH LEIGH, WITNEY, OXFORD OX29 6PU (01993 882292; Fax: 01993 883629). Stone country house with oak beams and flagstone floors. Large secluded garden, with grass tennis court. All rooms are en suite, with colour television. ETC/RAC ◆◆◆◆. [pw! 🐕]
e-mail: hamilton@gorselandshall.com website: www.gorselandshall.com

ETC The Travellers Rest Inn

◆◆◆ **Upper Affcot, Church Stretton, SY6 6RL**
Tel: 01694 781275 • Fax: 01694 781555

E-mail: reception@travellersrestinn.co.uk Website: www.travellersrestinn.co.uk

Situated between Church Stretton and Craven Arms, and surrounded by The South Shropshire Hills. We, Fraser and Mauresia Allison, the owners assure you a warm welcome, good food, good beers, good accommodation, and good old fashioned service. For those wishing to stay overnight with us at The Travellers Rest we have 12 very nice en suite guest bedrooms: six of these being on the ground floor with easy access, and two of these are suitable for accompanied wheel chair users. The bedrooms are away from the main area of the Inn and have their own entrance to the car park and garden, ideal if you have brought your pet with you and a midnight walk is needed. Our well stocked Bar can satisfy most thirsts; cask ales, lagers, stouts, spirits, wines and minerals, throughout the day and the Kitchen takes care of your hunger; be it for a snack or a full satisfying meal, vegetarians no problem, food being served until 9pm in the evening.

Idyllic rural hamlet in the Stretton Hills – Mynd House Hotel

An Edwardian house offers a warm welcome and comfortable en suite rooms with great views. Centrally located for Ludlow, Shrewsbury, Ironbridge. Walks from the doorstep. Excellent home-cooked meals in a fusion of Eastern and Western cuisine, using local produce. Short Breaks available. No charge for dogs.

Mynd House Hotel, Ludlow Road, Little Stretton, Church Stretton, Shropshire SY6 6RB
Tel: 01694 722212 • web: www.myndhouse.co.uk • e-mail: info@myndhouse.co.uk • AA ★★

Oaklands Farm Cottages

In an Area of Outstanding Natural Beauty... Oaklands Farm is the perfect place for those seeking escape. Two traditional stone cottages, sleeping 5/6, private garden and freedom of adjoining fields and shared woodland.

Contact: Paul & Sallyann Swift,
Oaklands Farm, Kinton, Leintwardine SY7 0LT • Tel: 01547 540635

Built in 1789, the Moor Hall is a splendid example of Georgian Palladian style and enjoys breathtaking views over miles of unspoilt countryside. The atmosphere is relaxed and friendly. The gardens, which extend to five acres, provide a perfect setting in which to idle away a few hours, whilst the hills beyond offer wonderful discoveries for the more energetic. B&B from £25 pppn.

Near Ludlow, Shropshire SY8 3EG. Tel: 01584 823209; Fax: 08707 443725
e-mail: info@moorhall.co.uk website: www.moorhall.co.uk

FHG

Other specialised FHG PUBLICATIONS

Published annually: available in all good bookshops or direct from the publisher.

- **Recommended COUNTRY HOTELS OF BRITAIN £6.99**
- **Recommended SHORT BREAK HOLIDAYS IN BRITAIN £6.99**
- **Recommended WAYSIDE INNS OF BRITAIN £6.99**
- **PETS WELCOME £7.99**
- **THE GOLF GUIDE Where to Play / Where to Stay £9.99**

FHG PUBLICATIONS LTD, Abbey Mill Business Centre, Seedhill, Paisley, Renfrewshire PA1 1TJ
Tel: 0141-887 0428 • Fax: 0141-889 7204
e-mail: fhg@ipcmedia.com • website: www.holidayguides.com

GOOD HOTEL GUIDE
Country Hotel of the Year 2003

ETC
★★★
(Silver Award)

★★★ 77%

Food Award

Pen-y-Dyffryn Country Hotel

RHYDYCROESAU, NEAR OSWESTRY, SHROPSHIRE SY10 7JD

This silver stone former Georgian Rectory, set almost a thousand feet up in the Shropshire/Welsh hills, is in a dream situation for both pets and their owners. Informal atmosphere, no traffic, just buzzards, badgers and beautiful country walks, yet Shrewsbury, Chester, Powis Castle & Lake Vyrnwy are all close by. The well-stocked bar and licensed restaurant are always welcoming at the end of another hard day's relaxing. All bedrooms en suite etc; four have private patios, ideal for pets; one has a double spa bath. Short breaks available from £69 pppd, Dinner, B&B. Pets free.

TEL: 01691 653700 **MILES AND AUDREY HUNTER**
E-MAIL: stay@peny.co.uk **WEBSITE: www.peny.co.uk**

See also Colour Advertisement on page 52

Red House Farm is a late Victorian farmhouse in Longdon-on-Tern, a small village noted for the aqueduct built by Thomas Telford in 1796.

• Friendly welcome • Spacious rooms • Home comforts • Families welcome • Local pubs serving good food • Bed & Breakfast from £20 per person • Tel: 01952 770245

Contact Mrs Mary Jones, Red House Farm, Longdon-on-Tern, Wellington, Telford, Shropshire TF6 6LE
website: www.virtual-shropshire.co.uk/red-house-farm • e-mail: rhf@virtual-shropshire.co.uk

SELF CATERING COTTAGES
From £160 - £550 per week ETC ★★★
Sleeps 2 - 8 people, some ground floor bedrooms
3 beautifully converted barn cottages equipped and furnished to a high standard. Wheelchair friendly. Enclosed patio gardens.

BED & BREAKFAST
From £25 per person
Enjoy large country breakfast and a warm welcome.
Four poster, en suite and single rooms.
Central for Ironbridge, Shrewsbury, Welsh Border, Ludlow.

Church Farm, Rowton, Near Wellington, Telford, Shropshire TF6 6QY
Tel: 01952 770381 Website: www.virtual-shropshire.co.uk/churchfarm

FHG

FHG PUBLICATIONS

publish a large range of well-known accommodation guides. We will be happy to send you details or you can use the order form at the back of this book.

Church Stretton

Delightful little town in lee of Shropshire Hills. Walking and riding country. Facilities for tennis, bowls, gliding and golf. Knighton 22 miles, Bridgnorth 19, Ludlow 15, Shrewsbury 12.

DON AND RITA ROGERS, BELVEDERE GUEST HOUSE, BURWAY ROAD, CHURCH STRETTON SY6 6DP (01694 722232). Pleasant, centrally heated family Guest House – attractive gardens. Parking. Hairdryers, shaver points, Teasmaids all rooms. Two lounges – TV. Packed lunches available. Bed and Breakfast from £26. 10% reduction for weekly/party bookings. ETC ◆◆◆◆, AA◆◆◆◆ APPROVED. [🐕]

F. & M. ALLISON, TRAVELLERS REST INN, UPPER AFFCOT, NEAR CHURCH STRETTON SY6 6RL (01694 781275; Fax: 01694 781555). Fully licensed inn on the main A49. Good base for touring. Ample parking space. Children and dogs welcome. SAE or phone for further details. ETC ◆◆◆ [pw! 🐕]
e-mail: reception@travellersrestinn.co.uk website: www.travellersrestinn.co.uk

MYND HOUSE HOTEL, LUDLOW ROAD, LITTLE STRETTON, CHURCH STRETTON SY6 6RB (01694 722212). Comfortable small family-run hotel and restaurant in quiet village. Fully en suite. Walks from the doorstep. Convenient for Ludlow, Shrewsbury, Ironbridge etc. Short Breaks available. Dogs free. AA ★★ [🐕]
e-mail: info@myndhouse.co.uk website: www.myndhouse.co.uk

Craven Arms

Attractive little town with some interesting old half-timbered houses. Weekly cattle and sheep sales. Nearby is imposing Stokesay Castle (13th cent.) Bridgnorth 21 miles, Shrewsbury 20, Ludlow 8.

PAUL & SALLYANN SWIFT, OAKLANDS FARM COTTAGES, KINTON, LEINTWARDINE SY7 0LT (01547 540635). In an Area of Outstanding Natural Beauty, two renovated stone cottages sleeping 5/6. Share private garden. Central heating. Bed linen provided. Pets by arrangement.

Ludlow

Lovely and historic town on Rivers Teme and Corve with numerous old half-timbered houses and inns. Impressive Norman castle; river and woodland walks. Golf, tennis, bowls, steeplechase course. Worcester 29 miles, Shrewsbury 27, Hereford 24, Bridgnorth 19, Church Stretton 16.

CLIVE & CYNTHIA PRIOR, MOCKTREE BARNS, LEINTWARDINE, LUDLOW SY7 0LY (01547 540441). Self-catering cottages around sunny courtyard. Sleep 2-6. Comfortable, well-equipped. Friendly owners nearby. Dogs and children welcome. Lovely country walks from door. Ludlow, seven miles. Brochure. ETC ★★★ [🐕] **See also colour advertisement page 52.**
e-mail: mocktreebarns@care4free.net website: www.mocktreeholidays.co.uk

SALLY AND TIM LOFT, GOOSEFOOT BARN, PINSTONES, DIDDLEBURY, CRAVEN ARMS, SHROPSHIRE SY7 9LB (01584 861326). Converted in 2000 from stone and timbered barns, the three cottages are individually decorated to the highest standards. Each cottage has en suite facilities and private garden or seating area. Situated in a secluded valley. Ideally located for exploring south Shropshire. ETC ★★★★ [🐕]
e-mail: sally@goosefoot.freeserve.co.uk website: www.goosefootbarn.co.uk

THE MOOR HALL, NEAR LUDLOW SY8 3EG (01584 823209; Fax: 08707 443725). Built in 1789, a splendid example of the Georgian Palladian style. Breathtaking views, 5 acre garden. B&B from £25 pppn. AA ◆◆◆◆ [🐕]
e-mail: info@moorhall.co.uk website: www.moorhall.co.uk

SYMBOLS

🐕 **Indicates that pets are welcome free of charge.**

£ **Indicates that a charge is made for pets: nightly or weekly.**

pw! **Shows some special provision for pets; exercise facility, feeding or accommodation arrangement.**

⌂ **Indicates separate pets accommodation.**

Oswestry

Borderland market town. Many old castles and fortifications including 13th century Chirk Castle, Whittington Castle, Oswestry's huge Iron Age hill fort, Offa's Dyke. Shrewsbury 16, Vyrnwy 18.

PEN-Y-DYFFRYN COUNTRY HOUSE HOTEL, NEAR RHYDYCROESAU, OSWESTRY SY10 7JD (01691 653700). Picturesque Georgian Rectory quietly set in Shropshire/ Welsh Hills. Ten en suite bedrooms, two with private patios. 5-acre grounds. No passing traffic. Johansens recommended. Dinner, Bed and Breakfast from £69.00 per person per day. AA/ETC ★★★. [🐕 pw!]
e-mail: stay@peny.co.uk website: www.peny.co.uk

Telford

New town (1963). Ten miles east of Shrewsbury. Includes the south bank of the River Severn above and below Ironbridge, site of the world's first iron bridge (1777).

MRS MARY JONES, RED HOUSE FARM, LONGDON-ON-TERN, WELLINGTON, TELFORD TF6 6LE (01952 770245). Late Victorian farmhouse with friendly welcome. Spacious rooms, home comforts. Families welcome. Local pubs serving good food. Bed & Breakfast from £20 per person. Please come and visit our area. [🐕]
e-mail: rhf@virtual-shropshire.co.uk website: www.virtual-shropshire.co.uk/red-house-farm

CHURCH FARM, ROWTON, NEAR WELLINGTON TF6 6QY (01952 770381).B&B and self-catering in quiet village central for Shrewsbury, Ludlow, Ironbridge and Welsh Borders. En suite rooms, country breakfasts. Barn conversion. sleeps 2 - 8. [Pets £5 per week S/C, B&B no charge]
website: www.virtual-shropshire.co.uk/churchfarm

Exmoor • The Pack Horse Allerford, Near Porlock, Somerset TA24 8HW

Tel/Fax: 01643 862475 • www.thepackhorse.net • e-mail: holidays@thepackhorse.net

Our self-catering apartments and cottage are situated within a picturesque National Trust village which has local amenities. Enjoy immediate access from our doorstep to the beautiful surrounding countryside, pretty villages, spectacular coast, and Exmoor. OPEN ALL YEAR • PRIVATE PARKING • SHORT BREAKS • ETC ★★★

See also Colour Advertisement on page 54

TOGHILL HOUSE FARM Cottages and B&B Accommodation

Luxury barn conversions on working farm just north of Bath. Each cottage is equipped to a very high standard with bed linen provided. You are welcome to roam amongst our many animals and enjoy the outstanding country views. We also provide Bed and Breakfast accommodation in our warm and cosy 17th century farmhouse where all rooms are en suite with TV and tea making facilities. Pets £2 per night, £8 per week.

Brochure - Tel: 01225 891261 • Fax: 01225 892128 • website: www.toghillhousefarm.co.uk

David and Jackie Bishop, Toghill House Farm, Freezing Hill, Wick, Near Bath BS30 5RT

WESTWARD RISE HOLIDAY PARK

Brean, Near Burnham-on-Sea, Somerset TA8 2RD Tel & Fax: 01278 751310

Highly Recommended Luxury 2/6 berth Chalet-Bungalows on a small quiet family-owned Park adjoining sandy beach. ◆ 2 Double Bedrooms ◆ Shower ◆ Toilet ◆ Colour TV ◆ Fridge ◆ Cooker ◆ Duvets and Linen ◆ Open all year ◆ Centrally Heated during winter months ◆ Laundry on Park ◆ Caravan Sales Available ◆ Shops ◆ Clubs ◆ Amusements & Restaurants Nearby ◆ Dogs Welcome

Call now for a FREE BROCHURE. website: www.breansands.freeserve.co.uk

When making enquiries please mention FHG Publications

Beachside Holiday Park

Coast Road, Brean Sands, Somerset TA8 2QZ
Tel: 01278 751346 • Fax: 01278 751683

• Chalets and Caravan holiday homes on quiet park. Direct access to beach (pets £20 per week) •
• Full facilities • Colour television • Golf courses nearby • Bars and restaurant nearby •

FREE BROCHURE • FREEPHONE 08000 190322 • www.beachsideholidaypark.co.uk

BROADWAY HOUSE

Holiday Touring Caravan & Camping Park
Cheddar, Somerset BS27 3DB

•Holiday caravans for hire •Premier touring and camping pitches •Heated swimming pool •Adventure playground •Corner shop •English Pub and Family Room Launderette •Amusements • Bike hire • Activity programme • Nature trails • Skateboard park •BMX track •

Tel: 01934 742610 • Fax: 01934 744950 • e-mail: enquiries@broadwayhouse.uk.com
website: www.broadwayhouse.uk.com ETC★★★★

Spring Cottages

Three single bedroomed cottages with twin or double beds in a converted barn. Each sleeps 2/3 persons using extra folding bed as necessary. Linen, colour TV and basic heating included. Ample car parking. The Gorge/Caves are within walking distance. An acre of paddock to exercise your dog.

£205 – £290 per week. Short breaks out of season.

ETC ★★★★ SELF-CATERING Non-Smoking

Mrs Jennifer Buckland, Spring Cottage, Venns Gate, Cheddar BS27 3LW.
Tel/Fax: 01934 742493 • E-mail: buckland@springcottages.co.uk
Web: www.springcottages.co.uk

CHEDDAR - SUNGATE HOLIDAY APARTMENTS

Church Street, Cheddar, Somerset BS27 3RA

Delightful apartments in Cheddar village, each fully equipped. Sleep two/four. Laundry facilities. Private parking. Family, disabled and pet friendly.

For full details contact Mrs M. Fieldhouse.
Tel: 01934 842273/742264. Fax: 01934 844994 ETC ★★★

Highercombe Farm

Dulverton, Exmoor, Somerset TA22 9PT.
Tel & Fax: 01398 323616

A 450 acre farm on Exmoor and 100 acres of woodland in peaceful setting. Spectacular views. All rooms en suite. Bring your dog or horse and enjoy walking/riding directly onto moorland. Log fires, farmhouse cooking and much more. **ETC ◆◆◆◆ Silver Award.**

***Brochure available.* Contact: Abigail Humphrey**
e-mail: abigail@highercombe.demon.co.uk
website: www.highercombe.demon.co.uk

See also Colour Advertisement on page 52

THE YARN MARKET HOTEL

High Street, Dunster TA24 6SF
***Tel:* 01643 821425**
***Fax:* 01643 821475**
e-mail: yarnmarket.hotel@virgin.net
web: www.yarnmarkethotel.co.uk

In the centre of quaint English village, an ideal location for walking and exploring Exmoor, the surrounding coastline and the many local attractions. Comfortable, family-run hotel which provides a friendly, relaxed atmosphere, home cooking, en suite rooms with colour TV, tea making facilities and a residents' lounge. Packed lunches and drying facilities available. Non-smoking. Well behaved dogs welcome.

Party bookings and mid-week breaks a speciality

Pets Welcome *B&B From £30* *ETC ★★★ Hotel*

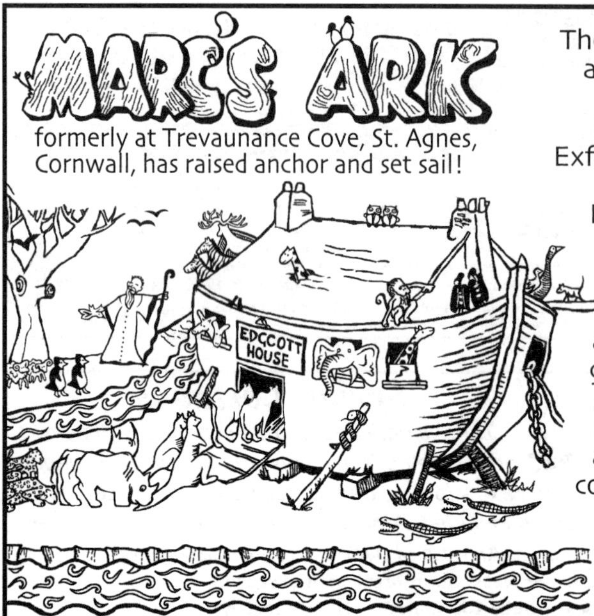

MARC'S ARK
formerly at Trevaunance Cove, St. Agnes, Cornwall, has raised anchor and set sail!
EDGCOTT HOUSE

The arc has come ashore at Edgcott House, a 17th Century country house in the village of Exford, right in the heart of the magnificent Exmoor National Park.

Edgcott is a country house of great charm and character set amidst mature, secluded gardens in beautiful lush countryside. Experience the sound of birdsong and bubbling brook, the comfort of open log fires, newly refurbished bedrooms - all with ensuite, and delicious full English breakfast.

The location may be new, but Marc's warm hospitality is unchanging.

Edgcott House, Exford, Somerset, TA247QG Tel/Fax: 01643 831 495

See colour advertisement on page 54

HUNTERS MOON

ETC ◆◆◆

Exford, Near Minehead, Somerset TA24 7PP

Cosy bungalow smallholding in the heart of Exmoor

★★ Glorious views ★★ Good food ★★ Friendly atmosphere ★★ Open all year ★★

Pets welcome free Optional Evening Meal

Bryan and Jane Jackson Tel: 01643 831695

e-mail: huntersmoon@bushinternet.com • website: www.exmooraccommodation.co.uk

Riscombe Farm Holiday Cottages – Exmoor National Park

Four charming self-catering stone cottages converted from barns surrounding an attractive courtyard with stables. Very comfortable, with log fires and equipped to a high standard, sleeping 2-7.

Peaceful, relaxing location beside the River Exe in the centre of Exmoor National Park.

Excellent walking and riding country in the valleys, across the moors or along the spectacular coast.

One and a half miles from Exford Village.

Dogs and horses welcome. Stabling provided.

Open all year. ETC ★★★★

Leone & Brian Martin,
Riscombe Farm, Exford,
Somerset TA24 7NH
Tel & Fax: 01643 831480
www.riscombe.co.uk ***(with vacancy info.)***

Please mention Pets Welcome when writing to enquire about accommodation

See also Colour Advertisement on page 53

See also Colour Advertisement on page 55

UPTON, NEAR WIVELISCOMBE, TAUNTON, SOMERSET TA4 2JH
Tel: 01398 371258 • Fax: 01398 371123
e-mail: ghughes@irisi.u-net.com • website: www.exmoor-cottages.com

West Withy Farm offers you and your dog a haven of peace and tranquillity in the beautiful, undiscovered Brendon Hills on the edge of Exmoor. The glorious countryside of Exmoor, the Brendons and the Quantocks provides a walker's paradise. Two local stone barns have been skilfully converted to provide well-equipped, detached character cottages with full central heating and stoves, sleeping 2- 6.

- **Panoramic views**
- **Private south-facing, enclosed, dog-proof gardens**
- **Colour TVs • Bed linen and towels provided**
- **Fully inclusive prices**
- **Short breaks available**
- **Residents carp lake**
- **Excellent fly fishing at Wimbleball and Clatworthy Reservoirs**

SIMONSBATH HOUSE HOTEL

Simonsbath, Exmoor, Somerset TA24 7SH
Tel: 01643 831259 • Fax: 01643 831557

The first house built on Exmoor in 1654 in the heart of the moor overlooking the River Barle and surrounded by moorland, making this the ideal location for those long walks on or off the lead with your pets.

Original features abound in the hotel - wood panelling and log fires to warm by on those chilly evenings. All bedrooms are en suite, centrally heated, colour television, direct dial telephone, hospitality tray, hairdryer and some with four-posters. There is a relaxing lawned garden and ample off-road parking.

Relax and enjoy a five-course evening dinner in our informal restaurant. Dogs are welcome to stay free of charge with you in your hotel bedroom or in one of our kennels with runs at the rear of the hotel. Open all year. Telephone Andrew or Louise for our Brochure and Tariff.

AA ★★ 74% **website: www.simonsbathhouse.co.uk** **B&B/B&B & Evening Dinner.**

Brochure from resident owners

Val & Mike Warner, Westerclose House, Withypool, Somerset TA24 7QR

Holiday Cottages – Exmoor National Park

Quality cottages, including bungalows in the grounds of an old hunting lodge. Wonderful moorland location. Totally peaceful with superb views. So much to do locally – beautiful coast and countryside. Shop and pub 300 metres. Excellent walking and riding straight from your cottage.Very cosy with log burners and hand-made furnishings. Dogs & horses welcome. Individual gardens. Sleep 2-6. Open all year. Short breaks available.

Tel/Fax: 01643 831302 • www.westerclose.f9.co.uk

The Crown Hotel

Exford, Exmoor National Park, Somerset TA24 7PP

Situated in the middle of Exford, one of the prettiest villages on the Moor and known as the Capital of Exmoor, The Crown is very much the centre of village life. After a day out in the open, where better to return than the Comfort of The Crown Hotel, with its log fires, comfortable lounges, en suite bedrooms, ancient bar and elegant restaurant where Head Chef Scott Dickson serves some of the most wonderfully exciting food on Exmoor. Dogs are welcome in guests' rooms or can be accommodated in our stable block free of charge. Why not bring your horse and enjoy a day's hunting with one of the local hunts. (There is a small charge for horses).

AA ★★★ **Tel: 01643 831554/5 • Fax: 01643 831665**  RESTAURANT AWARD

MINEHEAD – 16th CENTURY THATCHED COTTAGES

ROSE-ASH – Sleeps 2 ✦ Prettily furnished ✦ All electric.
WILLOW – Inglenook ✦ Oak panelling ✦ Electricity, Gas, CH ✦ Sleeps 6.
LITTLE THATCH – Sleeps 5 ✦ Inglenook ✦ Cosy location ✦ Electricity. Gas, CH.
SAE please to: Mr T. STONE, Troytes Farmstead, Tivington, Somerset TA24 8SU
Private car park – Enclosed gardens – Pets Welcome **Tel: 01643 704531**

THE SHIP INN Porlock TA24 8QD (01643 862507)

The thatched 13th century Ship Inn is within walking distance of sea and moor. There is a genuine old bar with stone floors and roaring log fires in winter. There are 10 bedrooms, mainly en suite. Local produce used. Real food, real ales and great accommodation. Gardens to enjoy. Ship's log details special events.

e-mail: mail@shipinnporlock.co.uk • website: www.shipinnporlock.co.uk

The Castle Hotel Porlock, Somerset TA24 8PY

Tel: 01643 862504• E-mail: castlehotel@btconnect.com

The Castle Hotel is a small, fully licensed family-run Hotel in the centre of the lovely Exmoor village of Porlock. There are 13 en suite bedrooms, all fully heated, with colour TV and tea/coffee making facilities. The Hotel offers everything from bar snacks to three-course meals which may be taken in the bar or restaurant. All well-behaved children and pets most welcome*, **Pool, darts & skittles.***

see also colour advertisement on page 56

ANDREWS ON THE WEIR Restaurant with Rooms

Overlooking Porlock Weir, where Exmoor meets the sea, is a restaurant with rooms where every meal is an experience; where each room is individual; and where pets are just as welcome as their owners. Discover the perfect break on Exmoor at Andrews.

Porlock Weir, Porlock, Somerset TA24 8PB
Tel: 01643 863300 Fax: 01643 863311 www.andrewsontheweir.co.uk

See also Colour Advertisement on page 56

Please mention *Pets Welcome*
when enquiring about accommodation featured in these pages.

Ralegh's Cross Inn Brendon Hill, Exmoor, Somerset TA23 0LN

High in the beautiful Brendon Hills, the warmest of welcomes awaits everyone at this 16th century coaching inn. A walker's, rider's and fisherman's paradise, with many places of interest nearby. Locally famous farmer's carvery. All rooms en suite. Seasonal leisure breaks. Please phone for colour brochure or our view website.

Tel: 01984 640343 • Fax: 01984 641111 • enquiry@raleghscross.co.uk • www.raleghscross.co.uk

See also Colour Advertisement on page 54

Lorna Doone HOLIDAY PARK, Watchet, Somerset TA23 0BJ.

A small, quiet family-run 5-star park with beautiful views over the sea, the coastline and the Quantock Hills. Fleet of highest quality luxury caravans with exceptional standards of cleanliness. Park facilities include shop, tourist information centre, launderette, patio/barbecue area, garden area and telephone.

Please telephone Ros and Brodie McIntyre on 01984 631206 for a colour brochure or write to the above address.
Website: www.lornadoone.co.uk E-mail: mail@lornadoone.co.uk

Croft Holiday Cottages • The Croft, Anchor Street, Watchet. TA23 0BY

Contact: Mrs K. Musgrave • Tel: 01984 631121 • Fax: 01984 631134 • ETC ★★★★

Courtyard of six cottages/bungalows situated in a quiet backwater of the small harbour town of Watchet. Parking, central heating. TV, washing machine, fridge, microwave. Use of heated indoor pool. Sleeps 2-8 persons £115-£530 per property per week. • **E-mail: croftcottages@talk21.com • www.cottagessomerset.com**

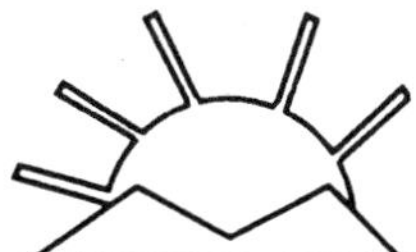

SUNNY BANK HOLIDAY CARAVANS

DONIFORD, WATCHET, SOMERSET TA23 0UD

SMALL PICTURESQUE FAMILY-RUN PARK
OVERLOOKING THE SEA NEAR MINEHEAD/ EXMOOR
CLOSE TO THE STEAM RAILWAY

Top quality caravans • Colour TV • Shower/Bath
• Heated Swimming Pool • Shop • Launderette • Good country walks • Access to Beach

Graded Exceptional by Tourist Board

Also caravans for sale.

Please telephone Peter & Anne Harrison on 01984 632237 for a coloured brochure or visit our website: www.sunnybankcp.co.uk

INFIELD HOUSE 36 Portway, Wells, Somerset BA5 2BN

Victorian townhouse a few minutes from city centre and Cathedral. Wonderful walks on Mendip Hills. Bountiful breakfasts. Dinners by arrangement.
No smoking. Parking. Well behaved dogs over 1 year old. AA ◆◆◆◆

Tel: 01749 670989 • Web: www.infieldhouse.co.uk • UK Local Rate tel: 0845 1304645

BRAESIDE HOTEL

Tel/Fax: (01934) 626642

2 VICTORIA PARK, WESTON-SUPER-MARE BS23 2HZ

Delightful, Family-run Hotel, ideally situated near sandy beach (dogs allowed all year) and park. All rooms en suite. Unrestricted on street parking. Open all year. Although fairly small, we have been awarded ◆◆◆◆ by the AA and the English Tourism Council.... expect quality and service.

Special B&B Offer: November to April inclusive (excl. Easter weekend) THIRD NIGHT FREE.

E-mail: braeside@tesco.net www.braesidehotel.co.uk

POWELLS COTTAGE HOLIDAYS, 51 HIGH STREET, SAUNDERSFOOT, PEMBROKESHIRE SA69 9EJ. Many of our top quality holiday properties accept pets. Cottages in Devon, Cornwall, Cotswolds, Pembrokeshire and Heart of England. For colour brochure FREEPHONE 0800 378771 (24 hours).
website: www.powells.co.uk

CLASSIC COTTAGES (01326 565 555). Featuring 500 hand selected coastal and country holiday homes throughout the West Country.
website: www.classic.co.uk

Allerford

Village 2 miles east of Porlock.

THE PACK HORSE, ALLERFORD, NEAR PORLOCK TA24 8HW (Tel/Fax: 01643 862475). Self-catering apartments and cottage within picturesque National Trust village. Immediate access to the beautiful surrounding countryside. Open all year. ETC ★★★
e-mail: holidays@thepackhorse.net website: www.thepackhorse.net

Bath

The best-preserved Georgian city in Britain, Bath has been famous since Roman times for its mineral springs. It is a noted centre for music and the arts, with a wide range of leisure facilities.

DAVID & JACKIE BISHOP, TOGHILL HOUSE FARM, FREEZING HILL, WICK, NEAR BATH BS30 5RT (01225 891261; Fax: 01225 892128). Luxury barn conversions on working farm 3 miles north of Bath. Each equipped to very high standard, bed linen provided. Also en suite B&B accommodation in 17th century farmhouse. [pw! Pets £2 per night, £8 per week]
website: www.toghillhousefarm.co.uk

Brean

Coastal village with extensive sands. To north is the promontory of Brean Down. Weston-Super-Mare 9 miles.

WESTWARD RISE HOLIDAY PARK, SOUTH ROAD, BREAN, NEAR BURNHAM ON-SEA TA8 2RD (01278 751310). Highly Recommended Luxury 2/6 berth Chalet bungalows. 2 double bedrooms, shower, toilet, TV, fridge, cooker, duvets and linen. Open all year. Call for free brochure. [Pets £10 per week.]
website: www.breansands.freeserve.co.uk

BEACHSIDE HOLIDAY PARK, COAST ROAD, BREAN SANDS TA8 2QZ (FREEPHONE 08000 190322; Tel: 01278 751346; Fax: 01278 751683). Chalets and Caravan holiday homes on quiet park. Direct access to beach (dogs allowed). Full facilities. Colour TV. Golf courses nearby. Bars and restaurant nearby. Free brochure. [Pets £20 per week]
website: www.beachsideholidaypark.co.uk

SEE PAGE 81 FOR FULL DETAILS

Cheddar

Picturesque little town in the Mendips, famous for its Gorge and unique caves. Cheese-making is a speciality. Good touring centre. Bath 24 miles, Burnham-on-sea 13, Weston-Super-Mare 11.

BROADWAY HOUSE HOLIDAY TOURING CARAVAN & CAMPING PARK, CHEDDAR BS27 3DB (01934 742610; Fax: 01934 744950). Holiday caravans for hire; premier touring and camping pitches. Heated pool, adventure playground, pub, shop, launderette. Superb range of activities - skateboard park, BMX track. ETC ★★★★
e-mail: enquiries@broadwayhouse.uk.com website: www.broadwayhouse.uk.com

MRS JENNIFER BUCKLAND, SPRING COTTAGES, VENNS GATE, CHEDDAR BS27 3LW (Tel & Fax: 01934 742493). Three single bedroomed cottages sleeping 2/3 persons. The Gorge/Caves are within walking distance. An acre of paddock to exercise your dog. Non-smoking. Short breaks. ETC ★★★★. [Dogs £3 per night, £20 per week].
e-mail: buckland@springcottages.co.uk website: www.springcottages.co.uk

SUNGATE HOLIDAY APARTMENTS, CHURCH STREET, CHEDDAR, SOMERSET BS27 3RA. Ideally situated for walking, cycling and touring the Mendips and the West Country. Competitively priced for short or longer holidays. For full details contact Mrs M. FIELDHOUSE (01934 842273/742264; Fax: 01934 844994) ETC ★★★ [Pets £10 per week].

Dulverton

Attractively set between Exmoor and Brendon Hills. Good fishing. In vicinity, prehistoric Tarr Steps (A.M. and N.T.). Exeter 27 miles, Taunton 26, Lynton 23, Minehead 19, Tiverton 13.

HIGHERCOMBE FARM, DULVERTON, EXMOOR TA22 9PT (01398 323616). A 450 acre farm on Exmoor and 100 acres of woodland in peaceful setting. Spectacular views. All rooms en suite. Bring your dog or horse and enjoy walking/riding directly onto moorland. Brochure available. Contact Abigail Humphrey. ETC ◆◆◆◆ and Silver Award. ETC ★★★ Self Catering [Pets £2 per night].

Dunster

Pretty village with interesting features, including Yarn Market, imposing 14th century Castle. Priory Church and old houses and cottages. Minehead 3 miles.

THE YARN MARKET HOTEL, HIGH STREET, DUNSTER TA24 6SF (01643 821425; Fax: 01643 821475). An ideal location for walking and exploring Exmoor. Family-run hotel with a friendly, relaxed atmosphere, home cooking, en suite rooms with colour TV and tea making facilities. Non-smoking. Mid-week breaks a speciality – Pets Welcome. ETC ★★★ Hotel [pw! 🐕]
e-mail: yarnmarket.hotel@virgin.net website: www.yarnmarkethotel.co.uk

Exford

Fine touring centre for Exmoor and North Devon, on River Exe. Dulverton 10 miles.

EDGCOTT HOUSE, EXFORD, NEAR MINEHEAD TA24 7QG. (Tel & Fax 01643 831495). Spacious, comfortable, old country house in the heart of Exmoor. Good food, private bathrooms. Wonderful walking. Pets welcome. [pw! 🐕]

BRYAN & JANE JACKSON, HUNTERS MOON, EXFORD, NEAR MINEHEAD TA24 7PP (01643 831695). Cosy bungalow smallholding in the heart of Exmoor. Good food (optional Evening Meal), glorious views, friendly atmosphere. Pets welcome free. Open all year. ETC ◆◆◆ [pw! 🐕].
e-mail: huntersmoon@bushinternet.com website: www.exmooraccommodation.co.uk

LEONE & BRIAN MARTIN, RISCOMBE FARM HOLIDAY COTTAGES, EXFORD, EXMOOR NATIONAL PARK, SOMERSET. TA24 7NH (Tel & Fax: 01643 831480). Four self-catering stone cottages in the centre of Exmoor National Park. Excellent walking and riding country. Dogs and horses welcome. Stabling provided. Open all year. ETC ★★★★ [Pets £1.50 per night, £10 per week.]
website: www.riscombe.co.uk (with up-to-date vacancy info.)

Exmoor

265 square miles of unspoiled heather moorland with deep wooded valleys and rivers, ideal for a walking, pony trekking or fishing holiday.

LYNDALE COTTAGE, ROADWATER, EXMOOR NATIONAL PARK TA23 0QY (01984 641426) 18th century stone cottage, combining character with comfort. Located in pretty village, near inn and shop. Sleeps 4 + 2. Open fire and woodburner. Beamed ceilings throughout. Parking and garden 50 yards from door. Excellent walking, inland and coastal. £200 - £400 per week. Please phone, e-mail or check our website for details.
e-mail: jojo@lyndale200.fslife.co.uk website: www.uk-holiday-cottages.co.uk/lyndale

DUNKERY BEACON HOTEL, WOOTTON COURTENAY TA24 8RH (01643 841241). Country House Hotel with superb views. Fully en suite rooms, colour TV. Lots of lovely "walkies". Spring/Summer/Autumn Breaks. Write or phone Kenneth or Daphne Midwood for details.[🐕] .
e-mail: Dunkery.Beacon@virgin.net website: www.dunkerybeaconhotel.co.uk

THE EXMOOR WHITE HORSE INN, EXFORD TA24 7PY (01643 831229; Fax: 01643 831246). Family-run 16th century inn situated in charming Exmoor village. 26 bedrooms all en suite, with colour TV and tea making. Fully licensed. Restaurant with varied menu. [🐕 - one dog].
e-mail: user@exmoorwhitehorse.demon.co.uk

MRS P. EDWARDS, WESTERMILL FARM, EXFORD, MINEHEAD TA24 7NJ (01643 831238; Fax: 01643 831216). Cottages in grass paddocks (Disabled Category 2), with woodburners. Separate campsite by river. Way-marked walks. Wonderful for dogs and owners. ETC up to ★★★★ [pw! Pets 50p per night (camp), £10 per week in cottages].
e-mail: holidays@westermill-exmoor.co.uk website: www.exmoorfarmholidays.co.uk

WEST WITHY FARM, UPTON, NEAR WIVELISCOMBE, TAUNTON TA4 2JH. (01398 371258; Fax: 01398 371123). Two cottages sleeping 2-6. Fully inclusive prices. Walker's paradise in the Brendons and Quantocks. Excellent fly-fishing. Enclosed, dog-proof gardens.Short breaks available. ETC ★★★★ [Pets £8 per week]
e-mail: ghughes@irisi.u-net.com website: www.exmoor.cottages.com

SIMONSBATH HOUSE HOTEL, SIMONSBATH, EXMOOR, SOMERSET TA24 7SH. (01643 831259; Fax: 01643 831557). Built on Exmoor in 1654 in the heart of the moor overlooking the River Barle. Original features. 8 En suite bedrooms. Open all year. B&B/B&B & Evening Dinner. Phone for brochure & tariff. AA ★★ 74% [pw! 🐕 ⌂]
website: www.simonsbathhouse.co.uk

WESTERCLOSE HOUSE, WITHYPOOL, EXMOOR NATIONAL PARK TA24 7QR (01643 831302). Five cosy cottages including two bungalows in grounds of old hunting lodge overlooking Barle Valley. Dogs and horses welcome. Shop and pub 300 metres. [pw! Dogs £8 per week]
website: www.westerclose.f9.co.uk

WOODCOMBE LODGES, BRATTON, NEAR MINEHEAD TA24 8SQ (Tel & Fax: 01643 702789). Four self-catering lodges in a tranquil rural setting on the edge of Exmoor National Park, standing in a beautiful 2½ acre garden with wonderful views. [Pets £5 per week]
e-mail: nicola@woodcombelodge.co.uk website: www.woodcombelodge.co.uk

STILEMOOR, EXFORD, EXMOOR NATIONAL PARK TA24 7NA. Charming cosy centrally heated detached bungalow with enclosed garden, superb views, walking, fishing, riding. Sleeps 6. ETC ★★★★. JOAN ATKINS, 2 EDGCOTT COTTAGE, EXFORD, MINEHEAD TA24 7QG (Tel & Fax: 01643 831564). [Pets £10 per week]
e-mail: info@stilemoorexmoor.co.uk website: www.stilemoorexmoor.co.uk

JANE STYLES, WINTERSHEAD FARM, SIMONSBATH TA24 7LF (01643 831222). Five tastefully furnished and well-equipped cottages situated in the midst of beautiful Exmoor. Pets welcome, stabling and grazing, DIY livery. Colour brochure on request. ETC ★★★★ [Dogs and horses £12 per week.]
website: www.wintershead.co.uk

CLEMENTS COTTAGE, TIVINGTON, NEAR MINEHEAD, SOMERSET TA24 8SU (01643 703970). 16th Century cross-passage house with spectacular views of the Bristol Channel and Dunkery Beacon. Central heating. Evening meals. Spring and summer bargain breaks. B&B from £18.50. Ring Una or Gordon for brochure. [Pets from £1.50 per night].
e-mail: clementscottage@exmoorbandb.co.uk website: www.exmoorbandb.co.uk

CUTTHORNE, LUCKWELL BRIDGE, WHEDDON CROSS TA24 7EW (01643 831255). Enjoy a touch of sheer luxury at our 14th century country house in glorious Exmoor. En suite facilities, log fires, candlelit dinners. ETC ◆◆◆◆ Gold Award. ETC ★★★★ Self Catering available [🐕 in B&B; Pets £15 per week S/C]
e-mail: durbin@cutthorne.co.uk website: www.cutthorne.co.uk

THE CROWN HOTEL, EXFORD TA24 7PP (01643 831554/5; Fax: 01643 831665). Situated in rural England. All bedrooms with bath, colour television, hairdryer. Excellent cuisine and fine wines. Bargain Breaks. Superb dog holiday country. Horses stable £20.00 per night. AA ★★★ and Two Rosettes. [🐕]

Minehead

Neat and stylish resort on Bristol Channel. Sandy bathing beach, attractive gardens, golf course and good facilities for tennis, bowls and horse riding. Within easy reach of the beauties of Exmoor.

MINEHEAD 16TH CENTURY THATCHED COTTAGES. Rose Ash - Sleeps 2, prettily furnished, all electric. Willow - Inglenook, oak panelling, electricity, gas, CH, Sleeps 6. Little Thatch - Sleeps 5, Inglenook, Cosy location, Electricity. Gas, CH. Private car park. Enclosed gardens. Pets welcome. SAE: MR T. STONE, TROYTES FARMSTEAD, TIVINGTON, MINEHEAD TA24 8SU (01643 704531). [🐕]

Porlock

Most attractive village beneath the tree-clad slopes of Exmoor. Picturesque cottages, old Ship Inn and interesting church. Good bathing from pebble beach at delightful Porlock Weir (2 miles).

JACKIE & ALAN COTTRELL, THE SHIP INN, HIGH STREET, PORLOCK TA24 8QD (01643 862507). Thatched 13th century inn within walking distance of sea and moor. There are 10 bedrooms, mainly en suite. Local produce used, international country cooking. Real ales. Resident dogs Bubbles & Monty. Sam the black labrador is a regular eater and recent 'best man'. [🐕]
e-mail: mail@shipinnporlock.co.uk website: www.shipinnporlock.co.uk

CASTLE HOTEL, PORLOCK TA24 8PY (01643 862504). Fully licensed, family-run hotel in centre of lovely Exmoor village. 13 en suite bedrooms, all with colour TV. Pool, darts & skittles. Bar snacks and meals. Well-behaved children and pets welcome. Five acres of fields for exercising dogs. [🐕]

ANDREWS ON THE WEIR, PORLOCK WEIR, PORLOCK, SOMERSET TA24 8PB (01643 863300; Fax: 01643 863311). Overlooking Porlock Weir is a restaurant with rooms where every meal is an experience; where each room is individual; and where pets are just as welcome as their owners.
website: www.andrewsontheweir.co.uk

Sherborne

Town with abbey and two castles, one of which was built by sir Walter Raleigh with lakes and gardens by Capability Brown.

MRS S. STRETTON, BEECH FARM, SIGWELLS, CHARLTON HORETHORNE, NEAR SHERBORNE, DORSET DT9 4LN (Tel & Fax: 01963 220524). Comfortable, relaxed farmhouse accommodation on our 137 acre dairy farm, with horses. Centrally heated with double room en suite, a twin room and a family room with guest bathroom, all with TV, tea/coffee trays. B&B £18 per person. Open all year except Christmas. Pets and horses welcome. [🐕]

When making enquiries or bookings, a stamped addressed envelope is always appreciated

Taunton

County town, rich in historical associations. Good touring centre. Many sporting attractions. Bristol 43 miles, Exeter 32, Weston-Super-Mare 29.

RALEGH'S CROSS INN BRENDON HILL, EXMOOR, SOMERSET TA23 0LN (01984 640343; Fax: 01984 641111). High in beautiful Exmoor, Ralegh's Cross Inn offers the warmest of welcomes. All en suite. Home-cooked food, farmer's carvery. A walker's, rider's and fisherman's paradise. Colour brochure available.[🐕]
e-mail: enquiry@raleghscross.co.uk website: www.raleghscross.co.uk

Watchet

Small port and resort with rocks and sands. Good centre for Exmoor and the Quantocks. Bathing, boating, fishing, rambling. Tiverton 24 miles, Bridgwater 19, Taunton 17, Dunster 6.

LORNA DOONE HOLIDAY PARK, WATCHET TA23 0BJ (01984 631206). Small quiet 5 star holiday park with beautiful views of the coastline and Quantock Hills. Luxury, fully-equipped Rose Award caravans. [Pets £2 per night]
e-mail: mail@lornadoone.co.uk website: www.lornadoone.co.uk

MRS K. MUSGRAVE, CROFT HOLIDAY COTTAGES, THE CROFT, ANCHOR STREET, WATCHET TA23 0BY. (01984 631121; Fax: 01984 631134). Courtyard of six cottages/bungalows situated in a quiet backwater of the small harbour town of Watchet. Parking, central heating. TV, washing machine, fridge, microwave. Use of heated indoor pool. Sleeps 2-8 persons £115-£530 per property per week. ETC ★★★★ [🐕]
e-mail: croftcottages@talk21.com website: www.cottagessomerset.com

SUNNY BANK HOLIDAY CARAVANS, DONIFORD, WATCHET TA23 0UD (01984 632237). Small picturesque family-run park overlooking sea. All caravans with mains services. Colour TV. Heated swimming pool. Shop. Launderette. ETC ★★★★★. Also caravans for sale. Brochure. [Pets £2 per night, £14 per week.]
website: www.sunnybankcp.co.uk

Wells

England's smallest city. West front of Cathedral built around 1230, shows superb collection of statuary.

MRS CATHERINE HAY, HILLVIEW COTTAGE, CROSCOMBE, NEAR WELLS BA5 3RL (01749 343526). Attractive cottage in stunning, quiet location surrounded by our own 8 acres of land. Near village with two pubs. En suite accommodation. City of Wells 2 miles. Pets most welcome.
e-mail: cathyhay@yahoo.co.uk website: www.SmoothHound.co.uk/hotels/hillview.html

INFIELD HOUSE, 36 PORTWAY, WELLS BA5 2BN (01749 670989; UK Local Rate 0845 1304645). Richard and Heather invite you and your dog (if older than one year) to visit England's smallest city. Wonderful walks on Mendip Hills. No smoking. Bountiful breakfasts, dinners by arrangement. AA ◆◆◆◆ [🐕]
website: www.infieldhouse.co.uk

Weston-Super-Mare

Popular resort on the Bristol Channel with a wide range of entertainments and leisure facilities. An ideal base for touring the West Country.

BRAESIDE HOTEL, 2 VICTORIA PARK, WESTON-SUPER-MARE BS23 2HZ (Tel & Fax: 01934 626642). Delightful, family-run Hotel, close to shops and sea front. All rooms en suite, colour TV, tea/coffee making. November to April (excl Easter weekend)THIRD NIGHT FREE. See display advertisement. ETC/AA ◆◆◆◆ [🐕]
e-mail: braeside@tesco.net website: www.braesidehotel.co.uk

Terms quoted in this publication may be subject to increase if rises in costs necessitate

---

Marl Flat Farm • Newtown • Staffordshire Moorlands

Stunning moorland views from our 10-acre farm quietly located close to Rudyard Lake with hiking and biking trails and superb moorland walks. Visit the famous Potteries and stately homes and gardens nearby, then relax by a real fire with fine home-cooked fare, before enjoying the comfort of our well-appointed balcony rooms with en suite facilities, TV, tea/coffee Iron/board, with open views of the Staffordshire moorlands.

Self-catering apartment available early 2004.

- Dogs most welcome.
- Holiday with your horse.
- Excellent Stabling & Kennel.
- Prices from £19pppn.

LITTLE PARK HOLIDAY HOMES

Barn Conversion Units. Full self-catering. Facilities situated next to medieval castle and tourist village. Spectacular views. Near Alton Towers and other theme parks. Ample parking. Please phone for brochure.

Park Lane, Tutbury, Near Burton-on-Trent, Staffordshire DE13 9JQ
Tel & Fax: 01283 812654 • Mobile: 07884 343460

Biddulph Moor

Located 2 miles north east of Biddulph town, 7 miles north of Stoke-on-Trent.

MARL FLAT FARM, NEWTOWN, BIDDULPH MOOR ST8 7SW (01782 379145). 10-acre farm with superb moorland walks. Rooms with en suite facilities, TV, tea/coffee. Dogs most welcome; holiday with your horse. Terms from £19pppn. [pw!]

Leek

Village 10 miles from Stoke-on-Trent.

EDITH & ALWYN MYCOCK, 'ROSEWOOD COTTAGE and ROSEWOOD FLAT', LOWER BERKHAMSYTCH FARM, BOTTOM HOUSE, NEAR LEEK ST13 7QP (Tel & Fax: 01538 308213). One cosy three bedroomed cottage with four poster. Also delightful flat which sleeps up to six. Both fully equipped and carpeted throughout. Electricity and linen inclusive, laundry room. Ideal base for Alton Towers, Potteries and Peak District. Terms £160 to £315. [Pets £5]

Tutbury

Village 4 miles north west of Burton-upon-Trent. Ruins of 14th century castle.

LITTLE PARK HOLIDAY HOMES, PARK LANE, TUTBURY, NEAR BURTON-ON-TRENT DE13 9JQ (Tel & Fax: 01283 812654; Mobile: 07884 343460). Barn Conversion Units. Full self-catering. Facilities situated next to medieval castle and tourist village. Spectacular views. Near Alton Towers and other theme parks. Ample parking. Please phone for brochure. [Pets £1 per night, £5 per week]

FREE or REDUCED RATE entry to Holiday Visits and Attractions – see our READERS' OFFER VOUCHERS on pages 103-118

Suffolk's No 1 holiday cottage letting agency.

A fine choice of individually selected cottages now available.
We are a friendly, local and independent firm.

For Brochure Tel: 01603 873378.

www.suffolkcountrycottages.co.uk

Aldeburgh, Diss, Dunwich, Kessingland

WENTWORTH HOTEL

AA ★★★ 76%

WENTWORTH ROAD, ALDEBURGH, SUFFOLK IP15 5BD

The Wentworth Hotel, privately run since 1920, offers a perfect welcome retreat. 37 comfortable, elegantly furnished bedrooms, most en suite, have colour television, radio and direct dial telephone. Fresh local produce such as fish, crab and lobster is extensively used in the relaxed atmosphere of the restaurant.

For a reservation, please Telephone: 01728 452312 or Fax: 01728 454343.
E-mail: stay@wentworth-aldeburgh.co.uk Website: www.wentworth-aldeburgh.com

See also Colour Advertisement on page 57

Country Bed and Breakfast

4B&B STRENNETH

Airfield Road, Fersfield, Diss
Norfolk IP22 2BP
Telephone: 01379 688182
Fax: 01379 688260
E-mail: pdavey@strenneth.co.uk
Website: www.strenneth.co.uk

STRENNETH is a well-established, family-run business, situated in unspoiled countryside just a short drive from Bressingham Gardens and the picturesque market town of Diss. Offering first-class accommodation, the original 17th Century building has been carefully renovated to a high standard with a wealth of exposed oak beams and a newer single storey courtyard wing. There is ample off road parking and plenty of nice walks nearby. All seven bedrooms, including a Four Poster and an Executive, are tastefully arranged with period furniture and distinctive beds. Each has remote-control colour television, hospitality tray, central heating and full en suite facilities. The establishment is smoke free and dinners are served by arrangement. There is an extensive breakfast menu using local produce. Ideal touring base. Pets most welcome at no extra charge. Outside kennels with runs if required. ETC ◆◆◆◆
Bed and Breakfast from £25.00

See also Colour Advertisement on page 48

THE CLOSE **MIDDLEGATE BARN, DUNWICH IP17 3DW**

Situated in a quiet, private road 200 yards from the sea. Furnished and equipped to a high standard. Please ask for our brochure. Centrally heated; available all year. Bookings taken from 1/1/2004.

Tel: 01728 648741

KNIGHTS HOLIDAY HOMES • KESSINGLAND

Quality **SEASIDE BUNGALOWS.** Open all year, central heating, colour TV, parking, bed linen, heating and lighting included. Sleep 1/6 persons. Direct access to award-winning beach.

BROCHURE ◆ CALENDAR ◆ OFFER LETTER ◆ BOOKING FORM
KNIGHTS HOLIDAY HOMES, 198 CHURCH ROAD, KESSINGLAND, SUFFOLK NR33 7SF
Tel: 01502 588533

CHILDREN AND PETS WELCOME

Freephone: 0800 269067

SHORT BREAK SPECIALS

See also Colour Advertisement on page 56

See also Colour Advertisement on page 57

SUFFOLK COUNTRY COTTAGES (01603 873378). Suffolk's No. 1 holiday cottage letting agency. A fine choice of individually selected cottages now available. We are a friendly, local and independent firm.
website: www.suffolkcountrycottages.co.uk

Aldeburgh

Coastal town 6 miles south-east of Saxmundham. Annual music festival at Snape Maltings.

WENTWORTH HOTEL, ALDEBURGH IP15 5BD (01728 452312). Country House Hotel overlooking the sea. Immediate access to the beach and walks. Two comfortable lounges with log fires and antique furniture. Refurbished bedrooms with all facilities and many with sea views. Restaurant specialises in fresh produce and sea food. AA ★★★ 76% One Rosette. [Pets £2 per day]
e-mail: stay@wentworth-aldeburgh.co.uk website: www.wentworth-aldeburgh.com

Bury St Edmunds

This prosperous market town on the River Lark lies 28 miles east of Cambridge.

RAVENWOOD HALL COUNTRY HOUSE HOTEL AND RESTAURANT, ROUGHAM, BURY ST EDMUNDS IP30 9JA (01359 270345; Fax: 01359 270788). 16th century heavily beamed Tudor Hall set in seven acres of perfect dog walks. Individually furnished en suite bedrooms; renowned restaurant; relaxing inglenook fires. AA ★★★, AA Rosette. [🐕 pw!]
e-mail: enquiries@ravenwoodhall.co.uk website: www.ravenwoodhall.co.uk

Diss

Small market town on the River Waveney 19 miles south west of Norwich.

PAUL AND YOLANDA DAVEY, STRENNETH, AIRFIELD ROAD, FERSFIELD, DISS IP22 2BP (01379 688182; Fax 01379 688260). Family run, fully renovated period property. All rooms en suite, colour TVs, hospitality trays. Ground floor rooms. Non-smoking. Extensive breakfast menu. Licensed. Bed and Breakfast from £25. ETC ◆◆◆◆. [🐕]
e-mail: pdavey@strenneth.co.uk website: www.strenneth.co.uk

Dunwich

Small village on coast, 4 miles south west of Southwold.

MR & MRS COLE, THE CLOSE, MIDDLEGATE BARN, DUNWICH IP17 3DW (01728 648741). Situated in a quiet, private road 200 yards from the sea. Furnished and equipped to a high standard. Centrally heated; available all year. Bookings taken from 1/1/2004. [🐕]

Hadleigh

Historic town on River Brett with several buildings of interest including unusual 14th century church. Bury St Edmunds 20 miles, Colchester 14, Sudbury 11, Ipswich 10.

EDGEHALL HOTEL, 2 HIGH STREET, HADLEIGH IP7 5AP (01473 822458; Fax: 01473 827751). 16th-century property offering a warm welcome. Comfortable accommodation and good home-cooked food. Licensed. SAE or telephone for details. Pets welcome. ETC ◆◆◆◆. [🐕]

Kessingland

Little seaside place with expansive beach, safe bathing, wildlife park, lake fishing. To the south is Benacre Broad, a beauty spot. Norwich 26 miles, Aldeburgh 23, Lowestoft 5.

Comfortable well-equipped bungalow on lawned site overlooking beach, next to Heritage Coast. Panoramic sea views. Easy beach access. Unspoiled walking area. ETC ★★ MR AND MRS J. SAUNDERS, 159 THE STREET, ROCKLAND ST MARY, NORWICH NR14 7HL (01508 538340). [Pets £10 per week].

Quality seaside bungalows in lawned surrounds overlooking the sea. Open all year, central heating, colour TV, parking, bed-linen, microwave, video recorder, heat and light included. Sleep 1/6. Direct access to award winning beach. Pets very welcome. APPLY– KNIGHTS HOLIDAY HOMES, 198 CHURCH ROAD, KESSINGLAND, SUFFOLK NR33 7SF (FREEPHONE 0800 269067).

Long Melford

Small town 3 miles north of Sudbury. Melford Hall and Kentwell Hall of interest.

BLACK LION HOTEL & RESTAURANT, THE GREEN, LONG MELFORD CO10 9DN (01787 312356; Fax: 01787 374557). 17th Century hotel opposite The Green. Leave your car and walk the dog. Contemporary restaurant, bar meals. Stylish en suite bedrooms, cosy lounge. Short breaks available. AA ★★★ 1 Rosette for Food [🐕 pw!]
e-mail: enquiries@blacklionhotel.net website: www.blacklionhotel.net

Lowestoft

Holiday resort and fishing port. Britain's most easterly point. Maritime museum traces seafaring history.

THE ALBANY HOTEL, 400 LONDON ROAD SOUTH, LOWESTOFT NR33 0BQ (01502 574394; Fax: 01502 581198) Warm welcome at this delightful hotel, close to beach and town centre. Individually decorated bedrooms, dining room with corner bar. AA ◆◆◆◆ [🐕]
e-mail: geoffrey.ward@btclick.com

Sudbury

Birthplace of Thomas Gainsborough, with a museum illustrating his career. Colchester 13 miles.

Situated in small, picturesque village within 15 miles of Sudbury, Newmarket Racecourse and historic Bury St Edmunds. Bungalow well equipped to accommodate 4 people. All facilities. Car essential, parking. Children and pets welcome. Terms from £61 to £122 per week. For further details send SAE to MRS M. WINCH, PLOUGH HOUSE, STANSFIELD, SUDBURY CO10 8LT (01284 789253). [🐕]

Woodbridge

Town on River Deben, 8 miles east of Ipswich.

THE CROWN AND CASTLE, ORFORD, WOODBRIDGE IP12 2LJ (01394 450205). Comfortable and very dog-friendly hotel situated close to 12th century castle in historic and unspoilt village of Orford. Honest good food served in award-winning Trinity Restaurant. [🐕]
e-mail: info@crownandcastle.co.uk website: www.crownandcastle.co.uk

Chase Lodge Hotel

An Award Winning Hotel

with style & elegance, set in tranquil surroundings at affordable prices.

10 Park Road Hampton Wick Kingston-Upon-Thames KT1 4AS

Pets welcome

Tel: 020 8943 1862 . Fax: 020 8943 9363

E-mail: info@chaselodgehotel.com Website: www.chaselodgehotel.com

Quality en suite bedrooms
Close to Bushy Park
Full English Breakfast
A la carte menu
Licensed bar
Wedding Receptions
Honeymoon suite
available with jacuzzi & steam area
20 minutes from Heathrow Airport
Close to Kingston town centre & all major transport links.

All Major Credit Cards Accepted

AA * * * Les Routiers RAC * * *

See also Colour Advertisement on page 57

Kingston-upon-Thames

Market town, Royal borough and administrative centre of Surrey. Kingston is ideally placed for London and environs.

CHASE LODGE HOTEL, 10 PARK ROAD, HAMPTON WICK, KINGSTON-UPON-THAMES KT1 4AS (020 8943 1862; Fax: 020 8943 9363). Award-winning hotel offering quality en suite bedrooms. Easy access to town centre and major transport links. A la carte menu, licensed bar. ETC/AA/RAC ★★★ [🐕]

e-mail: info@chaselodgehotel.com website: www.chaselodgehotel.com

EAST SUSSEX

Battle, Camber

Little Hemingfold Hotel, Battle

TELHAM, BATTLE, EAST SUSSEX TN33 0TT

Tel: 01424 774338 • Fax: 01424 775351

Email: littlehemingfoldhote@tiscali.co.uk • Web: www.littlehemingfoldhotel.co.uk

Relax and enjoy the friendly, tranquil atmosphere of our part 17th century and early Victorian farmhouse.
Treat your pets to one of our courtyard garden rooms, all en suite and some with log-burning stoves
Fish, row and swim in our two-acre trout lake or play on our grass tennis court.
Special breaks available all year including Christmas and New Year. 2 days DB&B £64 pppn

Discounts for children and FREE accommodation for pets.

ETC◆◆◆ ***Special Places to Stay*** **RAC**

See also Colour Advertisement on page 58

Camber Sands Holiday Park **ETC★★★**

Camber, Near Rye, East Sussex TN31 7RT

Lively park opposite award-winning, blue flag beach. Great range of hire caravans. Four indoor fun pools, sauna, spa bath and solarium, outdoor play area, café and a choice of bar and entertainment venues. Visit Historic Hastings and 1066 Country. Attractions include Underwater World and Smugglers Adventure. Tourers and tents welcome.

www.gbholidayparks.co.uk Call **0870 442 9284** for brochure

Chiddingly, East Sussex

Adorable, small, well-equipped cottage in grounds of Tudor Manor

• Full central heating • Two bedrooms • Colour TV • Fridge/freezer, microwave, dishwasher, laundry facilities, • Telephone • Use of indoor heated swimming pool, sauna/jacuzzi, tennis and badminton court • Large safe garden

From £385 – £675 per week inclusive. Pets and children welcome

Breaks available £225 – £305 ETC ★★★

Apply: Eva Morris, "Pekes", 124 Elm Park Mansions, Park Walk, London SW10 0AR

Tel: 020-7352 8088 Fax: 020-7352 8125 e-mail: pekes.afa@virgin.net web:www.pekesmanor.com

FAIRLIGHT COTTAGE

Warren Road, Fairlight, East Sussex TN35 4AG Tel: 01424 812545

Country house in idyllic location with clifftop walks and panoramic views from balcony. Centrally heated en suite rooms, with beverage trays and colour TV. Comfortable guest lounge. Delicious home cooking, generous breakfasts. Bring your own drinks. ETC ◆◆◆◆ No smoking. Ample parking. Dogs stay with owners.

See also Colour Advertisement on page 59

LITTLE OAKS, FARLEY WAY, FAIRLIGHT ETC ★★★★ ***Tel & Fax: 01424 812545***

Luxury bungalow, on one level, set in quiet coastal village with clifftop parklands, close to ancient towns of Rye, Battle and Hastings. Furnished to a very high standard, the spacious accommodation comprises double bedroom with en suite shower and sauna, twin bedroom, lounge with TV, dining room, fully equipped kitchen/diner, bathroom, conservatory and balcony overlooking beautiful secluded garden, garage. No smoking in bungalow. Pets welcome. Rates from £275 per week to include central heating, electric and linen.

Contact: Ray and Janet Adams, Fairlight Cottage, Warren Road, Fairlight, East Sussex TN35 4AG

See also Colour Advertisement on page 59

BEAUPORT PARK HOTEL

A Georgian Country House Hotel set amid 33 acres of formal gardens and woodland. All rooms have private bath, satellite colour TV, trouser press, hairdryer and auto-dial telephone. Outdoor Swimming Pool, Tennis, Squash, Badminton, Outdoor Chess, French Boules, Croquet Lawn, Putting, Golf and Riding School. Own woodland walks. Special Country House Breaks available all year. Please telephone for Brochure and Tariff.

BEAUPORT PARK HOTEL
Battle Road, Hastings TN38 8EA
Tel: Hastings (01424) 851222

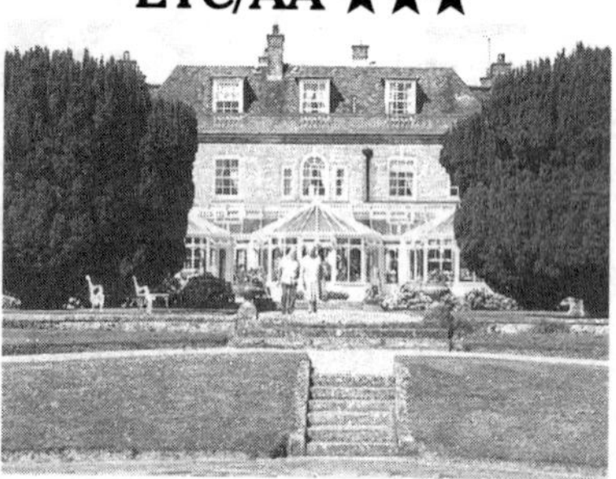

***The* FHG**

GOLF GUIDE

Where to Play Where to Stay

2004

Available from most bookshops, the 2004 edition of **THE GOLF GUIDE** covers details of every UK golf course – well over 2800 entries – for holiday or business golf. Hundreds of hotel entries offer convenient accommodation, accompanying details of the courses – the 'pro', par score, length etc.

In association with 'Golf Monthly' and including Holiday Golf in Ireland, France, Portugal, Spain, The USA, South Africa and Thailand.

£9.99 from bookshops or from the publishers (postage charged outside UK) • FHG Publications, Abbey Mill Business Centre, Paisley PA1 1TJ

See colour advertisement on page 58

Battle

Site of the famous victory of William the Conqueror; remains of an abbey mark the spot where Harold fell.

FOX HOLE FARM, KANE HYTHE ROAD, BATTLE TN33 9QU (Tel & Fax: 01424 772053). Beautiful secluded 18th century woodcutter's cottage, nestling in over 40 acres of its own rolling, lush East Sussex land. Surrounded by Forestry Commission woodland. AA ◆◆◆◆ [🐕]

HOUNDS RETREAT, BATTLE (01303 812636). Mobile home on Beauport Park, twixt Battle and Hastings. Quiet woodland site, nice walks. Own fenced garden, deck and parking place (level access). Adults only. [pw!🐕]

LITTLE HEMINGFOLD HOTEL, TELHAM, BATTLE TN33 0TT (01424 774338; Fax: 01424 775351). In the heart of 1066 Country, 40 acres of bliss for you and your pets. Farmhouse hotel, all facilities. Fishing, boating, swimming, tennis. Special Breaks all year. Discounts for children 7-14 years old. FREE accommodation for pets. [🐕]

Brighton

Famous resort with shingle beach and sand at low tide. Varied entertainment and nightlife; excellent shops and restaurants. Portsmouth 48 miles, Hastings 37, Newhaven 9.

BEST OF BRIGHTON & SUSSEX COTTAGES has available a very good selection of houses, flats, apartments and cottages in Brighton and Hove as well as East and West Sussex from Eastbourne to Chichester. Town centre/seaside and countryside locations – many taking pets. (01273 308779; Fax: 01273 390211). [Pets £15/£20 per week.]

Camber

Seaside resort on Rye Bay, 3 miles east of Rye.

CAMBER SANDS HOLIDAY PARK, CAMBER, NEAR RYE TN31 7RT. Lively park opposite award-winning blue flag beach. Great range of hire caravans. Four indoor pools; choice of bar and entertainment venues. Visit Historic Hastings and 1066 Country. Tourers and tents welcome. Call 0870 442 9284 for brochure. ETC★★★[🐕]
website: www.gbholidayparks.co.uk

Chiddlingly

Charming village, 4 miles north-west of Hailsham. Off the A22 London-Eastbourne road.

Adorable, small, well-equipped cottage in grounds of Tudor Manor. Two bedrooms. Full central heating. Colour TV. Fridge/freezer, laundry facilities. Large safe garden. Use indoor heated swimming pool, sauna/jacuzzi and tennis. From £385 to £675 per week inclusive. ETC ★★★. Contact: EVA MORRIS, "PEKES", 124 ELM PARK MANSIONS, PARK WALK, LONDON SW10 0AR (020 7352 8088; Fax: 020 7352 8125). [2 dogs free, extra dog £5 (max. 4) pw!].
e–mail: pekes.afa@virgin.net website: pekesmanor.com

Fairlight

Village 3 miles east of Hastings.

JANET & RAY ADAMS, FAIRLIGHT COTTAGE, WARREN ROAD, FAIRLIGHT TN35 4AG (01424 812545). Country house in idyllic location with clifftop walks. Tasteful en suite rooms, comfortable guest lounge. Delicious breakfasts. No smoking. Dogs stay with owners. ETC ◆◆◆◆ [🐕]

LITTLE OAKS, FARLEY WAY, FAIRLIGHT. Luxury bungalow set in quiet coastal village close to Rye, Hastings and Battle. Beautiful secluded garden, balcony and conservatory. No smoking. ETC ★★★★ Contact: RAY & JANET ADAMS, FAIRLIGHT COTTAGE, WARREN ROAD, FAIRLIGHT, EAST SUSSEX TN35 4AG (Tel & Fax: 01424 812545).[🐕]

Hastings

Seaside resort with a famous past - the ruins of William the Conqueror's castle lie above the Old Town. Many places of historic interest in the area, plus entertainments for all the family.

BEAUPORT PARK HOTEL, BATTLE ROAD, HASTINGS TN38 8EA (01424 851222). Georgian country mansion in 33 acres. All rooms private bath, colour television, trouser press, hairdryer, telephone. Country house breaks available all year. ETC/AA ★★★ [pw! 🐕]

Polegate

Quiet position, 5 miles from the popular seaside resort of Eastbourne. London 58 miles, Lewes 12.

MRS P. FIELD, 20 ST JOHN'S ROAD, POLEGATE BN26 5BP (01323 482691). Homely private house. Quiet location; large enclosed garden. Parking space. Ideally situated for walking on South Downs and Forestry Commission land. All rooms, washbasins and tea/coffee making facilities. Bed and Breakfast. Pets very welcome. [pw!]

Rye

Picturesque hill town with steep cobbled streets. Many fine buildings of historic interest. Hastings 12 miles, Tunbridge Wells 28.

FLACKLEY ASH HOTEL, PEASMARSH, RYE TN31 6YH (01797 230651). Georgian Country House Hotel in beautiful grounds. Indoor swimming pool and Leisure Centre. Beauty and massage. Visit Rye and the castles and gardens of East Sussex and Kent. AA/RAC ★★★ [pw at £7.50 per night]
website: www.flackleyashhotel.co.uk

CADBOROUGH FARM, UDIMORE ROAD, RYE TN31 6AA (01797 225426; Fax: 01797 224097). Five newly converted individual cottages. Each sleeps two, some with own courtyards. Double and Twin available. One small well-behaved dog welcome. Non-smoking. Sorry, no children. ETC ★★★★ [🐕].
e-mail: info@cadborough.co.uk website: www.cadborough.co.uk

JEAKE'S HOUSE, MERMAID STREET, RYE TN31 7ET (01797 222828; Fax: 01797 222623). Dating from 1689, this Listed Building has oak-beamed and panelled bedrooms overlooking the marsh. TV, radio, telephone. Book-lined bar. £37.00-£58.00 per person. ETC/AA/RAC ◆◆◆◆◆ [Pets £5 per night]
e-mail: jeakeshouse@btinternet.com website: www.jeakeshouse.com

Seaford

On the coast midway between Newhaven and Beachy Head.

BEACH COTTAGES, CLAREMONT ROAD, SEAFORD. Well-equipped, three-bedroomed terraced cottage on seafront. CH, open fire and woodburner. South-facing patio overlooking sea. Downland walks (wonderful for dogs), fishing, golf, wind-surfing, etc. Details from JULIA LEWIS, 47 WANDLE BANK, LONDON SW19 1DW (020 8542 5073). [🐕]
e-mail: julialewis@beachcottages.info website: www.beachcottages.info

Wandleys Caravan Park

Eastergate, West Sussex PO20 6SE
Telephone: 01243 543235
or 01243 543384 (evenings/weekends)

You will find peace, tranquillity and relaxation in one of our comfortable holiday caravans. All have internal WC and shower. Dogs welcome. The Sussex Downs, Chichester, Bognor Regis, Arundel, Littlehampton – all these historic and interesting places are only 15 minutes from our beautiful, small and quiet country park. SAE please for brochure.

CHEQUERS HOTEL

Old Rectory Lane, Pulborough,
West Sussex RH20 1AD
Tel: 01798 872486
e-mail: chequershotel@btinternet.com

Delightful small Queen Anne Hotel on the edge of the village, overlooking the Arun Valley towards the South Downs. All bedrooms with private bathrooms, plus colour TV, telephone, trouser press, hairdryer and tea/coffee making facilities. Restaurant serves fresh market produce from daily changing menu. Garden Conservatory and Coffee Shop. Car park. Superb centre for walking or touring, with safe walks for your dog available directly from the hotel in our 9-acre meadow.

Walk for miles along the South Downs Way, or along the banks of the River Arun, or visit one of the many local places of interest such as Parham House and Gardens, Petworth House and Park, Goodwood, Arundel, or the Weald and Downland Open Air Museum.

Children are also very welcome. Major Credit Cards accepted. BARGAIN BREAKS all through the year from £49.50 per person for Dinner, Bed and Breakfast. Reduced rates for longer stays. Winter Bargain - any 3 nights DB&B from £119.
AA ★★★, 2 RAC Merit Awards, 2 AA Rosettes for Good Food.

No charge for dogs belonging to readers of Pets Welcome!

ST ANDREWS LODGE

Chichester Road, Selsey, West Sussex PO20 0LX
Tel: 01243 606899 • Fax: 01243 607826
e-mail: info@standrewslodge.co.uk
web: www.standrewslodge.co.uk

Welcoming, family-run hotel with a reputation for an excellent hearty breakfast. Situated on the Manhood peninsula just south of Chichester, close to unspoilt beaches and countryside. Ten bedrooms, all en suite, with direct-dial telephones, TV, fridge and tea-making facilities; some on ground floor. Spacious lounges with log fire; friendly bar for residents only. Wheelchair accessible room. Large secure car park. Dogs welcome in rooms overlooking large garden. Bed & Breakfast from £30 pppn. Apply for brochure, prices and details of special winter offers October to February.

See also colour advertisement on page 59

See also Colour Advertisement on page 59

Eastergate

Village between the sea and the South Downs. Fontwell Park nearby. Bognor Regis 5 miles south.

WANDLEYS CARAVAN PARK, EASTERGATE PO20 6SE (01243 543235 or 01243 543384 evenings/weekends). You will find peace, tranquillity and relaxation in one of our comfortable holiday caravans. All have internal WC and shower. Dogs welcome. Many historic and interesting places nearby. SAE for brochure. [🐕]

Pulborough

Popular fishing centre on the River Arun. South Downs Way nearb; Arundel 8 miles.

BEACON LODGE, LONDON ROAD, WATERSFIELD, PULBOROUGH RH20 1NH (Tel & Fax: 01798 831026). Charming self-contained annexe. B&B accommodation, en suite, TV, coffee/tea making facilities. Wonderful countryside views. B&B from £25pppn. No charge for your pets!. Telephone for more details. ETC ◆◆◆◆ [🐕]
e-mail: beaconlodge@hotmail.com website: www.beaconlodge.co.uk

CHEQUERS HOTEL, PULBOROUGH RH20 1AD (01798 872486). Lovely Queen Anne house in village overlooking Arun Valley. Excellent food. Children and dogs welcome. No charge for dogs belonging to readers of Pets Welcome! ETC ★★★ Silver Award, AA/RAC ★★★ [pw! 🐕]

A useful Index of Towns/Villages and Counties appears on page 427 – please also refer to Contents Page 3.

Selsey

Seaside resort 8 miles south of Chichester. Selsey Bill is headland extending into the English Channel.

ST ANDREWS LODGE HOTEL, CHICHESTER ROAD, SELSEY PO20 0LX (01243 606899; Fax: 01243 607826). 10 bedrooms, all en suite, with direct dial telephones and modem point, some on ground floor. Spacious lounges with log fire; friendly bar for residents only. Wheelchair accessible room. Dogs welcome in rooms overlooking large garden. Apply for brochure and prices. ETC/AA ◆◆◆◆ [🐕]
e-mail: e-mail: info@standrewslodge.co.uk web: www.standrewslodge.co.uk

Steyning

Town below South Downs, 5 miles north west of Shoreham-by-Sea.

PEPPERSCOMBE FARM, NEWHAM LANE, STEYNING BN44 3LR (01903 813868). Two self-catering cottages, each designed to sleep two adults. Spacious and comfortable with oak beams. Direct access to South Downs and foot and bridle path network. Terms from £350 to £475 per week. [Pets £15 each per week].
e-mail: johncamilleri@btopenworld.com

Worthing

Residential town and seaside resort with 5 mile seafront. Situated 10 miles west of Brighton.

CAVENDISH HOTEL, 115 MARINE PARADE, WORTHING BN11 3QG (01903 236767; Fax: 01903 823840). Ideal base for touring Sussex villages and the rolling South Downs. All rooms are en suite, have TV, direct-dial telephone and tea/coffee facilities. No charge for dogs belonging to readers of Pets Welcome! AA/RAC ★★ [🐕].
e-mail: cavendishworthing@btinternet.com website: www.cavendishworthing.co.uk

TYNE & WEAR

Whitley Bay

Whitley Bay

North Sea coast resort 2 miles north of Tynemouth. Extensive sands to the north.

WHITLEY BAY HOLIDAY PARK, THE LINK, WHITLEY BAY NE26 4RR. Popular park with well appointed holiday caravans for hire. Indoor heated pool, café/take away, multi-sports court, play area, shop, club and entertainment venue. Good beach. Tourers welcome. Call 0870 442 9282 for brochure. ETC★★★★ [🐕]
website: www.gbholidayparks.co.uk

SYMBOLS

- 🐕 **Indicates that pets are welcome free of charge.**
- £ **Indicates that a charge is made for pets: nightly or weekly.**
- pw! **Shows some special provision for pets; exercise facility, feeding or accommodation arrangement.**
- ⌂ **Indicates separate pets accommodation.**

"Waverley" Wolverton Fields, Norton Lindsey, Warwickshire CV35 8JN

Located on the outskirts of the Warwickshire village of Norton Lindsey. Facing due south with extensive unbroken views towards Stratford-upon-Avon (6 miles). Guests will receive a warm welcome from Doreen and her Bernese Mountain Dog. En suite double bedrooms comfortably furnished with antiques and period furniture. Ideal for pet lovers using nearby town. M40 and Warwick 3 miles, NEC twenty minutes. Half-acre garden paddock available for dogs.

Tel: 01926 842446

Stratford-upon-Avon

RAYFORD CARAVAN PARK - ON THE BANKS OF THE RIVER AVON

Features at a Glance:
- Pets Welcome
- River Taxi to and from Town Centre
- Club House • Shop & Café
- Bowling Green
- Kids Playground
- Snooker Table
- 1½ miles of Free Fishing
- Only 1 mile to Town Centre

Rayford Park is ideally placed for visiting all Shakespearian attractions and the beautiful Cotswolds. In Stratford itself there is everything you could wish for: shops, pubs, restaurants, swimming pool, sports centre, The Royal Shakespeare Theatre, and a generous helping of history and the Bard! The luxury 12ft wide Caravan Holiday Homes accommodate up to 6 persons in comfort. All have kitchen with cooker and fridge, bathroom with shower/washbasin/WC, two bedrooms, one double bedded, one with two single beds, (cots available), lounge, eating area, electric fire, colour TV, carpeted throughout. Also available, TWO COTTAGES, "Sleepy Hollow" and "Kingfisher Cottage", both with modern facilities set on the river bank.

Rayford Caravan Park, Riverside, Tiddington Road, Stratford-Upon-Avon, Warwickshire CV37 7BE
Telephone: 01789 293964 **www.stratfordcaravans.co.uk**

Mrs Hazel Mellor
ARRANDALE
208 Evesham Road,
Stratford-upon-Avon CV37 9AS

Comfortable family Guest House situated at the town end of Evesham Road on the B439 (Bidford). 10 minutes' walk to River Avon, Shakespearean properties, theatre. One hour's drive to Cotswolds. Tea-making facilities and TV in bedrooms; centrally heated. Pets in room. Parking, though car not essential. Lift from bus or train station by arrangement.

Bed and Breakfast: room with shower, washbasin £17.50 per person; en suite toilet, shower, washbasin £20 per person. Weekly terms £115-£130. Evening Meals £8.00 extra.

Tel: (01789) 267112 • website: www.arrandale.netfirms.com

Please mention ***PETS WELCOME*** when making enquiries about accommodation featured in these pages.

Norton Lindsay

Village 4 miles west of Warwick.

DOREEN BROMILOW, "WAVERLEY", WOLVERTON FIELDS, NORTON LINDSEY, WARWICK CV35 8JN (01926 842446) Overlooking Stratford-upon-Avon. A warm welcome from Doreen and her Bernese Mountain Dog. En suite double bedrooms. Ideal for pet lovers. M40 and Warwick 3 miles, NEC twenty minutes. Half-acre garden paddock available for dogs. [Pets £2 per night].

Stratford-upon-Avon

Historic town famous as Shakespeare's birthplace and home. Birmingham 24, Warwick 8.

RAYFORD CARAVAN PARK, TIDDINGTON ROAD, STRATFORD-UPON-AVON CV37 7BE (01789 293964). Luxury Caravans, sleep 6. Fully equipped kitchens, bathroom/ shower/WC. Also two riverside Cottages, all modern facilities to first-class standards. Private fishing. On banks of River Avon. [Pets £15 weekly.]
website: www.stratfordcaravans.co.uk

MRS H. J. MELLOR, ARRANDALE, 208 EVESHAM ROAD, STRATFORD-UPON-AVON CV37 9AS (01789 267112). Guest House situated near River Avon, theatre, Shakespeare properties. Washbasins, tea making, TV, central heating, en suite available. Children, pets welcome. Parking. Bed and Breakfast £17.50-£20. Weekly terms £115-£130. Evening Meal £8.00. [🐕]
website: www.arrandale.netfirms.com

DEREK & SUSAN LEARMOUNT, GREEN HAVEN, 217 EVESHAM ROAD, STRATFORD-UPON-AVON CV37 9AS (01789 297874; Fax: 01789 550487). Cosy, pretty, refurbished guest house. Central heating, colour TV, courtesy trays. All en suite. Private parking. Payphone. Easily accessible to Cotswolds and Warwick. Non-smoking. Pets by arrangement only. ETC ◆◆◆◆ [🐕]
e-mail: susanlearmount@green-haven.co.uk OR information@green-haven.co.uk
website: www.green-haven.co.uk

Warwick

Town on the River Avon, 9 miles south-west of Coventry. Medieval castle and many fine old buildings.

DAVID & PATRICIA CLAPP, CROFT GUESTHOUSE, HASELEY KNOB, WARWICK CV35 7NL (Tel & Fax: 01926 484447). All bedrooms en suite or with private bathroom, some ground floor. Non-smoking. Picturesque rural setting. Central for NEC, Warwick, Stratford, Stoneleigh and Coventry. B&B single £35, double/twin £52. [Dogs £3]
e-mail: david@croftguesthouse.co.uk website: www.croftguesthouse.co.uk

Birmingham

The second largest city in Britain, with Art Galleries to rival London. The Bull Ring has been modernised and includes an impressive shopping centre, but there is still plenty of the old town to see; the town hall, the concert hall and the Cathedral Church of St Philip.

ANGELA AND IAN KERR, THE AWENTSBURY HOTEL, 21 SERPENTINE ROAD, SELLY PARK, BIRMINGHAM B29 7HU (0121 472 1258). Victorian Country House. Large gardens. All rooms have colour TV, telephones and tea/coffee making facilities. Some rooms en suite, some with showers. All rooms central heating, wash basins. Near Birmingham University and BBC Pebble Mill. B&B from £40 single room, £54 twin room (inclusive of VAT). [🐕]

WILTSHIRE

Chippenham, Malmesbury

Chippenham

Town on River Avon 12 miles north-east of Bath.

KATE & DAVID HUMPHREY, ROWARD FARM, DRAYCOT CERNE, CHIPPENHAM SN15 4SG (01249 758147). Three self-catering cottages full of character and charm, set in peaceful Wiltshire countryside. Excellent touring centre for Cotswolds and Bath. Sleep two to four people in fully-equipped accommodation. Non-smoking. Pets welcome. Call or write for brochure.
ETC ★★★★ [🐕]
e-mail: d.humphrey@roward.demon.co.uk website: www.roward.demon.co.uk

Malmesbury

Country town on River Avon with a late medieval market cross. Remains of medieval abbey.

JOHN AND EDNA EDWARDS, STONEHILL FARM, CHARLTON, MALMESBURY SN16 9DY (01666 823310). Family-run dairy farm, ideal for touring. 3 comfortable rooms, one en suite. Also 2 fully equipped bungalow-style barns, each sleeps 2/3 plus cot, self catering. ETC ★★★ [Pets £5 per week].
e-mail: johnedna@stonehillfarm.fsnet.co.uk
website: www.SmoothHound.co.uk/hotels/stonehill.html

Salisbury

13th century cathedral city, with England's highest spire at 404ft. Many fine buildings.

MR A. SHERING, SWAYNES FIRS FARM, GRIMSDYKE, COOMBE BISSETT, SALISBURY SP5 5RF (01725 519240). Small working farm with horses, poultry, geese and duck ponds. Spacious rooms, all en suite with colour TV. Ideal for visiting the many historic sites in the area. ETC ◆◆◆ [🐕]
e-mail: swaynes.firs@virgin.net website: www.swaynesfirs.co.uk

The 17th-century Dormy House Hotel is set high in the rolling Cotswold countryside between the picturesque villages of Broadway and Chipping Campden, with Stratford-upon-Avon only a short drive away. Adjacent to Broadway Golf Course, it is a really lovely place in which to relax with your dog(s) and enjoy a one night stay or Classic Dormy Break. **Telephone: 01386 852711 for brochure/booking.**

Willersey Hill, Broadway, Worcestershire WR12 7LF
Telephone: (01386) 852711 Fax: (01386) 858636
E-Mail: reservations@dormyhouse. co.uk • Web: www.dormyhouse.co.uk

Quality of food

See also Colour Advertisement on page 60

Beautiful landmark Georgian building in the centre of Malvern with direct access to the Hills from beside the gate. Family-run hotel that provides a relaxed, friendly country house atmosphere with high standards of service tailored by its staff for its guests, not the other way round. Good, fresh local food served in the Auberge brasserie and Number 50 restaurant. Children and dogs welcome. Ask about special break rates. **AA ★★**

Mount Pleasant Hotel

Belle Vue Terrace, Great Malvern WR14 4PZ.

Tel: 01684 561837 • e-mail: mountpleasanthotel@btinternet.com • website: www.mountpleasanthotel.co.uk

Croft Guest House, Bransford, Worcester WR6 5JD

16th-18th Century country house, 10 minutes from Worcester, Malvern and M5. En suite rooms, tea/coffee trays, central heating. Dinners available; residential licence. TV in all bedrooms. Children and dogs welcome; cot and baby listening service; family room. Bed & Breakfast from £23 to £33 single, £41 to £56 double. Open Christmas and New Year. Credit / debit cards accepted.

Ann & Brian Porter: Tel: 01886 832227 Fax: 01886 830037 AA ◆◆◆

For a brochure call 01684 575859
www.cottageinthewood.co.uk

WHITEWELLS FARM COTTAGES

ETC ★★★★

Ridgeway Cross, Near Malvern, Worcestershire WR13 5JR • www.whitewellsfarm.co.uk
Tel: 01886 880607 • Fax: 01886 880360 • e-mail: info@whitewellsfarm.co.uk

Seven well-established cottages converted from old farm buildings and a hop kiln, full of charm and character with original exposed timbering. These award-winning cottages are exceptionally clean and comfortable and equipped to the highest standards. One cottage suitable for the disabled with full wheelchair access. Idyllically set around a duckpond with two and a half acres of the property being a fully-fenced woodland plantation, ideal for exercising dogs, on or off the lead.

Set in unspoilt countryside with outstanding views of the **Malvern Hills** on the **Herefordshire/Worcestershire border. Ideal base for touring Worcestershire, Herefordshire, the Malverns, Gloucestershire, Welsh mountains, Cotswolds and Shakespeare country**. Electricity and linen included in price. Short breaks and long lets, suitable for relocation. Children and pets welcome. Open all year.

Colour brochure available from: Kate and Denis Kavanagh.

Broadway

Small town below escarpment of Cotswold Hills, 5 miles south-east of Evesham.

DORMY HOUSE, WILLERSEY HILL, BROADWAY WR12 7LF (01386 852711; Fax: 01386 858636). The 17th-century Dormy House Hotel is set high in the rolling Cotswold countryside. Adjacent to Broadway Golf Course, it is a really lovely place in which to relax with your dog(s) and enjoy a one night stay or Classic Dormy Break. AA/RAC ★★★ [Pets £5 per dog per night]
e-mail: reservations@dormyhouse.co.uk website: www.dormyhouse.co.uk

Great Malvern

Fashionable spa town in last century with echoes of that period.

MALVERN HILLS HOTEL, WYNDS POINT, MALVERN WR13 6DW (01684 540690). Enchanting family-owned and run hotel nestling high in the hills. Direct access to superb walking with magnificent views. Oak-panelled lounge, log fire, real ales, fine food and friendly staff. Great animal lovers. ETC/AA/RAC ★★ [🐕]
website: www.malvern-hotel.co.uk

JULIE & ALAN JOSEY. MOUNT PLEASANT HOTEL, BELLE VUE TERRACE, GREAT MALVERN WR14 4PZ (01684 561837). Beautiful landmark Georgian building in the centre of Malvern. Family-run hotel with a relaxed, friendly country house atmosphere. Ask about special break rates. Children and dogs welcome. AA★★. [Pets £5 per stay].
e-mail: mountpleasanthotel@btinternet.com website: www.mountpleasanthotel.co.uk

ANN AND BRIAN PORTER, CROFT GUEST HOUSE, BRANSFORD, WORCESTER WR6 5JD (01886 832227; Fax: 01886 830037). 16th-18th century country house. 10 minutes from Worcester, Malvern and M5. En suite rooms, tea coffee trays, central heating, TV in all bedrooms. Dinners available; residential licence. Children and dogs welcome. Cot and baby listening service; family room. Credit cards accepted. AA ◆◆◆. [🐕]

THE COTTAGE IN THE WOOD (01684 575859). High on Malvern hills. Accommodation over three buildings. 2 AA Restaurants, Rosettes, over 600 wines. "Best view in England" - The Daily Mail. Call for brochure. ★★★ [🐕]
website: www.cottageinthewood.co.uk

KATE AND DENIS KAVANAGH, WHITEWELLS FARM COTTAGES, RIDGEWAY CROSS, NEAR MALVERN WR13 5JR (01886 880607; Fax: 01886 880360). Charming converted Cottages, sleep 2–6. Fully equipped with colour TV, microwave, barbecue, fridge, iron, etc. Linen, towels also supplied. One cottage suitable for the disabled with full wheelchair access. Short breaks, long lets, large groups. ETC ★★★★ [Pets £10 per week. p.w!] Also see adverts under Great Malvern, Worcestershire.
e-mail: info@whitewellsfarm.co.uk website: www.whitewellsfarm.co.uk

Barmby Moor

Village 2 miles west of Pocklington.

MR AND MRS THORPE, PARKLANDS, YORK ROAD, BARMBY MOOR, YORK YO42 4HT (Tel & Fax: 01759 380260). Tastefully converted stables in private grounds. Ideally placed for wolds, moors, coast. Self-contained, self-catering, sleeps two. Full central heating. No smoking. Pets welcome. [pw! 🐕]

Bridlington

Traditional family resort with picturesque harbour and a wide range of entertainments and leisure facilities. Ideal for exploring the Heritage coastline and the Wolds.

THE TENNYSON HOTEL, 19 TENNYSON AVENUE, BRIDLINGTON YO15 2EU (Tel & Fax: 01262 604382). 1994 Golden Bowl Award Winner for the Most Pet-Friendly Hotel in Yorkshire. Offering fine cuisine in attractive surroundings. Close to beach and cliff walks. ETC ◆◆◆◆. [🐕 pw!]

CHRIS & JACKY SHORT, HEATHFIELD GUEST HOUSE, 34 TENNYSON AVENUE, BRIDLINGTON YO15 2EP ((01262 672594). Easy walking to beach and all amenities. En suite rooms available. B&B from £16pppn. TV, tea and coffee in all rooms. Non-smoking. Dogs welcome free of charge. ETC ◆◆◆ [🐕]
e-mail: chrisbshort2002@yahoo.co.uk

SARAH AND RAY ROLLINSON, CROMER LICENSED GUEST HOUSE, 78 TRINITY ROAD, BRIDLINGTON YO15 2HF (Tel & Fax: 01262 679452). Only steps from Bridlington's North Beach, our guest house is the ideal base for a fantastic seaside holiday, local sightseeing, or a relaxing break from your busy life. [🐕]
e-mail: stay@cromerguesthouse.com website: www.cromerguesthouse.com

Driffield

Town 11 miles south west of Bridlington.

MRS TIFFY HOPPER, KELLEYTHORPE FARM, DRIFFIELD YO25 9DW (01377 252297). Lovely Georgian farmhouse overlooking small lake. Friendly atmosphere, attractive bedrooms. Aberdeen Angus herd with beef sold in shop. Children welcome. B&B from £22. Evening Meal by prior arrangement.[🐕]

Flamborough

Village 4 miles north-east of Bridlington.

THORNWICK & SEA FARM HOLIDAY CENTRE, NORTH MARINE ROAD, FLAMBOROUGH YO15 1AV (01262 850369; Fax: 01262 851550) Set on the spectacular Heritage Coast with unrivalled coastal scenery. Six-berth caravans and chalets for hire. Tents and tourers welcome. Bars, entertainment, shop, pool and gym on site. [Pets £5 per week.] ETC ★★★.
e-mail: enquiries@thornwickbay.co.uk website: www.thornwickbay.co.uk

Kilnwick Percy

Located 2 miles east of Pocklington.

PAWS-A-WHILE, KILNWICK PERCY, POCKLINGTON YO42 1UF (01759 301168; Mobile: 07711 866869). Small family B & B set in forty acres of parkland twixt York and Beverley. Fishing, golf, sauna, walking, riding. Pets and horses most welcome. Brochure available. ETC ◆◆◆◆ [pw! 🐕]
e-mail: paws.a.while@lineone.net website: www.pawsawhile.net

Withernsea

Coastal resort 15 miles east of Hull.

WITHERNSEA HOLIDAY VILLAGE, NORTH ROAD, WITHERNSEA HU19 2BS. Small, modern fleet of caravans for hire. Clubhouse offering tasty snacks, nature trail, shop. Excellent access to beach. Pavilion Leisure Centre nearby. Tourers and tents welcome. Call 0870 442 9313 for brochure. ETC★★★ [🐕]
website: www.gbholidayparks.co.uk

Readers are requested to mention this guidebook when seeking accommodation (and please enclose a stamped addressed envelope).

See also Colour Advertisement on page 5

Bishop Thornton, Clapham,

See also Colour Advertisement on page 47

The Fox & Hounds Inn ***Ainthorpe, Danby YO21 2LD***

Residential 16th Century Coaching Inn. Freshly prepared dishes served every day.
Superb en suite accommodation available. Ideal centre for the moors and coast.
Open all year. Pets: £1.50 per night. ETC ◆◆◆◆
Situated between Castleton and Danby on the Fryup Road.
For bookings please Tel: 01287 660218 Fax: 01287 660030

"SEA CABIN" **16 Gap Road, Hunmanby Gap, Near Filey YO14 9QP**

Warm and friendly hospitality plus good food at our well-appointed twin-bedroomed Granny annexe. En suite, own private lounge. Located on the cliff top, with easy access to the golden sands of Filey Bay. Private parking, quiet location, five minutes' drive from Filey town. Full English Breakfast. Bookings for B&B plus Evening Meal. Pet friendly beach and area.

for brochure & terms:
Leonard & Diane Hunter Tel: 01723 891368 **Dogs come free of charge!** **ETC ◆◆◆**

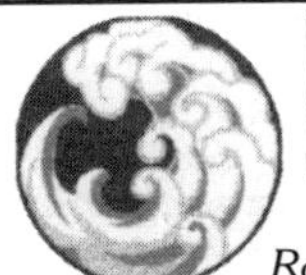

ETC ★★

Sea Brink Hotel

ETC ★★

3 The Beach, Filey, North Yorkshire YO14 9LA
Tel: 01723 513257 Fax: 01723 514139 Website: www.seabrink.co.uk

Licensed seafront hotel with nine en suite rooms, many overlooking Filey Bay.
Room amenities: colour TV, clock/radio, central heating, direct-dial phones and tea/coffee tray.

The Foresters Arms

MAIN STREET, GRASSINGTON, SKIPTON
NORTH YORKSHIRE BD23 5AA
Tel: 01756 752349 • Fax: 01756 753633

The Foresters Arms, Grassington, once an old coaching inn, situated in the heart of the Yorkshire Dales. An ideal centre for walking or touring. A family-run business for over 35 years. Serving hand-pulled traditional ales. Bar meals served lunchtime and evenings. All bedrooms are en suite and have satellite TVs and tea/coffee making facilities. Prices £30 single; £60 double.

Proprietor: Rita Richardson

JERRY AND BEN'S HOLIDAY COTTAGES

Seven comfortable properties on a private estate near Grassington in the Yorkshire Dales National Park, with wooded mountain becks, waterfalls, rocky crags and surrounded by accessible hill and footpath walking. £100 to £420. Brochure from:

Mrs J. M. Joy, Jerry and Ben's Holiday Cottages, Hebden, Skipton, North Yorkshire BD23 5DL. Tel: 01756 752369; Fax: 01756 753370
e-mail: dawjoy@aol.com website: www.yorkshirenet.co.uk/stayat/jerryandbens

---

A useful Index of Towns/Villages and Counties appears on page 427 – please also refer to Contents Page 3.

Grassington House Hotel & Restaurant

AA ★★ E.T.C. ★★ *HOTEL*

The Square, Grassington, Skipton
North Yorkshire BD23 5AQ
Tel: 01756 752406 Fax: 01756 752135

The hotel is situated in the quaint cobbled square and is renowned for its atmosphere of warmth and friendliness. Our restaurant, serving à la carte, is very popular for its good food where we use produce from local suppliers. We also serve a large selection of meals and snacks in the bar and conservatory. The hotel is well situated for walking in the beautiful dales or touring. Large private car park.

HELME PASTURE LODGES AND COTTAGES • Old Spring Wood
FREEDOM HOLIDAYS
Ideal for Discriminating Dogs

Rosemary Helme,
Helme Pasture,
Hartwith Bank, Summerbridge,
Harrogate, N. Yorks HG3 4DR

See also Colour Advertisement on page 62

* Great sniffing trails, highest paw category walks in the heart of unspoilt Nidderdale.
* Renowned snooze spots while owners explore.
* Central for Harrogate, York, Herriot and Brontë Country. National Trust area; outstanding natural beauty.
* After your hard day, stretch out and watch woodland wildlife from the luxurious comfort of your Scandinavian lodge or converted Yorkshire Dales barn.
* David Bellamy Gold Conservation Award
* ETC Welcome Host Award.
* Accessible Category 1.

Tel: 01423 780279 Fax: 01423 780994
E-mail: info@helmepasture.co.uk
Website: www.helmepasture.co.uk

RUDDING HOLIDAY PARK

LUXURY COTTAGES AND TIMBER LODGES IN BEAUTIFUL SURROUNDINGS

FOLLIFOOT,
HARROGATE HG3 1JH

TEL: 01423 870439
FAX: 01423 870859

e-mail - holidaypark@ruddingpark.com
www.ruddingpark.com

- Deer House family pub
- Children's adventure playground
- Pets welcome
- Heated outdoor swimming pool and paddling pool
- Games room
- 18 hole pay & play golf course plus floodlit driving range

RELAX IN THE HEART OF YORKSHIRE

See also Colour Advertisement on page 60

STONE HOUSE HOTEL

★★

Licensed Country House Hotel & Restaurant overlooking Magnificent Wensleydale

~ 21 Quality En Suite Bedrooms ~

(some with private conservatories opening onto Gardens)

~ Delicious Food & Fine Wines ~

The Perfect Venue for a relaxing break deep in the heart of the Yorkshire Dales.
Dogs genuinely welcome – Short Breaks available now

Sedbusk, Hawes, North Yorkshire DL8 3PT
Tel: 01969 667571 • Fax: 01969 667720
website: www.stonehousehotel.com

See also Colour Advertisement on page 61

Experience the Unique Atmosphere and Traditional Hospitality at

SIMONSTONE HALL COUNTRY HOUSE HOTEL

Hawes, Wensleydale, North Yorkshire DL8 3LY
Tel: 01969 667255 Fax: 01969 667741

Outstanding Bar Meals and Sunday Lunches served in the Game Tavern. Our restaurant provides an elegant setting for our wide selection of fine food and wines. Set in magnificent countryside near the market town of Hawes, Simonstone Hall is a beautifully restored Country House hotel with spectacular views over the Dale and surrounding Fell. An excellent base for walking and exploring the Dales. Pets welcome in most rooms. Kennels provided if required. A relaxed friendly establishment with open fires, Four Poster Beds and experienced staff to look after all your needs. AA ★★ and One Rosette.

e-mail: information@simonstonehall.demon.co.uk **website: www.simonstonehall.co.uk**

See also Colour Advertisement on page 60

1637 OVER 350 YEARS OF GOOD SERVICE 2003

Formerly a Posting House in coaching days, and full of character, a convenient centre for the North Yorkshire Moors and east coast, with Castle Howard and Rievaulx and Byland Abbeys within easy distance. 12 en suite rooms, all with colour TV, tea and coffee facilities, radio, and direct-dial telephone. One private lounge. Jacobean dining room offering traditional country-style cooking, with many choices. Special Breaks all year. Dogs welcome (no charge). Under the same ownership for 43 years. Brochure sent on request.

Dinner, Bed and Breakfast from £44.00.

AA/RAC ★★
Ashley Courtenay

THE CROWN HOTEL

Helmsley, North Yorkshire YO62 5BJ Tel: Helmsley (01439) 770297

★★ HOTEL

Stoney End **ETC 4 Diamonds Silver Award**
for quality B&B and Self Catering
in the heart of the Yorkshire Dales

Worton, Near Askrigg, Leyburn, North Yorkshire DL8 3ET

Tel: +44(0) 1969 650652 • e-mail: pmh@stoneyend.co.uk • website: www.stoneyend.co.uk

Malham - Miresfield Farm

In beautiful gardens bordering village green and stream. Well known for excellent food. 11 bedrooms, all with private facilities. Full central heating. Two well-furnished lounges and conservatory for guests' use. 3 Diamonds Commended. B&B from £24pppn.

Mr. C. Sharp, Miresfield Farm, Malham, Skipton BD23 4DA Tel: 01729 830414

Hill House Farm, Little Langton, Northallerton DL7 0PZ

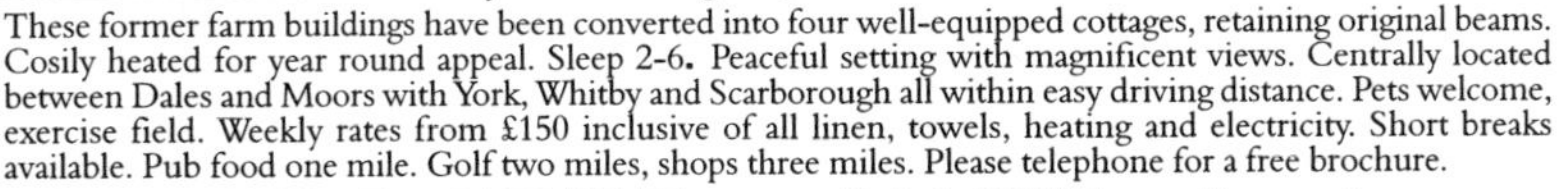

These former farm buildings have been converted into four well-equipped cottages, retaining original beams. Cosily heated for year round appeal. Sleep 2-6. Peaceful setting with magnificent views. Centrally located between Dales and Moors with York, Whitby and Scarborough all within easy driving distance. Pets welcome, exercise field. Weekly rates from £150 inclusive of all linen, towels, heating and electricity. Short breaks available. Pub food one mile. Golf two miles, shops three miles. Please telephone for a free brochure.

Tel: 01609 770643 Fax: 01609 760438 e-mail: info@Hillhousefarmcottages.com

See also Colour Advertisement on page 62

FHG PUBLICATIONS

publish a large range of well-known accommodation guides. We will be happy to send you details or you can use the order form at the back of this book.

The Black Swan Inn Oldstead

Coxwold, York YO61 4BL
Telephone: 01347 868387

e-mail: blackswan@oldstead.fsworld.co.uk • website: www.theblackswaninn.com

Charming, family-run 18th century Inn set in the stunning scenery of the North York Moors National Park.
Magnificent views — perfect dog walking country.
2 miles Kilburn, 20 miles York. Superb chalet-style en suite accommodation with colour TV, central heating and tea/coffee making facilities.

★ Hand-pumped real ale ★
★ Yorkshire farmhouse cooking ★
★ A la carte Restaurant ★
★ Bar meals ★ Fine wines ★

Bed and Breakfast from £25.00pp

For bookings and brochures telephone: 01347 868387

BANAVIE

ETC ◆◆◆◆

Mrs Ella Bowes, Banavie, Roxby Road, Thornton-le-Dale, Pickering YO18 7SX * Tel: 01751 474616

Large stone-built semi-detached house set in Thornton-le-Dale. Ideal for touring. One family bedroom and two double bedrooms, all en suite. All with TV, shaver points, central heating and tea-making facilities. Open all year. Car park, cycle shed. B&B from £21-£24.00 pppn. Hygiene Certificate held. Your pets are very welcome.

website: www.banavie.uk.com **e-mail: ella@banavie.fsbusiness.co.uk**

NORTH YORKSHIRE MOORS NATIONAL PARK

Stone Cottage with log fire in North York Moors National Park. Sleeps 4. Near Cleveland coastal footpath, sea view. Non-smoking. Whitby 9 miles. Brochure available.

Mrs J. Hiley, 3 Valley Gardens, Stockton-On-Tees, Teesside TS19 8BE.
Tel & Fax: 01642 613888 E-mail: comesatime.cottage@ntlworld.com

HARMONY COUNTRY LODGE

ETC

Limestone Road, Burniston, Scarborough YO13 0DG. (Non-Smoking)

Unique octagonal peaceful retreat in own grounds with superb 360º views of National Park and sea. Two miles from Scarborough. Parking facilities and fully licensed. Fragrant massage available. B&B – £22 to £33.50. Five-berth caravan available for self-catering. Local dog walks. Pets welcome.

Sue & Tony Hewitt • Tel: 0800 2985840 • website: www.harmonylodge.net

Please mention Pets Welcome when writing to enquire about accommodation

See also Colour Advertisement on page 61

See also Colour Advertisement on page 61

Foxhills Hideaways *Felixkirk, Thirsk. YO7 2DS*

Quiet, no hassle holidays in cosy Scandinavian log cabins. Secluded garden setting. Central for the Moors, Dales, York and the coast. Village pub round the corner. Fully inclusive prices (£180 to £340 per week).

Open all year.

Out of season short breaks from £90 inclusive.
Please write or phone for a brochure

TELEPHONE 01845 537575

ST EDMUNDS COUNTRY COTTAGES

Cottages in Wensleydale

Properties sleeping two to seven persons plus cot. These recently renovated cottages are fully equipped and are an ideal base for exploring the Dales and Moors.

PETS WELCOME

For a brochure send SAE to:

Sue Cooper, St Edmunds, The Green, Crakehall, Bedale, North Yorkshire DL8 1HP

Tel: 01677 423584 Web: www.crakehall.org.uk ETC★★/★★★

Moorcote *Three delightful cottages around a sunny courtyard*

- **Granary Cottage** sleeps four in double and bunk rooms.
- **Hayloft Cottage** sleeps four in double and twin rooms.
- **Stable Cottage** sleeps six in double and twin rooms.

All equipped to a very high standard. Central heating, linen and towels provided. Large gardens and private patios.

Overlooking Jervaulx Abbey with fabulous views of forty miles. All the peace and quiet you could wish for, yet only one hour to York and under half an hour to the A1.

Children and pets welcome. Open all year round. Short Breaks from £85. Weekly prices from £170.

Details from: Mrs Pat Cooper, Moorcote Farm, Ellingstring, Masham, North Yorkshire HG4 4PL • Tel: 01677 460315

Panoramic views, waterfalls, wild birds and tranquillity

See also Colour Advertisement on page 60

Stone farmhouse with panoramic views, high in the Yorkshire Dales National Park (Herriot family's house in 'All Creatures Great and Small' on TV). Three bedrooms (sleeps 6-8), sitting and dining rooms with wood-burning stoves, kitchen, bathroom, WC. House has electric storage heating, cooker, microwave, fridge, washing machine, colour TV, telephone. Garden, large barn, stables. Access from lane, private parking, no through traffic. Excellent walking from front door, near Wensleydale. Pets welcome. Self-catering from £400 per week.

Westclose House (Allaker), West Scrafton,
Coverdale, Leyburn, North Yorkshire DL8 4RM
For bookings telephone 020 8567 4862
e-mail: ac@adriancave.com • website: www.adriancave.com/yorks

The Seacliffe Hotel 12 North Promenade, West Cliff, Whitby YO21 3JX

Friendly family-run hotel overlooking the sea. Licensed à la carte restaurant specialising in fresh local seafoods, steaks and vegetarian dishes. Open all year.

Freephone 0800 0191747 www.seacliffe.co.uk ETC/AA ◆◆◆◆

PARTRIDGE NEST FARM

Eskdaleside, Sleights, Whitby YO22 5ES Tel: 01947 810450

Six caravans on secluded site, five miles from Whitby and sea. Ideal touring centre. All have mains electricity, colour TV, fridge, gas cooker. Also cottages to let.

e-mail: barbara@partridgenestfarm.com web: www.partridgenestfarm.com

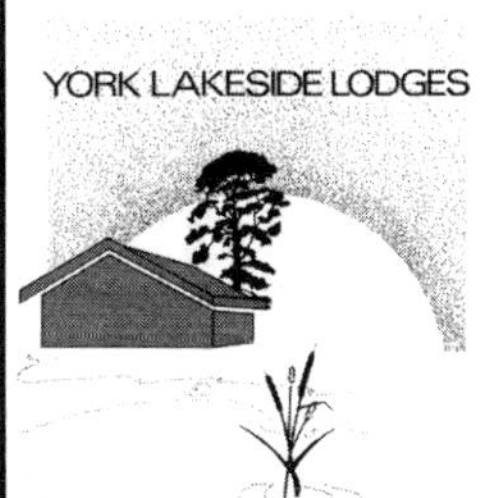

YORK LAKESIDE LODGES

Moor Lane, York YO24 2QU

Tel: 01904 702346 •Fax: 01904 701631

E-mail: neil@yorklakesidelodges.co.uk

Unique in a city! Luxurious Scandinavian lodges, and cottages in mature parkland overlooking large private fishing lake. Nearby superstore with coach to centre every 10 minutes. Easy access to ring road for touring. Open year round.

YORKSHIRE & HUMBERSIDE TOURIST BOARD WHITE ROSE AWARDS FOR TOURISM

WINNER

Award – British Holiday Home Parks Association

4-5 STARS SELF-CATERING **Website: www.yorklakesidelodges.co.uk**

HIGH BELTHORPE

Set on an ancient moated site at the foot of the Yorkshire Wolds, this comfortable Victorian farmhouse offers huge breakfasts, private fishing and fabulous walks. With York only 13 miles away, it is a peaceful rural idyll that both dogs and owners will love. Open all year except Christmas. From £20 + VAT.

Bishop Wilton, York YO42 1SB

Tel: 01759 368238; Mobile: 07786 923330

Tel: 01653 698251 • *"the best of Yorkshire – coast, city and countryside"* • **Fax: 01653 691962**

Coronation Farm Cottage

Deceptively spacious luxury cottage in conservation village, sleeps 2-8 + cot in 4 bedrooms. South-facing patio area with gas barbecue for lazy summer evenings. Off-street parking. Pets and children very welcome. Non-smoking. Open all year. Other properties available – all ETC 4 Star.

enquiries@coronationfarmcottage.co.uk • www.coronationfarmcottage.co.uk

See also Colour Advertisement on page 62

Visit the FHG website

www.holidayguides.com

for details of the wide choice of accommodation featured in the full range of FHG titles

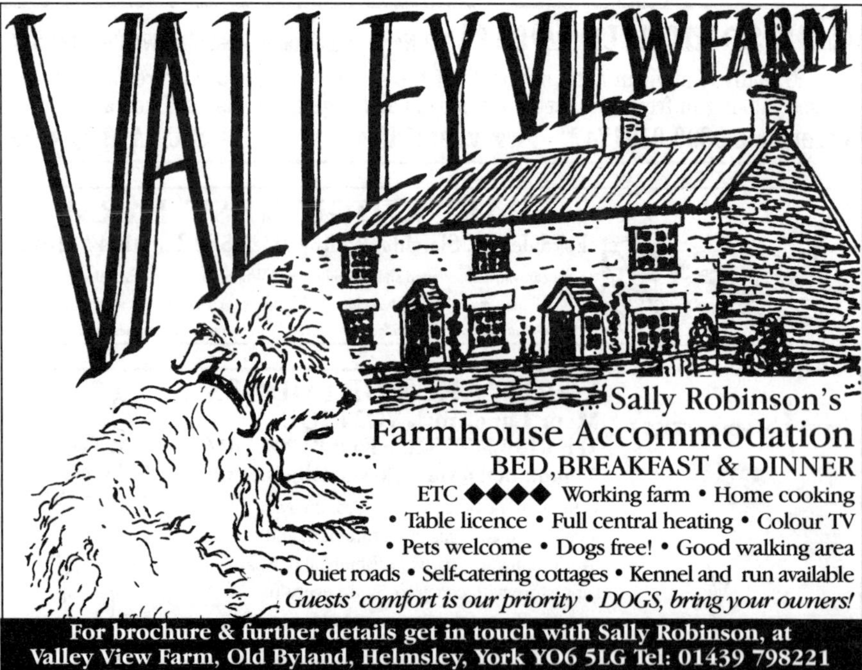

RECOMMENDED COTTAGE HOLIDAYS. 1st Choice for dream cottages at very competitive prices in all holiday regions of beautiful Britain. Pets welcome. All properties inspected. For a brochure call: 08700 718718.
website: www.recommended-cottages.co.uk

DALES HOLIDAY COTTAGES offer a choice of over 350 superb, personally inspected holiday properties, in beautiful rural and coastal locations. Including the Calendar Girls and Bronte, Heartbeat and Herriot areas. Cosy cottages to Country houses, many open all year. FREE brochure on request. DALES HOLIDAY COTTAGES, CARLETON BUSINESS PARK, SKIPTON, NORTH YORKSHIRE BD23 2AA (01756 799821 & 790919.
website: www.dalesholcot.com

Bentham

Quiet village amidst the fells. Good centre for rambling and fishing. Ingleton 5 miles north-east.

MRS L. J. STORY, HOLMES FARM, LOW BENTHAM, LANCASTER LA2 7DE (015242 61198). Cottage conversion in easy reach of Dales, Lake District and coast. Central heating, fridge, TV, washer, games room. ★★★★. [🐕]

SYMBOLS

- 🐕 **Indicates that pets are welcome free of charge.**
- £ **Indicates that a charge is made for pets: nightly or weekly.**
- pw! **Shows some special provision for pets; exercise facility, feeding or accommodation arrangement.**
- ⌂ **Indicates separate pets accommodation.**

Bishop Thornton

Village 2 miles north-west of Ripley.

THE COURTYARD AT DUKE'S PLACE, BISHOP THORNTON, NEAR HARROGATE HG3 3YJ (01765 620229; Fax: 01765 620454). In the heart of Nidderdale, group of well maintained and equipped holiday cottages. Sleep 2/6; linen, fully equipped kitchens. Riding stables on site. Pets and children most welcome. ETC ★★★/★★★★ [🐕]
e-mail: jakimoorhouse@onetel.net.uk

Clapham

Attractive village with caves and pot holes in vicinity, including Gaping Ghyll. Nearby lofty peaks include Ingleborough (2,373ft) to the north. Kendal 24 miles. Settle 6.

NEW INN HOTEL, CLAPHAM, NEAR INGLETON, NORTH YORKSHIRE LA2 8HH (015242 51203; Fax: 01524 251496). 'Jewel of the Dales'. A comfortable hotel in the Yorkshire Dales National Park. The ideal holiday destination for your pet, be assured of a warm and friendly reception, sit back, close your eyes and soak up the history and atmosphere.
e-mail: info@newinn-clapham.co.uk website: www.newinn-clapham.co.uk

DAVID & JACKIE KINGSLEY, ARBUTUS GUEST HOUSE, RIVERSIDE, CLAPHAM (NEAR SETTLE) LA2 8DS (015242 51240). Restored Georgian vicarage in a delightful setting. All rooms en suite, or private facilities. TV, tea/coffee. Central heating. Delicious home cooking. Open all year round. ETC ◆◆◆◆ Pets welcome. [🐕]
e-mail: info@arbutus.co.uk website: www.arbutus.co.uk

Coverdale

Small village set in Yorkshire Dales, in heart of Herriot Country.

MRS JULIE CLARKE, MIDDLE FARM, WOODALE, COVERDALE, LEYBURN DL8 4TY (01969 640271). Peacefully situated farmhouse away from the madding crowd. B&B with optional Evening Meal. Home cooking. Pets sleep where you prefer. Ideally positioned for exploring the beautiful Yorkshire Dales. [🐕 pw!]
e-mail: julie-clarke@amserve.com

Danby

Village on River Esk 12 miles west of Whitby.

THE FOX & HOUNDS INN, AINTHORPE, DANBY YO21 2LD (01287 660218; Fax: 01287 660030). Residential 16th Century Coaching Inn. Comfortable en suite bedrooms available. Enjoy our real ales or quality wines. Special mid-week breaks available Oct - May. Open all year. ETC ◆◆◆◆ [Pets £1.50 per night.]

Filey

Well-known resort with sandy beach. Off-shore is Filey Brig. Hull 40 miles, Bridlington 11, Scarborough 7.

LEONARD & DIANE HUNTER, "SEA CABIN", 16 GAP ROAD, HUNMANBY GAP, NEAR FILEY YO14 9QP (01723 891368). En suite, twin-bedroomed Granny annexe with private lounge. Full English breakfast. Vegetarians catered for. B&B plus Evening Meal. Open all year. Pet friendly beach. ETC ◆◆◆ [🐕 pw!]

SEA BRINK HOTEL, 3 THE BEACH, FILEY YO14 9LA (01723 513257 Fax: 01723 514139). Licensed seafront accommodation. Room amenities: colour TV, clock/radio, central heating, direct dial phones, coffee/tea making facilities, sea views. ETC ★★ [Pets £2 per night]
website: www.seabrink.co.uk

PLEASE SEND A STAMPED ADDRESSED ENVELOPE WITH ENQUIRIES

Grassington

Wharfedale village in attractive moorland setting. Ripon 22 miles, Skipton 9.

FORESTERS ARMS, MAIN STREET, GRASSINGTON, SKIPTON BD23 5AA (01756 752349; Fax: 01756 753633). The Foresters Arms is situated in the heart of the Yorkshire Dales and provides an ideal centre for walking or touring. Within easy reach of York and Harrogate. ETC ◆◆◆ [🐕]

JERRY AND BEN'S HOLIDAY COTTAGES. Seven comfortable properties on private estate near Grassington in Yorkshire Dales National Park. Wooded mountain becks, waterfalls, rocky crags and accessible hill and footpath walking. Brochure from: MRS J. M.JOY, JERRY AND BEN'S HOLIDAY COTTAGES, HEBDEN, SKIPTON BD23 5DL (01756 752369; Fax: 01756 753370). [pw! one pet free, subsequent pets £5 per week] [🐕]
e-mail: dawjoy@aol.com website: www.yorkshirenet.co.uk/stayat/jerryandbens

GRASSINGTON HOUSE HOTEL, THE SQUARE, GRASSINGTON BD23 5AQ (01756 752406; Fax: 01756 752135). A small hotel with a big reputation. All rooms en suite, colour TV, tea making. Parking. Ideal for walking or touring. AA/ETC ★★, [🐕]

Harrogate

Charming and elegant spa town set amid some of Britain's most scenic countryside. Ideal for exploring Herriot Country and the Moors and Dales. York 22 miles, Bradford 19, Leeds 16.

ROSEMARY HELME, HELME PASTURE LODGES & COTTAGES, OLD SPRING WOOD, HARTWITH BANK, SUMMERBRIDGE, HARROGATE HG3 4DR (01423 780279, Fax: 01423 780994). Country accommodation for dogs and numerous walks in unspoilt Nidderdale. Central for Harrogate, York, Herriot and Bronte country. National Trust area. ETC ★★★★ [pw! Pets £5 per night, £25 per week.]
e-mail: info@helmepasture.co.uk website: www.helmepasture.co.uk

RUDDING HOLIDAY PARK, FOLLIFOOT, HARROGATE HG3 1JH (01423 870439; Fax: 01423 870859). Luxury cottages and lodges sleeping two to ten people. All equipped to a high standard. Pool, licensed bar, golf and children's playground on estate. Illustrated brochure available. ETC ★★★. [🐕]

Hawes (near Mallerstang)

12 miles north-west on the Hawes to Kirkby Stephen road.

COCKLAKE HOUSE, MALLERSTANG CA17 4JT (017683 72080). Charming, High Pennine Country House B&B in unique position above Pendragon Castle in Upper Mallerstang Dale, offering good food and exceptional comfort to a small number of guests. Two double rooms with large private bathrooms. Three acres riverside grounds. Dogs welcome.

STONE HOUSE HOTEL, SEDBUSK, HAWES DL8 3PT (01969 667571; Fax: 01969 667720). This fine Edwardian country house has spectacular views and serves delicious Yorkshire cooking with fine wines. Comfortable en suite bedrooms, some ground floor. Phone for details. [🐕]
website: www.stonehousehotel.com

SIMONSTONE HALL, HAWES, WENSLEYDALE DL8 3LY (01969 667255; Fax: 01969 667741). Facing south across picturesque Wensleydale. All rooms en suite with colour TV. Fine cuisine. Extensive wine list. Friendly personal attention. A relaxing break away from it all. AA ★★. [🐕 ⌂]
e-mail: information@simonstonehall.demon.co.uk website: www.simonstonehall.co.uk

Helmsley

A delightful stone-built town on River Rye with a large cobbled square. Thirsk 12 miles.

CROWN HOTEL, MARKET SQUARE, HELMSLEY YO62 5BJ (01439 770297). Fully residential old coaching inn. Bedrooms are very well appointed, all have tea and coffee-making facilities, colour TV, radio and telephones. Traditional country cooking. ETC/AA/RAC ★★. [🐕]

Kirkbymoorside

Small town below North Yorkshire Moors, 7 miles west of Pickering. Traces of a medieval castle.

MRS F. WILES, SINNINGTON COMMON FARM, KIRKBYMOORSIDE, YORK YO62 6NX (Tel & Fax: 01751 431719). Newly converted cottages, tastefully furnished and well equipped, on working family farm. Sleep 2/8 from £135 per week including linen and heating. Also spacious ground floor accommodation (teamakers, colour TV, fridge, radio). Disabled facilities, separate outside entrances. B&B from £19.00. ETC ◆◆◆◆ (B&B), ★★★/★★★★ (SC) [🐕 pw!]
e-mail: felicity@scfarm.demon.co.uk website: www.scfarm.demon.co.uk

Leeming Bar

Small, pretty village two miles north-east of Bedale.

THE WHITE ROSE HOTEL, LEEMING BAR, NORTHALLERTON DL7 9AY (01677 422707/424941; Fax: 01677 425123). Ideally situated for touring the spectacular scenery of two National Parks,Yorkshire Dales, coastal resorts, Herriot & Heartbeat Country. 18 rooms, all private bathroom, Colour TV/radio, tea & coffee, hair dryer, trouser press and telephone. B&B £42 single, £56 double/twin, £62 family room. RAC ★★ [🐕]
e-mail: john@whiterosehotel.co.uk website: www.whiterosehotel.co.uk

Leyburn

Small market town, 8 miles south-west of Richmond, standing above the River Ure in Wensleydale.

BARBARA & BARRIE MARTIN, THE OLD STAR, WEST WITTON, LEYBURN DL8 4LU (01969 622949). Former 17th century Coaching Inn now run as a guest house. Oak beams, log fire, home cooking. En suite from £21. ETC ◆◆◆. [🐕]

STONEY END, WORTON, NEAR ASKRIGG, LEYBURN DL8 3ET (01969 650652). For quality Bed and Breakfast and Self-Catering in the heart of the Yorkshire Dales.[🐕]
e-mail: pmh@stoneyend.co.uk website: www.stoneyend.co.uk

Malham

In picturesque Craven District with spectacular Malham Cove (300ft) and Gordale Scar with waterfalls. Malham Tarn (N.T.) is 4 miles north, Skipton 12 miles.

MR C. SHARP, MIRESFIELD FARM, MALHAM, SKIPTON BD23 4DA (01729 830414). In beautiful gardens bordering village green and stream. Excellent food. 11 bedrooms, all with private facilities. Full central heating. Two well-furnished lounges and conservatory. B&B from £24pppn. ETC ◆◆◆ [🐕 pw!]

Northallerton

Town 14 miles south of Darlington.

JULIE & JIM GRIFFITH, HILL HOUSE FARM, LITTLE LANGTON, NORTHALLERTON DL7 0PZ (01609 770643; Fax: 01609 760438). Four well-equipped, converted cottages. Sleep 2-6. Centrally located between Dales and Moors. Pub food 1 mile, golf 2 miles, shops 3 miles. Rate from £150 per week inclusive of linen, towels, heating and electricity. Short breaks available. Phone for free brochure. ETC ★★★★ [🐕 pw!]
e-mail: info@Hillhousefarmcottages.com

Oldstead

Hamlet 7 miles east of Thirsk in beautiful North Yorkshire Moors.

THE BLACK SWAN INN, OLDSTEAD, COXWOLD, YORK YO61 4BL (01347 868387). 18th-century Country Freehouse offers chalet-style accommodation, en suite, colour TV, central heating, tea/coffee facilities. Real ale. A la carte restaurant. Fine wines. Brochure available. [Pets £1 per night]
e-mail: blackswan@oldstead.fsworld.co.uk website: www.theblackswaninn.com

Pickering

Pleasant market town on southern fringe of North Yorkshire Moors National Park with Moated Norman Castle. Bridlington 31 miles, Whitby 20, Scarborough 16, Helmsley 13, Malton 3.

MRS S. M. PICKERING, 'NABGATE', WILTON ROAD, THORNTON-LE-DALE, PICKERING YO18 7QP (01751 474279). All rooms en suite. TV, courtesy trays, central heating. Good food and a very warm welcome for pets and owners. Central for coast, steam railway, moors. Nearby walks for dogs. Own keys. Car park. Hygiene and Welcome Host Certificates. Open all year. Bed and Breakfast from £20. Also Self-Catering Cottage available. ETC ◆◆◆◆ [🐕]
website: www.nabgateguesthouse.co.uk

MRS ELLA BOWES, BANAVIE, ROXBY ROAD, THORNTON-LE-DALE, PICKERING YO18 7SX (01751 474616). Large stone-built semi-detached house set in Thornton-le-Dale. Ideal for touring. One family bedroom and two double bedrooms, all en suite. All with TV, shaver points, central heating and tea-making facilities. Open all year. Car park, cycle shed. B&B from £21-£24.00 pppn. Welcome Host and Hygiene Certificate held. ETC ◆◆◆◆, **[🐕]**
e-mail: ella@banavie.fsbusiness.co.uk website: www.banavie.uk.com

Port Mulgrave

Located 1km north of Hinderwell.

NORTH YORK MOORS NATIONAL PARK. Stone Cottage (sleeps) 4 in North York Moors National Park. Sea view, near Cleveland coastal footpath. Log fire, non-smoking. Whitby 9 miles. Brochure available (Tel & Fax: 01642 613888). [🐕]
e-mail: comesatime.cottage@ntlworld.com

Scarborough

Very popular family resort with good sands. York 41 miles, Whitby 20, Bridlington 17, Filey 7.

SUE AND TONY HEWITT, HARMONY COUNTRY LODGE, LIMESTONE ROAD, BURNISTON, SCARBOROUGH YO13 0DG (0800 2985840). A peaceful retreat set in two acres of private grounds with 360° panoramic views of the National Park and sea. An ideal centre for walking or touring.En suite centrally heated rooms with superb views. Fragrant massage available. B&B from £24 to £31.50. Non-smoking, licensed, private parking facilities. ETC ◆◆◆◆
website: www.harmonylodge.net

SUE AND TONY HEWITT, HARMONY COUNTRY LODGE, LIMESTONE ROAD, BURNISTON, SCARBOROUGH YO13 0DG (0800 2985840). A peaceful retreat set in two acres of private grounds with 360° panoramic views of the National Park and sea. An ideal centre for walking or touring. En suite centrally heated rooms with superb views. Fragrant massage available. B&B from £22 to £33.50. Non-smoking, licensed, private parking facilities. Pets welcome. ETC ◆◆◆◆
website: www.harmonylodge.net

FORGE VALLEY COTTAGES (01653 698251; Fax: 01653 691962). Luxury stone cottages in lovely village near Scarborough. Sleep 2-5 + cot in 2 bedrooms. Private patio/garden and car park. Pets and children very welcome. Non-smoking available. Open all year. Other properties available. All ETC ★★★★. [🐕]
e-mail: enquiries@forgevalleycottages.co.uk website: www.forgevalleycottages.co.uk

NEW SOUTHLANDS HOTEL, SOUTH CLIFF, SCARBOROUGH YO11 2QW (01723 361461; Fax: 01723 376035). Ideally situated close to Italian Rose Gardens, Esplanade and South Bay, with easy access to Conference Centre and theatre. 60 en suite bedrooms. Excellent food, well stocked cellar. ETC ★★ HOTEL. [Pets £3 per night.]
e-mail: sales@southlandshotel.co.uk website: www.southlandshotel.co.uk

Skipton

Airedale market town, centre for picturesque Craven district. Fine 14th century castle. York 43 miles, Manchester 42, Leeds 26, Harrogate 22, Settle 16.

Over 200 super self-catering Cottages, throughout the Yorkshire Dales, York, Moors, Lancs Coast, Peak and Lake District. For our fully illustrated brochure apply: HOLIDAY COTTAGES (YORKSHIRE) LTD, WATER STREET, SKIPTON (18) BD23 1PB (01756 700872). [🐕]
e-mail: p@holidaycotts.co.uk website: www.holidaycotts.co.uk

THE CONISTON HOTEL, CONISTON COLD, SKIPTON BD23 4EB (01756 748080; Fax: 01756 749487). Set in a 1200 acre estate, an ideal base for business or leisure guests. 40 en suite bedrooms with full facilities. Special rates for leisure breaks and family rooms. ETC ★★★ Silver Award, AA ★★★ & Rosette. [pw! Pets £5 per night]
e-mail: info@theconistonhotel.com website: www.theconistonhotel.com

Staithes

Fishing village surrounded by high cliffs on North Sea coast 9 miles north west of Whitby.

MS M.J. HEALD, BROOKLYN, BROWN'S TERRACE, STAITHES, SALTBURN-BY-THE-SEA TS13 5BG (01947 841396). Sea captain's house in quiet location in old part of this picturesque, historic fishing village. Views across rooftops to Cowbar Cliffs. Pets and children welcome. [🐕]

Thirsk

Market town with attractive square. Excellent touring area. Northallerton 3 miles.

GOLDEN FLEECE HOTEL, MARKET SQUARE, THIRSK YO7 1LL (01845 523108; Fax: 01845 523996). Characterful Coaching Inn offering good food and up to date facilities. All rooms have new bathrooms, satellite TV, phone, trouser press, hairdryer. ETC/AA ★★, [🐕]
e-mail: goldenfleece@bestwestern.co.uk website: www.goldenfleecehotel.com

FOXHILLS HIDEAWAYS, FELIXKIRK, THIRSK YO7 2DS (01845 537575). Scandinavian log cabins, heated throughout, linen provided. A supremely relaxed atmosphere on the edge of the North Yorkshire Moors National Park. Open all year. Village pub round the corner. [🐕]

Wensleydale

Possibly the most picturesque of all the Dales, ideal for touring some of the most beautiful parts of Yorkshire and nearby Herriot Country. Kendal 25 miles, Kirkby Stephen 15.

MRS SUE COOPER, ST EDMUNDS, CRAKEHALL, BEDALE DL8 1HP (01677 423584). Set in Wensleydale, these recently renovated cottages are fully equipped and are an ideal base for exploring the Dales and Moors. Sleep 2–7 plus cot. ETC★★/★★★, Brochure available. [🐕]
website: www.crakehall.org.uk

MRS PAT COOPER, MOORCOTE FARM, ELLINGSTRING, MASHAM HG4 4PL (01677 460315). Three delightful cottages around a sunny courtyard, sleeping 4-6. All equipped to a very high standard. Children and pets welcome. Open all year round. [Pets £10 per week]

West Scrafton

Village 3 miles south of Wensley.

ADRIAN CAVE, WESTCLOSE HOUSE (ALLAKER), WEST SCRAFTON, COVERDALE, NEAR LEYBURN DL8 4RM (020 8567 4862 for bookings). Stone farmhouse with panoramic views. Three bedrooms sleeping 6-8. Well-equipped with electric storage heating and woodburning stoves. Garden, barn, stables. Ideal for families/walkers. Self-catering from £400 per week. [pw 🐕]
e-mail: ac@adriancave.com website: www.adriancave.com/yorks

Whitby

Charming resort with harbour and sands. Of note is the 13th century ruined Abbey. Stockton-on-Tees 34 miles, Scarborough 20, Saltburn-by-the-Sea 19.

MRS JILL McNEIL, SWALLOW HOLIDAY COTTAGES, THE FARM, STAINSACRE, WHITBY YO22 4NT (01947 603790). Discover historic Whitby, pretty fishing villages, countryside with way-marked walks, etc. Four cottages. One or two bedrooms, plus a three bedroom detached house. Private parking. Children and dogs welcome. Non-smoking accommodation available. Weekly rates from £120 to £450. Please phone or write for a brochure. ETC ★★ [🐕]

ARCHES GUESTHOUSE, 8 HAVELOCK PLACE, HUDSON STREET, WHITBY YO21 3ER. Pet friendly, family-run guesthouse, where a warm welcome and large breakfast is always assured. The ideal base for experiencing the old world charms of this historic seaside town, exploring the beautiful North Yorkshire Moors, or just relaxing. Strictly Non-Smoking. Tariff: £20 - £24. RUTH & DICK BREW (01947 601880). ETC ◆◆◆◆ [🐕 pw!]
e-mail: archeswhitby@freeola.com website: www.whitbyguesthouses.co.uk

SNEATON HALL, SNEATON, NEAR WHITBY YO22 5HP (01947 605929). Country House Hotel situated 3 miles south of Whitby. En-suite rooms with tea/coffee making facilities. Delightful restaurant, bar and residents' lounge. Pets most welcome (£3 - £5 per night).
e-mail: sneatonhall@supanet.com

WHITE ROSE HOLIDAY COTTAGES, NEAR WHITBY. Superior centrally heated village cottages and bungalows, also flat in Whitby. Available all year. Ideal for coast and country. Up to ETC ★★★★. APPLY: MRS J. ROBERTS (PW), 5 BROOK PARK, SLEIGHTS, NEAR WHITBY YO21 1RT (01947 810763) [£5 per week, pw!]
e-mail: enquiries@whiterosecottages.co.uk website: www.whiterosecottages.co.uk

THE SEACLIFFE HOTEL, WEST CLIFF, WHITBY Y021 3JX (Freephone 0800 0191747). Friendly family-run hotel overlooking the sea. Licensed à la carte restaurant specialising in fresh local seafoods, steaks and vegetarian dishes. Tel & Fax: 01947 603139. ETC/AA ◆◆◆◆. [🐕]
website: www.seacliffe.co.uk

PARTRIDGE NEST FARM, ESKDALESIDE, SLEIGHTS, WHITBY YO22 5ES (01947 810450). Six caravans on secluded site, five miles from Whitby and sea. Ideal touring centre. All have mains electricity, colour TV, fridge, gas cooker. Also cottages to let. [Dogs £1 per day per dog]
e-mail: barbara@partridgenestfarm.com website: www.partridgenestfarm.com

York

Historic cathedral city and former Roman Station on River Ouse. Magnificent Minster and 3 miles of ancient walls. Facilities for a wide range of sports and entertainments. Horse-racing on Knavesmire. Bridlington 41 miles, Filey 41, Leeds 24, Harrogate 22.

ST GEORGE'S HOUSE HOTEL, 6 ST GEORGE'S PLACE, YORK YO24 1DR (01904 625056). Family-run Hotel in quiet cul-de-sac near racecourse. All rooms en suite with colour TV, tea/coffee making facilities. Private parking. Pets welcome. ETC/RAC/AA ◆◆◆ [🐕]
e-mail: sixstgeorg@aol.com website: http://members.aol.com/sixstgeorg/

MR G. JACKSON, VICTORIA VILLA GUEST HOUSE, 72 HESLINGTON ROAD, YORK YO10 5AU (01904 631647). Ten minutes' walk from city centre. Comfortable double, twin, single and family bedrooms, all with TV. Open all year. B&B from £16 to £25 per person. Children and pets welcome. [🐕 pw!]

NOTE

All the information in this book is given in good faith in the belief that it is correct. However, the publishers cannot guarantee the facts given in these pages, neither are they responsible for changes in policy, ownership or terms that may take place after the date of going to press. Readers should always satisfy themselves that the facilities they require are available and that the terms, if quoted, still apply.

YORK LAKESIDE LODGES, MOOR LANE, YORK YO24 2QU (01904 702346; Fax: 01904 701631). Self-catering pine lodges. Mature parkland setting. Large fishing lake. Nearby superstore with coach to centre every 10 mins. ETC ★★★★/★★★★★ [pw! Pets £18 per week]
e-mail:neil@yorklakesidelodges.co.uk website: www.lakesidelodges.co.uk

HIGH BELTHORPE, BISHOP WILTON, YORK YO42 1SB (01759 368238; Mobile: 07786 923330). Set on an ancient moated site at the foot of the Yorkshire Wolds, this comfortable Victorian farmhouse offers huge breakfasts, private fishing and fabulous walks. Dogs and owners will love it! Open all year except Christmas. Prices from £20 +VAT. ETC ◆◆◆ [pw!]

CORONATION FARM COTTAGE (01653 698251; Fax: 01653 691962). Luxury cottage in conservation village, sleeps 2-8 + cot in four bedrooms. South-facing patio area with gas barbecue; off-street parking. Pets and children very welcome. Non-smoking. Open all year. Other properties available – all ETC 4 Star. [ ]
enquiries@coronationfarmcottage.co.uk website: www.coronationfarmcottage.co.uk

MRS SALLY ROBINSON, VALLEY VIEW FARM, OLD BYLAND, HELMSLEY, YORK YO6 5LG (01439 798221). B&B £30. BB&D £43.50 Working farm, home cooking, table licence, private parking, full central heating, colour TV. Self catering cottages. Kennel and run available. Pets Welcome. [ ] ETC ◆◆◆◆
e-mail: sally@valleyviewfarm.com website: www.valleyviewfarm.com

WEST YORKSHIRE

Meltham

Bingley

Town on River Aire 5 miles north-west of Bradford.

MRS P. OXLEY, FIVE RISE LOCKS HOTEL, BECK LANE, BINGLEY BD16 4DD (01274 565296; Fax: 01274 568828). Charming Victorian Mill owner's house in mature terraced gardens, minutes walk from the famous Five Rise Locks. Individually designed and furnished en suite bedrooms with panoramic views of the Aire Valley. Relaxed atmosphere complemented by interesting menus and wine list. ETC SILVER AWARD , RAC DINING AWARD, ETC/RAC/AA ◆◆◆◆ [ ]
e-mail: info@five-rise-locks.co.uk website: www.five-rise-locks.co.uk

Meltham

Town 5 miles south west of Huddersfield.

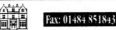

DURKER ROODS HOTEL, BISHOPSWAY, MELTHAM, HUDDERSFIELD HD9 4JA (01484 851413; Fax: 01484 851843). Extensively refurbished hotel, all bedrooms en suite with TV. Elegant restaurant and friendly bar. Ideal for Peak District Park and 'Last of Summer Wine' country. West Yorkshire's warmest welcome.
e-mail: spencer@durkerroodshotel.co.uk website: www.durkerroodshotel.co.uk

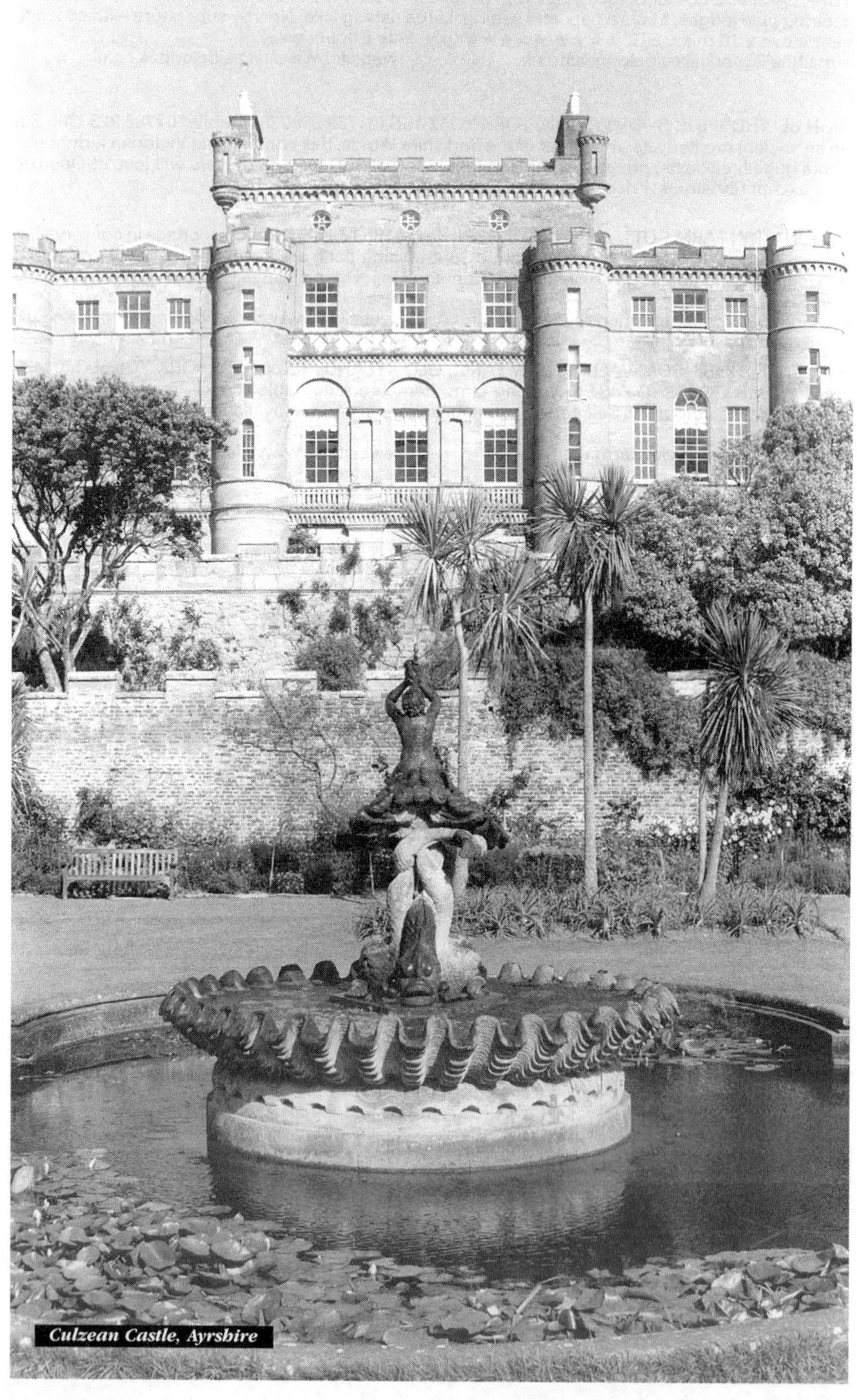

Culzean Castle, Ayrshire

SCOTLAND from BORDERS to HIGHLANDS

Dales Holiday Cottages

Superb, personally inspected, self catering holiday properties in beautiful rural and coastal locations including Burns country, Cowal, the West Coast & Isles and Speyside. Cosy cottages to country houses, many welcome pets and most are open all year.

01756 799821 & 790919
www.dalesholcot.com

See also Colour Advertisement on page 5

The best holidays on four legs

We have over 50 holiday parks in Scotland where your pet is as welcome as you are. For those who love long walks, there are secluded pine lodges surrounded by acres of picturesque countryside. Or loch side locations with miles of shoreline to explore. Nearly all offer mid-week and weekend breaks. Many are open all year round. **01502 502 601** Quote H0006

HOSEASONS. We have over 50 holiday parks in Scotland where your pet is as welcome as you are. For those who love long walks, there are secluded pine lodges surrounded by acres of picturesque countryside. Or loch side locations with miles of shoreline to explore. Nearly all offer mid-week and weekend breaks. Many are open all year round. (01502 502601) Quote H0006. website: www.hoseasons.co.uk

Visit the FHG website
www.holidayguides.com
for details of the wide choice of accommodation featured in the full range of FHG titles

Have your pet's photo featured in Pets Welcome! and receive a FREE Live-a-Lot Pack

As the sponsor of **Pets Welcome! 2004** Winalot is offering readers the chance to win a **Live-a-Lot Pack** for every picture featured.
The special packs include a rucksack, fold away bowl, water bottle, frisbee and dog towel – an essential kit for everyday doggie outings.

SEE PAGE 81 FOR FULL DETAILS

See also Colour Advertisement on page 63

Crathie

Village on River Dee, 1km east of Balmoral Castle.

INVER HOTEL, CRAITHIE, BY BRAEMAR, ABERDEENSHIRE AB35 5YR. (013397 42345)Family run Hotel located in the village of Crathie, close to Balmoral Castle. All 9 bedrooms are en-suite with bath and shower along with TV and tea/coffee making facilities. Lounge bar, residents' lounge and beer garden. Ideal for fishing, deerstalking, mountaineering and ski-ing. Highland Games held throughout the summer.

Cullen

Fishing village on Cullen Bay on the north coast, 6 miles east of Buckie.

CULLEN BAY HOTEL, CULLEN, MORAY AB56 4XA (01542 840432; Fax: 01542 840900). Outstanding position on prominent headland overlooking Moray Firth - dolphins, porpoises and whales. 14 well-equipped en suite bedrooms. Wholesome Scottish menus and warm hospitality.[🐕]
e-mail: info@cullenbayhotel.com website: www.cullenbayhotel.com

Grantown-on-Spey

Market town 19 miles south of Forres.

MR AND MRS J. R. TAYLOR, MILTON OF CROMDALE, GRANTOWN-ON-SPEY PH26 3PH (01479 872415). Fully modernised Cottage with large garden and views of River Spey and Cromdale Hills. Golf, tennis and trekking within easy reach. Fully equipped except linen. Two double bedrooms. Shower, refrigerator, electric cooker, colour television. Car desirable. Open March to October. £100 per week. Children and pets welcome. [🐕]

Kintore

Village on the River Don, 4 miles south of Inverurie.

THE TORRYBURN HOTEL, SCHOOL ROAD, KINTORE AB51 0XP (01467 632269). Situated 12 miles north of Aberdeen, set in 3 acres of grounds, the hotel has 12 en suite rooms all individually decorated with tea/coffee making, satellite TV and direct dial telephones.
website: www.torryburnhotel.co.uk

Methlick

Village 9 miles from Ellon and 7 miles from Fyvie, between Haddo House and Fyvie Castle.

MRS CHRISTINE STAFF, SUNNYBRAE FARM, GIGHT, METHLICK, ELLON AB41 7JA (Tel & Fax: 01651 806456). Comfortable accommodation on a working farm situated in a quiet, peaceful location with superb views. Centrally situated for many places of interest. Double, twin, single rooms, some en suite. Open all year. Dogs and owners most welcome. STB ★★. [🐕]
e-mail: sunnybrae-farm@talk21.com

Newburgh

Village with quay on west side of River Ythan estuary. 4 miles south east of Ellon.

UDNY ARMS HOTEL, MAIN STREET, NEWBURGH AB41 6BL (01358 789444; Fax: 01358 789012). Short breaks with a wealth of sporting activities available for you to try. 3 golf courses nearby. Please contact for further details and rates. [⌂]
e-mail: enquiry@udny.demon.co.uk website: www.udny.co.uk

Rattray Head (Near Peterhead)

Headland with lighthouse on north east coast 7 miles north of Peterhead.

SAND DUNES & SECLUDED 10 MILE BEACH. Homely, relaxed non-smoking B&B for cyclists, walkers, carnivores, vegetarians and pets (even giant dogs). Wet/dry room for washing and drying clothes, pets etc. Breakfast available all morning. Hot and cold drinks available 24/7. ROB & VAL, LIGHTHOUSE COTTAGES, RATTRAY HEAD, PETERHEAD AB42 3HB (01346 532236). [🐕, pw!]
website: www.rattrayhead.net

Turriff

Small town in agricultural area, 9 miles south of Banff.

MRS P E. BATES, COUNTRY COTTAGES, FORGLEN ESTATE, TURRIFF AB53 4JP (01888 562918/ 562518; Fax 01888 562 252). Estate on the beautiful Deveron River. Sea only nine miles away, Turriff two miles. 10 cottages sleeping 6–9. From £159 weekly. Special Winter lets. Children and reasonable dogs welcome. [🐕]
website: www.forglen.co.uk

FREE or REDUCED RATE entry to Holiday Visits and Attractions – see our READERS' OFFER VOUCHERS on pages 103-118

HOUSE IN THE WOOD HOLIDAYS

Glenachulish, Ballachulish, Argyll PH49 4JZ Telephone: 01855 811379

Cottage and Chalets in Natural Woodland sleeping two to six people.
From £155–£270.

GOOD AREA FOR WALKING – AND NATURE LOVERS

PETS WELCOME *BROCHURE AVAILABLE* *NO VAT* *REGRET NO SMOKERS*

AT THE HEAD OF LOCH FYNE. Two comfortable holiday cottages at the head of the longest sea loch in Scotland. INVERFYNE, a very spacious cottage with 4 twin-bedded rooms and BRIDGE COTTAGE, sleeps four. Linen and electricity are included. Achadunan Estate is set amidst lovely walking country. The bird life is fascinating and the deer graze the river banks and the hills behind the cottages.

Brochures available from Mrs Delap, Achadunan, Cairndow, Argyll PA26 8BJ.
Tel & Fax: 01499 600238 website: www.argyllholidaycottages.com

See also Colour Advertisement on page 64

Rockhill Waterside Country House

Est 1960

Ardbrecknish, By Dalmally, Argyll PA33 1BH Tel: 01866 833218

17th century guest house in spectacular waterside setting on Loch Awe with breathtaking views to Ben Cruachan, where comfort, peace and tranquillity reign supreme. Small private Highland estate breeding Hanoverian competition horses. 1200 metres free trout fishing. Five delightful rooms with all modern facilities. First-class highly acclaimed home cooking with much home-grown produce. Wonderful area for touring the Western Highlands, Glencoe, the Trossachs and Kintyre. Ideal for climbing, walking, bird and animal watching. Boat trips locally and from Oban (30 miles) to Mull, Iona, Fingal's Cave and other islands. Dogs' Paradise!

Also Self-Catering Cottages.

ABBOT'S BRAE HOTEL West Bay, Dunoon, Argyll PA23 7QJ

Tel: 01369 705021 • Fax: 01369 701191

e-mail: info@abbotsbrae.co.uk • website: www.abbotsbrae.co.uk

Award-winning, small Country House Hotel set in its own secluded woodland garden with breathtaking views of the sea and hills. Spacious en suite bedrooms. Welcoming, homely atmosphere, peaceful surroundings. Pets stay free. Ideal base to explore the Western Highlands. For further details contact either Helen or Gavin.

See also Colour Advertisement on page 65

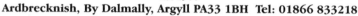

Terms quoted in this publication may be subject to increase if rises in costs necessitate

ELERAIG HIGHLAND CHALETS

Near OBAN, ARGYLL

Gateway to the Highlands and Islands

Well-equipped Norwegian chalets on secluded Eleraig Estate 12 miles from Oban.

PERFECT FOR PETS

In the breathtaking scenery of a private glen within 1800-acre working sheep farm. The chalets are ideal for a holiday with dogs. Widely spaced, sleeping four to seven. Parking by each chalet. Cots and high chairs available. By Loch Tralaig. Free fishing and boating. Peace and tranquillity are features of this walkers' and birdwatchers' paradise. Riding, golf, watersports and evening entertainment available locally. Open March to November.

From £205 weekly per chalet, including electricity & bed linen.
Colour brochure from resident owners:

Anne and Robin Grey,
Eleraig Highland Chalets,
Kilninver, by Oban, Argyll PA34 4UX.
Tel/Fax: 01852 200225
Website: www.scotland2000.com/eleraig
E-mail: robingrey@eleraig.co.uk

Scottish Tourist Board ★★ Self Catering — Scottish Tourist Board ★★★ Self Catering

Loch Melfort Hotel & Restaurant

Enjoy stunning views down the Sound of Jura to the Islands. Located between Inveraray and Oban, beside the famous Arduaine Gardens. Join our regular guests and relax with excellent award-winning cuisine, comfortable accommodation, and friendly and attentive service. The perfect place for a relaxing holiday or short break.

Arduaine, By Oban, Argyll PA34 4XG Tel: 01852 200233
Fax: 01852 200214 • www.lochmelfort.co.uk

MELFORT PIER & HARBOUR

KILMELFORD, BY OBAN PA34 4XD
Tel: 01852 200333; Fax: 01852 200329

"A Luxury Dog's Life!". Private beach, Hillwalking, Underfloor heating. Dog sitter. Superb Lochside Houses, each with Sauna, Spabath, Satellite TV, Telephone, E-mail hook-up, right on the shores of Loch Melfort. Close by restaurants/bars. Excellent base for touring Argyll and the Isles. From £80 to £220.00 per house/night. Sleep 2/6. Min 2 nights, start any day of the week. 2 pets welcome. Mention Pets Welcome and 1 pet stays FREE! STB ★★★★★ Self-Catering.

E-mail: melharbour@aol.com Website: www.scotland2000.com/melfort

See also Colour Advertisement on page 63

Colin and Jo Mossman, Lerags, Oban, Argyll, PA34 4SE
• Tel: 01631 562746 • Fax: 01631 570225
• E-mail: lagnakeil@aol.com • Website: www.lagnakeil.co.uk

Our timber lodges and three houses are set in a tranquil, scenic wooded glen overlooking Loch Feochan, only 3½ miles from the picturesque harbour town of Oban "Gateway to the Isles", offering a wonderful holiday at any time of the year. Free loch fishing. Pets welcome. O.A.P. discount. Sleep 2-10 comfortably. *Mini breaks from £39 per lodge per night, weekly from £195. ASSC Member.* **STB ★★★★** *SC*

See also Colour Advertisement on page 63

STB ★★★ **WILLOWBURN HOTEL** AA ★★

Clachan Seil, By Oban, Argyll PA34 4TJ Tel: 01852 300276

Peaceful, relaxing, informal and addictive. Superb setting overlooking the Sound of Seil. Walk, fish, birdwatch or simply just laze. Completely non-smoking. Tempted? Bring your owners too! **www.willowburn.co.uk**

See also Colour Advertisement on page 63

See also Colour Advertisement on page 64

See also Colour Advertisement on page 64

Appin

Mountainous area bounded by Loch Linnhe, Glen Creran and Glencoe.

MRS J PERY, ARDTUR, APPIN PA38 4DD (01631 730223 or 01626 834172). Two adjacent cottages in secluded surroundings. Ideal for hill walking, climbing, pony trekking, boating and fly fishing. Shop one mile; sea 200 yards; car essential; pets allowed.
e-mail: pery@eurobell.co.uk

Ballachulish

Impressively placed village at entrance to Glencoe and on Loch Leven. Magnificent mountain scenery including Sgorr Dhearg (3362ft). Good centre for boating, climbing and sailing. Glasgow 89 miles, Oban 38, Fort William 14, Kinlochleven 9.

Cottages and Chalets in Natural Woodland sleeping two to six people. The Glencoe area is lovely for walking and perfect for nature lovers too. Regret no smokers. No VAT. Brochure available. APPLY: HOUSE IN THE WOOD HOLIDAYS, GLENACHULISH, BALLACHULISH PH49 4JZ (01855 811379). Pets welcome. [🐕]

Cairndow

Village at mouth of Kinglas Water on Loch Fyne in Argyll, near head of Loch.

Two comfortable holiday cottages at the head of the longest sea loch in Scotland, in lovely walking country. Sleep four and eight. Linen and electricity included. STB ★★★ Self Catering.MRS DELAP, ACHADUNAN, CAIRNDOW, ARGYLL PA26 8BJ (Tel & Fax: 01499 600238).
website: www.argyllholidaycottages.com

Dalmally

Small town in Glen Orchy. To the south-west of Loch Awe with romantic Kilchurn Castle (14th century). Edinburgh 98 miles, Glasgow 69, Ardrishaig 42, Oban 25, Inveraray 16.

ROCKHILL WATERSIDE COUNTRY HOUSE, ARDBRECKNISH, BY DALMALLY PA33 1BH (01866 833218). 17th Century guest house on waterside with spectacular views over Loch Awe. Five delightful rooms with all modern facilities. First class home cooking with much home grown produce.

Dunoon

Lively resort reached by car ferry from Gourock. Cowal Highland Gathering held at end of August.

ENMORE HOTEL, MARINE PARADE, DUNOON PA23 8HH (01369 702230; Fax: 01369 702148). Small luxury Hotel with well-tended grounds, situated overlooking the beautiful Firth of Clyde. Own shingle beach. Promenade and superb walking in the hills and forests within five minutes' drive. Owners have two labrador cross dogs. STB ★★★★ HOTEL. AA ★★. AA Rosette. [Dogs £4.25 per night, pw!]
e-mail: enmorehotel@btinternet.com website: www.enmorehotel.co.uk

ABBOT'S BRAE HOTEL, WEST BAY, DUNOON PA23 7QJ (01369 705021; Fax: 01369 701191). Small welcoming hotel at the gateway to the Western Highlands with breathtaking views. Comfortable, spacious, en suite bedrooms, quality home cooking and select wines. [🐕]
e-mail: info@abbotsbrae.co.uk website: www.abbotsbrae.co.uk

Please mention ***PETS WELCOME*** when making enquiries about accommodation featured in these pages.

Oban

Popular Highland resort and port, yachting centre, ferry services to Inner and Outer Hebrides. Sandy bathing beach at Ganavan Bay. McCaig's Tower above town is Colosseum replica built in 1890's.

MRS STEWART, GLENVIEW, SOROBA ROAD, OBAN PA34 4JF (01631 562267). Small family-run guest house, 10 minutes' walk from train, boat and bus terminal. A warm welcome awaits you all year round. [🐕]

Well-equipped Scandinavian chalets in breathtaking scenery near Oban. Chalets sleep 4–7, are widely spaced and close to Loch Tralaig. Car parking. From £205 per week per chalet. Available March to November. STB ★★ & ★★★ Self Catering. APPLY – ANNE & ROBIN GREY, ELERAIG HIGHLAND CHALETS, KILNINVER, BY OBAN PA34 4UX (01852 200225) [🐕]
e-mail: robingrey@eleraig.co.uk website: www.scotland2000.com/eleraig

LOCH MELFORT HOTEL & RESTAURANT, ARDUAINE, BY OBAN PA34 4XG (01852 200233; Fax: 01852 200214). Stunning views down the Sound of Jura to the Islands. Located between Inveraray and Oban, beside the famous Arduaine Gardens. Excellent award-winning cuisine, comfortable accommodation, and friendly and attentive service. [🐕]
website: www.lochmelfort.co.uk

MELFORT PIER AND HARBOUR, KILMELFORD, BY OBAN PA34 4XD (01852 200333; Fax: 01852 200329). Superb Lochside houses each with Sauna, Spabath, Satellite TV, Telephone, E-mail hook-up, on the shores of Loch Melfort. Excellent base for touring Argyll and the Isles. From £80 to £220 per house/night. Minimum stay 2 nights. 2 pets welcome.STB ★★★★★ Self Catering. [Pets £10 each per stay]
e-mail: melharbour@aol.com. website: www.scotland2000.com/melfort

LAGNAKEIL HIGHLAND LODGES, LERAGS, OBAN, ARGYLL PA34 4SE (01631 562746; Fax: 01631 570225). Our Timber Lodges and three houses are set in a tranquil, scenic wooded glen overlooking Loch Feochan, only 3½ miles from the picturesque harbour town of Oban: "Gateway to the Isles". Fully equipped Lodges to a high standard, including linen and towels, country pub a short walk. O.A.P. discount. Free loch fishing. Special Breaks from £39 per lodge per night, weekly from £195. Sleep 2-10 comfortably. Our colour brochure will tell lots more. STB ★★★★ *SELF-CATERING*. [Pets £10 per week].
e-mail: lagnakeil@aol.com website: www.lagnakeil.co.uk

WILLOWBURN HOTEL, CLACHAN SEIL, BY OBAN PA34 4TJ (01852 300276). Peaceful, relaxing, informal and addictive. Superb setting overlooking the Sound of Seil. Walk, fish, birdwatch or simply just laze. Completely non-smoking. Tempted? Bring your owners too! STB ★★★ Small Hotel, AA ★★ [🐕]
website: www.willowburn.co.uk

TRALEE BAY HOLIDAYS, BENDERLOCH BY OBAN PA37 1QR (01631 720255/217). Overlooking Ardmucknish Bay. The wooded surroundings and sandy beaches make Tralee the ideal destination for a self-catering lodge or caravan holiday anytime of the year. STB ★★★★.
e-mail: tralee@easynet.co.uk website: www.tralee.com

MRS LINDA BATTISON, COLOGIN COUNTRY CHALETS, LERAGS GLEN, BY OBAN PA34 4SE (01631 564501; Fax: 01631 566925). Cosy timber chalets, sleep two to six, all conveniences. Situated on farm, wildlife abundant. Games room, launderette, licensed bar serving home-cooked food. Free fishing. Playpark. Live entertainment. STB ★★★/★★★★ Self-Catering [pw! Pets £10 per week.]
e-mail: cologin@west-highland-holidays.co.uk website: www.west-highland-holidays.co.uk

Tarbert

Fishing port on isthmus connecting Kintyre to the mainland.

WEST LOCH HOTEL, BY TARBERT, LOCH FYNE PA29 6YF (01880 820283; Fax: 01880 820930). Attractive traditional coaching inn on the shore of West Loch. Bright, comfortable accommodation, cosy atmosphere, superb food and wines. Fishing, golf, boat hire. Open all year. [🐕]

AMANDA MINSHALL, DUNMORE COURT, WEST LOCH TARBERT PA29 6XZ (01880 820 654). Six cottages on 1000 acre estate with three miles of shore on West Loch Tarbert. Sleeping 2-8 people. Bird-watching, sea fishing, unrestricted walking, easy access to island ferries. Terms from £175 - £490. ASSC member. STB ★★ SELF CATERING [Pets £10 per week]. Open all year.
e-mail: dunmorecourtsc@aol.com website: www.dunmorecourt.com

HORIZON HOTEL Esplanade, Ayr KA7 1DT

A welcome guest. *In all my years of experience of this business, I have never received a complaint about a dog slamming bedroom doors late at night, talking loudly in the corridors or driving away noisily from the car park when other guests are trying to sleep. Never has a dog made cigarette burns on the carpets, furniture or in the bath. No dog has ever stolen my towels, sheets or ashtrays. No cheque written by a dog has ever bounced and no dog has ever tried to pay with a stolen credit card. Never has a dog insulted my waitress or complained about food or wine. Neither have we ever had a dog who was drunk. In short you are welcome whenever you wish to come to this hotel and if you can vouch for your master, you are welcome to bring him along too!!*

Ayr's only seafront hotel, just five minutes' walk from town centre. Lunches, dinners and bar suppers served. Phone now for free colour brochure.

Under the personal supervision of Mr & Mrs A.H. Meikle.

Tel: 01292 264384 Fax: 01292 264011

E-mail: mail@horizonhotel.com Website: www.horizonhotel.com

LAGGAN HOUSE LEISURE PARK

Ballantrae, Near Girvan KA26 0LL

Roger & Marilyn Bourne

Tel: 01465 831229

Fax: 01465 831511

STB ★★★★

Peaceful parkland setting in the grounds of an old country house overlooking secluded countryside and the sea. Luxury caravans and chalets for hire, with heated indoor pool, sauna, bar and children's playground. Pets are welcome. The park provides a superb base from which to explore the magnificent coastline, the inland hills and Galloway Forest. Local activities include fishing, golf, cycling, walking or just doing nothing. Short Breaks available.

Boars Head Hotel, Main Street, Colmonell KA26 0RY

Tel: 01465 881 371

Situated in the pretty Conservation village of Colmonell, ideal for golf, salmon and trout fishing and hill walking. 7 en suite rooms, some with views over Stinchar valley to Craigneil Castle. Friendly and relaxed atmosphere, meal times to suit you. Good variety of draught ales and malt Whiskies. Come and explore more of this unspoilt part of Scotland!

e-mail: alasdair@boarshead-colmonell.freeserve.co.uk • www.boarshead-colmonell.freeserve.co.uk

Sandylands Holiday Park

Auchenharvie Park, Saltcoats,Ayrshire KA21 5JN

Park on edge of Saltcoats, a popular Ayrshire coastal holiday resort. Access to beach. Take a ferry trip to Arran and other scenic islands. Great facilities include indoor pool, 3 clubrooms, kid's club and mini market. Tourers and tents welcome. Tenpin bowling, golf courses and leisure centre situated nearby.

www.gbholidayparks.co.uk Call **0870 442 9312** for brochure

ISLE OF ARRAN

Catacol

catacol Bay hotel

Catacol, Isle of Arran KA27 8HN

Tel: 01770 830231 or 0870 908 9303 Fax: 01770 830350

Escape from the pressures of mainland life. Stay awhile by clear shining seas, rocky coast, breathtaking hills and mountains. Comfortable, friendly, small country house hotel where good cooking is our speciality. Extensive bar menu, meals are served from noon until 10pm. Centrally heated. Open all year. Details of Special Breaks and brochure on request. Children and pets welcome.

Find us on the web at www.catacol.co.uk E-mail: davecatbay@lineone.net

FHG PUBLICATIONS

publish a large range of well-known accommodation guides. We will be happy to send you details or you can use the order form at the back of this book.

Ayr

Popular family holiday resort with sandy beaches. Excellent shopping, theatre, racecourse.

HORIZON HOTEL, ESPLANADE, AYR KA7 1DT (01292 264383; Fax: 01292 264011). Highly recommended for golf breaks; special midweek rates. Coach parties welcome. Lunches, dinners and bar suppers served. Phone now for free colour brochure. [🐕]
e-mail: mail@horizonhotel.com website: www.horizonhotel.com

Ballantrae

Small fishing port 12 miles south-west of Girvan.

ROGER AND MARILYN BOURNE, LAGGAN HOUSE LEISURE PARK, BALLANTRAE KA26 0LL (01465 831229; Fax: 01465 831511). Luxury caravans and chalets for hire. Overlooking secluded countryside and sea. Heated indoor pool, sauna, bar, children's playground. Short Breaks available. STB ★★★★

Girvan

Fishing town and resort at mouth of Water of Girvan, 17 miles south-west of Ayr.

BOARS HEAD HOTEL, MAIN STREET, COLMONELL KA27 0RY (01465 881371). Come and explore this unspoilt part of Scotland. Situated in village of Colmonell, 7 bedrooms with en suite bath/shower rooms and tea/coffee making facilities. [🐕]
e-mail: alasdair@boarshead-colmonell.freeserve.co.uk
website: www.boarshead-colmonell.freeserve.co.uk

Saltcoats

Town and resort on Firth of Clyde adjoining Ardrossan to south east.

SANDYLANDS HOLIDAY PARK, AUCHENHARVIE PARK, SALTCOATS KA21 5JN. Park on edge of Saltcoats. Access to beach. Indoor pool, 3 clubrooms, kid's club, mini market. Tourers and tents welcome. Tenpin bowling, golf and leisure centre nearby. Ferry trips to Arran. Call 0870 442 9312 for brochure. [🐕]
website: www.gbholidayparks.co.uk

Brodick (Isle of Arran)

Small port and resort on east coast of Arran. Brodick Castle (NTS) 2km north.

MR GILMORE, ORMIDALE HOTEL, BRODICK, ISLE OF ARRAN KA27 8BY (01770 302 293; Fax: 01770 302 098). Family-owned inn, very convenient for both hill-walking and golfing. Excellent bar meals, malt whiskies and CAMRA recommended ales. Three twin rooms, three double rooms, one family room, one single room. All rooms with colour television and tea making facilities. B&B £30 en suite.
e-mail: reception@ormidale-hotel.co.uk website: www.ormidale-hotel.co.uk

Catacol (Isle of Arran)

Location on north side of Catacol Bay on north-west coast of Arran.

CATACOL BAY HOTEL, CATACOL, LOCHRANZA KA27 8HN (01770 830231 or 0870 908 9303; Fax: 01770 830350). Comfortable, friendly, small country house hotel where good cooking is our speciality. Extensive bar menu, meals are served from noon until 10pm. Centrally heated. Open all year. Details of Special Breaks and brochure on request. Children and pets welcome. [🐕]
e-mail: davecatbay@lineone.net website: www.catacol.co.uk

PLEASE SEND A STAMPED ADDRESSED ENVELOPE WITH ENQUIRIES

Saughs Farm Cottages

STB ★★★★ Self Catering

Superb character cottages set in historic landscape on the Cumbrian/Scottish Borders. Conservation farm. Panoramic views. Quality furnishings. Wood burning stoves. Stabling facilities. Great for walking, cycling, riding. Explore the Lake District, Hadrian's Wall and Solway Coast and return to a barbecue on your own patio or relax by the fire. Children and pets welcome. Terms from £250 to £450. Open all year. **Contact: Jane Gray, Saughs Farm, Bailey, Newcastleton, Roxburghshire TD9 0TT**

Tel: 01697 748346/748000 • Fax: 01697 748180

e-mail: skylark@onholiday.co.uk • website: www.skylarkcottages.co.uk

See also Colour Advertisement on page 65

The Barniken House Hotel

Give you and your dogs a quality break in beautiful Duns, South East Scotland.

Special breaks available. All prices include VAT. *For free colour brochure write to:*

The Barniken House Hotel, Duns, Berwickshire, S.E. Scotland TD11 3DE

Tel: 01361 882466

See also Colour Advertisement on page 65

We are 9 Yorkshire Terrier "ladies" and would love you to come and spend a few days or longer in our former farmhouse home. We live in the heart of the Scottish Border country among rolling hills and green valleys. Our people would like to meet your people, as long as they are well behaved. We all look forward to seeing you. Love from ***Fudge, Amy, Buttons, Poppy, Amber, Joy, Debbie, Penny and Skye.***

WILLIAMHOPE HOUSE, OLD PEEL, CLOVENFORDS, NEAR GALASHIELS TD1 3LL

TEL: 01896 850243

Scottish ★★★ B&B

Westwood House – Kelso

Overlooking Scotland's famous River Tweed

TOTAL "OFF LEAD" FREEDOM FOR DOGS IN ENCLOSED AND SECLUDED GROUNDS

Renovated riverside cottage with 12 acres of paths, through walled gardens and on own private island.
4 bedrooms sleeping 2 - 8 (+ child), 2 bathrooms, period features, cosy log fire and centrally heated.
• ½ mile Kelso town • one hour Edinburgh/Newcastle • ½ hour Berwick (station) and Northumberland coast

DOGS WELCOME FREE

For Brochure and tariff, from £325 per week fully inclusive of all linen and towels, electricity and heating.
2-person discounts available. Trout fishing also included.

Debbie Crawford, Tel: 07788 134 832
Pippin Heath Farm, Holt, Norfolk NR25 6SS
e-mail: westwood.house@btinternet.com

ACHIEVING GOLD IN GREEN TOURISM AND 'HIGHLY COMMENDED' IN SCOTTISH THISTLE AWARDS

See also Colour Advertisement on page 65

The Crook Inn

Tweedsmuir,
Scottish Borders, ML12 6QN

Tel: 01899 880272 • Fax: 01899 880294
e-mail: thecrookinn@btinternet.com
website: www.crookinn.co.uk

This comfortable, family-run hotel is set in the Upper Tweed Valley 35 miles south of Edinburgh. The Crook is the oldest licensed inn in Scotland and retains many notable and historic features. The 17th century bar where Robert Burns wrote 'Willie Wastle's Wife' is a real time capsule. In the 1930's the hotel was refurbished in the Art Deco style and many of these features have been retained. Meals both in the bar and the restaurant are prepared to order with as much fresh local ingredients as possible. Step back in time at The Crook - an ideal base for touring the Borders, hillwalking or just relaxing.

When making enquiries please mention FHG Publications

Slipperfield House
West Linton EH46 7AA

America Cottage

Two well-equipped cottages a mile from West Linton at the foot of the Pentland Hills, set in 100 acres of lochs and woodlands. Only 19 miles from Edinburgh City Centre. Both Cottages have sitting rooms with dining areas and digital colour TV; modern bathrooms and kitchens with washing and drying machines, microwave oven and telephone.

Loch Cottage

Details from Mrs C.M. Kilpatrick

• Dogs welcome • Ample parking
• Car essential • Central Edinburgh 19 miles
• Golf and private fishing • Available all year.

This is an ideal dog-friendly location for a family holiday near Edinburgh.

Tel and Fax: 01968 660401 e-mail: cottages@slipperfield.com website: www.slipperfield.com

See also Colour Advertisement on page 65

Bailey/Newcastleton

Border town on Liddel Water, 17 miles south of Hawick.

JANE GRAY, SAUGHS FARM COTTAGES, BAILEY, NEWCASTLETON, ROXBURGHSHIRE TD9 0TT (01697 748346/748000; Fax: 01697 748180). Superb character cottages on Cumbrian/Scottish Borders. Panoramic views. Quality furnishings. Stabling facilities. Great for walking, cycling, riding. Children and pets welcome. Open all year. STB ★★★★ SELF CATERING
e-mail: skylark@onholiday.co.uk website: www.skylarkcottages.co.uk

Bonchester Bridge

Village on Rule Water, 6 miles east of Hawick. To east is Bonchester Hill surmounted by ancient earthworks.

WAUCHOPE COTTAGES, BONCHESTER BRIDGE, HAWICK TD9 9TG (01450 860630). Sleeps 2-4. Three detatched cottages each with kennel in enclosed garden. Quiet location with stunning scenery near Wauchope Forest. Ideal for walking. STB ★★★ SELF CATERING. [🐕]

Duns

Picturesque Borders town with nearby ancient fort, castle and Covenanters' stone to commemorate the army's encampment here in 1639. Excellent touring centre. Berwick-upon-Tweed 13 miles.

BARNIKEN HOUSE HOTEL, MURRAY STREET, DUNS TD11 3DE (01361 882466). Dogs most welcome, colour TV and tea coffee facilities in all rooms. Luxurious bar, sun lounge, large garden and car park. Central heating. Near spectacular scenery and ideal walks for dogs. [🐕]

NOTE

All the information in this book is given in good faith in the belief that it is correct. However, the publishers cannot guarantee the facts given in these pages, neither are they responsible for changes in policy, ownership or terms that may take place after the date of going to press. Readers should always satisfy themselves that the facilities they require are available and that the terms, if quoted, still apply.

Galashiels

Town on Gala Water, 14 miles north of Hawick.

WILLIAMHOPE HOUSE, OLD PEEL, CLOVENFORDS, NEAR GALASHIELS TD1 3LL (01896 850243). Fudge, Amy, Buttons, Poppy, Amber, Joy, Debbie, Penny and Skye (Yorkshire Terriers) invite you to spend a few days in their former farmhouse home in the heart of the Scottish Borders, among rolling hills and green valleys. STB ★★★ B&B.[🐕]

Jedburgh

Small town on Jed water, 10 miles north-east of Hawick. Ruins of abbey founded in 1138.

ALAN & CHRISTINE SWANSTON, FERNIEHIRST MILL LODGE & RIDING CENTRE, JEDBURGH TD8 6PQ (Tel & Fax: 01835 863279). A chalet style guest house set in grounds of 25 acres. All rooms en suite with tea/coffee making facilities. Licensed for residents. Well behaved pets (including horses) welcome by arrangement. STB, AA, RAC, TRSS Approved. [🐕]
e-mail: ferniehirstmill@aol.com website: www.ferniehirstmill.co.uk

Kelso

Market town 18 miles north-west of Hawick and 20 miles south-west of Berwick-upon-Tweed.

WESTWOOD HOUSE, OVERLOOKING SCOTLAND'S FAMOUS RIVER TWEED. (07788 134 832; Fax: 01263 712128) Enclosed and secluded riverside cottage with walled gardens and own private island. Sleep 2-8 persons plus child, from £325 per week. 2 person discounts. STB ★★★ For brochure contact: DEBBIE CRAWFORD, PIPPIN HEATH FARM, HOLT, NORFOLK NR25 6SS [🐕]
e-mail: westwood.house@btinternet.com

Peebles

On the River Tweed, famous for tweeds and knitwear.

MS S. BELL, THE CROOK INN, TWEEDSMUIR, SCOTTISH BORDERS ML12 6QN (01899 880272; Fax: 01899 880294). All rooms en suite. Full breakfast included in charge. Bar meals always available as well as dining-room menu in evenings. Children and pets welcome.
e-mail: thecrookinn@btinternet.com website: www.crookinn.co.uk

West Linton

Village on east side of Pentland hills, 7 miles south-west of Penicuick. Edinburgh 18 miles.

MRS C. M. KILPATRICK, SLIPPERFIELD HOUSE, WEST LINTON EH46 7AA (Tel & Fax: 01968 660401). Two well-equipped converted cottages set in 100 acres of lochs and woodlands. Sleep 4/6. Available all year. Central Heating. Car essential. Self Catering. Ideal, dog-friendly location. STB ★★★/★★★★ [🐕]
e-mail: cottages@slipperfield.com website: www.slipperfield.com

FREE or REDUCED RATE entry to Holiday Visits and Attractions – see our READERS' OFFER VOUCHERS on pages 103-118

See also Colour Advertisement on page 65.

A useful Index of Towns/Villages and Counties appears on page 427 – please also refer to Contents Page 3.

See also Colour Advertisement on page 66

Auchencairn

Spectacular cliffs, and sandy beaches lie near this whitewashed village.

MR AND MRS BARDSLEY, THE ROSSAN, CASTLE DOUGLAS, SOLWAY COAST DG7 1QR (01556 640269; Fax: 01556 640278). STB ★★ B&B. Small, homely, early Victorian guest house. B&B. Optional evening meal. Organic produce when possible. Ideal centre for bird watching, golf, hill walking. [🐕],
e-mail: bardsley@rossan.freeserve.co.uk website: www.the-rossan.co.uk

Borgue

Village south west of Kirkcudbright, setting for Robert Louis Stevenson's "Master of Ballantrae".

MRS MILLARD BARNES, BALMANGAN BEAG, BY BORGUE, KIRKCUDBRIGHT DG6 4TR. (01557 870 499). Comfortable bungalow with magnificent country and sea views. Dedicated dogs' garden. Good long and short walks, lots of beaches. Ten minutes by car from Kirkcudbright.

Castle Douglas

Old market town at the northern end of Carlingwalk Loch, good touring centre for Galloway

URR VALLEY HOTEL, ERNESPIE ROAD, CASTLE DOUGLAS, DUMFRIES & GALLOWAY DG7 3JG (01556 502188; Fax: 01556 504055). Hotel within easy walking distance of Castle Douglas. Sandy beaches, grouse moors, harbour villages and forest walks. Log fires, Sportsman's bar, 17 en suite rooms, colour TV, tea/coffee making facilities, and direct dial telephones. AA ★★ [🐕]
e-mail: info@urrvalleyhotel.co.uk website: www.urrvalleyhotel.co.uk

MRS CELIA PICKUP, "CRAIGADAM", CASTLE DOUGLAS DG7 3HU (Tel & Fax: 01556 650233). Family-run 18th century famhouse. All bedrooms en suite. Billiard room. Lovely oak-panelled dining room offering Cordon Bleu cooking using local produce such as venison, pheasant and salmon. Trout fishing, walking and golfing available. STB ★★★★ Hotel, RAC ◆◆◆◆◆ & Little Gem Award, AA ◆◆◆◆ Premier Collection. [🐕]
website: www.craigadam.com

MR P. W. BALL, BARNCROSH FARM, CASTLE DOUGLAS DG7 1TX (01556 680216; Fax: 01556 680442). Self-catering. Comfortable Cottages and flats. Fully equipped, including linen. Colour TV. Children and dogs welcome. Beautiful rural surroundings. Brochure on request. STB ★/★★★ Disabled Category 2. [Pets £40 weekly, £5 per short break]
e-mail: enq@barncrosh.co.uk website: www.barncrosh.co.uk

Dumfries

County town of Dumfries-shire and a former seaport. Dumfries contains many interesting buildings including an 18th century windmill containing a camera obscura. Robert Burns lived in the town before his death in 1796.

DAVID & GILL STEWART, AE FOREST COTTAGES, GUBHILL FARM, DUMFRIES DG1 1RL (01387 860369/860648). Listed farm steading flats in peaceful pastoral valley surrounded by wooded hills and forest lanes. Nature-friendly management. Lower flat wheelchair compatible. Riding, fishing, mountain biking and hillwalking all nearby. STB ★★★ SELF CATERING, CATEGORY ONE DISABILITY. [🐕]
e-mail: gill@gubhill.co.uk

Gatehouse of Fleet

Small town near mouth of Water of Fleet, 6 miles north-west of Kirkcudbright.

RUSKO HOLIDAYS, GATEHOUSE OF FLEET, CASTLE DOUGLAS DG7 2BS (01557 814215; Fax: 01557 814679). Spacious farmhouse and charming, cosy cottages near beaches, hills, gardens, castles and golf course. Walking, fishing, tennis, pets, including horses, welcome. Sleeps 2-10. Rates £168-£799. STB ★★ to ★★★★ Self-Catering. Disabled Awards.
email: info@ruskoholidays.co.uk website: www.ruskoholidays.co.uk

Glenluce

Village 9 miles east of Stranraer.

KELVIN HOUSE HOTEL, GLENLUCE, NEWTON STEWART DG8 0PP (Tel & Fax: 01581 300303). Situated in picturesque village of Glenluce. Long renowned for its good food, good cheer and cosy bedrooms. STB ★★★ HOTEL AA★★
e-mail: kelvinhouse@lineone.net website: www.kelvin-house.co.uk

Kirkcudbright

Small town on River Dee estuary 10 miles south of Castle Douglas.

GORDON HOUSE HOTEL, 116 HIGH STREET, KIRKCUDBRIGHT DG6 4JQ (Tel & Fax: 01557 330670). 8 en suite bedrooms with TV, tea/coffee, radio alarm and central heating. Restaurant - Scottish cuisine. Lounge and public bar. Garden. Dogs welcome! STB ★★★ Hotel.

MIRIAM BAKER, NUMBER 3 B&B, 3 HIGH STREET, KIRKCUDBRIGHT DG6 4JZ (01557 330881). 'B' Listed Georgian townhouse. Rich in ambience, the property charms those seeking period surroundings. Non-smoking. STB ★★★★
e-mail: ham_wwk@hotmail.com website: www.number3-bandb.co.uk

Lockerbie

Market town 11 miles east of Dumfries.

LOCKERBIE MANOR COUNTRY HOTEL, LOCKERBIE DG11 2RG (01576 202610/ 203939). Splendid Georgian mansion house set in 78 acres of beautiful grounds. Ideal base for exploring countryside. Single, twin, double and family rooms, all en suite, and equipped with colour TV, tea-making etc. [pw! 🐕]
e-mail: info@lockerbiemanorhotel.co.uk website: www.lockerbiemanorhotel.co.uk

Moffat

At head of lovely Annandale, grand mountain scenery. Good centre for rambling, climbing, angling and golf. The 'Devil's Beef Tub' is 5 miles, Edinburgh 52, Peebles 33, Dumfries 21.

ALLANTON HOTEL, 20-22 HIGH STREET, MOFFAT DG10 9HL (01683 220343). Situated in a quiet country town, many walks, golf course and lcoal fishing. A homely place to visit all year round.
website: www.allantonhotel.com

BARNHILL SPRINGS COUNTRY GUEST HOUSE, MOFFAT DG10 9QS (01683 220580). Early Victorian country house overlooking some of the finest views of Upper Annandale. Comfortable accommodation, residents' lounge with open fire. Situated on the Southern Upland Way half-a-mile from A74/M74 Moffat Junction. Pets free of charge. Bed & Breakfast from £22; Evening Meal (optional) from £15. STB ★★ Guest House. AA ◆◆◆. [pw! 🐕]

MORLICH GUEST HOUSE, BALLPLAY ROAD, MOFFAT DG10 9JU (01683 220589; Fax: 01683 220887). Set in beautiful 'Burns Country' Morlich House is a superb Victorian country house. Rooms are en suite with TV, radio alarm, tea/coffee, four-poster available. Private car park. B&B from £22pp. Weekly terms. Open all year. [🐕]
e-mail: info@morlichhouse.co.uk website: www.morlichhouse.co.uk

BUCCLEUCH ARMS HOTEL, HIGH STREET, MOFFAT DG10 9ET (01683 220003; Fax: 01683 221291). Ideally situated for exploring the unspoilt South West of Scotland. Single, double/twin and family rooms, all with private bathroom. Open all year. B&B from £40 single, £35.00 double/twin. [🐕]

ANNANDALE ARMS HOTEL, HIGH STREET, MOFFAT DG1O 9HF (01683 220013; Fax: 01683 221395). A warm welcome is offered at the Annandale Arms to dogs with well-mannered and house-trained owners. Excellent restaurant and a relaxing panelled bar. Large private parking area. £75 per room for two; £47.50 per room for one. [pw! 🐕]

Portpatrick

Picturesque fishing village located at the most westerly point of Dumfries & Galloway.

PORTPATRICK HOLIDAY COTTAGES. Very comfortable accommodation and outstanding value. The perfect base for golfing, walking or simply getting away from it all. Pets welcome by prior arrangement. Open all year. MR PERRATT, PORTPATRICK HOLIDAY COTTAGES LTD, 37 CABLE DEPOT ROAD, RIVERSIDE ESTATE, CLYDEBANK, WEST DUNBARTONSHIRE G81 1UY (0141 941 3800; Fax: 0141 941 3800)
website: www.portpatrickholidays.co.uk

Thornhill

Small town on River Nith 13 miles north-west of Dumfries. Site of Roman signal station lies to the south.

MRS S. STANNETT, HOPE COTTAGE, HOLESTANE FARM, THORNHILL, DUMFRIESSHIRE DG3 5BD (01848 500228; Fax: 01848 500337). Pretty stone cottage in the peaceful conservation village of Durisdeer. Well-equipped self-catering cottage with large secluded garden. Sleeps 6. Towels, linen, heating and electricity included. Self-catering. Phone for brochure. STB ★★★★ [🐕]
e-mail: a.stann@btinternet.com website: www.hopecottage.co.uk

DUNBARTONSHIRE

Drymen

Village 7 miles north-east of Balloch. To the west is the site of Buchanan Castle, formerly the Seat of the Duke of Montrose.

CROFTBURN BED & BREAKFAST, CROFTAMIE, DRYMEN, LOCH LOMOND G63 0HA (01360 660796; Fax: 01360 661005). Rural location set in one acre of gardens with views of the Campsie Fells and the Strathendrick Valley. Excellent base for walking, touring etc. Pets welcome. STB ★★★, AA ◆◆◆◆. [🐕]
e-mail: johnreid@croftburn.fsnet.co.uk
website: www.dellta.org/croftburn or www.croftburn.co.uk

Loch Lomond

Largest stretch of inland water in Britain. Extends from Ardlui in the north to Balloch in the south.

MRS SALLY MACDONELL, MARDELLA FARMHOUSE, OLD SCHOOL ROAD, GARTOCHARN, LOCH LOMOND G83 8SD (01389 830428). Set on a quiet country lane, surrounded by fields. Friendly and comfortable, where the kettle's always boiling. AA "Landlady of the Year" 1995 Finalist; Winner AA Scotland B&B of the Year 1995. Dogs welcomed and loved.

Edinburgh

Scotland's capital with magnificent castle overlooking "The Athens of the North".

PETER FRASER, RIMSWELL HOUSE HOTEL, 33 MAYFIELD GARDENS, EDINBURGH EH9 2BX (Tel & Fax: 0131 667 5851). A convenient and comfortable private hotel. 9 bedrooms, most en suite with TV and tea/coffee facilities. Private off-road parking. Bed and full Scottish Breakfast from £20 to £30 per person.
e-mail: reception@rimswellhouse.co.uk website: www.rimswellhouse.co.uk

FIFE

Anstruther, St Andrews

Anstruther

Resort and fishing port on Firth of Forth, 9 miles south-east of St Andrews. Site of Scottish Fisheries Museum.

SPINDRIFT GUEST HOUSE, PITTENWEEM ROAD, ANSTRUTHER KY10 3DT (Tel & Fax: 01333 310573). Relax in our beautifully restored Victorian home. Individually furnished en suite bedrooms. Elegant guest lounge and dining room. 10 minutes from St Andrews and 1 hour from Edinburgh. AA & RAC (Sparkling Diamond) ◆◆◆◆. Taste of Scotland. STB ★★★★ Guest House.
e-mail: info@thespindrift.co.uk website: www.thespindrift.co.uk

St Andrews

Home of golf - British Golf Museum has memorabilia dating back to the origins of the game. Remains of castle and cathedral. Sealife Centre and beach Leisure Centre. Excellent sands. Ideal base for exploring the picturesque East Neuk of Fife.

MR & MRS PATRICK WEDDERBURN, ST ANDREWS COUNTRY COTTAGES, MOUNTQUHANIE ESTATE, FREEPOST, CUPAR KY15 4BR (01382 330318; Mobile: 07966 373007; Fax: 01382 330480). Quality self-catering houses and cottages on tranquil Country Estate. Central heating, TV, phone. Enclosed gardens. STB ★★★ to ★★★★★ Self Catering. [pw! Dogs £10 per week, Cats F.O.C.].
e-mail: enquiries@standrews-cottages.com website: www.standrews-cottages.com

Glasgow

Scotland's largest city with a fascinating mix of modern and Victorian architecture, as well as art galleries, theatres, museums and excellent shopping.

THE BRUNSWICK HOTEL 106/108 BRUNSWICK STREET, GLASGOW G1 1TF (0141 552 0001; Fax: 0141 552 1551) Very modern small city hotel, centrally situated in a prime location. Intimate, bold and very friendly. 18 en suite bedrooms."Small Dogs Welcome"
e-mail: enquiry@brunswickhotel.co.uk website: www.brunswickhotel.co.uk

HIGHLANDS

Alvie, Aultbea, Aviemore

See also Colour Advertisement on page 67.

See also Colour Advertisement on page 66

Linnhe Lochside Holidays

Corpach, Fort William PH33 7NL

Tel: 01397-772376 Fax: 01397-772007
www.linnhe-lochside-holidays.co.uk
e-mail: holidays@linnhe.demon.co.uk

"Best Park in Scotland 1999 Award"

Almost a botanical garden and stunningly beautiful. Wonderful views and ideal for touring or simply relaxing and soaking up the scenery. Licensed shop, private beach & free fishing. Colour brochure sent with pleasure.

Scottish Tourist Board ★★★★★ Holiday Park

★ ***Luxury holiday caravans*** *for hire from £190/week*
★ ***Touring*** *pitches from £13.00/night.* ***Camping*** *from £10.00/night.*

Inchbae Lodge Hotel *by Garve, Ross-shire, IV23 2PH* STB ★★★

Situated six miles west of Garve, this old hunting lodge nestles on the bank of the River Blackwater. Ideal location for bird watching, hunting, fishing and walking. There are nine bedrooms, all with en-suite bathrooms or shower rooms. The warm and friendly atmosphere is felt in all the reception rooms - the home from home feel of the lounge, the cosy bar and the elegant diningroom.

Tel: 01997 455269 • Fax: 01997 455207
e-mail: info@inchbae-lodge-hotel.co.uk website: www.inchbae-lodge-hotel.co.uk

COLUMBA HOUSE
HOTEL & GARDEN RESTAURANT

Among tall Scots pines and beech trees, nestling in large grounds and walled garden, an oasis in the beautiful Spey Valley. Family-run, with attentive staff, friendly and homely atmosphere. Garden Restaurant, with patio, offers superb traditional Scottish cuisine. Relax by the fire, in our comfortable lounge or enjoy a drink in the cosy bar. Your comfort and enjoyment is our priority. Beautiful en suite bedrooms with views of mountains and gardens, mini-bar, TV, phone, radio, hairdryer, tea/coffee facilities. Ground floor rooms with own front doors, ideal for doggies. Romantic four-poster rooms and double baths. Ample private parking. Full disabled facilities.

AA ♦♦♦♦ Bed and Breakfast from £35 STB ★★★

Manse Road, Kingussie PH21 1JF
Tel: 01540 661402 • Fax: 01540 661652
e-mail: pets@columbahousehotel.com • www.columbahousehotel.com

Readers are requested to mention this guidebook when seeking accommodation (and please enclose a stamped addressed envelope).

South Loch Ness • WILDSIDE HIGHLAND LODGES

Set on the banks of a rocky river deep in the countryside, amidst spectacular scenery, with a choice of accommodation.

• Cosy studio units built for two. • Well appointed stone and cedar lodges for up to six. Some with log fires. • Spacious grounds and private lawns. • Large picture windows to enjoy the scenery. • Country pub nearby and a choice of places to eat out. • Open all year round, with free central heating. • Mini breaks available and pets welcome. • See our colour brochure or visit our web site.

ASSC

Wildside, Whitebridge, Inverness IV2 6UN Tel: 01456 486 373 E-mail: info@wildsidelodges.com
Website: www.wildsidelodges.com STB ★★★★ SELF CATERING

See also Colour Advertisement on page 67

WILDERNESS COTTAGES, LOCH NESS - SELF-CATERING

Open all year - Sleeps 2-14 - Pets are welcome

Easter Boleskine is situated on the beautiful south side of Loch Ness 18 miles from Inverness, set in spectacular countryside of forests and mountains, with many lochs, large and small, dotted around the area like jewels in this undiscovered landscape. Easter Boleskin, a former croft, provides privacy, perfect peace, breathtaking views of Loch Ness, miles of forest walks, which start at the back door. For dog owners, this is possibly the best location you will ever find for 'mans best friend'.
We have a selection of 4-star quality self-catering cottages in the area that welcome you and your pets. Please check our website for full details of this and our other self-catering cottages, or send for a brochure.

For a colour brochure contact: **Gordon & Corinne Roberts, Roebuck Cottage, Errogie, Stratherrick Inverness-shire IV2 6UH • Tel & Fax: 01456 486358**

e-mail: corinne@wildernesscottages.co.uk • website: www.wildernesscottages.co.uk

SPEYSIDE COTTAGES, NETHY BRIDGE, Scottish Highlands

Choice of very comfortable modern cottages or converted smithy of unique character, set individually in this quiet Highland village. Fenced gardens. Sleep 2-9. Linen, towels, visitors' laundry, September to May storage heating included. Good walking and touring centre. Close to RSPB reserve with river and forest walks at your doorstep.

Write or phone for brochure to:
Mr & Mrs J. B. Patrick,
1 Chapelton Place, Forres, Moray IV36 2NL
Tel/Fax: 01309 672505
e-mail: brian@speysidecottages.co.uk
website: www.speysidecottages.co.uk

See also Colour Advertisement on page 67

Crubenbeg Holiday Cottages

Newtonmore, Inverness-shire PH20 1BE

Tel: 01540 673566 Fax: 01540 673509
E-mail: enquiry@crubenbeg.com
Website: www.crubenbeg.com

Rural self catering cottages in the central part of the Highlands where one can relax and stroll from the doorstep or take part in the choice of many sporting activities in the area. We have a Children's play area, a Games Room, Pond stocked with trout for fishing and a barbecue. Pets welcome.

CROFTERS COTTAGES

15 Croft, Poolewe, Ross-shire IV22 2JY • Tel: 01445 781268 • Fax: 01445 781704

Three traditional cottages sleeping 4, 5 and 9 persons. Situated in a scenic and tranquil area, ideal for a "get away from it all" holiday. Crofters Cottages are comfortably furnished, some with antiques and all the essential modern gadgets of today, such as auto-washer/dryer, microwave, fridge, bath and shower. Poolewe is a good base to tour the North West Highlands or for those who enjoy walking, fishing, climbing, golf or maybe just a stroll along one of the many sandy beaches. There are also indoor activities to be enjoyed such as the heated pool and leisure and fitness areas. Close by lie the famous Inverewe Gardens. Pets made welcome.

Low season from £120 – £230 • High season from £250 – £490
Midweek and short breaks available from November – March

MR A. URQUHART **croftcottages@btopenworld.com www.croftcottages.btinternet.co.uk**

Gull Cottage, Rhiconich, Sutherland

Situated on the wild and unspoilt west coast of Scotland overlooking Loch Inchard, the last sea loch on the north west coast. Superb scenery with excellent walks on mountains, moors, and the many beaches in the area. Recently built, high quality accommodation with full central heating. Sleeps 2/3. Pets welcome, dogs must be kept under firm control.

All enquiries to: **Lynn and Graham, Gull Cottage, Achriesgill, Rhiconich, Lairg, Sutherland IV27 4RJ**
Telephone: 01971 521717

RHICONICH HOTEL Rhiconich, Sutherland, N.W. Highlands IV27 4RN

• Tel: 01971 521224 • Fax: 01971 521732 • e-mail: rhiconichhotel@aol.com • website: www.rhiconichhotel.co.uk

SHE'S YOUR BEST FRIEND, so why leave her at home, bring her to RHICONICH HOTEL, she'll be made equally as welcome as you will. A place where we put service, hospitality and really fresh food as a priority, but why don't you come and see for yourself? *For further details contact Jasmine Campbell.* **STB ★★★**

RIVERSIDE LODGES Invergloy, Spean Bridge PH34 4DY • Tel: 01397 712684

Peace and quiet are synonymous with Riverside, where our three identical lodges each sleep up to six people. Accessible from the A82 but totally hidden from it, our 12 acres of woodland garden front on Loch Lochy, Gorge and waterfalls. Barbecue for hire. Pets welcome. Easy access and assistance to launch boats from our own beach. Free fishing from loch or private lochan. Brochures provided on request. Open all year.

Scottish TOURIST BOARD ★★★★ SELF CATERING

e-mail: enquiries@riversidelodge.org.uk • website: www.riversidelodge.org.uk

BORGIE LODGE HOTEL Skerray, Tongue, Sutherland KW14 7TH

"As featured in STV Scottish Passport Holiday Programme"

Set in a secluded Highland glen by one of Scotland's most beautiful beaches lies Borgie Lodge. Billie Maclean tunes his bagpipes while tales of massive salmon and red deer stags mingle with peaty malt whisky. Your hosts "The MacGregors" will ensure you are very well looked after, Peter taking guests fishing and shooting and Jacqui preparing local venison, salmon, lobster and lamb served with her own organic vegetables. Try pony trekking along the sands, cycling, swimming or hillwalking – we have it all. Good Hotel Guide.

Tel: 01641 521 332
e-mail: info@borgielodgehotel.co.uk
website: www.borgielodgehotel.co.uk

Sammy, Susie & Sandy, Borgie Lodge pets, would like to make new friends.

Alvie, By Aviemore (Inverness-shire)

Locality in Badenoch and Strathspey District, 3 miles south-west of Aviemore.

THE ROWAN TREE COUNTRY HOTEL, LOCH ALVIE, BY AVIEMORE PH22 1QB (Tel & Fax: 01479 810207). Award-winning small, friendly Country Hotel. Ideal location for a holiday or short break in the Highlands. Stunning setting, comfortable, individually decorated en suite bedrooms, cosy lounges and bar, crackling fires. Taste of Scotland. Inn of the Year 2001. STB ★★★ Small Hotel. [🐕]
e-mail: enquiries@rowantreehotel.com website: www.rowantreehotel.com

Aultbea (Ross-shire)

Village on east shore of Loch Ewe, 5 miles north of Poolewe.

COVE VIEW, 36 MELLON CHARLES, AULTBEA IV22 2JL (01445 731351). Wester Ross is ideal for hill walking or a quiet restful holiday. Detached chalet with two small bedrooms, sitting area, bathroom and mini kitchen. From £150 to £200 per week. A warm welcome awaits you and your pet. [🐕]

Aviemore (Inverness-shire)

Scotland's leading ski resort in Spey valley with superb sport and entertainment facilities. All-weather holiday centre with accommodation to suit all pockets. Excellent fishing. Centre for exploring Cairngorms. Edinburgh 129 miles, Grantown-on-Spey 14, Kingussie 12. Carrbridge 7.

CAIRNGORM HIGHLAND BUNGALOWS, GLEN EINICH, 29 GRAMPIAN VIEW, AVIEMORE, INVERNESS-SHIRE PH22 1TF. (01479 810653, Fax: 01479 810262). Well equipped bungalows ranging from one to four bedrooms. Open all year. Leisure facilities nearby. Children and pets welcome. Phone for brochure. [🐕]
e-mail: linda.murray@virgin. net website: www.cairngorm-bungalows.co.uk

PINE BANK CHALETS, DALFABER ROAD, AVIEMORE PH22 1PX (01479 810000; Fax: 01479 811469). Cosy Log Cabins and 9 Quality Chalets, situated in a secluded area near the River Spey. Superb Family/Activity Holidays by mountains. Ideal skiing, walking, fishing and golf. Sky TV. Short breaks available. Pets welcome. Open all year. ASSC Member. Brochure. [Pets £2.50 per night, £10 per week.]
e-mail: pinebankchallets@btopenworld.com website: www.pinebankchalets.co.uk

Boat of Garten (Inverness-shire)

Village on Speyside 5 miles from Aviemore.

CONIFER COTTAGES - Two adjacent, well-equipped cottages. Sleep 5/6. Large secure garden. Surrounding woodlands and walks, bird reserve (Ospreys), golf, Speyside walk and steam railway nearby. J. WEIR, GLENLORA COTTAGE, LOCHWINNOCH PA12 4DN (01505 842062). STB ★ [🐕]
e-mail: j.weir@ukonline.co.uk

THE BOAT, BOAT OF GARTEN IV25 3SD(01479 831258; Fax: 01479 831414). An individual hotel for individual guests. Award-winning cuisine. Pets welcome. STB ★★★★, AA ★★★ and Two Rosettes. [Pets £5 per night.]
website: www.boathotel.co.uk

Carrbridge (Inverness-shire)

Village on River Dulnain, 7 miles north of Aviemore. Landmark Visitor Centre has exhibition explaining history of local environment.

THE PINES COUNTRY GUESTHOUSE, DUTHIL, CARRBRIDGE PH23 3ND (FREEPHONE: 0800 9701763). Relax and enjoy our Highland hospitality, woodland setting; all rooms en suite. Traditional or vegetarian home cooking. B&B £21 daily; DB&B £208 weekly. Children and pets welcome. AA ◆◆◆ [🐕]
website: www.thepines-duthil.fsnet.co.uk

Drumnadrochit (Inverness-shire)

Village on the shores of Loch Ness with "Monster" visitor centre. Sonar scanning cruises.

CAROL HUGHES, GLENURQUHART LODGES, BY DRUMNADROCHIT IV3 6TJ (01456 476234; Fax: 01456 476286). Situated between Loch Ness and Glen Affric in a spectacular setting ideal for walking, touring or just relaxing in this tranquil location. Four spacious chalets all fully equipped for six people, set in wooded grounds. Owner's hotel adjacent where guests are most welcome in the restaurant and bar. [Pets £10 per week.]

Fort William (Inverness-shire)

Small town at foot of Ben Nevis, ideal base for climbers and hillwalkers.

MRS M. MATHESON, THISTLE COTTAGE, TORLUNDY, FORT WILLIAM PH33 6SN (01397 702428). Central for touring the Highlands – 3½ miles from Fort William. Double and family rooms with TV, tea/coffee making facilities. En suite available. Ample parking. B&B from £17pppn. STB ★★★ B&B [🐕]
e-mail: moragmatheson@btopenworld.com website: www.thistlescotland.co.uk

NETHER LOCHABER HOTEL, ONICH, FORT WILLIAM PH33 6SE (01855 821235; 01855 821545). Traditional home cooking goes hand in hand with homely service, comfortable accommodation and private facilities on the shores of beautiful Loch Linnhe. B&B from £25-£35 per person. [🐕]

THE CLAN MACDUFF HOTEL, ACHINTORE, FORT WILLIAM PH33 6RW (01397 702341; Fax: 01397 706174). This family-run hotel overlooks Loch Linnhe, two miles south of Fort William, excellent for touring the rugged mountains of the West Highlands. All rooms have TV, hair dryer and hospitality tray; all with private facilities. Three nights DB&B from £89 pppn. STB ★★ Hotel. Phone or write for colour brochure and tariff. [🐕]
website: www.clanmacduff.co.uk

ISLES OF GLENCOE HOTEL AND LEISURE CENTRE, BALLACHULISH, NEAR FORT WILLIAM PH49 4HL (0871 222 3415; Fax: 0871 222 3416). Almost afloat, this stylish, modern Hotel nestles on the lochside. Spacious bedrooms offer a commanding panorama of sky, mountain and loch. Delicious cuisine in Conservatory Restaurant. Heated pool and Leisure Centre. [pw! £5 per night] STB ★★★★
e-mail: reservations@freedomglen.co.uk website: www.freedomglen.co.uk

THE BALLACHULISH HOTEL, BALLACHULISH, NEAR FORT WILLIAM PH49 4JY (0871 222 3415; Fax: 0871 222 3416) Glide through the dramatic pass of Glencoe and the mountains divide to reveal this breathtaking lochside setting. Fulfill your dream of the perfect historic Highland Hotel by staying here amongst the turrets. STB ★★★★.
e-mail: reservations@freedomglen.co.uk website: www.freedomglen.co.uk

THE LODGE ON THE LOCH, CREAG DHU, ONICH, BY FORT WILLIAM PH33 6RY (0871 222 3415; Fax: 0871 222 3416). Discover seclusion and serenity - enjoy one of the West Coast's finest panoramas. Choice of individual luxury rooms with many personal touches. Taste of Scotland. STB ★★★★, AA ★★★.
e-mail: reservations@freedomglen.co.uk website: www.freedomglen.co.uk/ll

LINNHE LOCHSIDE HOLIDAYS, DEPT PW, CORPACH, FORT WILLIAM PH33 7NL (01397 772376). Almost a botanical garden Linnhe is stunning. "Best Park in Scotland Award 1999". Deluxe chalets and holiday caravans for hire. Touring pitches. Private beach, free fishing. Prices from £190 per week. Touring pitches from £13.00 per night, Camping from £10.00 per night. [pw! £2.50 per night, £15 per week]
e-mail: holidays@linnhe.demon.co.uk website: www.linnhe-lochside-holidays.co.uk

SYMBOLS

- **🐕 Indicates that pets are welcome free of charge.**
- **£ Indicates that a charge is made for pets: nightly or weekly.**
- **pw! Shows some special provision for pets; exercise facility, feeding or accommodation arrangement.**
- **⌂ Indicates separate pets accommodation.**

Garve (Ross-shire)

Locality in Ross and Cromarty District, 10 miles west of Dingwall.

INCHBAE LODGE HOTEL, BY GARVE IV23 2PH (01997 455269; Fax: 01997 455207). In outstanding mountain scenery between Inverness and Ullapool. Family-run Victorian hunting lodge in riverside eight acres. Good Scottish food. Real ale. Ideal centre for all outdoor activities. Bargain breaks eg: four nights DB&B £149 per dog, owner free. STB ★★★. [🐕 pw!]
e-mail: info@inchbae-lodge-hotel.co.uk website: www.inchbae-lodge-hotel.co.uk

Kincraig (Inverness-shire)

Attractive Highland village close to Loch Insh and Glenfeshie, midway between Aviemore and Kingussie.

NICK & PATSY THOMPSON, INSH HOUSE GUESTHOUSE AND SELF-CATERING COTTAGES, KINCRAIG, NEAR KINGUSSIE PH21 1NU (01540 651377). B&B in 1827 Telford Manse and two timber s/c cottages in superb rural location. Ideal for many outdoor activities and good touring base. Dogs and children welcome. STB ★★★. [🐕]
e-mail: inshhouse@btinternet.com website: www.kincraig.com/inshhouse

Kingussie (Inverness-shire)

Tourist centre on the River Spey 28 miles south of Inverness.

COLUMBA HOUSE HOTEL & GARDEN RESTAURANT, MANSE ROAD, KINGUSSIE PH21 1JF (01540 661402; Fax: 01540 661652). Nestling in large grounds. Restaurant & Patio in walled garden offers superb Scottish cuisine. En suite bedrooms with mini-bar, TV, phone, tea/coffee. Romantic four-posters and double baths. Parking. AA ◆◆◆◆, STB ★★★. [pw! Pets £5 per night, £15 per week]
e–mail: pets@columbahousehotel.com website: www.columbahousehotel.com

Lochcarron (Ross-shire)

Village on north shore of Loch Carron 2 miles below the head of the loch. Known for its ties and tartans.

THE COTTAGE, STROMECARRONACH, LOCHCARRON WEST, STRATHCARRON. Small, stone-built Highland cottage, double bedroom, shower room, open plan kitchen/living room, fully equipped. Panoramic views over Loch Carron and the mountains. For further details please phone. MRS A.G. MACKENZIE, STROMECARRONACH, LOCHCARRON WEST, STRATHCARRON IV54 8YH (01520 722284) [🐕]
website: www.lochcarron.org

Loch Ness (Inverness-shire)

Home of 'Nessie', extending for 23 miles from Fort Agustus to south of Inverness.

DAVID AND PATRICIA ALLEN, WILDSIDE HIGHLAND LODGES, WILDSIDE, WHITEBRIDGE, INVERNESS IV2 6UN. (01456 486373). Self-Catering. Cosy studio units built for two. Well appointed stone and cedar lodges for up to six. Some with log fires. Open all year round, with free central heating. Mini breaks available and pets welcome. See our colour brochure or visit our website. STB ★★★★. [Pets £15 per booking].
e-mail: info@wildsidelodges.com website: www.wildsidelodges.com

Former croft near Loch Ness, providing privacy, perfect peace and breathtaking views. Miles of forest walks, perfect for dogs/walking. Pets welcome. For a colour brochure contact: GORDON & CORINNE ROBERTS, ROEBUCK COTTAGE, ERROGIE, STRATHERRICK,INVERNESS-SHIRE IV2 6UH (Tel & Fax: 01456 486358). [1 dog free, extra dogs £10 each per week]
e-mail: corinne@wildernesscottages.co.uk website: www.wildernesscottages.co.uk

Nethy Bridge (Inverness-shire)

Popular Strathspey resort on River Nethy with extensive Abernethy Forest to the south. Impressive mountain scenery. Grantown-on-Spey 5 miles.

MONDHUIE CHALETS & B&B, NETHY BRIDGE, INVERNESS-SHIRE PH25 3DF (Tel & Fax: 01479 821062). Situated in the country between Aviemore and Grantown-on-Spey, two comfortable, self-catering chalets, or you can have B&B in the house. Guided walks. A warm welcome awaits you. Pets welcome. [🐕]
e-mail: david@mondhuie.com

NETHYBRIDGE, STRATHSPEY. Choice of modern cottages or converted smithy. Linen and visitor laundry included. September to May storage heating included. Good walking and touring area. STB ★★★/★★★★. Write or phone for brochure. MR AND MRS J. B. PATRICK, 1 CHAPELTON PLACE, FORRES, MORAY IV36 2NL (01309 672505). [One dog free, thereafter £25 per week.]
e-mail: brian@speysidecottages.co.uk website: www.speysidecottages.co.uk

Newtonmore (Inverness-shire)

Village on River Spey. 3 miles west of Kingussie. Holiday and ski centre. Clan Macpherson Museum..

CRUBENBEG FARM HOLIDAY COTTAGES, NEWTONMORE PH20 1BE (01540 673566 Fax: 01540 673509). Rural self catering cottages in the central part of the Highlands. Children's play area, a Games Room, Pond stocked with trout for fishing and a barbecue. Pets welcome. Please contact Jennifer Graham for more information and brochure. [Pets £15 per week]
e-mail: enquiry@crubenbeg.com website: www.crubenbeg.com

Poolewe (Ross-shire)

Village lying between Lochs Ewe and Maree with the river Ewe flowing through.

MR A. URQHART, CROFTERS COTTAGES, 15 CROFT, POOLEWE IV22 2JY (01445 781 268; Fax: 01445 781704). Three traditional cottages situated in a scenic and tranquil area, ideal for a "get away from it all" holiday. Comfortably furnished with all mod cons. [🐕]
e-mail: croftcottages@btopenworld.com website: www.croftcottages.btinternet.co.uk

Rhiconich (Sutherland)

Locality at the head of Loch Inchard on west coast of Sutherland District.

LYNN & GRAHAM, GULL COTTAGE, ACHRIESGILL, RHICONICH, SUTHERLAND IV27 4RJ (01971 521717). High quality accommodation on the wild and unspoilt west coast. Superb scenery and excellent walks on mountains, moors and beaches. Pets welcome under firm control. STB ★★★ Self-Catering. [🐕]

RHICONICH HOTEL, SUTHERLAND, N. W. HIGHLANDS IV27 4RN (01971 521224; Fax: 01971 521732). She's your best friend so why leave her at home, bring her to Rhiconich Hotel, she'll be made equally as welcome as you will. A place where we put service, hospitality and really fresh food as a priority, but why don't you come and see for yourself? For further details contact Jasmine Campbell. STB ★★★ [🐕]
e-mail: rhiconichhotel@aol.com website: www.rhiconichhotel.co.uk

Rogart

Location in Sutherland District 4 miles north-west of head of Loch Fleet on East Coast..

THE STEADING, 48 BLAIRMORE, ROGART IV28 3XE (01408 641409; Fax: 01408 641487). Converted barn with wild garden - two bedrooms, shower room, second toilet, fully equipped kitchen and open plan living area with woodburning stove. On a cul de sac road, good walks nearby. Available from end of May. [🐕]

Spean Bridge (Inverness-shire)

Village on River Spean at foot of Loch Lochy. Site of WWII Commando Memorial.

RIVERSIDE LODGES, INVERGLOY, SPEAN BRIDGE PH34 4DY (01397 712684). Peace and quiet. Three lodges, each sleep 6 in 12 acres of woodland garden on Loch Lochy. Free fishing. Open all year. Pets welcome. Brochure on request.
e-mail: enquiries@riversidelodge.org.uk website: www.riversidelodge.org.uk

Tongue (Sutherland)

Village near north coast of Caithness District on east side of Kyle of Tongue.

BORGIE LODGE HOTEL, SKERRAY, TONGUE KW14 7TH (Tel & Fax: 01641 521332). Set in a secluded Highland glen lies Borgie Lodge. Try pony trekking, cycling and fishing. Sammy, Susie and Sandy, Borgie Lodge pets, would like to make new friends. STB ★★★★ [🐕]
e-mail: info@borgielodgehotel.co.uk website: www.borgielodgehotel.co.uk

LANARKSHIRE

Biggar, Harthill

CARMICHAEL COUNTRY COTTAGES ★★ – ★★★★ *SELF-CATERING*

CARMICHAEL ESTATE, BY BIGGAR, LANARKSHIRE ML12 6PG
Tel: 01899 308336 • Fax: 01899 308481
website: www.carmichael.co.uk/cottages • e-mail:chiefcarm@aol.com

Our Stone Cottages nestle in the woods and fields of our Historic Family-run Estate. Ideal homes for families, pets and particularly dogs. Walking trails, private tennis, fishing, restaurant/farm shop. Off-road racing. 15 cottages, 32 bedrooms. Open all year. Central location. £180 to £500 per week.

Blair Mains Farm, Harthill ML7 5TJ Tel: 01501 751278

Attractive farmhouse on small farm of 72 acres. Immediately adjacent to Junction 5 of M8 motorway. Ideal centre for touring, with Edinburgh, Glasgow, Stirling 30 minutes' drive. One double, three twin, one single (three en suite); bathroom; sittingroom, diningroom; sun porch. Central heating. Children welcome. Pets welcome. Ample grounds for walking. Car essential – parking. Bed and Breakfast from £18; weekly rates available. Reduced rates for children. Open all year.
e-mail: heather@blairmains.freeserve.co.uk website: www.blairmains.co.uk

Biggar

Small town set round broad main street. Gasworks museum, puppet theatre seating 100, street museum displaying old shop fronts and interiors. Peebles 13 miles.

CARMICHAEL COUNTRY COTTAGES, CARMICHAEL ESTATE, BY BIGGAR ML12 6PG (01899 308336; Fax: 01899 308481). Our stone cottages nestle in the woods and fields of our historic family-run estate. Ideal homes for families, pets and dogs. 15 cottages, 32 bedrooms. STB ★★/★★★★ Self catering. Open all year. £180 to £550 per week. [pw! 🐕]
e-mail: chiefcarm@aol.com website: www.carmichael.co.uk/cottages

Harthill

Village 5 miles south-west of Bathgate.

MRS STEPHENS, BLAIR MAINS FARM, HARTHILL ML7 5TJ (01501 751278; Fax: 01501 753383). Attractive farmhouse on small farm. Ideal for touring. Children welcome. Bed and Breakfast from £18; weekly rates available. Reduced rates for children. Open all year. [🐕].
e-mail: heather@blairmains.freeserve.co.uk website: www.blairmains.co.uk

See also Colour Advertisement on page 68

Balrobin Hotel

STB ★★★ Hotel

Pitlochry PH16 5HT Tel: 01796 472901 Fax: 01796 474200 website: www.balrobin.co.uk

AA & RAC ★★ Scottish Country House Hotel. 15 en suite rooms, most with panoramic views, yet close to the town centre. Non-smoking. Owned and run by the Hohman family at value-for-money prices. Ideal for short or longer breaks. **e-mail:info@balrobin.co.uk**

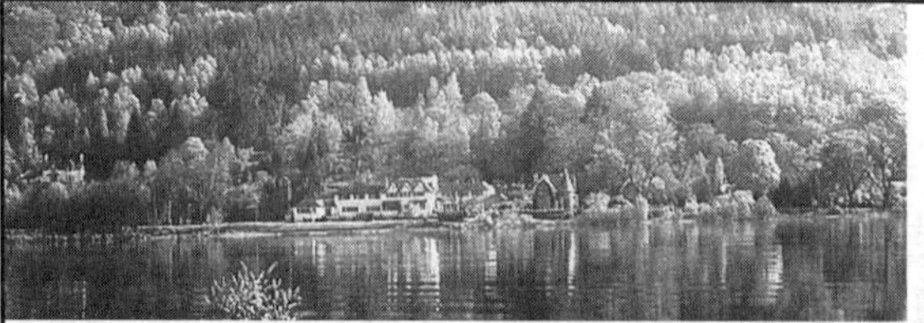

Woof Wuf Woof Woof

FREE for fellow four leggers (and other pets)

Please bring your well behaved charges.

The finest lochside location in the Southern Highlands

Meall Reamhar Restaurant for fine dining, and Tarken Room offer imaginative cuisine with a twist using only the best fresh Scottish Produce.

Well placed to enjoy many excellent days out within our area or further afield.

Hey, I am Sham, and this is my first year at the Hotel. As I dictate I must say that it is all very new to me, and I am still finding my way around, trying to take it all in. I am not sure what to say. I have heard a lot about my predecessor Whitfield, and I know I have much to live up to. But what a great part of the world in which to give it a go. We (both) offer you a warm welcome and friendly service.

The Four Seasons Hotel

St Fillans, Perthshire PH6 2NF

Tel: 01764 685333 e-mail: sham@thefourseasonshotel.co.uk

H.R.

See also Colour Advert on page 68

Ardoch Lodge

Yvonne & John Howes, Ardoch Lodge, Strathyre, Perthshire FK18 8NF

Exceptional walking and wildlife area – deer, red squirrels and a great variety of birds. Twelve acres of formal and informal gardens and grounds. Walk straight from the door through woodlands onto the hillsides or around the loch. The two log cabins and cottage are well furnished, equipped and heated.

Cleaned and beds freshly made for your arrival. All linen, towels and electricity included. In the lodge all our bedrooms, which have outstanding views of the mountains, are spacious and have either en suite or private bathrooms. Deliciously imaginative food using local produce plus a high level of service and comfort provides an excellent base from which to tour this beautiful part of Scotland. Truly a place to unwind.

Tel/Fax: 01877 384666 • E-mail: ardoch@btinternet.com

Perfect for pets. Dogs most welcome. Free of charge **Visit our web site at www.ardochlodge.co.uk**

See also Colour Advertisement on page 69

Aberfeldy

Small town standing on both sides of Uriar Burn near its confluence with the River Tay. Pitlochry 8 miles.

LOCH TAY LODGES, REMONY, ACHARN, ABERFELDY PH15 2HR (01887 830209). Enjoy hill walking, golf, sailing or touring. Salmon and trout fishing available. Log fires. Pets welcome. Walks along loch shore from house. STB ★★★★ SELF CATERING in village close to Loch. For brochure, contact MRS G. DUNCAN MILLAR at above address. [🐕]
e-mail: remony@btinternet.com website: www.lochtaylodges.co.uk

Blairgowrie

Town on the River Ericht 17 miles north west of Dundee.

ALTAMOUNT CHALETS, COUPAR ANGUS ROAD, BLAIRGOWRIE PH10 6JN (01250 873324; Fax: 01250 872464). Modern, fully equipped 1, 2 and 3 bedroom Scandinavian-style Chalets. Colour television. Centrally situated for touring Highlands. Children's amenities on site. Pets welcome. [Pets £1.80 per night].
e-mail: alastair@altamountchalets.co.uk website: www.altamountchalets.co.uk

Callander

Good base for walks and drives around the Trossachs and Loch Katrine. Stirling 14 miles.

LORNA AND ROBERT LECKIE, THE HIGHLAND HOUSE HOTEL, SOUTH CHURCH STREET, CALLANDER FK17 8BN (01877 330269; Fax: 01877 339004). Georgian town house built around 1790. Nine en suite bedrooms with colour TV, hospitality trays and full central heating. Comfortable lounge, evening meals, residents bar. B&B £20-£25 pp; Room only £17-£20 pp. [🐕]
e-mail: highland.house.hotel@lineone.net website: www.highlandhouseincallander.co.uk

LYNNE AND ALISTAIR FERGUSON, ROSLIN COTTAGE GUEST HOUSE, LAGRANNOCH, CALLANDER FK17 8LE (01877 330638; Fax: 01877 331448). Bed and good Scottish or continental Breakfast from £17.50 per person. Comfortable accommodation in 18th century Cottage, historic features. Ideal touring base. "Good walkies area" – dogs are especially welcome. [🐕 pw!]
e-mail: alifer@msn.com

Crieff

Town and resort above bank of River Earn 16 miles west of Perth.

CULCRIEFF COTTAGES, CRIEFF HYDRO, CRIEFF (01764 651670). Newly built cottages set in 900 acres all traditional style with en suite bedrooms. Woodland off-lead walks directly from the door. Free use of Crieff Hydro's leisure facilities included in your rate. Please contact us for more information.
website: www.crieffhydro.com

Killin

Village at confluence of Rivers Dochart and Lochay at head of Loch Tay.

GILL & DAVE HUNT, WESTER LIX HOLIDAY COTTAGES, WESTER LIX, KILLIN FK21 8RD (01567 820 990 & 07747 862641). All cottages are decorated and equipped to a high standard. All cottages have washing machines, freezers, oven, sky TV etc. Well behaved pets welcome by arrangement.
STB ★★★ SELF-CATERING. ASSC Member. [Pets £15 per animal]
e-mail: gill@westerlix.co.uk website: www.westerlix.co.uk

When making enquiries or bookings, a stamped addressed envelope is always appreciated

Kinloch Rannoch

Village at foot of Loch Rannoch.

KILVRECHT CAMP SITE, KINLOCH RANNOCH, PERTHSHIRE (01350 727284; Fax: 01350 727811). Secluded campsite on a level open area in quiet, secluded woodland setting. Fishing available for brown trout on Loch Rannoch. Several trails begin from campsite. Please write, fax or telephone for further information. [🐕]
e-mail: hamish.murray@forestry.gsi.gov.uk

Pitlochry

Popular resort on River Tummel in beautiful Perthshire Highlands. Excellent golf, loch and river fishing. Famous for summer Festival Theatre; distillery, Highland Games.

JACKY & MALCOLM CATTERALL, "TULLOCH", ENOCHDHU, BY KIRKMICHAEL, PITLOCHRY PH10 7PW (01250 881404; Fax: 01250 881304). Former farmhouse offers comfortable accommodation and good food. One family room with washbasin, one twin with washbasin; one en suite double room. All have tea/coffee making facilities and face open country to mountains beyond. Peace and quiet guaranteed. B&B from £19; Dinner if required from £10. Haven for wildlife and dogs. STB ★★★. [🐕]
e-mail: maljac@tulloch83.freeserve.co.uk website: www.maljac.com

BALROBIN HOTEL, HIGHER OAKFIELD, PITLOCHRY PH16 5HT (01796 472901; Fax: 01796 474200). Scottish Country House Hotel. 15 en suite rooms, most with panoramic views, yet close to the town centre. Non-smoking. Owned and run by the Hohman family at value-for-money prices. [🐕]
e-mail: info@balrobin.co.uk website: www.balrobin.co.uk

St Fillans

Village at foot of Lochearn, 5 miles west of Comrie.

THE FOUR SEASONS HOTEL, ST FILLANS PH6 2NF (01764 685333). Ideal holiday venue for pets and their owners. Spectacular Highland scenery, walking, fishing, watersports. Wonderful food. Full details on request. STB ★★★ Hotel, AA ★★★ and 2 Red Rosettes, RAC ★★★ Highly Recommended, Which? Hotel Guide, Taste of Scotland, Johansens, Best Loved Hotels. [🐕]
e-mail: sham@thefourseasonshotel.co.uk website: www.thefourseasonshotel.co.uk

Strathyre

Village set in middle of Strathyre Forest, just off A84 north of Callander. Information centre and picnic area.

ARDOCH LODGE, STRATHYRE (01877 384666). Log cabins and cottage in wonderful mountain scenery. Comfortably furnished and fully equipped. Country house accommodation also available. Phone for brochure. Open all year. Pets most welcome. STB ★★★★ [pw! 🐕]

PLEASE MENTION THIS GUIDE WHEN YOU WRITE OR PHONE TO ENQUIRE ABOUT ACCOMMODATION.

IF YOU ARE WRITING, A STAMPED, ADDRESSED ENVELOPE IS ALWAYS APPRECIATED.

ISLANDS & HIGHLANDS COTTAGES, THE ISLE OF SKYE ESTATE AGENCY, BRIDGE ROAD, PORTREE, ISLE OF SKYE IV51 9ER (01478 612123; Fax; 01478 612709). Awesome scenery, breathtaking sunsets, miraculous dawns and an abundance of wildlife to be found within the islands and highlands of Scotland. We have holiday properties to suit all tastes and pockets. Please send for our brochure. [pets from £14 per week]
website: www.islands-and-highlands.co.uk

ISLE OF MULL

Gruline

Gruline

Locality at the head of Loch na Keal, 3 miles south-west of Salen.

TORLOCHAN, GRULINE, ISLE OF MULL PA71 6HR (Tel & Fax: 01680 300380). Situated in centre of Mull. Panoramic views over Loch na Keal. Working croft of 40 acres. Two Cottages, Two Log Cabins for self-catering and en suite Bed & Breakfast. Friendly welcome awaits. Pets free of charge.[🐕]
e-mail: torlochan@btopenworld.com website: www.holidaymull.org/members/torlochan.html

Westray

Part hilly, part low lying island.

MOUNT PLEASANT, WESTRAY KW17 2DH (01857 677229). Relax on this beautiful island. Lovely sandy beaches, shops and swimming pool nearby. Ideal for children. Pets welcome. Caravans to let from £10 per night. Long or short let. Special prices for students. All linen provided. [🐕]

ISLE OF SKYE

Breakish

Breakish

Location 2 miles east of Broadford on the Isle of Skye

TIGH HOLM COTTAGES, SCULAMUS MOSS, BREAKISH IV42 8QB (01471 822848; Fax: 01471 822328). Open plan spacious ground floor with all modern appliances. Upper level comprises bathroom with shower, one twin and one double bedroom. All bedding and linen supplied, electricity included.
e-mail: info@tigh-holm-cottages.com

Staffin

Crofting and fishing village on rocky coast around Staffin bay, 12 miles north of Portree.

IAN STRATTON & DOREEN HARBEN, GLENVIEW HOTEL, CULNACNOC, STAFFIN IV51 9JH (01470 562248; Fax: 01470 562211). Traditional island house, ideally situated for exploring North East Skye. Comfortable en suite bedrooms. Restaurant renowned for fresh seafood and traditional home cooking. Dogs most welcome. STB ★★ Hotel, WHICH? Best B&B. [🐕]
e-mail: enquiries@glenview-skye.co.uk website: www.glenview-skye.co.uk

MR P.W. REES, "QUALITY COTTAGES', CERBID, SOLVA, HAVERFORDWEST, PEMBROKESHIRE SA62 6YE (01348 837871). Cottages set in all coastal areas, unashamed luxury, highest residential standards. Dishwashers, microwaves, washing machines. Log fires. Linen supplied. Pets welcome. [pw! 🐕]
website: www.qualitycottages.co.uk

ANGLESEY & GWYNEDD

Blaenau Ffestiniog, Caernarfon, Criccieth

OFFEREN COTTAGE, CWMBOWYDD LANE, BLAENAU FFESTINIOG LL41 3EE
Fully equipped three bedroomed cottage. Sleeps six plus small child. Two bathrooms. Small gated courtyard and colourful garden. Secluded but near shops, restaurants and pubs. Porthmadog 12 miles. £89 to £300 per week; prices include linen, towels and fuel. Short Breaks out of main holiday season. Brochure on request.
Apply: Mr & Mrs E. H. Preston, 14 Scott Green Drive, Gildersome, Leeds LS27 7DA
Tel: 0113 252 1006 or 01766 830982

Plas-Y-Bryn Chalet Park Bontnewydd, Near Caernarfon LL54 7YE (01286 672811)

Our small park is situated two miles from the historic town of Caernarfon. Set into a walled garden it offers safety, seclusion and beautiful views of Snowdonia. It is ideally positioned for touring the area. Shop and village pub nearby. A selection of chalets and caravans available at prices from £95 to £370 per week for the caravans and £95 to £290 per week for the chalets. Well behaved pets always welcome.
WTB ★★★ **website: www.plasybrynholidayscaernarfon.co.uk**

Rhos Country Cottages

Quality self-catering. Traditional cosy cottages in an idyllic setting which enjoy their very own quiet seclusion away from the crowds. 4½ miles from Criccieth and the beach.

Olde Worlde Charm and Character with oak beams, inglenook fireplace, log fires, antiques and lovely country furnishings. Some have four poster beds, own snooker table, sauna or jacuzzi. Open all year. Always warm and inviting with home from home comforts.

Rhos Country Cottages, Ynys, Criccieth, Gwynedd LL52 0PB
Telephone & Fax: 01758 720047 E-mail: cottages@rhos.freeserve.co.uk
Website: www.rhos-cottages.co.uk **WTB★★★★★**

Tai Gwyliau DWYFACH Country Cottages

Tel: 01766 810208 Fax: 01766 810064
5 Star cottages near Criccieth.
Our luxury cottages are set in peaceful, beautiful countryside with stunning views of Cardigan Bay and Snowdonia. They are superbly equipped with dishwasher, microwave, washer/dryer, C/H, linen and barbecue. With numerous attractions, country walks, leisure centres, fishing and beaches nearby this is the ideal place to unwind and relax. Special rates off season. Exciting choice of eating places.
Enquiries and brochure:

W & S. Edwards, Pen-y-Bryn, Llanystumdwy, Criccieth, Gwynedd LL53 6SX.
E-mail: llyredwards@ukonline.co.uk • Website: www.dwyfach.co.uk

WERNOL CARAVAN & CHALET PARK Chwilog, Pwllheli, Gwynedd LL53 6SW
Tel & Fax: 01766 810506 • Website: www.wernol.com
Peaceful and quiet, family-run park adjacent to a working farm with panoramic views of Cardigan Bay. Conveniently situated between Llyn and Snowdonia and within 3 miles of the beach. Coarse fishing lake on farm with lovely country walks. Cycle route, horse riding, golf courses and ranges nearby. Two or three bedroom chalets, and luxury caravans. Playing area, games room, pay-phone and laundry room. Personal attention. Colour brochure available. *Also caravans for sale. **WTB Grade 4**

Small Georgian cottage overlooking the magnificent beach at Harlech. Central for unspoiled beaches and countryside, yet within easy reach of Porthmadog and Lleyn Peninsula. Good home cooking. Dinner, Bed and Breakfast at reasonable prices. Pretty bedrooms overlooking sea.
Pets welcome. Open March-November.

Fron Deg Guest House, Llanfair, Harlech, Gwynedd LL46 2RE
Tel: 01766 780448

Gwesty Minffordd Hotel

Talyllyn LL36 9AJ
Tel: 01654 761665 Fax: 01654 761517
E-mail: hotel@minffordd.com; Website: www.minffordd.com

Small 17th century Drovers' Inn at the base of Cader Idris, ideal for 'walkies' or as a centre for touring. For the two legged guest enjoy a Minffordd dinner, cooked on an Aga using local Welsh produce, organic vegetables, Welsh flavouring. Residential and restaurant licence; seven bedrooms all en suite, two ground floor. Non-smoking. Pets welcome. No children under 12. Dolgellau six miles, Machynlleth eight miles, Cader Idris 2,697 ft. Hosts: **Gordon & Michelle Holt**.

WTB ★★★ AA ★★ • Founder Member Taste of Wales • Good Food Guide 2000

Cliff Cottages and Plas Darien Apartments

All year round holidays and short breaks in a choice of centrally heated apartments with wonderful sea views or stone-built cottages in village-like situation very near sea. Own private indoor leisure complex with adults' pool and children's pool, saunas, solarium, gym, snooker, bowls, table tennis. Outdoor heated pool, tennis courts, badminton, small golf, bowls, croquet. Adjacent 18 hole golf course, horse riding, windsurfing, canoeing, fishing.

Phone or write for brochure:
Plas Darien
The Cliff
Trearddur Bay
Anglesey LL65 2UR
Tel: 01407 860789
Fax: 01407 861150

FREE or REDUCED RATE entry to Holiday Visits and Attractions
– see our READERS' OFFER VOUCHERS on pages 103-118

MR P.W. REES, "QUALITY COTTAGES', CERBID, SOLVA, HAVERFORDWEST, PEMBROKESHIRE SA62 6YE (01348 837871). Cottages set in all coastal areas, unashamed luxury, highest residential standards. Dishwashers, microwaves, washing machines. Log fires. Linen supplied. Pets welcome. [pw! 🐕]
website: www.qualitycottages.co.uk

Bala

Natural touring centre for Snowdonia. Narrow gauge railway runs along side of Bala lake, the largest natural lake in Wales. Golf, sailing, fishing, canoeing.

TY GWYN. Self-catering annexe. Twin bedded studio type with shower/bathroom, colour TV. Situated just two miles from Bala in beautiful country area. Ideal for - walking, sailing, canoeing and fishing. Also 6-berth caravan with all mod cons available to let. Contact: MRS G. SKINNER, TY GWYN, RHYDUCHAF, BALA (01678 520234 or 521267). [🐕]

Barmouth

Modern seaside resort with two miles of sandy beaches. Surrounding hills full of interesting archaeological remains.

LAWRENNY LODGE HOTEL, BARMOUTH LL42 1SU (01341 280466; Fax: 01341 281551). Quiet, family-run hotel overlooking harbour and estuary but only 5 minutes from town. Most rooms en suite, all with TV, tea/coffee making facilities and clock radio alarms. Restaurant menu includes vegetarian dishes. Residential licence. Large car park. WTB ★★ Hotel [🐕]

Beaumaris

Elegant little town dominated by castle built by Edward I in 13th century. Museum of Childhood has Victorian toys and music boxes.

MR P. W. REES, "QUALITY COTTAGES", CERBID, SOLVA, HAVERFORDWEST, PEMBROKESHIRE SA62 6YE (01348 837871). Cottages set in all coastal areas, unashamed luxury, highest residential standards. Dishwashers, microwaves, washing machines. Log fires. Linen supplied. Pets welcome. [pw! 🐕]
website: www.qualitycottages.co.uk

SYMBOLS

- 🐕 **Indicates that pets are welcome free of charge.**
- £ **Indicates that a charge is made for pets: nightly or weekly.**
- pw! **Shows some special provision for pets; exercise facility, feeding or accommodation arrangement.**
- ⌂ **Indicates separate pets accommodation.**

Blaenau Ffestiniog

Good touring centre amidst dramatic scenery. Well-known slate quarries. Betws-y-Coed 12 miles, Ffestiniog 3.

OFFEREN COTTAGE, BLAENAU FFESTINIOG. Fully equipped 3-bedroomed centrally heated cottage. Sleeps 6 adults plus small child. 2 bathrooms. £89 to £300 per week. Brochure on request from: MR & MRS E.H. PRESTON, 14 SCOTT GREEN DRIVE, GILDERSOME, LEEDS LS27 7DA (0113 252 1006 or 01766 830982). [🐕]

Bodorgan

A rural area in South West Anglesey.

MRS J. GUNDRY, FARMYARD LODGE, BODORGAN, ANGLESEY LL62 5LW (01407 840977). Comfortable three-bedroomed house. Enclosed garden. Near beaches, common, forest. Fully equipped, bedding and electricity inclusive. Colour TV/video, microwave. Dogs and children welcome. WTB ★★★★ [🐕]

Caernarfon

Historic walled town and resort, ideal for touring Snowdonia. Museums, Segontium Roman Fort, magnificent 13th century castle. Old harbour, sailing trips.

PRINCE OF WALES HOTEL, BANGOR STREET, CAERNARFON, GWYNEDD LL55 1AR (01286 673367; Fax: 01286 676610). Ideally located for exploring Snowdonia and Anglesey. Three minutes' walk to Caernarfon Castle, harbour and steam trains. 21 bedrooms, bar and restaurant meals. Traditional home cooking. Guest ales. Special breaks available. [🐕]
e-mail: info@prince-of-wales-hotel.co.uk website: www.prince-of-wales-hotel.co.uk

PLAS-Y-BRYN CHALET PARK, BONTNEWYDD, NEAR CAERNARFON LL54 7YE (01286 672811). Two miles from Caernarfon. It offers safety, seclusion and beautiful views of Snowdonia. Ideally positioned for touring. Well behaved pets always welcome. WTB ★★★ [Pets £10 per week].
website: www.plasybrynholidayscaernarfon.co.uk

Criccieth

Popular family resort with safe beaches divided by ruins of 13th century castle. Salmon and sea trout fishing. Festival of Music and Arts in the summer.

A warm welcome awaits you in comfortable self-catering cottages. Easily accessible to numerous attractions, or enjoy tranquillity of countryside. Short breaks available. MRS M. WILLIAMS, MGAER WEN FARM, YNYS, CRICCIETH LL52 0NU (01766 810324).
e-mail: gaerwen@btinternet.com

MRS LENA HUGHES JONES, TYDDYN HEILYN, CHWILOG, CRICCIETH LL53 6SW (01766 810441). Cosy, comfortably renovated Welshstone country cottage with historic features, double glazing and centrally heated. Cardigan Bay sea views and mild Gulf Stream climate. Suitable parking and spacious garden, ideal for dogs. Three miles South Criccieth, on Llyn Peninsula and edge Snowdonia. Beautiful river walks amid wildlife, tree lined walks through farmland. Double glazed and centrally heated. Also Norwegian home to let, furnished. [🐕]

MR P. W. REES, "QUALITY COTTAGES", CERBID, SOLVA, HAVERFORDWEST, PEMBROKESHIRE SA62 6YE (01348 837871). Cottages set in all coastal areas, unashamed luxury, highest residential standards. Dishwashers, microwaves, washing machines. Log fires. Linen supplied. Pets welcome. [pw! 🐕]
website: www.qualitycottages.co.uk

MRS A. M. JONES, RHOS COUNTRY COTTAGES, YNYS, CRICCIETH LL52 0PB (Tel & Fax: 01758 720047/01766 810295). Quality self-catering, traditional cosy cottages in an idyllic setting with oak beams, inglenook fireplace, log fires, antiques and lovely country furnishings. Some have four poster beds, own snooker table, sauna or jacuzzi. WTB★★★★★ [🐕]
e-mail: cottages@rhos.freeserve.co.uk website: www.rhos-cottages.co.uk

DWYFACH COUNTRY COTTAGES, NEAR CRICCIETH (01766 810208; Fax: 01766 810064). Five Star luxury cottages in the countryside with stunning views of Cardigan Bay and Snowdonia. Numerous attractions. Enquiries and brochure: W & S EDWARDS, PEN-Y-BRYN, LLANYSTUMDWY, CRICCIETH, GWYNEDD LL53 6SX. [🐕]
e-mail: llyredwards@ukonline.co.uk website: www.dwyfach.co.uk

WERNOL CARAVAN & CHALET PARK, CHWILOG, PWLLHELI LL53 6SW (Tel & Fax: 01766 810506). Family-run park adjacent to farm. Cycle route, horse riding and golf courses nearby. Two or three bedroom chalets, and luxury caravans. Playing area, games room, pay-phone and laundry room. Colour brochure. WTB Grade 4. [Pets £10 per week.]
website: www.wernol.com

Dulas Bay

On north-east coast of Anglesey, between Amlwch and Moelfre.

MRS G. McCREADIE, DERI ISAF, DULAS BAY LL70 9DX (01248 410536; Mobile: 077 21 374471). Beautiful Victorian Country House standing in 20 acres of woodland, gardens and fields. High standard of accommodation in two family rooms and one double all en suite. Pets welcome. Stabling available. ★★★★ [Pets £2 per night, £10 per week]
e-mail: mccreadie@deriisaf.freeserve.co.uk website: www.deriisaf.freeserve.co.uk

Dwyran

Village on Anglesey 2 miles east of Newborough.

JUDY HUTCHINGS, TAL-Y-FOEL STUD FARM AND RIDING CENTRE, DWYRAN, ANGLESEY LL61 6LQ (Tel & Fax: 01248 430377) Rural waterfront location with spectacular views of Snowdonia. Luxury en suite rooms with whirlpool baths and many facilities. Walking, birdwatching, fishing, riding and horse livery. Brochure on application. WTB ★★★★ FARM [🐕]
e-mail: riding@talyfoel.u-net.com website: www.tal-y-foel.co.uk

Ffestiniog

Village 9 miles east of Porthmadog.

NEIL & MOIRA RICHARDS, SNOWDONIA HOLIDAYS LTD, PLAS BLAENDDOL, LLAN FFESTINIOG, GWYNEDD LL41 4PH (01766 762786; Fax: 01766 762796) Sophisticated self-catering holidays in the heart of Snowdonia. Free booking service for a wide range of activities, e.g. pony trekking, golf, quad biking etc., all within easy reach. Brochure on application. [Pets £18 per week]
e-mail: pw@snowdonia-holidays.co.uk website: www.snowdonia-holidays.co.uk

Harlech

Small stone-built town dominated by remains of 13th century castle. Golf, theatre, swimming pool, fine stretch of sands.

MR P. W. REES, "QUALITY COTTAGES", CERBID, SOLVA, HAVERFORDWEST, PEMBROKESHIRE SA62 6YE (01348 837871). Cottages set in all coastal areas, unashamed luxury, highest residential standards. Dishwashers, microwaves, washing machines. Log fires. Linen supplied. Pets welcome. [pw! 🐕]
website: www.qualitycottages.co.uk

FRON DEG GUEST HOUSE, LLANFAIR, HARLECH LL46 2RE (01766 780448). Small Georgian cottage overlooking beach at Harlech. Pretty bedrooms. Central for unspoiled beaches and countryside, yet within easy reach of Porthmadog. Reasonable terms for Bed and Breakfast, also Dinner. Open March-November. [🐕]

When making enquiries or bookings, a stamped addressed envelope is always appreciated

Holyhead

Principal town of the Isle of Anglesey. Passenger terminal for Republic of Ireland.

PAM BRONNIE MONTGOMERY-CROFT, TY GWRTHYN FARMHOUSE, LLANFAIR-YN-NEUBWLL, HOLLYHEAD LL65 3LD (01407 741025). Ideal "out of town" stopover near the beach. Within easy reach of all 'Irish Ferries'. All rooms en suite. Country and beach walks. Farmhouse with family atmosphere. Reasonably priced. Drive safely! [🐕]

Llanddona

Village on Anglesey 3 miles north west of Beaumaris.

MR P. W. REES, "QUALITY COTTAGES", CERBID, SOLVA, HAVERFORDWEST, PEMBROKESHIRE SA62 6YE (01348 837871). Cottages set in all coastal areas, unashamed luxury, highest residential standards. Dishwashers, microwaves, washing machines. Log fires. Linen supplied. Pets welcome. [pw! 🐕]
website: www.qualitycottages.co.uk

Morfa Nefyn

Picturesque village 2 miles west of Nefyn.

MR P. W. REES, "QUALITY COTTAGES", CERBID, SOLVA, HAVERFORDWEST, PEMBROKESHIRE SA62 6YE (01348 837871). Cottages set in all coastal areas, unashamed luxury, highest residential standards. Dishwashers, microwaves, washing machines. Log fires. Linen supplied. Pets welcome. [pw! 🐕]
website: www.qualitycottages.co.uk

Pentraeth

Village on Anglesey 5 miles north of Menai Bridge

PEN-Y-GARNEDD FARM, NEAR PENTRAETH, ISLE OF ANGLESEY LL75 8YW (01248 450580). Anglesey holiday cottage and touring caravan site with hook-ups. Cosy cottage on friendly working small-holding. Sleeps 5, log burner and heating. Well behaved children and pets welcome. Close to beaches and mountains (Snowdonia). Open all year. Winter breaks - 4 nights for the price of 3 fully inclusive when available. WTB ★★★ [pw! Pets £10 per week].

Porthmadog

Harbour town with mile-long Cob embankment, along which runs Ffestiniog Narrow Gauge Steam Railway to Blaenau Ffestiniog. Pottery, maritime museum, car museum. Good beaches nearby.

BLACK ROCK SANDS, PORTHMADOG. Private site, beach 150 yards.14 Caravans only. Fully equipped 6-berths. Own flush toilets. Showers and TVs. Shop and tavern nearby. APPLY: M. HUMPHRIES, 251 HEDNESFORD ROAD, NORTON CANES, CANNOCK, STAFFORDSHIRE WS11 3RZ (01543 279583).

MR P. W. REES, "QUALITY COTTAGES", CERBID, SOLVA, HAVERFORDWEST, PEMBROKESHIRE SA62 6YE (01348 837871). Cottages set in all coastal areas, unashamed luxury, highest residential standards. Dishwashers, microwaves, washing machines. Log fires. Linen supplied. Pets welcome. [pw! 🐕]
website: www.quaiitycottages.co.uk

Porth Neigel

Bay on south side of Lleyn peninsula, also known as Hell's Mouth.

Attractive cottage set in meadow near beach, quiet rural area. Sleeps 6, open fire, all comforts. Local carer. Near Abersoch. Details from MRS E.M. COOPER, 18 ST MARY'S LANE, LOUTH, LINCOLNSHIRE LN11 0DT (01507 604408 or 01507 354892).

Red Wharf Bay

Deep curving bay with vast expanse of sand, very popular for sailing and swimming.

MR P. W. REES, "QUALITY COTTAGES", CERBID, SOLVA, HAVERFORDWEST, PEMBROKESHIRE SA62 6YE (01348 837871). Cottages set in all coastal areas, unashamed luxury, highest residential standards. Dishwashers, microwaves, washing machines. Log fires. Linen supplied. Pets welcome. [pw! 🐕]
website: www.qualitycottages.co.uk

Talyllyn

Lake in course of River Dysynni, 2 miles south of summit of Cader Idris.

GWESTY MINFFORDD HOTEL, TALYLLYN LL36 9AJ (01654 761665; Fax: 01654 761517). Small 17th century Drovers' Inn at the base of Cader Idris, ideal for 'walkies' or as a centre for touring. Residential and restaurant licence; seven en suite bedrooms. WTB ★★★, AA ★★, Founder Member Taste of Wales, Good Food Guide 2000. [pw! £3 per night]
e-mail: hotel@minffordd.com website: www.minffordd.com

Trearddur Bay

Attractive holiday spot set amongst low cliffs on Holy Island, near Holyhead. Golf, sailing, fishing, swimming.

CLIFF COTTAGES AND PLAS DARIEN APARTMENTS, TREARDDUR BAY LL65 2UR (01407 860789; Fax: 01407 861150). Fully equipped holiday cottages, sleeping 4/8 plus cot. Near sea. Children's playground. Indoor and outdoor heated pools. Colour television. Choice of centrally heated apartments or stone-built cottages. Own private leisure complex with bowls, sauna, snooker, table tennis etc. Also tennis, croquet. Adjacent golf course. [🐕]

Tywyn

Pleasant seaside resort, start of Talyllyn Narrow Gauge Railway. Sea and river fishing, golf.

MR P. W. REES, "QUALITY COTTAGES", CERBID, SOLVA, HAVERFORDWEST, PEMBROKESHIRE SA62 6YE (01348 837871). Cottages set in all coastal areas, unashamed luxury, highest residential standards. Dishwashers, microwaves, washing machines. Log fires. Linen supplied. Pets welcome. [pw! 🐕]
website: www.qualitycottages.co.uk

Fully equipped coastal house, close to sandy beach. 3 bedrooms, sleeps five. Gardens; garage. Pets welcome free of charge. APPLY – MR IAN WESTON, 18 ELIZABETH ROAD, BASINGSTOKE, HAMPSHIRE RG22 6AX (01256 352364; 01256 412233 evenings).[🐕]
e-mail: i.weston1@ntlworld.com

PLEASE NOTE

All the information in this book is given in good faith in the belief that it is correct. However, the publishers cannot guarantee the facts given in these pages, neither are they responsible for changes in policy, ownership or terms that may take place after the date of going to press. Readers should always satisfy themselves that the facilities they require are available and that the terms, if quoted, still apply.

Betws-y-Coed, Conwy

When making enquiries or bookings, a stamped addressed envelope is always appreciated

Sychnant Pass House

Sychnant Pass Road, Conwy LL32 8BJ
Telephone: 01492 596868
e-mail: bresykes@sychnant-pass-house.co.uk
website: www.sychnant-pass-house.co.uk

Nellie and Molly our lovely collies would love to welcome your four legged friends to their home in the hills above Conwy. Sychnant Pass House is a lovely Victorian House set in two acres with a little pond and stream running through it. Step out of our garden and straight onto Snowdonia National Park land where you can walk for miles with your dogs. Just over two miles from the beach and one-and-a-half miles from Conwy it is an ideal base from which to tour Wales. All our rooms are en suite, our garden rooms have French windows opening into the garden which are ideal for pets. We have a lovely sitting room that you can share with your best friends after dinner which is served in our informal, friendly restaurant, doggie bags are always available. Your four legged friends and their folk are most welcome here.

Bre & Graham C. Sykes (FHG Diploma Winner)
Great Little Places & AA & RAC 5 Diamonds
AA Best Guest Accomodation Wales 2003
Bed & Breakfast from £35 pp
"Booker Prize for Excellence 2002"
RAC Little Gem Award 2003

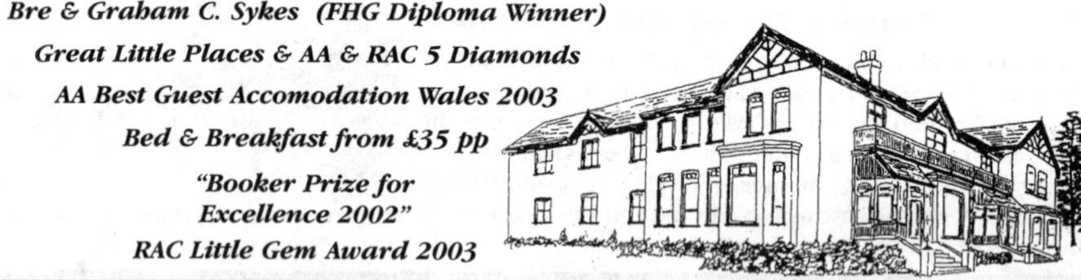

TREFRIW • CONWY VALLEY • SNOWDONIA

Secluded cottages, log fire and beams
Dogs will love it – a place of their dreams
Plenty of walks around mountains and lakes
Cosy and tranquil – it's got what it takes.
It's really a perfect holiday let
For up to 2-7 people, plus their pet(s).

Apply: Mrs Williams
Tel: 01724 733990 or 07711 217 448 (week lets only)

GOOD HOTEL GUIDE
Country Hotel of the Year 2003

ETC
★★★
(Silver Award)

★★★ 77%

Food Award

Pen-y-Dyffryn Country Hotel

RHYDYCROESAU, NEAR OSWESTRY, SHROPSHIRE SY10 7JD

This silver stone former Georgian Rectory, set almost a thousand feet up in the Shropshire/Welsh hills, is in a dream situation for both pets and their owners. Informal atmosphere, no traffic, just buzzards, badgers and beautiful country walks, yet Shrewsbury, Chester, Powis Castle & Lake Vyrnwy are all close by. The well-stocked bar and licensed restaurant are always welcoming at the end of another hard day's relaxing. All bedrooms en suite etc; four have private patios, ideal for pets; one has a double spa bath. Short breaks available from £69 pppd, Dinner, B&B. Pets free.

TEL: 01691 653700 **MILES AND AUDREY HUNTER**
E-MAIL: stay@peny.co.uk **WEBSITE: www.peny.co.uk**

See also Colour Advertisement on page 52

The Golden Pheasant is an 18th Century country hotel and inn ideally situated to welcome all pets, especially dogs. Dogs can take their mistress or master for quiet country walks along the country lanes in the summer and on their return enjoy a refreshing drink or sit outside in our garden. If their owners are well-behaved they can enjoy a relaxing drink too! In winter you can warm in front of our old range fire in our 'olde worlde' bar. Ted & Fred, our two Labradors love making new friends and will be waiting to greet you & your companions on arrival. They will wait for the phone to ring or chase the postman for your enquiries, as they have not yet mastered surfing the web. So please ask your mistress or master to bring you for a break – they would be barking mad not to come and stay with us all at The Golden Pheasant where Ted & Fred will be waiting to greet you!!

THE GOLDEN PHEASANT *Country* Hotel & Inn

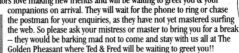

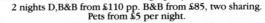

AA ★★★ WTB ★★★

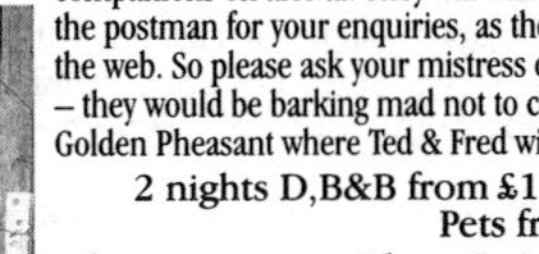

2 nights D,B&B from £110 pp. B&B from £85, two sharing.
Pets from £5 per night.

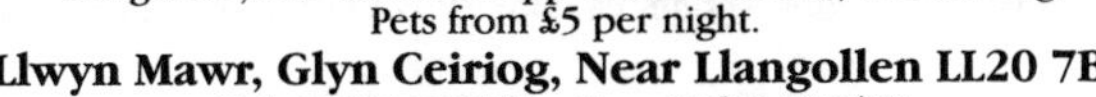

Llwyn Mawr, Glyn Ceiriog, Near Llangollen LL20 7BB
Tel: 01691 718281 • Fax: 01691 718479
e-mail: goldenpheasant@micro-plus-web.net
website: www.goldenpheasanthotel.co.uk

See also Colour Advertisement on page 70

FHG PUBLICATIONS LIMITED

publish a large range of well-known accommodation guides. We will be happy to send you details or you can use the order form at the back of this book.

When making enquiries please mention FHG Publications

Sunnydowns Hotel

WTB ★★★ *Quality Hotel*

66 Abbey Road, Rhos-on-Sea, Colwyn Bay, Conwy, North Wales LL28 4NU

Tel: 01492 544256 Fax: 01492 543223

(Proprietor: Mike Willington)

A 3 star family-run hotel situated in a quiet area and just a 2 minute level walk to the beach & shops. High standard of comfort and cleanliness, car park, bar, games room with pool table, Nordic sauna, restaurant, TV lounge.

Our restaurant is non-smoking, serving freshly prepared good home cooking. Special diets are catered for and our speciality is Thai cuisine. There is a choice of menu at all times. The towns of Llandudno, Colwyn Bay & Conwy are only 5 minutes' drive away and just 10 minutes to the mountains and castles of Snowdonia and the Isle of Anglesey.

OAP discounts, large family rooms & family suites available. All en suite bedrooms have remote control TV (teletext, video & satellite), clock radio, tea/coffee making facilities, hairdyer, mini-bar, refrigerator, telephone and central heating. Available on request are irons, trouser press, room service and laundry service.

New this year all rooms fitted with personal digital room safe. Microwave available for guests' use. Also a fitness/exercise machine in games room all available free of charge for all our guests.

Dogs are very welcome and can stay at a small charge. They are allowed in your bedroom with you and in the hotel except the restaurant. Meals also served in the bar where dogs are allowed.

For further information, please phone or write for our colour brochure.

e-mail: sunnydowns-hotel@tinyworld.co.uk • website: www.hotelnorthwales.co.uk

MR P.W. REES, "QUALITY COTTAGES', CERBID, SOLVA, HAVERFORDWEST, PEMBROKESHIRE SA62 6YE (01348 837871). Cottages set in all coastal areas, unashamed luxury, highest residential standards. Dishwashers, microwaves, washing machines. Log fires. Linen supplied. Pets welcome. [pw!]
website: www.qualitycottages.co.uk

SEASIDE COTTAGES. MANN'S, SHAW'S AND SNOWDONIA TOURIST SERVICES (01758 701 702). Large selection of self-catering seaside and country cottages, bungalows, farmhouses, caravans etc. offering superb, reasonably priced accommodation for owners and their pets. Please telephone for brochure.
websites: www.manns-holidays.com www.shaws-holidays.co.uk www.snowdoniatourist.com

Betws-y-Coed

Popular mountain resort in picturesque setting where three rivers meet. Trout fishing, craft shops, golf, railway and motor museums, Snowdonia National Park Visitor Centre. Nearby Swallow Falls are famous beauty spot.

MRS MORRIS, TY COCH FARM-TREKKING CENTRE, PENMACHNO, BETWS-Y-COED LL25 0HJ (01690 760248). Hill farm in Wales. TV, teamaking, en suite. Set in National Park/Snowdonia. Very quiet and well off the beaten track. A great welcome and good food. Many return visits. £18 B&B. [ ]
e-mail: tycoch@amserve.net

SUMMER HILL NON-SMOKERS' GUEST HOUSE, BETWS-Y-COED LL24 0BL (01690 710306). Quiet location, overlooking river. 150 yards from main road and shops. En suite and standard rooms, tea-making facilities. Residents' lounge. TV. Ideal for walkers. B&B from £18. [Pets £1.50 per night.]

HAFOD COUNTRY HOUSE, TREFRIW, CONWY VALLEY LL27 0RQ (01492 640029; Fax: 01492 641351). Small informal hotel. Over two acres of grounds. Excellent food in restaurant. Short breaks available. Well behaved dogs welcome. Non-smoking. WTB ★★★★ Country House AA ★★ 71%, Good Hotel Guide 2004. [Pets £5 per night, £30 per week]
e-mail: hafod@breathemail.net website: www.hafodhouse.co.uk

Conwy

One of the best preserved medieval fortified towns in Britain on dramatic estuary setting. Telford Suspension Bridge, many historic buildings, lively quayside (site of smallest house in Britain). Golf, pony trekking, pleasure cruises.

YENTON, PROMENADE, LLANFAIRFECHAN LL33 0BY(01248 680075). Self-contained, seafront apartments. Fully equipped. Sleeps 2 to 6. Sandy beach, scenic views. Easy seaside or mountain walks. Good touring position. Short Break details on request. Ring BARBARA ALLIX for brochure. [Pets £15 per week.]
e-mail: yenton@llan-holidays.freeserve.co.uk website: www.the-yenton.co.uk

NORTH WALES HOLIDAYS, BRON-Y-WENDON AND NANT-Y-GLYN HOLIDAY PARKS, WERN ROAD, LLANDDULAS, COLWYN BAY LL22 8HG (01492 512903/512282). Cottages with sea views at Bron-Y-Wendon or chalets, cottages & coach house in picturesque valley at Nant-Y-Glyn. WTB ★★★/★★★★/★★★★★ [Pets £10 per week].
e-mai: bron-y-wendon@northwales-holidays.co.uk website: www.northwales-holidays.co.uk

BRONGAIN, TY'N-Y-GROES, CONWY. Homely Victorian stone cottage, picturesque Conwy Valley. Snowdonia Mountain views. Enjoy lakes, mountains, walking, bird watching, beaches, Bodnant, RSPB, Conwy Castle. £145-£300. Contact: MRS G. M. SIMPOLE, 105 HAYGREEN ROAD, TERRINGTON ST CLEMENT, KINGS LYNN, NORFOLK PE34 4PU (Tel: 01553 828897; Mobile: 0798 9080 665) [🐕]

SYCHNANT PASS HOUSE, SYCHNANT PASS ROAD, CONWY LL32 8BJ (01492 596868). Sychnant Pass House is a lovely Victorian House set in two acres with a little pond and stream running through it. Step out of our garden and straight onto Snowdonia National Park land where you can walk for miles with your dogs. All rooms en suite. [🐕]
e-mail: breskyes@sychnant-pass-house.co.uk website: www.sychnant-pass-house.co.uk

Conwy Valley

Scenic area with many places of interest.

Secluded cottages with log fire and beams. Dogs will love it. Plenty of walks around mountains and lakes. For 2 - 7 people plus their pet(s). MRS WILLIAMS (01724 733990 or 07711 217 448) week lets only. [🐕]

Llandudno

Premier holiday resort of North Wales coast flanked by Great Orme and Little Orme headlands. Wide promenade, pier, two beaches; water ski-ing, sailing, fishing trips from jetty. Excellent sports facilities: golf, indoor pool, tennis, pony trekking, Leisure Centre. Summer variety shows, Alice In Wonderland Visitor Centre.

CLIFFBURY HOTEL, 34 ST DAVID'S ROAD, LLANDUDNO LL30 2UH (01492 877224; Fax: 01492 873524) Pets and well-behaved owners very welcome at our non-smoking hotel situated in a quiet area close to town centre and both beaches. Car park. En suite rooms with TV and beverage making facilities. Please contact John or Rita for brochure. WTB ★★ Hotel. [🐕]
e-mail: cliffburyhotel@tiscali.co.uk website: www.cliffburyhotel.co.uk

Llangollen

Famous for International Music Eisteddfod held in July. Plas Newydd, Valle Crucis Abbey nearby. Standard gauge steam railway; canal cruises; ideal for golf and walking.

PEN-Y-DYFFRYN COUNTRY HOUSE HOTEL, NEAR RHYDYCROESAU, OSWESTRY SY10 7JD (01691 653700). Picturesque Georgian Rectory quietly set in Shropshire/ Welsh Hills. Ten en suite bedrooms, two with private patios. 5-acre grounds. No passing traffic. Johansens recommended. Dinner, Bed and Breakfast from £69.00 per person per day. AA/ETC ★★★. [🐕 pw!]
e-mail: stay@peny.co.uk website: www.peny.co.uk

GOLDEN PHEASANT COUNTRY HOTEL, GLYN CEIRIOG, NEAR LLANGOLLEN LL20 7BB (01691 718281; Fax: 01691 718479). Situated in the beautiful Ceiriog Valley. All 19 rooms en suite, colour TV and tea/coffee making facilities. Pets welcome in all rooms (except restaurant and lounge). WTB/AA ★★★ [£5 per night per pet]
e-mail: goldenpheasant@micro-plus-web.net website: www.goldenpheasanthotel.co.uk

Rhos-on-Sea

Popular resort at east end of Penrhyn Bay, adjoining Colwyn Bay to the north-west.

SUNNYDOWNS HOTEL, 66 ABBEY ROAD, RHOS-ON-SEA, CONWY LL28 4NU (01492 544256; Fax: 01492 543223). A WTB ★★★ luxury family hotel just 2 minutes' walk to beach & shops. All rooms en suite with colour TV, video & satellite channels, tea/coffee facilities and central heating. Hotel has bar, pool room and car park. [pets £1.50 per night]
e-mail: sunnydowns-hotel@tinyworld.co.uk website: www.hotelnorthwales.co.uk

Trefriw

Hillside village, popular as spa in Victorian times. Local beauty spots at Llyn Crafnant and Llyn Geironnydd. Woollen mill demonstrating traditional techniques.

MRS B. COLE, GLANDWR, TREFRIW, NEAR LLANRWST LL27 0JP (01492 640431). Large Country House on outskirts of Trefriw village. Good touring area with Llanrwst, Betws-y-Coed and Swallow Falls five miles away. Fishing, walking, golf, pony trekking close by. Comfortable bedrooms, lounge with TV, diningroom. Good home cooking. Parking. B&B from £22.50.

CARMARTHENSHIRE

Laugharne

See also Colour Advertisement on page 70

Laugharne

Village on the River Taf estuary 4 miles south of St Clears, burial place of Dylan Thomas.

SIR JOHN'S HILL FARM HOLIDAY COTTAGES, LAUGHARNE, CARMARTHENSHIRE SA33 4TD (01994 427667) In one of the finest locations in West Wales with spectacular views of coast and countryside. Three very comfortable cottages are the perfect place for a relaxing break. Lots of great country walks and long sandy beaches nearby too. [pw! £15 per week.]
e-mail: liz.handford@sirjohnshillfarm.co.uk website: www.sirjohnshillfarm.co.uk

MR P.W. REES, "QUALITY COTTAGES', CERBID, SOLVA, HAVERFORDWEST, PEMBROKESHIRE SA62 6YE (01348 837871). Cottages set in all coastal areas, unashamed luxury, highest residential standards. Dishwashers, microwaves, washing machines. Log fires. Linen supplied. Pets welcome. [pw! 🐕]
website: www.qualitycottages.co.uk

Aberaeron

Attractive little town on Cardigan Bay, good touring centre for coast and inland. The Aeron Express Aerial ferry offers an exciting trip across the harbour. Marine aquarium; Aberarth Leisure Park nearby.

GILFACH HOLIDAY VILLAGE, LLWYNCELYN, NEAR ABERAERON SA46 OHN (01545 580288). Choice of modern Bungalows (up to 6 persons) or luxury 2/3 person apartments. Fully equipped, linen available, colour TV. Horse and pony riding. Tennis. Write or phone for brochure pack to the Manager. [Pets £15 per week.]
e-mail: info@stratfordcaravans.co.uk website: www.stratfordcaravans.co.uk

Aberporth

Popular seaside village offering safe swimming and good sea fishing. Good base for exploring Cardigan Bay coastline.

MISS M. ALLEN, YR YSGUBOR, PANTYFFWRN, ABERPORTH, CARDIGAN SA43 2DT (01239 810509). Sleeps 2. Delightful stone cottage on beautiful unspoilt West Wales coast. Quiet, comfortable. All amenities. Large dog-friendly garden. Ample parking. From £80 plus electricity.[🐕]

MR P. W. REES, "QUALITY COTTAGES", CERBID, SOLVA, HAVERFORDWEST, PEMBROKESHIRE SA62 6YE (01348 837871). Cottages set in all coastal areas, unashamed luxury, highest residential standards. Dishwashers, microwaves, washing machines. Log fires. Linen supplied. Pets welcome. [pw! 🐕]
website: www.qualitycottages.co.uk

MRS JANN TUCKER, PENFFYNNON, ABERPORTH, CARDIGAN SA43 2DA (01239 810387; Fax: 01239 811401). Comfortable, self-contained, fully-equipped cottage, houses and apartments adjacent to safe and sandy beaches. Dogs welcome by arrangement. Local attractions include water sports, Cardigan Bay dolphins and walking in the Presceli Hills. £200-£950 per week. WTB ★★★★/★★★★★ SELF CATERING[pw! 🐕]
e-mail: jann@aberporth.com website: www.aberporth.com

Ciliau Aeron

Village in undulating country just inland from the charming Cardigan Bay resorts of New Quay and Aberaeron. New Quay 12 miles, Aberaeron 6.

MR P. W. REES, "QUALITY COTTAGES", CERBID, SOLVA, HAVERFORDWEST, PEMBROKESHIRE SA62 6YE (01348 837871). Cottages set in all coastal areas, unashamed luxury, highest residential standards. Dishwashers, microwaves, washing machines. Log fires. Linen supplied. Pets welcome. [pw! 🐕]
website: www.qualitycottages.co.uk

Llangrannog

Pretty little seaside village overlooking a sandy beach. Superb cliff walk to NT Ynys Lochtyn, a secluded promontory.

MR P. W. REES, "QUALITY COTTAGES", CERBID, SOLVA, HAVERFORDWEST, PEMBROKESHIRE SA62 6YE (01348 837871). Cottages set in all coastal areas, unashamed luxury, highest residential standards. Dishwashers, microwaves, washing machines. Log fires. Linen supplied. Pets welcome. [pw! 🐕]
website: www.qualitycottages.co.uk

Parcllyn

Located 1 mile north of Aberporth.

MR & MRS MILLAR, PARK NEWYDD FACH, PARCLLYN, ABERPORTH, CARDIGAN SA43 2DR (01239 811325). Quality self-contained cottage, stunning views over Cardigan Bay, peaceful location, garden, close to dog friendly beach. Parking. Sleeps 2/4. Pets welcome. Terms from £150 to £275 per week. [🐕]

Raglan

Village 7 miles south-west of Monmouth. Remains of 15th century castle lie to the north.

MRS J.E.THOM, THE GRANGE, PENRHOS, RAGLAN, MONMOUTHSHIRE NP15 2LQ (01600 780202). Traditional mixed farm (115 acres). Local golf and fishing, or simply sit and enjoy the views. On the Offa's Dyke footpath. Bring dogs and horses! En suite rooms. Bed and Breakfast from £22 pp. WTB ★★★ [pw!]

PEMBROKESHIRE

See also Colour Advertisement on page 70

Terms quoted in this publication may be subject to increase if rises in costs necessitate

Nolton Cross Caravan Park

WTB ★★★

Small quiet family park, set in open countryside overlooking St Brides Bay. Ideal base for touring Pembrokeshire. Luxury caravans for hire, short breaks available. 15 touring pitches. Open March to November.

Contact Philip and Helen Thomas, Nolton Cross Caravan Park, Nolton, Haverfordwest, Pembrokeshire SA62 3NP

Tel: 01437 710701 Fax: 01437 710329

E-mail: noltoncross@nolton.fsnet.co.uk Website: www.noltoncross-holidays.co.uk

LLANTEGLOS ESTATE

Charming self-contained Woodland Lodges in quiet estate. Wonderful views of coast and country. Safe children's play area. Fully licensed clubhouse. Miles of sandy beaches. Attractions for all ages and interests. For further details/ colour brochure: **(01834) 831677/ 831739**

TONY & JANE BARON, LLANTEGLOS ESTATE, LLANTEG, NEAR AMROTH, PEMBROKESHIRE SA67 8PU

e-mail: llanteglosestate@supanet.com

Scamford Holidays

Richard & Christine White
Scamford Holidays Keeston
Haverfordwest Pembrokeshire SA62 6HN
Tel: 01437 710304
Email:holidays@scamford.com
Web Page www.stdavids.co.uk/folkeston/

Folkeston Hill Holiday Bungalows

A small group of bungalows in a sheltered valley which winds down to the sea at Nolton Haven.

WTB Graded. Pets welcome (no charge)

Cosy cottages and farmhouses near superb beaches and coastal path, around beautiful St Brides Bay in Pembrokeshire.

WTB graded. Sleep 2-11. Pet welcome.

Tel: 0870 7572270

See also Colour Advertisement on page 72

Luxury cottage in quiet lane between St David's and Fishguard, with panoramic views over spectacular coastline. Ideal for walking; rocky coves and safe, sandy beaches nearby. The cottage is fully carpeted, warm, comfortable and very well-equipped, sleeping six in three bedrooms, plus cot. Washing machine, tumble dryer, freezer, microwave and video. Large games room, children's toys, pleasant secure garden. Perfect for early or late holidays, with central heating and double glazing. Parking. Shop one mile. Footpath to beach. Open all year. Terms from £240, including heating and electricity. Brochure on request.

FFYNNON DDOFN **Mrs B. Rees White, Brickhouse Farm, Burnham Road, Woodham Mortimer, Maldon, Essex CM9 6SR (01245 224611)**

The Ridgeway, Saundersfoot, Pembrokeshire SA69 9LA

David & Helen Trimmings, Tel: 01834 814422

Conveniently situated on outskirts of picturesque coastal village with shops, beaches and restaurants. We have large gardens and paddock for pets and owners' relaxation and exercise. Private parking for guests. Warm hospitality in relaxed atmosphere. Non-smoking throughout. All rooms en-suite with central heating, clock-radio, colour TV, hairdryer and hospitality tray. Children 6 to 16 years, half price when sharing with two adults. £1 per day per dog. Brochure and pet guidelines on request.

GUEST HOUSE

Email: enquiries@vinecottageguesthouse.co.uk

Website: www.vinecottageguesthouse.co.uk

When making enquiries please mention FHG Publications

WTB ★★★★★ Farm AA/RAC ◆◆◆◆◆ Award

A warm Welsh welcome awaits you at Lochmeyler, a dairy farm at the centre of the St David's peninsula. Luxury facilities including some four-poster beds for those romantic breaks. Vegetarian and traditional Pembrokeshire farmhouse fare served using home cooked local produce. Children welcome – with play area. Smoking and non-smoking lounges – sorry no smoking in bedrooms. National Park Activity Packs provided to help you to explore our beautiful coastline and countryside. Well-behaved dogs can sleep in bedrooms providing they have their own bedding on the floor, Credit cards accepted. For information pack and brochure please let us have your address. Closed Chrismas and New Year. Telephone for special offers.

Llandeloy, Pen-y-Cwm, Near Solva,
St Davids, Pembrokeshire SA62 6LL
Tel: 01348 837724 • Fax: 01348 837622
Website: www.lochmeyler.co.uk
E-mail: stay@lochmeyler.co.uk

B&B from £20–£27.50pp
Dinners 3 nights ie. Sat, Mon, & Wed @ £15 each.
Children half-price sharing family room.

See also Colour Advertisement on page 71

POWELLS COTTAGE HOLIDAYS, 51 HIGH STREET, SAUNDERSFOOT, PEMBROKESHIRE SA69 9EJ. Many of our top quality holiday properties accept pets. Cottages in Devon, Cornwall, Cotswolds, Pembrokeshire and Heart of England. For colour brochure FREEPHONE 0800 378771 (24 hours).
website: www.powells.co.uk

FBM HOLIDAYS, ST JULIAN STREET, TENBY, PEMBROKESHIRE SA70 7AU (01834 844565; Fax: 01834 844525). Over 300 properties achieving 3, 4 and 5 Star Wales Tourist Board Gradings. Character cottages or breathtaking seafront properties. Family accommodation or quiet retreats for couples where your pets are welcome. Call now for our 86 page colour brochure.
e-mail: info@fbmholidays.co.uk website: www.fbmholidays.co.uk

MR P.W. REES, "QUALITY COTTAGES', CERBID, SOLVA, HAVERFORDWEST, PEMBROKESHIRE SA62 6YE (01348 837871). Cottages set in all coastal areas, unashamed luxury, highest residential standards. Dishwashers, microwaves, washing machines. Log fires. Linen supplied. Pets welcome. [pw! 🐕]
website: www.qualitycottages.co.uk

Amroth

Village on Saundersfoot Bay 2 miles north-east of Saundersfoot.

GRANARY, STABLES AND FURZEWOOD COTTAGE. Just minutes from the safe sandy beach, Amroth village and the Pembrokeshire Coast Path, we welcome children, pets and their owners! Large safe garden play area and fields to walk the dogs. MRS GREEN, FURZEWOOD FARM, AMROTH, PEMBROKESHIRE SA67 8NQ (01834 814674) [Pets £10 per week.]
e-mail: info@amrothcottages.co.uk website: www.amrothcottages.co.uk

Bosherton

Village 4 miles south of Pembroke, bordered by 3 man-made lakes, a haven for wildlife and covered in water lilies in early summer.

MR P. W. REES, "QUALITY COTTAGES", CERBID, SOLVA, HAVERFORDWEST, PEMBROKESHIRE SA62 6YE (01348 837871). Cottages set in all coastal areas, unashamed luxury, highest residential standards. Dishwashers, microwaves, washing machines. Log fires. Linen supplied. Pets welcome. [pw! 🐕]
website: www.qualitycottages.co.uk

Broad Haven

Attractive little resort on St Bride's Bay in the Pembrokeshire Coast National Park. Superb sandy beach; National Park Information Centre.

PEMBROKESHIRE NATIONAL PARK. Sleeps 6. Three-bedroom fully furnished Holiday House. Walking distance sandy beaches and coastal footpath. £120 to £300 per week. MRS L.P. ASHTON, 10 ST LEONARDS ROAD, THAMES DITTON, SURREY KT7 0RJ (020-8398 6349). [🐕]
e-mail: lejash@aol.com

Croes Goch

Hamlet 6 miles north east of St Davids.

MR P. W. REES, "QUALITY COTTAGES", CERBID, SOLVA, HAVERFORDWEST, PEMBROKESHIRE SA62 6YE (01348 837871). Cottages set in all coastal areas, unashamed luxury, highest residential standards. Dishwashers, microwaves, washing machines. Log fires. Linen supplied. Pets welcome. [pw! 🐕]
website: www.qualitycottages.co.uk

Croft

Located 2 miles south west of Cardigan.

CROFT FARM & CELTIC COTTAGES, CROFT NEAR CARDIGAN SA43 3NT (01239 615179). Featured in Daily Mail. Stone barn conversions with luxury indoor heated pool, sauna, spa pool and gym. Colourful gardens, indoor and outdoor play areas. WTB ★★★★★ *SELF CATERING*. Pets welcome. [Pets £15 per week, pw!]
e-mail: croftfarm@compuserve.com website: www.croft-holiday-cottages.co.uk

Fishguard

Small town at end of Fishguard Bay

IVYBRIDGE, DRIM MILL, DYFFRYN, GOODWICK, PEMBROKESHIRE SA64 0FT. (01348 875366, Fax: 01348 872338). Stay at Ivybridge, swim in our heated pool or relax in our comfortable guest lounge. En suite rooms, home cooking, large off road carpark. Pets welcome! [🐕]
e-mail: ivybridge@cwcom.net website: www.ivybridge.cwc.net

FREE or REDUCED RATE entry to Holiday Visits and Attractions – see our READERS' OFFER VOUCHERS on pages 103-118

Haverfordwest

Administrative and shopping centre for the area; ideal base for explorlng National Park Historic town of narrow streets; museum in castle grounds; many fine buildings.

NOLTON HAVEN COTTAGES, NOLTON HAVEN, HAVERFORDWEST SA62 3NH. (01437 710200 or 01437 710298). Quality beach front cottages, sleep 2-6, adjacent sandy beach. Well equipped. Open all year. Winter breaks. [Pets £10 per week].
e-mail: havencottages@hotmail.com

SCAMFORD CARAVAN PARK, KEESTON, HAVERFORDWEST SA62 6HN (Tel & Fax: 01437 710304). 25 luxurious caravans (shower, fridge, microwave, colour TV). Peaceful park near lovely sandy beaches. Super playground. Launderette. Five touring pitches, hook-ups. Modern shower block. [Pets £5 per week]
e-mail: scamfordcaravanpark@talk21.com website: www.scamford-caravan-holidays.co.uk

PHILIP & HELEN THOMAS, NOLTON CROSS CARAVAN PARK, NOLTON, HAVERFORDWEST SA62 3NP (01437 710701; Fax: 01437 710329). Small, quiet, family park set in open countryside overlooking St Brides Bay. Ideal for touring. Luxury caravans for hire; short breaks available. Open March to November. WTB ★★★ Touring and Holiday Park. [🐕]
e-mail: noltoncross@nolton.fsnet.co.uk website: www.noltoncross-holidays.co.uk

Llanteg

Hamlet 4 miles south of Whitland.

TONY & JANE BARON, LLANTEGLOS ESTATE, LLANTEG, NEAR AMROTH, PEMBROKESHIRE SA67 8PU (01834 831677 / 831739). Self-contained Woodland Lodges. Sleep 6. Children's play area. Licensed bar & entertainment. Visitor attractions. Call for brochure. WTB ★★★★ Self Catering
e-mail: llanteglosestate@supanet.com

Lawrenny

Village near River Cresswell estuary, 8 miles south-west of Narberth

MRS VIRGINIA LORT PHILLIPS, KNOWLES FARM, LAWRENNY SA68 0PX (01834 891221). Come and relax with us in our lovely south-facing farmhouse. Listen to the silence and spoil yourselves and your dogs whilst discovering the delights of hidden Pembrokeshire. Walk along the shores of the Estuary which surrounds our organic farm. B&B from £25, Dinner on request. WTB ★★★ [First pet free, others £2 per pet per night.]
e-mail: ginilp@lawrenny.org.uk website: www.lawrenny.org.uk

Manorbier

Unspoiled village on South Pembrokeshire coast near Tenby. Sandy bay and fine coastal walks.

AQUARIUM COTTAGE, THE LOBSTER POT AND ORCHARD END, MANORBIER. Three pleasant country properties half-a-mile from the sea. Detached Cottage (sleeps 6). Ground-floor Flat (sleeps 4). Spacious detached Bungalow, three bedrooms (sleeps 6). Ample parking. Pets welcome. Electricity, central heating, bed linen and towels inclusive. Brochure available from: MRS J. HUGHES, ROSE COTTAGE, MANORBIER, TENBY, PEMBROKESHIRE SA70 7ST (01834 871408). [🐕]
website: www.aquariumcottage.co.uk

Newgale

On St Bride's Bay 3 miles east of Solva. Long beach where at exceptionally low tide the stumps of a submerged forest may be seen.

MR P. W. REES, "QUALITY COTTAGES", CERBID, SOLVA, HAVERFORDWEST, PEMBROKESHIRE SA62 6YE (01348 837871). Cottages set in all coastal areas, unashamed luxury, highest residential standards. Dishwashers, microwaves, washing machines. Log fires. Linen supplied. Pets welcome. [pw! 🐕]
website: www.qualitycottages.co.uk

Newport

Small town at mouth of the River Nyfer, 9 miles south west of Cardigan. Remains of 13th-century castle.

MR P. W. REES, "QUALITY COTTAGES", CERBID, SOLVA, HAVERFORDWEST, PEMBROKESHIRE SA62 6YE (01348 837871). Cottages set in all coastal areas, unashamed luxury, highest residential standards. Dishwashers, microwaves, washing machines. Log fires. Linen supplied. Pets welcome. [pw! 🐕]
website: www.qualitycottages.co.uk

Nolton Haven

Hamlet at head of inlet on St Bride's Bay. Fine coastal views.

FOLKESTON HILL HOLIDAY BUNGALOWS. A small group of bungalows in a sheltered valley which winds down to the sea. WTB Graded. Pets welcome – no charge. Brochure from RICHARD & CHRISTINE WHITE, SCAMFORD HOLIDAYS, KEESTON, HAVERFORDWEST SA62 6HN (01437 710304)
e-mail: holidays@scamford.com website:www.stdavids.co.uk/folkeston/

St Brides

Located on St Brides Bay 7 miles north west of Milford Haven.

ST BRIDES BAY COTTAGES (0870 7572270). Cosy cottages and farmhouses near superb beaches and coastal path, around beautiful St Brides Bay in Pembrokeshire. Sleep 2-11. Pet welcome.WTB graded.
website: www.stbridesbaycottages.com

St Davids

Smallest cathedral city in Britain, shrine of Wales' patron saint. Magnificent ruins of Bishop's Palace. Craft shops, farm parks and museums; boat trips to Ramsey Island.

FELINDRE COTTAGES, PORTHGAIN, ST DAVIDS, PEMBROKESHIRE SA62 5BH (01348 831220). Self-catering cottages overlooking spectacular coast. One well-behaved dog welcome, except August. Near coast path with spectacular cliff walks and pub. WTB graded. [pw! £10 per week]
e-mail: steve@felindrecottages.co.uk website: www.felindrecottages.co.uk

LOWER MOOR COTTAGES, ST DAVIDS. Beautifully restored stone and slate cottages. Panoramic views over coast and open countryside. Near coastal path and sandy beaches. Dishwashers, TV, games rooms, log fire, gas fired central heating. Open all year. Two to seven bedrooms; sleep four to sixteen. WTB ★★★★★. Correspondence: T. M. HARDMAN, HIGH VIEW, CATHERINE STREET, ST DAVIDS, PEMBROKESHIRE. Telephone: LILIAN MARLOW (01437 720616). [Pets £10 per week]
e-mail: enquiries@lowermoorcottages.co.uk

MR P. W. REES, "QUALITY COTTAGES", CERBID, SOLVA, HAVERFORDWEST, PEMBROKESHIRE SA62 6YE (01348 837871). Cottages set in all coastal areas, unashamed luxury, highest residential standards. Dishwashers, microwaves, washing machines. Log fires. Linen supplied. Pets welcome. [pw! 🐕]
website: www.qualitycottages.co.uk

FFYNNON DDOFN, LLANON, LLANRHIAN, NEAR ST DAVIDS. Comfortable, well-equipped cottage with panoramic coastal views. Sleeps 6. Fully carpeted with central heating. Large games room. Open all year. Pets welcome free of charge. Brochure on request from: MRS B. REES WHITE, BRICKHOUSE FARM, BURNHAM RD, WOODHAM MORTIMER, MALDON, ESSEX CM9 6SR (01245 224611). [🐕]

Saundersfoot

Popular resort and sailing centre with picturesque harbour and sandy beach. Tenby 3 miles

VINE COTTAGE, THE RIDGEWAY, SAUNDERSFOOT SA69 9LA (01834 814422). Former Farmhouse close to village and beaches. Central heating, log fires. All rooms en suite. Pets welcome – garden and paddock. Private parking. Non-smoking throughout. AA ◆◆◆◆. WTB ★★★ *GUEST HOUSE*, [pw! Pets £1 per night.]
e-mail: enquiries@vinecottageguesthouse.co.uk website: www.vinecottageguesthouse.co.uk

Solva

Picturesque coastal village with sheltered harbour and excellent craft shops. Sailing and watersports; sea fishing, long sandy beach.

MR P. W. REES, "QUALITY COTTAGES", CERBID, SOLVA, HAVERFORDWEST, PEMBROKESHIRE SA62 6YE (01348 837871). Cottages set in all coastal areas, unashamed luxury, highest residential standards. Dishwashers, microwaves, washing machines. Log fires. Linen supplied. Pets welcome. [pw! 🐕]
website: www.qualitycottages.co.uk

MRS M. JONES, LOCHMEYLER FARM GUEST HOUSE, LLANDELOY, PEN-Y-CWM, NEAR SOLVA, ST DAVID'S, PEMBROKESHIRE SA62 6LL (01348 837724; Fax: 01348 837622). Welcome Host Gold Award. 15 en suite luxury bedrooms, eight in the cottage suites adjacent to the house. All bedrooms non-smoking, with TV, video and refreshment facilities. Children welcome. WTB ★★★★★ *FARM*, AA/RAC ◆◆◆◆◆ [pw! 🐕]

Tenby

Popular resort with two wide beaches. Fishing trips, craft shops, museum. Medieval castle ruins, 13th-century church. Golf, fishing and watersports; boat trips to nearby Caldy Island with monastery and medieval church.

MR P. W. REES, "QUALITY COTTAGES", CERBID, SOLVA, HAVERFORDWEST, PEMBROKESHIRE SA62 6YE (01348 837871). Cottages set in all coastal areas, unashamed luxury, highest residential standards. Dishwashers, microwaves, washing machines. Log fires. Linen supplied. Pets welcome. [pw! 🐕]
website: www.qualitycottages.co.uk

Please mention Pets Welcome when writing to enquire about accommodation

SEE PAGE 81 FOR FULL DETAILS

Caer Beris Manor

Family-owned three star Country House Hotel set in 27 acres of parkland. Free salmon and trout fishing on River Wye (two rods) and on River Irfon. Superb walking and touring. 18 hole Golf Course nearby. Excellent cuisine.
All rooms en suite with telephone, TV and tea making.

DOGS WELCOME!

DB&B £57.50 pppn; £345 weekly; B&B £47.50pp.

Mrs Katharine Smith, Caer Beris Manor, Builth Wells
Powys LD2 3NP Tel: 01982 552601 • Fax: 01982 552586
E-mail: caerberismanor@btinternet.com • Website: www.caerberis.co.uk

Penllwyn Lodges

Set in a 30 acre woodland, all our lodges are individually designed and fully fitted throughout, including colour TV, microwave, full kitchen, bath/shower room and include all bedding. 19 lodges sleeping 2 – 8 people and one cottage which sleeps six. Fishing on the Montgomery canal, River Severn and our own private lake. Quad trekking and pony trekking nearby. Pets welcome. From £175 to £640 per cabin per week including VAT.

Short Breaks. Open all year round.

Tel/Fax 01686 640269 for a colour brochure
Penllwyn Lodges, Garthmyl, Powys SY15 6SB
www.penllwynlodges.co.uk
e-mail: penllwynlodges@supanet.com

See also Colour Advertisement on Outside Back Cover.

The Park Motel

Crossgates
Llandrindod Wells
Powys LD1 6RF
Tel: (01597) 851201
WTB ★★★ *Country Lodge*

Set in 3 acres of beautiful Welsh countryside and close to the famous Elan Valley. Accommodation includes static caravans, touring pitches and fully equipped motel units which have either a twin or double bedroom, shower room, and kitchen with a dinette that converts to a double bed. Sleeping up to 4, they can be booked for either self catering or B&B. On-site facilities include restaurant, bar and snug, games room, outdoor swimming pool, kids play area. Well behaved pets are very welcome.

MADOG'S WELLS, Llanfair Caereinion, Welshpool, Powys SY21 0DE

Beautiful, peaceful valley with lots of wildlife. Two bungalows, both wheelchair accessible, plus 4 berth caravan. Free gas, electricity, linen and cot available. Picnic benches, games room and children's play area. Daily rates available out of main school holidays. Three bedroom bungalow (**WTB ★★★★★**) from £135 to £375. Two bedroom bungalow (**WTB ★★★**) £110 to £310. Open all year. Caravan from £130 to £230 pw. Open April to November. Farmhouse B&B at £20 pppn.

Contact Michael & Ann Reed for further details. Tel/Fax: 01938 810446 e-mail: madogswells@btopenworld.com

See also Colour Advertisement on page 72

Brecon

Main touring centre for National Park. Busy market; Jazz Festival in summer. Brecknock Museum, ruined castle, cathedral of interest. Golf, walking, fishing, canal cruising, pony trekking.

Well-equipped, tastefully decorated and personally supervised, offering the highest standard of cleanliness. Bungalow sleeps 6 and ground floor apartment 2/4 in quiet, accessible rural location in heart of Breacon Beacons National Park. Lawns. Play area. Parking. Short Breaks. Superb walking. Excellent pub food locally. Ideal touring base. WTB ★★★★ / ★★★★★ Brochure: MRS ANN PHILLIPS, TYLEBRYTHOS FARM, CANTREF, BRECON LD3 8LR (Tel & Fax: 01874 665329; mobile: 07977 337523). [pw! £15 per week]
e-mail: ann@wernymarchog.co.uk website: www.wernymarchog.co.uk

ERW YR DANTY, TALYBONT-ON-USK, BRECON LD3 7YN (Tel & Fax: 01874 676498). Attractive village on Taff Trail; ideal location for all outdoor pursuits. Stylish barn conversion with wonderful views. Comfortable accommodation. Bed and Breakfast. Dogs welcome. WTB ★★★. Contact: LAURA KOSTORIS. [Pets £2 per night]
e-mail: kosto@ukonline.co.uk website: www.wiz.to/lifestyle/

GILFACH FARM, SENNYBRIDGE, POWYS LD3 8TY (01874 636818; mobile: 07899 892582). Charming barn conversion offering self-catering accommodation for four on picturesque farm. Fantastic location for walking/riding (Brecon 8 miles). Pets and horses welcome from £2 per night. Linen and fuel included. Open all year. Short Breaks available. From £258 per week.
e-mail: sm@mip.co.uk website: www.breconbeaconsriding.co.uk

Builth Wells

Old country town in lovely setting on River Wye amid beautiful hills. Lively markets; host to Royal Welsh Agricultural Show.

MRS KATHERINE SMITH, CAER BERIS MANOR, BUILTH WELLS LD2 3NP (01982 552601; Fax: 01982 552586). Family-owned country house hotel set in 27 acres of parkland. Free salmon and trout fishing; golf nearby, superb walking and touring. All rooms en suite. WTB/AA ★★★. [🐕]
e-mail: caerberismanor@btinternet.com website: www.caerberis.co.uk

Garthmyl

Situated on A483 between Welshpool and Newtown in unspoilt countryside.

Self-catering log cabins set in 30 acres of unspoilt woodland teeming with wildlife. Central heating, colour TV, microwave etc. Pets Welcome. From £175 – £640 per cabin per week breaks. Apply PENLLWYN LODGES, GARTHMYL, POWYS SY15 6SB or Tel & Fax: (01686 640269) for colour brochure. [Pets £15 per stay]
e-mail: penllwynlodges@supanet.com website: www.penllwynlodges.co.uk

Hay-on-Wye

Small market town at north end of Black Mountains, 15 miles north-east of Brecon.

PETER & OLWEN ROBERTS, YORK HOUSE, CUSOP, HAY-ON-WYE HR3 5QX (Tel & Fax: 01497 820705). Enjoy a relaxing holiday in this elegant Victorian Guest House quietly situated on the edge of Hay, "Town of Books". Excellent walking country for pets. AA ◆◆◆◆. [Pets £5.00 per visit.]
e-mail: roberts@yorkhouse59.fsnet.co.uk website: www.hay-on-wye.co.uk/yorkhouse

MRS E. BALLY, LANE FARM, PAINSCASTLE, BUILTH WELLS LD2 3JS (Tel & Fax: 01497 851605). 17th century farm in rural Radnorshire, five miles Hay-on-Wye. Wonderful walking country. Self-catering apartments and Bed and Breakfast accommodation. A warm welcome for you and your pet(s).WTB ★★★ [🐕]
e-mail: jbally@btclick.com

Llandrindod Wells

Popular inland resort, Victorian spa town, excellent touring centre. Golf, fishing, bowling, boating and tennis. Visitors can still take the waters at Rock Park Gardens.

THE PARK MOTEL, CROSSGATES, LLANDRINDOD WELLS LD1 6RF (01597 851201). In three acres, amidst beautiful countryside near Elan Valley. Static caravans, touring pitches and fully equipped motel units. Licensed restaurant, bar, games room. Swimming pool. Children's play area. Pets welcome. WTB ★★★ [Pets £1 per night, £5 per week]

Llanfair Caereinion

Small town on River Banwy, 8 miles west of Welshpool.

MRS ANN REED, MADOG'S WELLS, LLANFAIR CAEREINION, WELSHPOOL SY21 0DE (Tel & Fax: 01938 810446). Two self-catering bungalows, both wheelchair accessible, plus 4 berth caravan; farmhouse B&B. Astronomy available. WTB ★★★/★★★★★ *SELF-CATERING*. [🐕]
e-mail: madogswells@btopenworld.com

Llangurig

Village on River Wye, 4 miles south-west of Llanidloes. Ideal walking countryside.

MRS J. BAILEY, GLANGWY, LLANGURIG, LLANIDLOES SY18 6RS (01686 440697). Bed, breakfast and evening meals in the countryside. Plenty of walking locally. Prices on request.

Llanidloes

Small town 11 miles south-west of Newtown. Museum of local history and industry in Tudor Old Market Hall.

MR AND MRS ROBERT AND WENDY KNIGHT, BARN VIEW COTTAGES, LLANIDLOES SY18 6PW (01686 413527). A stone and timber-clad barn converted into three self-contained holiday cottages. Idyllic hillside position overlooking magnificent views through the Severn Valley. [🐕]
e-mail: wendy-robert-barn-view-@supanet.com

Machynlleth

Small market town and tourist centre on River Dovey Valley. 16 miles north-east of Aberystwyth

PETS WELCOME at The Wynnstay Hotel in historic Market Town of Machynlleth on the edge of Snowdonia, offering sandy beaches and glorious Welsh Countryside perfect for walking. Award winning food prepared by Chef Gareth Johns. WTB/AA/RAC ★★. Good Food Guide & Good Beer Guide Recommended. (01654 702941). [Pets free in kennels, £5 per night in rooms]
e-mail: info@wynnstay-hotel.com website: www.wynnstay-hotel.com

Rhayader

Small market town on River Wye north of Builth Wells. Popular for angling and pony trekking

OAK WOOD LODGES, LLWYNBAEDD, RHAYADER LD6 5NT (01597 811422). SELF-CATERING LOG CABINS. Luxurious Norwegian log cabins with spectacular views of the Elan Valley and Cambrian Mountains. Walking, pony trekking, mountain biking, fishing and bird watching in idyllic surroundings. WTB ★★★★ SELF CATERING. [Pets £20 per week].

BEST WESTERN ABERAVON BEACH HOTEL

Modern seafront hotel. A warm Welsh welcome awaits you and your pets. 2 miles of flat promenade and a pet friendly beach. Pets Paradise!! And for you..... comfortable rooms, fine cuisine, leisure centre and many local attractions.

Port Talbot, Swansea Bay, SA12 6QP TEL 01639 884949

AA ★★★ RAC ★★★

Cwrt-y-Gaer in the Vale of Usk and Wye Valley

One, four or more dogs welcome FREE. Three self catering units in well converted stone Welsh Longhouse, set in old hilltop fort in 20 acres with fine views across to mountains. Quiet area with good access to many places of interest. Good walking. Open all year. Brochure from Sue & John Llewellyn, Cwrt-y-Gaer, Wolvesnewton, Chepstow, Monmouthshire NP16 6PR Tel: (01291) 650700 E-mail: john.ll@talk21.com All units are WTB ★★★★. One unit is Grade 1 access for the disabled.

CASTLE NARROWBOATS, CHURCH ROAD WHARF, GILWERN, MONMOUTHSHIRE NP7 0EP (01873 830001; Fax: 01873 832341). Discover the beauty of the Brecon Beacons onboard one of our electric or diesel canal boats. 2-8 berth boats, short breaks available. Pets welcome. [Pets £15 per week]
e-mail: castle.narrowboats@btinternet.com website: www.castlenarrowboats.co.uk

Abergavenny

Historic market town at south-eastern gateway to Brecon Beacons National Park. Pony trekking, leisure centre; excellent touring base for Vale of Usk.

CHRISTINE SMITH, THE HALF MOON HOTEL, LLANTHONY, NEAR ABERGAVENNY NP7 7NN (01873 890611). Friendly 17th-Century Hotel. Serves good food and real ale. Enjoy wonderful scenery of Black Mountains. Good base. Walking, pony trekking. B&B accommodation. Dogs welcome. [🐕]
e-mail: halfmoonllanthony@talk21.com

Gower

Britain's first designated Area of Outstanding Natural Beauty with numerous sandy beaches and lovely countryside to explore.

CULVER HOUSE HOTEL, PORT EYNON, GOWER SA3 1NN (01792 390755). Small, friendly Hotel with fabulous food and quality service. Peacefully situated, with superb coast and countryside. En suite, sea views. WTB ★★ Country Hotel. [Pets £2 per night.]
website: www.culverhousehotel.co.uk

Llanmadoc

Village on Gower Peninsula, a secluded area with unspoilt beaches and many bird reserves

MRS A. MAIN, TALLIZMAND, LLANMADOC, GOWER SA3 1DE (01792 386373). Located near the splendid Gower coastline, surrounded by beautiful countryside. Tallizmand has tastefully furnished en suite bedrooms with tea/coffee facilities. Home cooking, packed lunches. Non-smoking. Pets by arrangement. WTB ★★★ Guest House [🐕].

Mumbles

Seaside resort of Swansea to west and north west of Mumbles Head

MUMBLES & SWANSEA Holiday Homes, some with sea views. Flat locations. Well equipped, modern conveniences – carpets throughout. Convenient for beaches, countryside and town's amenities. Personally supervised. WTB ★★★ and ★★★★. Cottage, Flat and Town house available. MRS JEAN GRIERSON, 112 MUMBLES ROAD, BLACKPILL, SWANSEA SA3 5AS (01792 402278). [🐕]

Redbrook on Wye

Village on the River Wye, 3 miles south-east of Monmouth.

OLD BREWERY HOUSE, BREWERY YARD, REDBROOK ON WYE, MONMOUTHSHIRE NP25 4LU (01600 713819). Welcoming en suite accommodation with courtyard garden and private parking. Scenic riverside and off-road walks. Two village pubs serve meals. B&B £55 per person per night. Dogs free. WTB ★★★ [🐕].
e-mail: enquiries@oldbreweryhouse.com website: www.oldbreweryhouse.com

Swansea

BEST WESTERN ABERAVON BEACH HOTEL, PORT TALBOT, SWANSEA BAY SA12 6QP (01639 884949). Modern seafront hotel. A warm Welsh welcome awaits you and your pets. 2 miles of flat promenade and a pet friendly beach. Pets Paradise!! And for you..... comfortable rooms, fine cuisine, leisure centre and many local attractions. AA/RAC ★★★.[🐕]

Wye Valley

Scenic area, ideal for relaxation.

MR & MRS J. LLEWELLYN, CWRT-Y-GAER, WOLVESNEWTON, CHEPSTOW NP16 6PR (01291 650700). 1, 4 or more dogs welcome free. Self-catering, attractively converted stone buildings of Welsh Longhouse. 20 acres, super views of Usk Vale. Brochure. Three units (one suitable for disabled). WTB ★★★★ Welcome Host Gold Award. [🐕 pw!].
e-mail: john.ll@talk21.com website: www.cwrt-y-gaer.co.uk

IRELAND

CO DUBLIN

Dublin

The capital city of Ireland, occupies an attractive site at the head of Dublin Bay. Many places of interest including cathedrals, libraries and many other historic buildings.

IONA HOUSE, 5 IONA PARK, GLASNEVIN, DUBLIN 9 (00 353 8306217/8306473; Fax: 00 353 8306732). Situated near the city centre, en route to Dublin Airport, in one of Dublin's unique Victorian quarters. All double rooms with private shower, colour TV, self-dial telephone and central heating. Comfortable lounge, charming patio. MasterCard, Visa accepted. Contact: JACK AND CONRAD SHOULDICE. ★★★ Guest House. [🐕]
e-mail: conrad.shouldice@btinternet.com

PLEASE MENTION THIS GUIDE WHEN YOU WRITE OR PHONE TO ENQUIRE ABOUT ACCOMMODATION.

IF YOU ARE WRITING, A STAMPED, ADDRESSED ENVELOPE IS ALWAYS APPRECIATED.

CASTLE NARROWBOATS Church Road Wharf, Gilwern, Monmouthshire NP7 0EP

Monmouthshire & Brecon Canal in South Wales. Discover the beauty of the Brecon Beacons onboard one of our electric or diesel canal boats. 2-8 berth boats, short breaks available. Pets welcome. For a free colour brochure call **Castle Narrowboats - Tel: 01873 830001; Fax: 01873 832341**
website: www.castlenarrowboats.co.uk • e-mail: castle.narrowboats@btinternet.com

See also colour Advertisement on page 73

Available from most bookshops, the 2004 edition of **THE GOLF GUIDE** covers details of every UK golf course – well over 2800 entries – for holiday or business golf. Hundreds of hotel entries offer convenient accommodation, accompanying details of the courses – the 'pro', par score, length etc.

In association with 'Golf Monthly' and including Holiday Golf in Ireland, France, Portugal, Spain, The USA, South Africa and Thailand .

£9.99 from bookshops or from the publishers (postage charged outside UK) • FHG Publications, Abbey Mill Business Centre, Paisley PA1 1TJ

PET PRODUCTS

QUALITY DOG COATS

Smart, light and custom designed for every size and breed of dog. Flectalon Thermal, Vent X Breathable Waterproof, Waterproof or Night Time Safety. Choice of Colours. Optional Extras: Tummy Protectors, Rear leg straps.

01271 376115 for a brochure
or www.gillrugs.com for the 'on-line' shop

PLEASE NOTE

All the information in this book is given in good faith in the belief that it is correct. However, the publishers cannot guarantee the facts given in these pages, neither are they responsible for changes in policy, ownership or terms that may take place after the date of going to press. Readers should always satisfy themselves that the facilities they require are available and that the terms, if quoted, still apply.

HOLIDAYS WITH HORSES

A selection of accommodation where horse and owner/rider can be put up at the same address – if not actually under the same roof! We would be grateful if readers making enquiries and/or bookings from this supplement would mention *Pets Welcome!*

ENGLAND

Devon

JAYE JONES & HELEN ASHER,
TWITCHEN FARM, CHALLACOMBE, BARNSTAPLE EX31 4TT
(Tel: 01598 763568)
e-mail: holidays@twitchen.co.uk • website: www.twitchen.co.uk

Comfort for country lovers in Exmoor National Park. All rooms en suite with TV. Meals prepared with local and some organic produce. Stabling £50 per week. Dogs no charge. B&B £22 - £30, DB&B £39.50 - £47.50. ETC ◆◆◆◆

DITTISCOMBE HOLIDAY COTTAGES & STABLES
SLAPTON, KINGSBRIDGE, DEVON TQ7 2QF
(Tel: 01548 521272)
e-mail: info@dittiscombe.co.uk • website: www.dittiscombe.co.uk

Riding, livery and stabling at the Dittiscombe Equestrian Centre. Hack across rolling Devon hills and down traffic-free lanes. Park your horse in the stables and enjoy the freedom of a comfortable self-catering cottage. Beaches nearby. Dogs welcome.

Dorset

MRS L.S. BARNES
LUCKFORD WOOD HOUSE, EAST STOKE, WAREHAM BH20 6AW
(Tel: 01929 463098; Fax: 01929 405715)
e-mail: info@luckfordleisure.co.uk website: www.luckfordleisure.co.uk

Spacious, peaceful surroundings, delightful scenery. B&B luxurious farmhouse. Farmhouse breakfast served in conservatory or dining room. Camping facilities include showers. [Pets £5 per night, £30 per week.]

Durham

MRS P A BOOTH,
IVESLEY EQUESTRIAN CENTRE, IVESLEY, WATERHOUSES, DURHAM DH7 9HB.
(Tel: 0191 373 4324; Fax: 0191 373 4757)
e-mail: ivesley@msn.com • website: ridingholidays-ivesley.co.uk

Beautifully furnished comfortable country house set in 220 acres in Durham but very quiet and rural. Excellent dog exercising facilities. En suite bedrooms. Excellent food. Licensed. Fully equipped Equestrian Centre adjacent.

Hampshire

MRS H.J. BEALE,
HACKNEY PARK, MOUNT PLEASANT LANE, SWAY, LYMINGTON SO41 8LS
(Tel: 01590 682049)

Coach House and two apartments in tranquil setting adjoining the New Forest. Superb walking, riding and driving country. Excellent stabling and grazing.

When making enquiries or bookings, a stamped addressed envelope is always appreciated

Oxfordshire

JUNE AND GEORGE COLLIER
55 NETHERCOTE ROAD, TACKLEY, KIDLINGTON, OXFORD OX5 3AT
(01869 331255; mobile: 07790 338225; Fax: 01869 331670)
e-mail: colliers.bnb@virgin.net

An ideal base for riding - superb network of Bridleways. Stop-over for Claude Duval route. Close to Blenheim. Regular train and bus service. Local Hostelries serve excellent food. ETC ◆◆◆ [🐕]

Somerset

LEONE & BRIAN MARTIN,
RISCOMBE FARM HOLIDAY COTTAGES, EXFORD,
EXMOOR NATIONAL PARK TA24 7NH
(Tel & Fax: 01643 831480)
website: www.riscombe.co.uk (with up-to-date vacancy info.)

Four self-catering stone cottages in the centre of Exmoor National Park. Excellent walking and riding country. Dogs and horses welcome. Open all year. ETC ★★★★

STILEMOOR,
EXFORD, SOMERSET
(Tel & Fax: 01643 831564)
e-mail: info@stilemoorexmoor.co.uk • website: www.stilemoorexmoor.co.uk

Charming, cosy, comfortable bungalow with garden and superb views. Ideally located for walking, fishing, riding. Stabling available. ETC ★★★★

WESTERCLOSE HOUSE,
WITHYPOOL, EXMOOR NATIONAL PARK TA24 7QR
(Tel: 01643 831302)
website: www.westerclose.f9.co.uk

Five cottages including two bungalows in grounds of old hunting lodge overlooking Barle Valley. Dogs and horses welcome. Shop and pub 300 metres. Cosy, quality and peaceful accommodation with excellent riding and superb stables.

JANE STYLES
WINTERSHEAD FARM, SIMONSBATH, EXMOOR, SOMERSET TA24 7LF
(Tel: 01643 831222)
Website: www.wintershead.co.uk

Five tastefully furnished and well-equipped cottages situated in the midst of beautiful Exmoor. Pets welcome, stables and grazing available. Colour brochure on request. ETC ★★★★ [Dogs and horses £12 per week, DIY Livery]

North Yorkshire

PAWS-A-WHILE
KILNWICK PERCY, POCKLINGTON YO42 1UF
Tel:01759 301168; Mobile: 07711 866869)
e-mail: paws.a.while@lineone.net • website: www.pawsawhile.net

Small family B & B set in forty acres of parkland twixt York and Beverley. Fishing, golf, sauna, walking, riding. Pets and horses most welcome. Brochure available. ETC ◆◆◆◆

MEG ABU HAMDAN,
HIGH BELTHORPE, BISHOP WILTON, YORK YO42 1SB
(Tel: 01759 368238; Mobile: 07786 923330)

BHS Approved Livery yard in lovely surroundings. Bring your horse to enjoy the most fabulous hacking over the Yorkshire Wolds, still unspoilt and quiet. Farmhouse B&B. ETC ◆◆◆

SCOTLAND

Argyll & Bute

ENMORE HOTEL
MARINE PARADE, DUNOON, ARGYLL PA23 8HH
(Tel: 01369 702230; Fax: 01369 702148)
e-mail: enmorehotel@btinternet.com • website: www.enmorehotel.co.uk

Small luxury hotel with well-tended grounds, situated overlooking the beautiful Firth of Clyde. Own shingle beach. Promenade and superb walking in the hills and forests within five minutes' drive. STB ★★★★ HOTEL. AA ★★. AA Rosette. [Dogs £4.25 per night, pw!]

Borders

JANE GRAY, SAUGHS FARM COTTAGES,
Saughs Farm, Bailey, Newcastleton, Roxburghshire TD9 0TT
(Tel: 01697 748346/748000; Fax: 01697 748180)
e-mail: skylark@onholiday.co.uk website: www.skylarkcottages.co.uk

Superb character cottages on the Cumbrian/Scottish Borders. Conservation farm. Panoramic views. Stabling facilities. Great for walking, cycling, riding. Children and pets welcome. Open all year. STB ★★★★ Self Catering.

Dumfries & Galloway

RUSKO HOLIDAYS,
GATEHOUSE OF FLEET, CASTLE DOUGLAS DG7 2BS
(Tel: 01557 814215; Fax: 01557 814679)
email: info@ruskoholidays.co.uk • website: www.ruskoholidays.co.uk

Spacious, traditional farmhouse and charming, cosy cottages near beaches, hills and forest park. Lots of off-road riding amid stunning scenery. Stabling and grazing available for your own horse. Beautiful walking and riding country, fishing and tennis. Rates £168 – £799. STB ★★ to ★★★★

WALES

Anglesey & Gwynedd

JUDY HUTCHINGS
TAL-Y-FOEL STUD FARM AND RIDING CENTRE
DWYRAN, ANGLESEY LL61 6LQ
(Tel & Fax: 01248 430377)
e-mail: riding@talyfoel.u-net.com • website: www.tal-y-foel.co.uk

Waterfront location with spectacular views of Snowdonia. Luxury en suite rooms with whirlpool baths. Riding and horse livery, indoor/outdoor arenas, etc. Brochures on application. WTB ★★★★ FARM

DERI ISAF, DULAS BAY LL70 9DX
(01248 410536; Mobile: 077 21 374471)
e-mail: mccreadie@deriisaf.freeserve.co.uk website: www.deriisaf.freeserve.co.uk

Beautiful Victorian Country House standing in 20 acres of woodland, gardens and fields. High standard of accommodation in two family rooms and one double all en suite. Pets welcome. Stabling available. ★★★★

When making enquiries please mention FHG Publications

Carmarthenshire

SIR JOHN'S HILL FARM HOLIDAY COTTAGES
LAUGHARNE, CARMARTHENSHIRE SA33 4TD

(Tel: 01994 427667)
e-mail: liz.handford@sirjohnshillfarm.co.uk • website: www.sirjohnshillfarm.co.uk

Great place to obring your horse or holiday. Stabling and grazing available. Lovely scenic country rides and 7 miles of beach to ride on.

Powys

MRS E. BALLY
LANE FARM, PAINSCASTLE, BUILTH WELLS LD2 3JS
(Tel & Fax: 01497 851605)
e-mail: jbally@btclick.com

Self-Catering and Bed and Breakfast accommodation. Nine good stables and ample grazing in the heart of rural Radnorshire with wonderful open riding. Some cross-country jumps. WTB ★★★

GILFACH EQUITATION & HOLIDAYS
GILFACH FARM, SENNYBRIDGE, POWYS LD3 8TY
(01874 636818; mobile: 07899 892582)
e-mail: sm@mip.co.uk website: www.breconbeaconsriding.co.uk

Charming self-catering accommodation for four plus grazing/stabling for your horse. Excellent equestrian facilities and instruction available. Fantastic riding country.

•• *Some Useful Guidance for Guests and Hosts* ••

Every year literally thousands of holidays, short breaks and overnight stops are arranged through our guides, the vast majority without any problems at all. In a handful of cases, however, difficulties do arise about bookings, which often could have been prevented from the outset.

It is important to remember that when accommodation has been booked, both parties – guests and hosts – have entered into a form of contract. We hope that the following points will provide helpful guidance.

GUESTS:

- When enquiring about accommodation, be as precise as possible. Give exact dates, numbers in your party and the ages of any children.
- State the number and type of rooms wanted and also what catering you require – bed and breakfast, full board etc. Make sure that the position about evening meals is clear – and about pets, reductions for children or any other special points.
- Read our reviews carefully to ensure that the proprietors you are going to contact can supply what you want. Ask for a letter confirming all arrangements, if possible.
- If you have to cancel, do so as soon as possible. Proprietors do have the right to retain deposits and under certain circumstances to charge for cancelled holidays if adequate notice is not given and they cannot re-let the accommodation.

HOSTS:

- Give details about your facilities and about any special conditions. Explain your deposit system clearly and arrangements for cancellations, charges etc. and whether or not your terms include VAT.
- If for any reason you are unable to fulfil an agreed booking without adequate notice, you may be under an obligation to arrange suitable alternative accommodation or to make some form of compensation.

While every effort is made to ensure accuracy, we regret that FHG Publications cannot accept responsibility for errors, omissions or misrepresentations in our entries or any consequences thereof. Prices in particular should be checked because we go to press early. We will follow up complaints but cannot act as arbiters or agents for either party.

A Guide to Pet-Friendly Pubs

ENGLAND

BERKSHIRE

UNCLE TOM'S CABIN
Hills Lane, Cookham Dean, Berkshire (01628 483339).
Dogs allowed throughout.
Pet Regulars: Flossie and Pipa. Free dog biscuit pub.

THE GREYHOUND (known locally as 'The Dog')
The Walk, Eton Wick, Berkshire (01753 863925).
Dogs allowed throughout the pub.
Pet Regulars: Harvey (Retriever), retrieves anything, including Beer mats. KIA - German Shepherd.

THE SWAN
9 Mill Lane, Clewer, Windsor, Berkshire (01753 862069).
Dogs allowed throughout the pub.
Pet Regulars: Mollie (Jack Russell).

THE TWO BREWERS
Park Street, Windsor, Berkshire (01753 855426).
Dogs allowed, public and saloon bars.
Pet Regulars: Harry (Pyrenean) and his mate Molly (Newfoundland) take up the whole bar, 'Bear' (Black Labrador), Tessa (Cocker Spaniel), Rufus (Springer Spaniel), Rosie (Chocolate Labrador), Jessie (Labrador/German Shepherd) and Liz (Malaysian).

BUCKINGHAMSHIRE

WHITE HORSE
Village Lane, Hedgerley, Buckinghamshire SL2 3UY (01753 643225).
Dogs allowed at tables on pub frontage, beer garden (on leads), public bar.

FROG AT SKIRMETT
Skirmett, Henley -on-Thames, Buckinghamshire RG9 6TG (01491 638996)
Dogs welcome, pet friendly.
Pet Regular: Resident cat "Cleo".

GEORGE AND DRAGON
High Street, West Wycombe, Buckinghamshire HP14 3AB (01494 464414)
Pet friendly.

CAMBRIDGESHIRE

YE OLD WHITE HART
Main Street, Ufford, Peterborough, Cambridgeshire (01780 740250).
Dogs allowed in non-food areas.

CHESHIRE

THE GROSVENOR ARMS
Chester Road, Aldford, Cheshire CH3 6HJ (01244 620228)
Pet friendly.
Pet Regulars: resident dog "Sadie" (Labrador).

JACKSONS BOAT
Rifle Road, Sale, Cheshire (0161 973 8549).
Dogs allowed throughout on lead.

CORNWALL

DRIFTWOOD SPARS HOTEL
Trevaunance Cove, St Agnes, Cornwall (01872 552428).
Dogs allowed everywhere except the restaurant.
Pet Regulars: Buster (Cornish Labrador cross with a Seal) - devours anything.

JUBILEE INN
Pelynt, Near Looe, Cornwall PL13 2JZ (01503 220312).
Dogs allowed in all areas except restaurant; accommodation for guests with dogs.

THE MILL HOUSE INN
Trebarwith Strand, Tintagel, Cornwall PL34 0HD (01840 770200).
Pet friendly.

THE MOLESWORTH ARMS HOTEL
Molesworth Street, Wadebridge, Cornwall PL27 7DP (01208 812055).
Dogs allowed in all public areas and in hotel rooms.
Pet Regulars: Thomson Cassidy (Black Lab), Ruby Cassidy and Lola (Black Lab).

CUMBRIA

THE BRITANNIA INN
Elterwater, Ambleside, Cumbria LA22 9HP (015394 37210).
Dogs allowed in all areas except dining room and residential lounge.
Pet Friendly.

THE MORTAL MAN HOTEL
Troutbeck, Windermere, Cumbria LA23 lPL (015394 33193).
Pets allowed everywhere except restaurant.

STAG INN
Dufton, Appleby, Cumbria (017683 51608).
Dogs allowed in non-food bar, beer garden, village green plus B&B and cottage.
Pet Regulars: Toffee (cross between Saluki and Golden Setter); Willow (cross between Great Dane and an Old English Sheepdog); Kim (Weimaraner), best bitter drinker; Toffee (cross between Chihuahua and Papillon – likes beef dinner. Seb 'chats up' Toffee.

WATERMILL INN
School Lane, Ings, Near Staveley, Kendal, Cumbria (01539 821309).
Dogs allowed in beer garden, Wrynose bottom bar.
Pet Regulars: Blot (sheepdog) and Scruffy (mongrel). Both enjoy a range of crisps and snacks. Scruffy regularly drinks Blacksheep special. Pub dogs Misty (Beardie) and Shelley (German Sheperd). Owners cannot walk dogs past pub, without being dragged in! Biscuits and water provided.

DERBYSHIRE

THE GEORGE HOTEL
Commercial Road, Tideswell, Near Buxton, Derbyshire SK17 8NU (01298 871382).
Dogs allowed in snug and around the bar, water bowls provided.

DOG AND PARTRIDGE COUNTRY INN & MOTEL
Swinscoe, Ashbourne, Derbyshire (01335 343183).
Dogs allowed throughout, except restaurant.
Pet Regulars: Include Mitsy (57); Rusty (Cairn); Spider (Collie/GSD) and Rex (GSD).

DEVONSHIRE ARMS
Peak Forest, Near Buxton, Derbyshire SK17 8EJ (01298 23875)
Dogs allowed in bar.
Pet Regulars: Fergie (Collie-cross), known as "The Fireguard".

DEVON

THE SHIP INN
Axmouth, Devon EX12 4AF (01297 21838).
A predominantly catering pub, so dogs on a lead please.
Pet Regulars: Cassie (dog) and Tiger, Whip and Sinbad (cats). Also resident Tawny Owls.

BRENDON HOUSE
Brendon, Lynton, North Devon EX35 6PS (01598 741206).
Dogs very welcome and allowed in tea gardens, guest bedrooms by arrangement.
Owner's dogs - Drummer (Labrador) and Piper (Labrador).

THE BULLERS ARMS
Chagford, Newton Abbot, Devon (01647 432348).
Dogs allowed throughout pub, except dining room/kitchen. "More than welcome".

CROWN AND SCEPTRE
2 Petitor Road, Torquay, Devon TQ1 4QA (01803 328290).
Dogs allowed in non-food bar, family room, lounge. All dogs welcome.
Pet Regulars: Four Jack Russells - Sprocket, Scrappy Doo, Mouse and Minnie Mouse.

THE JOURNEY'S END INN
Ringmore, Near Kingsbridge, South Devon TQ7 4HL (01548 810205).
Dogs allowed throughout the pub except in the dining room.

PALK ARMS INN
Hennock, Bovey Tracey, Devon TQ13 9QS (01626 836584).
Pets welcome.

THE ROYAL OAK INN
Dunsford, Near Exeter, Devon EX6 7DA (01647 252256).
Dogs allowed in bars, beer garden, accommodation for guests with dogs.
Pet Regulars: Cleo and Kizi.

THE POLSHAM ARMS
Lower Polsham Road, Paignton, Devon (01803 558360).
Dogs allowed throughout the pub.
Pet Regulars: Stella (German Shepherd) pub dog; C.J. (West Highland Terrier) loves pork scratchings; Freckles and Dina (German Pointers); Patch, owner brings his supply of dog biscuits and Bracken (German Shepherd).

THE SEA TROUT INN

Staverton, Near Totnes, Devon TQ9 6PA (01803 762274).
Dogs welcome in lounge and public bar, car park tables, beer garden, owners' rooms (but not on beds).
Pet Regulars: Buster (resident dog) partial to drip trays.

THE DEVONSHIRE INN

Sticklepath, Okehampton, Devon EX20 2NW (01837 840626).
Dogs allowed in non-food bar, car park, beer garden, family room and guest rooms.
Pet Regulars: Scampi and Tammy

THE TROUT & TIPPLE

(A386 - Tavistock to Okehampton Road), Parkwood Road, Tavistock,
Devon PL10 0JS (01822 618886)
Dogs welcome at all times in bar, games room and patio.
Pet regulars include: Jet (black Labrador) likes biscuits and his two sons Connor and Fenrhys - sometimes misbehave. Alf (GSD) visits occasionally - but has to stay off the Guinness. Also, our own two dogs Borgia (GBD 57) and Morgan (no brain lurcher).

THE WHITE HART HOTEL

Moretonhampstead, Newton Abbot, Devon TQ13 8NF (01647 440406).
Dogs allowed throughout, except restaurant.
Pet Regulars: Daisy (Collie).

DORSET

THE ANVIL HOTEL

Sailsbury Road, Pimperne, Blandford, Dorset DT11 8UQ (01258 453431).
Pets allowed in bar, lounge and bedrooms.

THE SQUARE AND COMPASS

Swanage, Dorset BH19 3LF (01929 439229).
Well-behaved dogs allowed - but beware of the chickens!

THE NOTHE TAVERN

Barrack Road, Weymouth, Dorset DT4 8TZ (01305 839255).
Pet friendly - well known for allowing pets.
Pet Regulars: get a warm welcome from the pub Alsatian.

DRUSILLA'S INN

Wigbeth, Horton, Dorset (01258 840297).
Well-behaved dogs welcome.

DURHAM

MOORCOCK INN

Hill Top, Eggleston, Teesdale, County Durham DL12 9AU (01833 650395).
Pet Regulars: Thor, the in-house hound dog, and Raymond, the resident hack, welcome all equine travellers; Gem (Jack Russell); Arnie (Ginger Tom); Poppy (Jack Russell); Haflinger - the horse.

TAP AND SPILE

27 Front Street, Framwellgate Moor, Durham DH1 5EE (0191 386 5451).
Dogs allowed throughout the pub.

THE ROSE TREE

Low Road West, Shincliff, Durham DH1 2LY (0191-386 8512).
Pets allowed in bar area only.
Pet Regulars: "Benson" (Boxer), "Ben" (Minature White Poodle) and "Jack" (Pomeranian).

THE SEVEN STARS

High Street North, Shincliff, Durham (0191-384 8454).
Dogs welcome in bar area only.

ESSEX

WHITE HARTE

The Quay, Burnham-on-Crouch, Essex CM0 8AS (01621 782106).
Pets welcome.
Pet Regulars: Resident dog "Tilly" (Collie) and "Elsie" the cat.

THE OLD SHIP

Heybridge Basin, Heybridge, Maldon, Essex (01621 854150).
Dogs allowed throughout pub.

GLOUCESTERSHIRE

THE OLD STOCKS HOTEL

The Square, Stow on the Wold, Gloucestershire GL54 1AF (01451 830666).
Dogs allowed in the beer garden, accommodation for dogs and their owners also available.
Pet Regulars: Ben (Labrador) enjoys bitter from the drip trays and Oscar (Doberman) often gets carried out as he refuses to leave.

THE OLD CROWN

The Green, Uley, Gloucestershire GL11 5SN (01453 861070).
Pets allowed throughout the pub.

GREATER LONDON

THE PHOENIX

28 Thames Street, Sunbury on Thames, Middlesex (01932 785358).
Dogs allowed on lead in non-food bar, beer garden, family room. Capability 2 Grading.
Pet Regulars: "Olly" (57 variety) and Monster (Shihtzu).

THE TIDE END COTTAGE

Ferry Road, Teddington, Middlesex (0208 977 7762).
Dogs allowed throughout the pub.
Pet Regulars: Mimi (Labrador).

HAMPSHIRE

THE SUN
Sun Hill, Bentworth, Alton, Hampshire GU34 5JT (01420 562338)
Pets welcome throughout the pub.
Pet Regualrs: "Rover" (Black Labrador) and "Dilweed" the cat.

HIGH CORNER INN
Linwood, Near Ringwood, Hampshire BH24 3QY (01425 473973).
Dogs, horses and even goats are catered for here.

THE CHEQUERS
Ridgeway Lane, Lower Pennington, Lymington, Hants (01590 673415).
Dogs allowed in non-food bar, outdoor barbecue area (away from food).
Pet Regulars: Rusty Boyd - parties held for him.

THE VICTORY
High Street, Hamble-le-Rice, Southampton, Hampshire (023 80 453105).
Dogs allowed.

HERTFORDSHIRE

THE BLACK HORSE
Chorley Wood Common, Dog Kennel Lane, Rickmansworth, Herts (01923 282252).
Dogs very welcome and allowed throughout the pub, on a lead.

THE RED LION
Chenies Village, Rickmansworth, Hertfordshire WD3 6ED (01923 282722).
Pets welcome in bar area only.
Pet Regulars: Resident dog "Bobby" (Terriers mixture), "Moss" and "Luke" (Boxer).

THE ROBIN HOOD AND LITTLE JOHN
Rabley Heath, near Codicote, Hertfordshire (01438 812361).
Dogs allowed in non-food bar, car park tables, beer garden.
Pet Regulars: Bonnie (Labrador), beer-mat catcher. The locals of the pub have close to 50 dogs between them, most of which visit from time to time. The team includes a two Labrador search squad dispatched by one regular's wife to indicate time's up. When they arrive he has five minutes' drinking up time before all three leave together.

KENT

KENTISH HORSE
Cow Lane, Mark Beech, Edenbridge, Kent (01342 850493).
Dogs allowed in reserved area.

THE OLD NEPTUNE
Marine Terrace, Whitstable, Kent CT5 lEJ (01227 272262).
Dogs allowed in beach frontage.

THE SWANN INN
Little Chart, Kent TN27 OQB (01233 840702).
Dogs allowed - everywhere except restaurant.

LANCASHIRE

ASSHETON ARMS
Downham, Clitheroe, Blackburn, Lancashire BB7 4BJ (01200 441227).
Dogs welcome.

MALT'N HOPS
50 Friday Street, Chorley, Lancashire PR6 0AH (01257 260967).
Dogs allowed throughout pub if kept on a lead.
Pet Regulars: Mork – says please for bag of crisps and Zac - likes his pint of beer.

LINCOLNSHIRE

THE HAVEN INN
Ferry Road, Barrow Haven, North Lincolnshire DN19 7EX (01469 530247).
Dogs allowed in the public bar, beer garden, and bedrooms on their own bed/blanket.

THE BLUE DOG INN
Main Street, Sewstern, Grantham, Lincs NG33 5QR (01476 860097).
Dogs allowed.
Pet Regulars: The Guv'nor (Great Dane), best draught-excluder in history; Cassie (Scottie) shares biscuits with pub cats; Jemma (98% Collie), atmosphere lapper-upper. Spud and Nelson – Terriers. Also two cats: Fred and Brahms.

MERSEYSIDE

THE SCOTCH PIPER
Southport Road, Lydiate, Merseyside (0151 526 0503).
Dogs allowed throughout the pub.

MIDLANDS

AWENTSBURY HOTEL
21 Serpentine Road, Selly Park, Birmingham B29 7HU (0121 472 1258).
Dogs allowed.
Pet Regulars: Well-behaved dogs welcome.

NORFOLK

THE OLD RAILWAY TAVERN
Eccles Road, Quidenham, Norwich, Norfolk NR16 2JG (01953 888223).
Dogs allowed in non-food bar, beer garden, must be on lead.
Pet Regulars: Roscow (Poodle) and pub dogs Flo (Scottish Terrier) and Benji (Jack Russell).

THE HOSTE ARMS
The Green, Burnham Market, King's Lynn, Norfolk PE31 8HD (01328 738777).
Dogs allowed throughout the pub.
Pet Regulars: "Augustus" and "Sweep" (Black Labradors).

THE ROSE AND CROWN
Nethergate Street, Harpley, King's Lynn, Norfolk (01485 520577).
Dogs allowed in non-food bar, car park tables. .

OXFORDSHIRE

THE BELL
Shenington, Banbury, Oxfordshire OX15 6NQ (01295 670274).
Pets allowed throughout.
Pet Regulars: Resident pub dogs "Oliver" (Great Dane) and "Daisy" (Labrador).

THE PLOUGH INN
High Street, Finstock, Chipping Norton, Oxfordshire (01993 868333).
Dogs more than welcome.
Pet Regulars: Resident dogs - "Jodi", "Charlie" and "Rosie" (Poodles); "Henry","Gertie" (Beagles) and "Zac" (Sheepdog) are regular visitors.

THE BELL INN
High Street, Adderbury, Oxon (01295 810338).
Dogs allowed throughout the pub with the exception of the restaurant and letting rooms.
Owner's dog: Elsa (Black Labrador).

SHROPSHIRE

THE TRAVELLERS REST INN
Church Stretton, Shropshire (01694 781275).
Well-mannered pets welcome - but beware of the cats!

LONGMYND HOTEL
Cunnery Road, Church Stretton, Shropshire SY6 6AG (01694 722244).
Dogs allowed in owners' hotel bedrooms but not in public areas.
Pet Regulars: Bruno and Frenzie; and owner's dogs, Sam and Sailor.

SOMERSET

CASTLE OF COMFORT HOTEL
Dodington, Nether Stowey, Bridgwater, Somerset TA5 1LE (01278 741264).
Pet friendly.

THE SPARKFORD INN
High Street, Sparkford, Somerset BA22 7JN (01963 440218).
Dogs allowed in bar areas but not in restaurant; safe garden and car park.

THE BUTCHERS ARMS
Carhampton, Somerset (01643 821333).
Dogs allowed in bar. B&B accommodation available.

HOOD ARMS
Kilve, Somerset TA5 1EA (01278 741210)
Pets welcome.

THE SHIP INN
High Street, Porlock, Somerset (01643 862507).
Dogs allowed throughout and in guests' rooms.
Pet Regulars: Include Silver (Jack Russell); Sam (Black Lab) and Max (Staffordshire). Bubbles and Monty (Pugs) are residents.

SUFFOLK

THE KINGS HEAD
High Street, Southwold, Suffolk IP18 6AD (01502 724517).
Well-behaved dogs welcome.

SIX BELLS AT BARDWELL
The Green, Bardwell, Bury St Edmunds IP31 1AW (01359 250820).
Dogs allowed in guest bedrooms but not allowed in bar and restaurant.

SURREY

THE PLOUGH
South Road, Woking, Surrey GU21 4JL (01483 714105).
Pets welcome throughout the pub.
Pet Regulars: Resident cats "Dixie" and "Bagerrha"

THE SPORTSMAN
Mogador Road, Mogador, Surrey (01737 246655).
Adopted dogs congregate at this pub.
Pet Regulars: "Ziggy" (Mongrel) and "Max" (German Shepherd).

THE CRICKETERS
12 Oxenden Road, Tongham, Farnham, Surrey (01252 333262).
Dogs allowed in beer garden on lead.

SUSSEX

THE FORESTERS ARMS
High Street, Fairwarp, Near Uckfield, East Sussex TN22 3BP (01825 712808).
Dogs allowed in the beer garden and at car park tables, also inside.
Dog biscuits always available.

THE PLOUGH
Crowhurst, Near Battle, East Sussex TN33 9AY (01424 830310).
Dogs allowed in non-food bar, car park tables, beer garden. .

QUEENS HEAD
Village Green, Sedlescombe, East Sussex (01424 870228).
Dogs allowed throughout the pub.

THE SLOOP INN
Freshfield Lock, Haywards Heath, West Sussex RH17 7NP (01444 831219).
Dogs allowed in public bar and garden.

THE SMUGGLERS' ROOST
125 Sea Lane, Rustington, West Sussex BN16 2SG (01903 785714).
Dogs allowed in non-food bar, at car park tables, in beer garden, family room.
Pet Regulars: Skip; Malcolm (Bull Mastiff); PJ and Mel (Staffs); Leo (Border Terrier), forms instant affections with anyone who notices him; Tim (King Charles Spaniel), quite prepared to guard his corner when food appears. The landlord owns an Alsatian.

THE SPORTSMAN'S ARMS
Rackham Road, Amberley, Near Arundel, West Sussex BN18 9NR (01798 831787).
Dogs allowed in the bar area.

WILTSHIRE

THE HORSE AND GROOM
The Street, Charlton, Near Malmesbury, Wiltshire (01666 823904).
Dogs welcome in bar.
Pet Regulars: Buster (Basset Hound); Troy (black Labrador).

THE PETERBOROUGH ARMS
Dauntsey Lock, Near Chippenham, Wiltshire SN15 4HD (01249 890409).
Guide dogs only, welcome in bar.
Pub dog - Bonny (Collie).

THE THREE HORSESHOES
High Street, Chapmanslade, Near Westbury, Wiltshire (01373 832280).
Dogs allowed in non-food bar and beer garden.
Resident Pets: Include Oscar (dog) and two cats. Three horses overlooking the beer garden.

YORKSHIRE

BARNES WALLIS INN
North Howden, Howden, East Yorkshire (01430 430639).
Guide dogs only

KINGS HEAD INN
Barmby on the Marsh, East Yorkshire DN14 7HL (01757 630705).
Dogs allowed in non-food bar.
Pet Regulars: Many and varied!

THE FORESTERS ARMS
Kilburn, North Yorkshire YO6 4AH (01347 868386).
Dogs allowed throughout, except restaurant.
Pet Regulars: Ainsley (Black Labrador).

NEW INN HOTEL
Clapham, Near Settle, North Yorkshire LA2 8HH (015242 51203).
Dogs allowed in bar, beer garden, bedrooms.

SIMONSTONE HALL
Hawes, North Yorkshire DL8 3LY (01969 667255).
Dogs allowed except dining area.
Dogs of all shapes, sizes and breeds welcome.

THE SPINNEY
Forest Rise, Balby, Doncaster, South Yorkshire DN4 9HQ (01302 852033).
Dogs allowed throughout the pub.
Pet Regulars: Shamus (Irish Setter), pub thief - fair game includes pool balls, beer mats, crisps, beer, coats, hats - jumped 15 feet off pub roof with no ill effect; Wyn (Labrador) a guide dog and Buster (Staff).

THE ROCKINGHAM ARMS
8 Main Street, Wentworth, Rotherham, South Yorkshire S62 7LO (01226 742075).
Pets welcome.
Pet Regulars: Sheeba (Springer Spaniel), Charlie and Gypsy (Black Labradors), Sally (Alsatian) and Rosie (Jack Russell).

THE GOLDEN FLEECE
Lindley Road, Blackley, near Huddersfield, West Yorkshire (01422 372704).
Dogs allowed in non-food bar.
Pet Regulars: Holly and Honey (Border Collies).

CHANNEL ISLANDS/JERSEY

LA PULENTE INN
La Pulente, St Brelade, Jersey (01534 744487).
Dogs allowed in public bar.
Pet Regulars: Taz (Golden Labrador). Owners dog - Ben (cross between Alsatian and black Labrador).

WALES

ANGLESEY & GWYNEDD

THE GRAPES HOTEL
Maentwrog, Blaenau Ffestiniog, Gwynedd LL41 4HN (01766 590365).
Pets allowed in bar area only.

THE BUCKLEY HOTEL
Castle Street, Beaumaris, Isle of Anglesey LL58 8AW (01248 810415).
Dogs allowed throughout the pub, except in the dining room and bistro.
Pet Regulars: Cassie (Springer Spaniel) and Rex (mongrel), dedicated 'companion' dogs, also Charlie (Spaniel).

NORTH WALES

THE WEST ARMS HOTEL
Llanarmon Dyffryn Ceiriog, Llangollen, North Wales LL20 7LD (01691 600665).
Welcome pets.

PEMBROKESHIRE

THE FARMERS
14-16 Goat Street, St David's, Pembrokeshire (01437 721666).
Pets welcome in the pub area only.

POWYS

SEVERN ARMS HOTEL
Penybont, Llandrindod Wells, Powys LD1 5UA (01597 851224).
Dogs allowed in the bar, but not the restaurant, and in the rooms - but not on the beds.

FREE or REDUCED RATE entry to Holiday Visits and Attractions – see our READERS' OFFER VOUCHERS on pages 103-118

SCOTLAND

ABERDEEN, BANFF & MORAY

THE CLIFTON BAR
Clifton Road, Lossiemouth, Moray (01343 812100).
Dogs allowed throughout pub.
Pet Regulars: Include Murphy (Miniature Dachshund), Stella, Jimmy (Collie); Poppy (Cocker Spaniel) is our resident dog.

ROYAL OAK
Station Road, Urquhart, Elgin, Moray (01343 842607).
Dogs allowed throughout pub.
Pet Regulars: Jack (Collie).

ARGYLL & BUTE

CAIRNDOW STAGECOACH INN
Cairndow, Argyll PA26 8BN (01499 600286).
Pet regulars: Our own dog Rocky is a Golden Labrador.

THE BALLACHULISH HOTEL
Ballachulish, Argyll PA39 4JY (01855 811606).
Dogs allowed in the lounge, beer garden and guests' bedrooms, excluding food areas.

BORDERS

CULGRUFF HOUSE HOTEL
Crossmichael, Castle Douglas, Kirkcudbrightshire DG7 3BB (01556 670230).
Dogs allowed in family room, guest bedrooms, but must be kept on leads outside.
Pet Regulars: A cross-section of canine visitors.

EDINBURGH & LOTHIANS

JOHNSBURN HOUSE
Johnsburn Road, Balerno, Lothians EH14 7BB (0131-449 3847).
Pets welcome in bar area only.
Pet Regulars: Resident dog "Topaz" (Great Dane).

LAIRD & DOG
Lasswade, Midlothian (0131-663 9219).
Dogs allowed in bar.
Pet Regulars: Many pet regulars. Drinking bowls .

HIGHLANDS

CLUANIE INN
Skye & Lochalsh, Glenmoriston, Inverness-shire IV63 7YW (01320 340238).
Pets welcome throughout the pub.

PERTH & KINROSS

FOUR SEASONS HOTEL
St Fillans, Perthshire (01764 685333).
Dogs allowed in all non-food areas.

Index of Towns and Counties

OTHER FHG TITLES FOR 2004

FHG Publications have a large range of attractive holiday accommodation guides for all kinds of holiday opportunities throughout Britain. They also make useful gifts at any time of year. Our guides are available in most bookshops and larger newsagents but we will be happy to post you a copy direct if you have any difficulty. POST FREE for addresses in the UK. We will also post abroad but have to charge separately for post or freight.

The original
Farm Holiday Guide to COAST & COUNTRY HOLIDAYS in England, Scotland, Wales and Channel Islands. Board, Self-catering, Caravans/Camping, Activity Holidays.

BED AND BREAKFAST STOPS
Over 1000 friendly and comfortable overnight stops. Non-smoking, Disabled and Special Diets Supplements.

BRITAIN'S BEST HOLIDAYS
A quick-reference general guide for all kinds of holidays.

Recommended
WAYSIDE AND COUNTRY INNS of Britain
Pubs, Inns and small hotels.

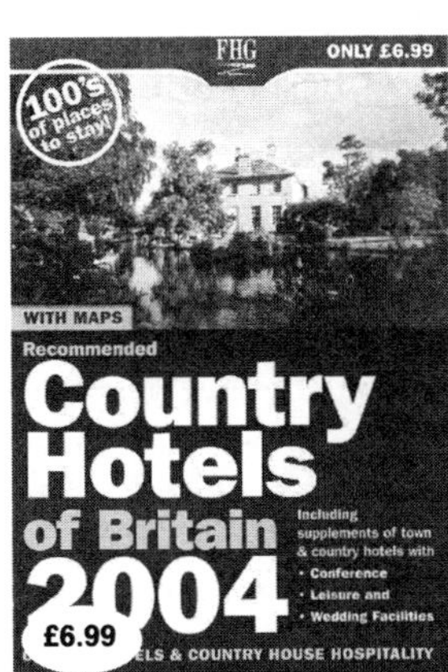

Recommended
COUNTRY HOTELS
of Britain
Including Country Houses, for the discriminating.

Recommended
SHORT BREAK HOLIDAYS IN BRITAIN
"Approved" accommodation for quality bargain breaks.

CHILDREN WELCOME! ☐
Family Holidays and Days Out guide.
Family holidays with details of amenities for children and babies.

The FHG Guide to ☐
CARAVAN & CAMPING HOLIDAYS,
Caravans for hire, sites and holiday parks and centres.

SELF-CATERING HOLIDAYS ☐
in Britain
Over 1000 addresses throughout for self-catering and caravans in Britain.

The GOLF GUIDE –
Where to play Where to stay £9.99
In association with GOLF MONTHLY. Over 2800 golf courses in Britain with convenient accommodation. Holiday Golf in France, Portugal, Spain, USA, South Africa and Thailand. ☐

Tick your choice and send your order and payment to

FHG PUBLICATIONS, ABBEY MILL BUSINESS CENTRE, SEEDHILL, PAISLEY PA1 1TJ
TEL: 0141- 887 0428; FAX: 0141- 889 7204
e-mail: fhg@ipcmedia.com

FHG

Deduct 10% for 2/3 titles or copies; 20% for 4 or more.

Send to: NAME ....

ADDRESS ....

....

....

POST CODE ....

I enclose Cheque/Postal Order for £ ....

SIGNATURE..DATE ....

Please complete the following to help us improve the service we provide. How did you find out about our guides?:

☐ Press ☐ Magazines ☐ TV/Radio ☐ Family/Friend ☐ Other

Your dog-friendly guide to Hertfordshire

There's far more to Hertfordshire than the beginnings of the M25 and London commuter housing estates; discover the county's more secluded spots with your dog.

The Ashridge estate

by Mary Welsh

This pleasing walk descends from an elegant monument to a pretty ancient village, then continues along part of a prehistoric track over the Chiltern Hills, returning through the famous beeches that provide a dramatic backdrop to the village.

Walk 1

Route planner

1 From the parking area walk along the road leading to the monument, then bear left of it to pass the National Trust visitor centre and shop. The thousands of acres of woodland of the Ashridge estate are now in the care of the Trust and are open to the public. Walk down the rough track and, at the Y-junction, take the right fork. Go on down to join the road and turn right to come to the much-photographed duck pond bordered by picturesque cottages. Go on towards the grey flintstone church, which you may wish to visit.

2 Beyond the church, take the footpath on the right, signposted Pitstone Hill. After the next stile, pass through a gate on the left to walk beside a barn. Stroll on along the stiled track where, in autumn, the blackthorn bushes are heavy with deep blue sloes. Ignore all left and right turns and head on alongside the golf course. At the top of the slope pass on through a small wood, where the dog can have some freedom and enjoy a few good

e picturesque duck pond at Aldbury is much otographed and is bordered by attractive cottages.

In autumn the blackthorn bushes are heavy with sloes.

The Bridgewater monument was erected in 1832.

Pic: Don Morgan.

Enjoying the woodland of the Ashridge estate.

sniffs. Bear left at a signpost and then right to join the Ridgeway.

3 Climb the steps and remain on the airy ridge with glorious woodland about you. Then follow the chalky Ridgeway out on to the open sheep-cropped downland turf and go over Pitstone Hill, with its superb views. Keep to the right of a knoll and then gently descend to a gate to the road. Cross and pass through another gate, then carry on along the delightful way to another. Beyond, turn right and saunter along this pretty route through the glorious Chiltern countryside.

4 At Clipper Down bear left following the arrowed way, part of the boundary trail of the Ashridge estate, which offers more freedom for the dog. From now on no instructions are needed as you stroll easily through the fine woodland, where great trails of chalk-loving clematis grow — known locally as 'daddy's beard'. This delightful way takes you all the way back to the foot of the monument. If you have any energy left why not climb the winding staircase to the top, perhaps leaving the dog in the charge of one of the party below?

Fact file

Distance: 6 miles.

Time: 3 hours.

Map: Explorer 181.

Start/parking: Parking area on the south side of the road leading to the foot of the Bridgewater monument; grid reference 975128. This lies between the villages of Northchurch and Ringshall, just off the B4506, three miles north of the A41.

Terrain: Grassy tracks over the downs; chalk and flint paths in the woodland. After rain some paths can be slippery.

Nearest town: Berkhamsted.

Public toilets: At visitor centre.

Refreshments: The Greyhound pub; Farm Tea Room; Trooper's restaurant; and The Valiant Trooper pub, all at Aldbury.

Public transport: Trains from Euston to Tring, bus to monument (summer only). For further information, contact tel. 0845 605 0600. Alternatively walk (it's under a mile) from Tring Station to Aldbury and start the walk from the village.

Suitable for: Everyone, but keep dogs under close control where there is stock.

● This is a chalkland walk and water is in short supply, so take plenty and a container for your dog to drink from.

Your dog-friendly guide to

Deeside & Angus

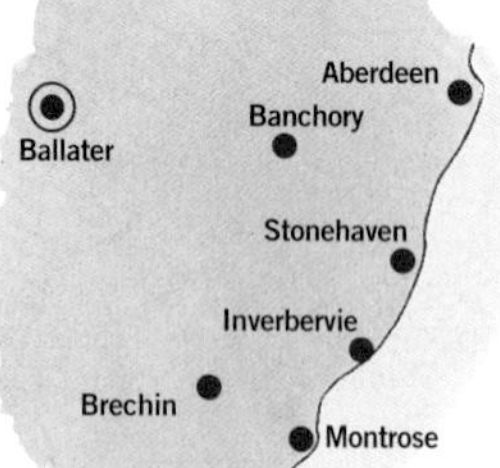

Explore the rugged, romantic landscape of central Scotland with this walk alongside the famed River Dee.

Ballater, Deeside

by Mary Welsh

This is a very attractive, short walk, with fine open views of the surrounding hills, skirting the golf course and following the banks of the river. It is a favourite dog walk offering plenty of interesting smells and the opportunity for lots of drinks and swims.

Walk 2

Route planner

1 Leave Ballater's square heading in a south-easterly direction and walk on along the A93, with the village's fine church to your left. Go along Bridge Street until you come to Ballater Bridge. Descend the waymarked steps, to the right of the bridge, to join the path beside the Dee. Turn right and walk upstream, keeping a look out for dippers bobbing on the rocks in, or close to, the water. Trees line the bank of the wide, surging, peat-stained river. Go through a gate where a sign welcomes walkers and on through the next gate to continue along a wide track in front of houses. Pass beside a caravan site and, at the Y-junction, take the left branch.

2 Walk along the signposted footpath that runs between the golf course and the river. At this point all dogs

The town of Ballater became popular with those who wanted to 'take the waters'.

The imposing Ballater Bridge spans the River Dee which is famous for its salmon.

The enchanting River Dee.

must be on the lead — watch out for flying golf balls! Eventually the path drifts away from the golf course and winds on beside alders; on either side heather and birch scrub flourish. The path then comes close beside the golf course again; from here you can see Lochnagar. Continue on beside the lovely Dee to reach a car park, with picnic tables set out among the trees.

3 Turn right to walk through the trees and join Old Line Road and then Dundarroch Road. Continue left up Invercauld Road to the A93. Now walk right to return to the village.

Your dog will find lots of interesting smells beside the River Dee.

Fact file

Distance: 2 miles.

Time: 1½ hours.

Map: Explorer 388.

Start/parking: Station Square car park, Ballater; grid reference 370958.

Terrain: Easy walking all the way.

Nearest village: Ballater.

Refreshments: The Alexandra Hotel, Ballater, allows dogs in the pub or you can tie them up outside; The Glen Lui in Invercauld Road has its own resident canine — Misty — and dogs are welcome here.

Public toilets: In the square.

Public transport: For rail information contact tel. 0345 484950; for bus information contact tel. 01224 212266 or tel. 01224 288828.

Stiles: One.

Suitable for: All.

Your dog-friendly guide to Somerset

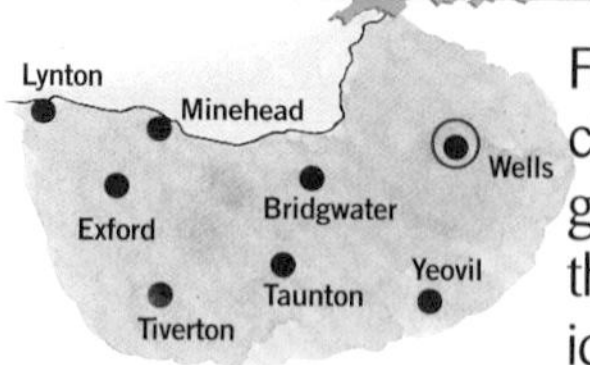

Famous for its Exmoor National Park, Cheddar cheese, cider, and as being the stamping ground of King Arthur and Alfred the Great, this west 'county of summer' provides the idyllic setting for wonderful dog walks.

Wells and Pen Hill

by Nick Channer

Discover one of England's smallest cathedral cities before climbing into the magnificent Mendips, a landscape of rolling hills, wooded combes and sleepy villages. En route there are impressive views of Wells Cathedral and glimpses of Glastonbury Tor.

Route planner

1 With your back to the west front of Wells Cathedral, turn right towards the city's museum and right again to Chain Gate. Turn immediately left into Vicar's Close and make for a narrow alleyway and some steps at the top. Turn right at the road and then left into College Road. Follow it to the A39.

2 Turn right, pass a bus stop and swing left into Walcombe Lane. Follow the road alongside a wall and woodland, passing Walcombe Farmhouse. Keep right at the fork and then turn right at the next junction. Take the bridleway on the right, further up the hill.

3 Follow the sunken woodland path and further up you'll catch glimpses of Glastonbury Tor on the left. Turn sharp right at a junction and follow the path along the grassy slopes and round

Wells is England's smallest city, its name originating from the three springs in the old Bishop's Palace.

Vicar's Close is one of the finest complete medieval streets in the UK.

Wells Cathedral is magnificent and definitely worth seeing.

to the right by a footpath sign. Keep to the hedgerow on the right and make for an intersection of tracks further down.

4 Turn left, pass Pen Hill Farm and continue ahead on the tarmac track. Pass a house called 'Gollege' and continue to a T-junction. Turn left and walk along to the A39. Cross over by a cottage, turn right and follow the path down the field boundary to a gate. Keep ahead along the woodland edge with a stream on the right. Cross a footbridge and follow the path just outside the trees. Rejoin the woodland and head up the grassy slope to a seat.

Chain Gate is one of Wells' most striking landmarks.

5 Turn right here and keep a house on the left. Follow the grassy path to a stile and cross the field, keeping to the left perimeter. Avoid the first stile and cross the second. Turn right and skirt the field to a kissing gate. Follow stone steps down through trees to a stream and cross a stone bridge.

6 Go over the junction and uphill, signposted Hawkers Lane. On reaching the field edge, keep left to a stile and cut through trees and alongside a fence. Pass through a wrought iron kissing gate and continue ahead in the field. Avoid a gate on the right and follow the path as it curves left in line with the boundary.

7 Walk down towards some houses and exit to the road. Turn left and walk through the housing estate to the B3139. Turn right here and return to the centre of Wells, passing the district hospital.

Fact file

Distance: 6 miles.

Time: 3 hours.

Map: OS Explorer 141.

Start: Wells Cathedral in the centre of the city.

Nearest towns: Wells, Shepton Mallet and Glastonbury.

Refreshments: Plenty of choice in Wells.

Public transport: Contact Traveline, tel. 0870 608 2608.

Stiles: Three.

Suitable for: Fit adults, dogs and older children. Some tracks and paths are suitable for dogs off the lead.

Your dog-friendly guide to

Nottinghamshire

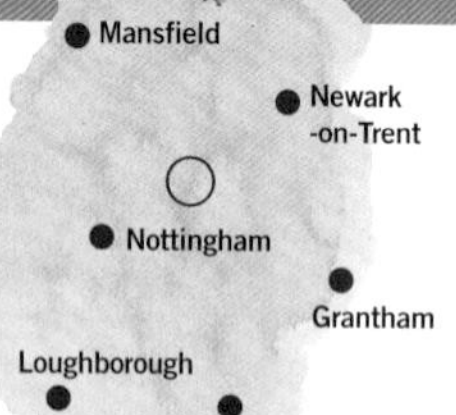

Famous as the legendary home of Robin Hood, and for its industrial heritage which inspired the novelist D.H. Lawrence, this county also has lovely countryside which our walk explores.

Gunthorpe and the River Trent

by Paul and Sandy Biggs

This is a walk to linger over, as there is so much to see and enjoy. Lovely countryside to savour, cream teas halfway round and a wonderful waterside walk beside the River Trent make this a grand day out for both the two and four-legged walkers.

Walk 4

Route planner

1 From the Unicorn Hotel walk away from the river along the road going through Gunthorpe village. Turn right into Peck Lane and continue ahead into open countryside. At the end of the lane locate a public footpath signpost in the hedge. Join the field path and walk ahead over several fields to the next signpost.

2 Turn right and carry on along a field footpath before turning left by crossing a footbridge over a stream. Go ahead, cross another footbridge and keep going in the same direction. Soon a third footbridge is crossed over Carr Dyke, where a stile leads you out on to a grassy field. This path now takes you ahead past the old mill to the main street in Caythorpe village. Turn right, and walk along Hoveringham Road to a public footpath signpost at Brackenhill.

3 Take the access drive towards the farm buildings then climb a stile to join a grassy path. Continue on over a couple of stiles to a track. Go past Fernhill House then, at the end of the track, go into a field. Turn right, then walk along the field edge following it round to the left, before

The Unicorn Hotel is the starting point for the walk.

The old watermill at Caythorpe is worth a visit.

Take great care when going past Gunthorpe Lock and remember that dogs must be on a lead.

going alongside a stream. Cross a footbridge and rejoin the field path. Continue ahead and in due course you'll reach Boat Lane, Hoveringham. Turn right and walk away from the village making for the River Trent. Follow the road around past Ferry Farm and the car park for the country park.

4 Continue along the road by the river to a public bridleway signpost. Go through the white gate to join the Trent Valley Way and a picturesque riverside path. Climb a large wooden stile and continue ahead on the riverside path. Cross Carr Dyke stream, which flows into the river, then go through two metal gates. Here a notice says that dogs must be kept on a lead — please comply. Continue ahead to reach the massive weir by Gunthorpe Lock.

5 Bear right away from the weir and pass the automatic lock gates. Join the access road passing the marina workshop and the Toll House Restaurant. Rejoin the riverside path by the moorings to return to the Unicorn Hotel.

The River Trent pictured from Ferry Farm, Hoveringham.

Fact file

Distance: 5 miles.

Time: 3 hours including stops.

Maps: Explorer 260, Landranger 129.

Start/parking: The Unicorn Hotel, Gunthorpe; grid reference SK683438; plenty of parking in Gunthorpe away from the hotel.

Terrain: Lovely picturesque walk by the River Trent. The whole route is well waymarked with no climbs.

Nearest town: Southwell.

Refreshments: There is a good selection of pubs and restaurants in Gunthorpe and Caythorpe. However, the Parlour Tea Rooms at Ferry Farm Country Park near Hoveringham are highly recommended. Dogs are allowed in the park but only outside the tea rooms. Gunthorpe Lock Tea Rooms also allow dogs outside at picnic tables.

Public toilets: None.

Public Transport: An hourly Nottingham to East Bridgford service, operated by Trent Buses,calls at Gunthorpe; contact Traveline, tel. 0870 608 2608.

Stiles: Less than ten; large dogs may need lifting over some.

Suitable for: All.

Your dog-friendly guide to

Outer London

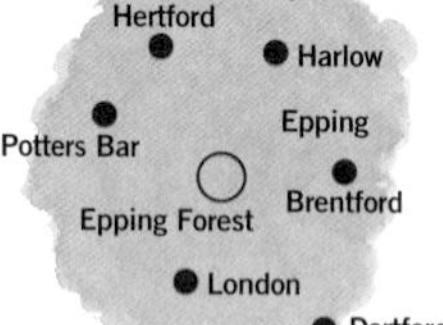

On the outskirts of one of the world's busiest cities there are some surprising oases of green which you and your dog can explore to escape the stresses of modern living. Enjoy!

Epping Forest

by Mary Welsh

Walk 5

However you reach Epping Forest there is road noise or railway noise and then it all ebbs away as you stroll through the lovely glades beneath glorious ancient trees. This is a great place for dogs, and their owners will enjoy it too. There are wonderful smells and sniffs en route; just remember to keep pets under control if you meet horse riders.

Route planner

1 From the car park just beyond the golf clubhouse, walk north along Bury Road with a large common, Chingford Plain, to your right. Take the second right to walk along Jubilee Ride, a grassy track across the common with woodland to your left and open pasture to your right. Go ahead at a junction of paths and where the path narrows to a 'squeeze', bear left on to a dirt track that takes you into oak and hornbeam woodland. At the next cross of tracks, turn left and walk on to come to Grimston's Oak — named after a famous cricketer. The oak stands in the centre of a small open space.

2 Just beyond turn left, with some railings to your left. Then after a few yards take a right turn along Grimston's Oak Ride. At a junction turn left and then almost immediately right. Ignore a right turn and go on ahead to reach Fairmead Road (which has been blocked off to all traffic) where you turn left. Walk on with woodland to your left and a common to the right — in summer both verges are bright with flowers. The old road

Grimston's Oak stands in a small clearing and is named after a famous cricketer.

Epping Forest is ancient woodland, complete with areas of grassland and ponds of varying sizes.

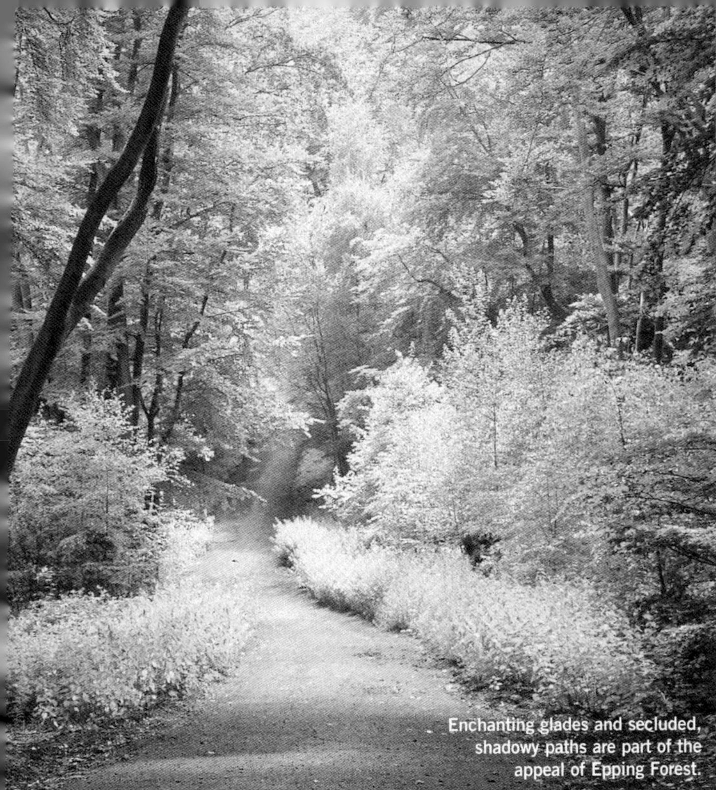

Enchanting glades and secluded, shadowy paths are part of the appeal of Epping Forest.

soon moves into woodland and you can enjoy the birdsong, the hornbeams, the trailing ivy and the honeysuckle.

3 Go on to pass some fine beeches. Continue to the tea hut, on the right, with picnic tables. Then cross the road and walk left, uphill. When opposite a sign for Epping Forest Centre turn right into the forest and take a narrow path, immediately left, to continue uphill parallel with the road. Rejoin the road just before you reach a building. Walk on to pass Paul's Nursery.

4 Pass the King's Oak pub, with a small snack bar beyond, where you turn right into a car park. Here, on the right, is the Epping Forest Centre, with some fine displays. Then, with your back to the entrance, walk ahead and turn right on to a wheelchair path through the forest. One hundred metres further on, turn right and then at the crossroads turn right again to stride the delightful and aptly named Up and Down Ride, passing through giant beech pollards, following the way as it curves slightly right.

5 Stride on to the road which you walked earlier. Cross and after two steps go ahead into the forest along the Centenary Walk. Keep to this wide way as it winds steadily left. Pass out of the trees, with woodland still on the right and pasture to the left. Keep to the main track as it winds right and then quickly curves left to continue as Green Ride, created for Queen Victoria to take a triumphal drive at the dedication of the forest in 1882.

6 Pass through more woodland and then an open space. At an island of trees, go ahead; ignore all other paths taken on your outward route. After the 'squeeze' in the path, you come to a junction of tracks. Ignore the one ahead and take the first diagonal right. Walk on until you catch a glimpse of a drinking fountain ahead through the trees and the weatherboarded Butlers' Retreat, now a tea room and restaurant. Here you should also glimpse Queen Elizabeth's Hunting Lodge. Take a right fork which brings you back to the junction of Bury Road with Station Road.

Fact file

Distance: $5\frac{1}{2}$ miles/8.8km.

Time: 3 hours.

Map: Explorer 174.

Start/parking: Just beyond the golf clubhouse in Bury Road, Chingford; grid reference 394948.

Terrain: Good paths and tracks, mainly level; a little road walking.

Nearest town: Chingford.

Public toilets: At the Queen Elizabeth Hunting Lodge if open (every day except Monday and Tuesday, 1 – 5pm) or the information centre.

Refreshments: At the tea huts you pass or the King's Oak pub.

Public transport: Take the train from London's Liverpool Street to Chingford. Turn right out of the station and walk down Station Road. Once you're opposite the golf clubhouse, cross and walk along Bury Road, which goes off left from Station Road.

Suitable for: Everyone.

● It might be difficult to find drinks for your dog so take water and a bowl with you.

Your dog-friendly guide to

Northumberland

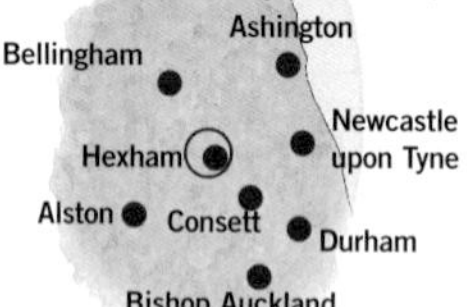

Northumberland is England's most northerly county with a beautiful North Sea coastline and stunning countryside punctuated by castles, Roman forts and attractive towns and villages.

Hexham and the Tyne Valley

by Mary Welsh

Explore the lovely town of Hexham, where pale stone houses cluster dramatically beneath the squat tower of the fine abbey church, high on a river terrace overlooking the Tyne Valley. Then set off with the dog for a walk along the delightful riverside path to where the North and South Tyne rivers unite to form the River Tyne.

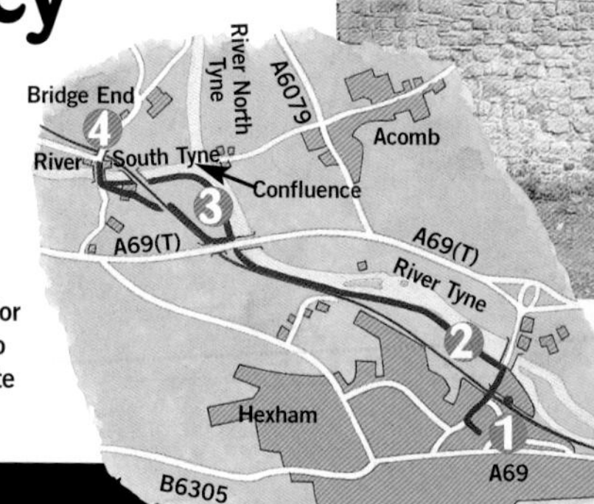

Walk 6

Route planner

1 To explore the beautiful town of Hexham, leave Wentworth car park by the steps to the right of the tourist information centre and then bear right up Hall Orchard Road. Hexham has a turbulent history, having been repeatedly attacked. Today it offers lots to see, good shops and places to eat. After your explorations return to the car park and leave it at the opposite end, in the direction of the supermarket and the roundabout. Cross the road and turn right and keep to the left side of each roundabout. Go over the railway bridge and head towards the splendid Hexham Bridge over the River Tyne. Immediately before it take a tarred path that leads left towards the side of the river to your right. Pause to look back on the fine nine-arched bridge designed by Robert Mylne in 1793. It replaced the two ferries which had to keep running when two previous bridges were swept away after snow, hurricanes and heavy rain caused great flooding.

The confluence of the South and North Tyne rivers; the River Tyne then flows into the North Sea.

The bridge on the Tyne at Hexham replaced ferries which had been used after previous bridges were swept away in floods.

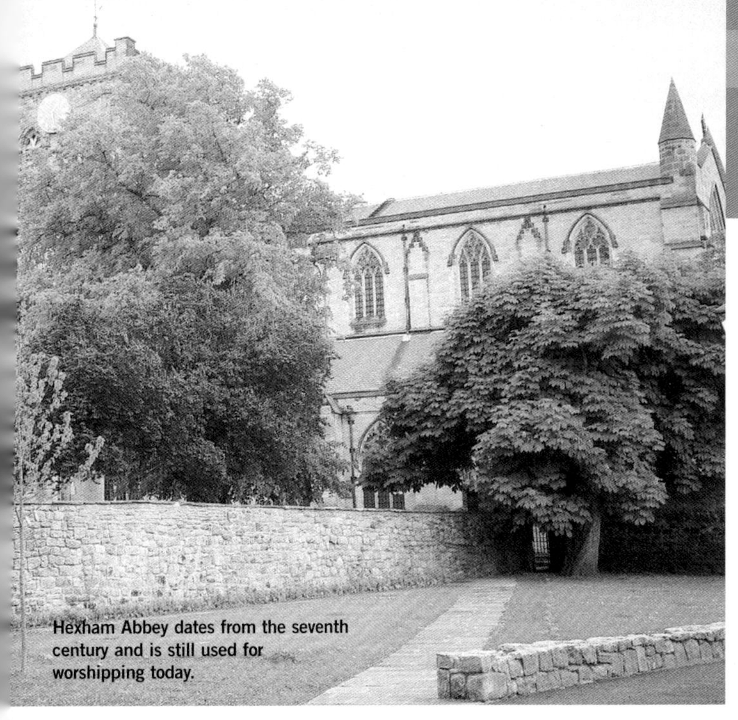

Hexham Abbey dates from the seventh century and is still used for worshipping today.

Your Dog Magazine is available from all good newsagents. For more information, contact the editorial department on tel. 01780 766199.

2 Continue beside the river, keeping to a path — sometimes a track — that passes below a splendid avenue of limes. The path and river eventually run beside the railway. When you can see the A69 road bridge ahead, watch out for the unmarked steps that drop right into an area of scrub. Continue on a grassy path that leads you to a rough patch of shingle, below the bridge. Beyond, climb the slope on the left to reach the top of the river embankment and walk along the way. If the river is high and you cannot pass under the bridge, return to climb the steps and continue on. Once under the road bridge, turn right to walk a scenic path that brings you to the top of the embankment.

3 Walk along the route where, in summer, the area between the embankment and the river is a glorious garden of wild flowers. Continue, and you come to the confluence of the two fine rivers, the North and South Tyne, where you and your dog will want to linger. Walk on beside the South Tyne until your way is barred. Turn left to join a narrow road. If you're ready for refreshments, walk right and then right again to cross Warden Bridge. Ahead is the Boatside Inn.

4 Then return from the inn by crossing the bridge and turning left into the narrow lane. Carry on until you near the A69 road bridge. Here you can choose whether to take the footpath just before it and retrace your steps back to Hexham, or to take the track you might have had to use earlier if the river was in spate.

The Moot Hall was once a meeting place for the county's magistrates.

Fact file

Distance: 4 miles.

Time: 2 hours.

Map: Explorer 43, Landranger 87.

Start/parking: Wentworth car park; grid reference 940645. It lies at the foot of the town, south end of Hexham Bridge.

Terrain: Good riverside paths and gentle climbs on easy tracks.

Nearest town: Hexham.

Refreshments: Wide choice of eating places in Hexham, plus the Boatside Inn at Warden.

Public toilets: Hexham car park.

Public transport: Good bus and train service from Newcastle and Carlisle. Contact TIC on tel. 01434 652220.

Stiles: None.

Suitable for: All.

Your dog-friendly guide to Deeside & Angus

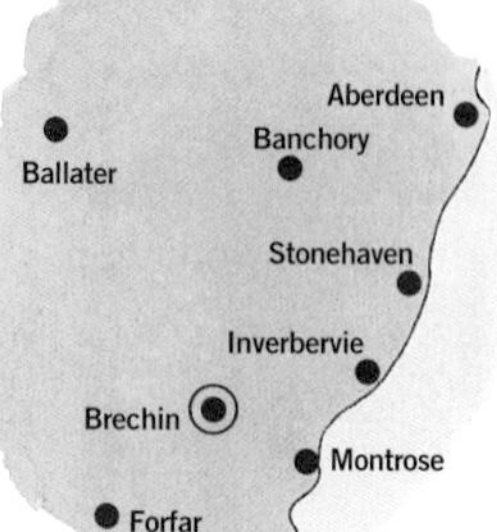

The second of two walks in this remote but beautiful region of central Scotland takes you to two ancient hill forts with superb views.

Two short walks to two ancient hill forts

by Mary Welsh

These two short, attractive walks start from the same car park in a remote area of Angus. The paths climb gently to two ancient hill forts from where the views are superb. There are no streams so take your own water supply for thirsty pets. Dogs must be kept under control and therefore should not be allowed to stray from the paths.

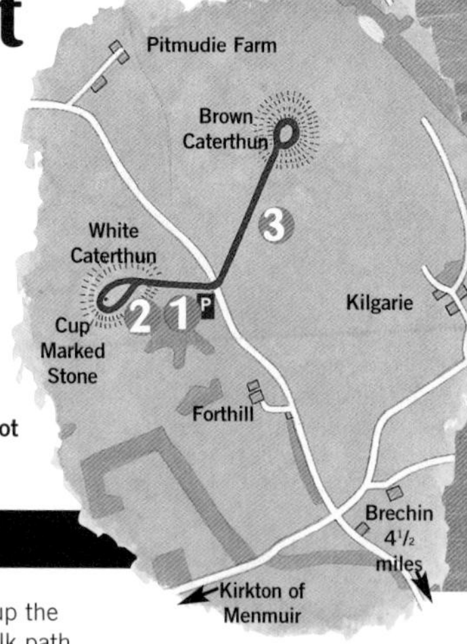

Walk 7

Route planner

1 From the car park and picnic area, set off up the clear, well-kept grassy path that ascends through heather to the White Caterthun (298m). Away to the left the slopes support scattered pine, spruce and larch. As you go enjoy the steadily improving views.

2 Continue up the easy-to-walk path to enter the extensive oval hollow, surrounded by a derelict dyke. Follow any of the little paths through the centre and then walk around the perimeter, pausing often

Conditions can get murky on the way up.

You can enjoy spectacular views from White Caterthun.

Looking out across Strathmore Valley.

to take in the superb view over to the hills around the Angus glens. Peer over the dyke to see the small ramparts. Find a corner to sit in the sun and enjoy the atmosphere of this high-level ancient site. Then return down the slope. Cross the road and take the path, a rougher and longer way, leading beside a fence, towards the Brown Caterthun.

Dogs need to be kept under close control on this walk.

3 The way climbs steadily over heather moorland to the top (287m) from where you can see south-east across the lovely valley of Strathmore and, west, across to the Angus hills. Again you will want to linger, especially when the air is perfumed by the heather, before you return by the same path.

Fact file

Distance: 2 miles.

Time: 1 – 2 hours.

Map: Explorer 389.

Start/parking: The car park, grid reference 552662, lies on the highest part of the road between the two forts, 4½ miles north-west of Brechin and 3½ miles south-west of Edzell.

Terrain: Easiest walking to the White Caterthun.

Nearest towns: Brechin or Edzell.

Refreshments: None on site; try the Old Bake House Coffee Shop at Brechin and the Glen Esk Hotel at Edzell.

Public toilets: None nearer than Brechin.

Public transport: Not accessible by public transport; a taxi ride from either Brechin or Edzell should cost no more that £10 (single journey).

Stiles: None.

Suitable for: All plus well-controlled dogs.

Publisher's Note

While every effort is made to ensure accuracy, we regret that FHG Publications cannot accept responsibility for errors, omissions or misrepresentations in our entries or any consequences thereof. Prices in particular should be checked because we go to press early. We will follow up complaints but cannot act as arbiters or agents for either party.

holidays together
feeding guide
great walks
Winalot
http://www.winalot-dog.co.uk
PURINA
LIVE A LOT WITH
winalot
Live Life to the Full
Mealtimes
Meeting Point
Newsletter
Get in Touch
"happy days, happy dogs"
Meet Holly living life to the full!
Every dog should live life to the full!
We all want our dogs to be happy and healthy; full of energy and sheer enthusiasm for life. Bright, alert, active - a wet nose and a shiny coat. Ready to get the best out of every day!
Winalot knows an important part of helping your dog get the most out of life is providing food that's nutritiously balanced, and tastes great too. A dog food your dog can really enjoy. That's why Winalot's range of meals, snacks and treats provide all the goodness your dog needs to go out and live a lot!
This site is dedicated to helping you and your dog make the most of time spent together. You'll find tips and advice, listings of the best dog-friendly pubs, hotels and holidays around the UK,
"dog friendly places"
Pubs
Hotels
Walks
Holidays
"Where should we take Holly?"
Log-In
Username
Password
Reset
Submit
dog friendly pubs
message boards